TRUE AND FALSE ACCUSATIONS OF CHILD SEX ABUSE

TRUE AND FALSE
ACCUSATIONS OF
CHILD SEX ABUSE

Richard A. Gardner, M.D.

Clinical Professor of Child Psychiatry
Columbia University
College of Physicians and Surgeons

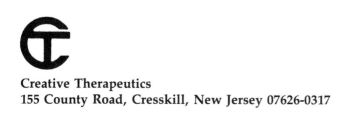

Creative Therapeutics
155 County Road, Cresskill, New Jersey 07626-0317

Library of Congress Cataloging-in-Publication Data

Gardner, Richard A.
   True and false accusations of child sex abuse : a guide for legal
and mental health professionals / Richard A. Gardner.
     p.   cm.
   Includes bibliographical references and index.
   ISBN 0-933812-25-6
   1. Child molesting. 2. Child molesting—Investigation.
3. Interviewing in child abuse. 4. Truthfulness and falsehood.
I. Title.
RC560.C46G377 1992
616.85′836—dc20   92-32957
                                                      CIP

PRINTED IN THE UNITED STATES OF AMERICA

10 9 8 7 6 5 4 3 2 1

To all who have taught me
About adult-child sexual encounters—
Both truly and falsely alleged

Other Books by Richard A. Gardner, M.D.

The Boys and Girls Book About Divorce
Therapeutic Communication with Children:
  The Mutual Storytelling Technique
Dr. Gardner's Stories About the Real World, Volume I
Dr. Gardner's Stories About the Real World, Volume II
Dr. Gardner's Fairy Tales for Today's Children
Understanding Children: A Parents Guide to Child Rearing
MBD: The Family Book About Minimal Brain Dysfunction
Psychotherapeutic Approaches to the Resistant Child
Psychotherapy with Children of Divorce
Dr. Gardner's Modern Fairy Tales
The Parents Book About Divorce
The Boys and Girls Book About One-Parent Families
The Objective Diagnosis of Minimal Brain Dysfunction
Dorothy and the Lizard of Oz
Dr. Gardner's Fables for Our Times
The Boys and Girls Book About Stepfamilies
Family Evaluation in Child Custody Litigation
Separation Anxiety Disorder: Psychodynamics and Psychotherapy
Child Custody Litigation: A Guide for Parents
  and Mental Health Professionals
The Psychotherapeutic Techniques of Richard A. Gardner
Hyperactivity, The So-Called Attention-Deficit Disorder,
  and the Group of MBD Syndromes
The Parental Alienation Syndrome and the Differentiation
  Between Fabricated and Genuine Child Sex Abuse
Psychotherapy with Adolescents
Family Evaluation in Child Custody Mediation, Arbitration,
  and Litigation
The Girls and Boys Book About Good and Bad Behavior
Sex Abuse Hysteria: Salem Witch Trials Revisited
The Parents Book About Divorce - Second Edition
The Psychotherapeutic Techniques of Richard A. Gardner - Revised
The Parental Alienation Syndrome: A Guide
  for Mental Health and Legal Professionals
Self-Esteem Problems of Children: Psychodynamics
  and Psychotherapy
Conduct Disorders of Children: Psychodynamics and Psychotherapy

CONTENTS

ACKNOWLEDGMENTS

I deeply appreciate the dedication of my secretaries, Donna La Tourette, Linda Gould, and Carol Gibbon, to the typing of the manuscript of this book in its various renditions. I am grateful to Muriel Jorgensen for her diligence in editing the manuscript. She provided useful suggestions and, at the same time, exhibited respect for my wishes regarding style and format. I am indebted, also, to Frances Dubner for her commitment to the editing of the early drafts. My daughter, Julie Anne Gardner, brought her psychological insights to the first chapter, and these are appreciated, especially from the point of view of the younger generation. I am grateful to the efforts of my son-in-law, Benjamin Rubin, for his input regarding biblical references to sex abuse.

I appreciate the efforts of Robert Tebbenhoff of Lind Graphics for his contributions to the production of this book from the original manuscript to the final volume. I am grateful to Barbara Bernstein for her diligence in the proofreading of the page proofs. I am grateful, as well, to Chris Saucier for her thorough and useful index.

I am enormously indebted to Holly Wakefield and Ralph Underwager for their availability and their willingness to share with me their knowledge and experience. I do not know of anyone who has more information in this area than Ralph and Holly. It took only a telephone call and a few minutes of inquiry for me to receive by fax a list of pertinent publications drawn from their extensive computer bank of information in this area.

It is unusual for an author to mention in the acknowledgments section of a book a particular reference. I myself do not recall having done so in the past. However, of all the references provided in this book there are two that, I believe, warrant special notice and acknowledgment. My deepest debt is to Mr. Richard Dawkins, author of *The Selfish Gene* (1976). At the time I write this, I am 61 years old and have been reading books since the age of five. (I first joined the Highbridge Public Library in The Bronx [a part of New York City] on May 12, 1936 – a date I easily recall because it was a landmark event in my life.) Of all the books I have read, Mr. Dawkins's has had, without question, the greatest influence on me. I consider his theory about the role of DNA in the evolution of living forms to be an important extension of Darwin's and a major contribution to human knowledge. My theory on the causes and purposes of "atypical" human sexuality (including pedophilia, homosexuality, and other forms of paraphilia) (Chapter One) is a derivative of Darwin's and an extension of Dawkins's.

Kenneth V. Lanning of the Federal Bureau of Investigation in Quantico, Virginia. Mr. Lanning, who is the Supervisory Special Agent at the National Center for the Analysis of Violent Crime, was the chief supervisor and analyst for hundreds of cases of ritual abuse reported in the United States between 1981 and 1991. His report, "Investigator's Guide to Allegations of 'Ritual' Child Abuse," is probably the most extensive analysis of such cases ever published. Certainly he had access to a much larger network of information than previously enjoyed by any investigator. Furthermore, his evaluators were primarily FBI agents, individuals particularly schooled in separating fact from fantasy. (This is just the opposite of what mental health professionals do, their professions to the contrary notwithstanding.) By the time of the report's publication (January 1992), the FBI had not found conclusive proof of even one case of murder, human sacrifice, kidnapping, or child abuse in association with satanic rituals. There was some evidence of minor crimes—such as trespassing, vandalism, cruelty to animals, and petty thievery—but none of the more formidable and dramatic activities ascribed to these alleged groups. But this is only one of the multiplicity of findings. The document is an extremely valuable one, and I recommend it to all readers of this book. I am not only indebted to Mr. Lanning for having written the report, but for having granted me permission to quote from it in various parts of this volume.

I am indebted, as well, to the patients I have seen who have alleged sex abuse. Those who have indeed been sexually abused have taught me much about its manifestations (or lack of manifestations) in childhood, adolescence, and even in adult years (for those who do suffer residual symptoms). And those who have falsely alleged sex abuse have taught me much about the manifestations of false allegations. Some of the patients in the first category have indeed been victims, and the word *abuse* certainly applies to them. There are others, however, whose sexual encounters I would not categorize as abuses in that they did not suffer any untoward psychiatric sequelae. Such people have confirmed for me that adult-child sexual encounters do not necessarily cause psychological damage, widespread opinion to the contrary notwithstanding. All of the children who have professed false allegations have been victims. All of them have been unnecessarily traumatized. It is to people in all of these categories that I am indebted because of what they have taught me.

INTRODUCTION

We are living in dangerous times. Sex-abuse hysteria is omnipresent. Open any newspaper or magazine and the likelihood of seeing an article on sex abuse is extremely high. Hardly a day goes by when there are not at least some television or radio programs devoted to the subject of sex abuse. There is no question that many accusations of child sex abuse are true, and this is especially so in settings such as homes and boarding schools (where the potential abuser has the opportunity for ongoing contact with the children). However, there is no question, as well, that many of the accusations are false, especially in child custody disputes (where the vengeance element and the opportunity for exclusion of a hated spouse is operative) and day-care centers and nursery schools (where the potential abuser has little opportunity for ongoing contact alone with the child).

The sexual abuse of children, like the abuse of women, is an ancient tradition and has been seen in every society in history. In fact, there is good reason to believe that there is less sexual exploitation of children in Western society (especially because of the proscriptions of the Judeo-Christian ethic) than has existed anywhere in the history of humanity. In recent years, we have become increasingly aware of how widespread sexual abuse of children is in Western society and have come to appreciate that there has been enormous denial of the phenomenon. At the same time, however, we have witnessed an exaggerated reaction to the phenomenon, so much so that the term *hysteria* is often warranted. The hysteria is seen at every level, from the time of the initial suggestion or suspicion to the final sentence meted out to an accused (whether truly guilty of the crime or not). A whole parade of individuals can predictably overreact—an overreaction that beclouds objectivity and lessens significantly the likelihood that a proper assessment will be conducted. I include here parents, police, detectives, prosecutors, psychologists, psychiatrists, social workers, "validators," "child advocates," teachers, school administrators, boards of education, lawyers, judges, juries, and legislators. In this atmosphere Constitutional safeguards of due process are ignored, people are jailed on the basis of the babbling of three-year-olds, traditional courtroom procedures designed to protect the defense are no longer followed, and excessively punitive sentences are the rule. I believe that the average murderer in the United States today will be out of jail much sooner than the average person convicted of sex abuse. When it comes to sex abuse, there seems to be an exception to the Eighth Amendment Constitutional safeguard against "cruel and unusual punishment."

Divorced fathers (and even those who are not divorced) have become afraid to bathe and shower their children, or even help them when they go to the bathroom. No sane teacher will spend time alone in a room with a girl. Scout masters on overnight hikes are sure to travel two at a time. Many nursery schools have ongoing videotapes, and no one takes a child alone to the bathroom. For at least a quarter of a century now, doctors have been ever-vigilant regarding their patients suing them for malpractice. Now, there is a new danger: accusations of sexual molestation, sexual abuse, and sexual harassment. The Salem witch trials are viewed by many as our country's most famous episode of mass hysteria. Many do not appreciate that the trials lasted less than five months (June 2, 1692-October 29, 1692). During this period 27 people were convicted of witchcraft.

Nineteen were hanged (the last hangings took place on September 22, 1692), one man (who refused trial by jury) was executed by being pressed to death with heavy stones (he took two days to die), and four died in prison. On October 26, 1692, the Massachusetts legislature, at the prodding of Reverend Increase Mather (president of Harvard University and United States ambassador to England), dictated to the Salem magistrates that they use much more stringent criteria before judging an individual guilty of witchcraft. On October 29, 1692, Massachusetts Governor Phips dismissed the court. This basically brought an end to the trials. For many years thereafter courts and churches declared days of penance and prayer in apology for the injustices perpetrated upon the accused. In January 1696 twelve of the jurors signed a statement of contrition, claiming that they had operated under the influence of the devil. In subsequent years survivors of the accused were granted redress and compensation for their losses, and such compensation continued until as recently as 1957.

The sex-abuse hysteria that we are witnessing today has been spiraling for approximately a decade. I am certain that the number of people who have died as a result of the current hysteria far exceeds the number who were executed in Salem. These people have not literally been executed; but they have been given psychological death sentences. These people have not been literally hanged or stoned to death, but many have been dealt with the equivalent treatment psychologically. I am convinced that there are hundreds (and possibly thousands) of people who are in jail in the United States today who have been convicted of sex crimes that they never committed. (I am not denying that there are many more incarcerated who actually did indeed commit such crimes.) There are hundreds, I am sure, who have committed suicide because of a false sex-abuse accusation. There are others who have died of heart attacks, strokes, and other diseases caused by the stresses and humiliations of a false sex-abuse accusation. Careers and marriages have been destroyed, reputations ruined, and people are suffering lifelong stigma because of such an accusation.

HYSTERIA AS A HISTORICAL PHENOMENON

To the best of my knowledge, hysteria was first described by Hippocrates in the 4th century B.C. He observed the condition almost exclusively in women who exhibited crying fits, agitated movements of their bodies, and exhibitionistic displays. He considered the disorder to be the result of the wandering of the uterus, which had somehow gotten loose from its fixations in the pelvic cavity. The word hysteria is derived from the Greek word *hystera,* which means uterus.

False accusations of sex abuse are certainly not new. Even the Bible provides an example, namely, Joseph being accused of sexual assault by his master's wife. The whole incident was a setup after he had spurned this woman's overtures because of loyalty to his master. As a result, Joseph was arrested and placed in a dungeon. Hysteria, too, is an ancient tradition, and the Salem witch trials were certainly not the only famous historical example. Human beings are sheeplike, and the desire to "go along with the crowd" is deep-seated and, I believe, possibly genetically determined. Obviously, it is safer to be one of the "herd" than to be a maverick. Those who are different inevitably suffer scorn and rejection. The word *gregarious* is derived from the Latin word *grex,* which means *flock of sheep.* In addition, human beings are amazingly suggestible and can, under proper circumstances, be brought to the point of believing anything, no matter how absurd. And I am not speaking of children in this regard, but adults as well. Other factors are then built upon these foundations, depending upon the particular needs of those involved in the mass hysteria. Society must provide acceptable releases for the pent-up hostilities that inevitably result from the predictable frustrations of life. When the mass has found a scapegoat for such hostilities, then this element may contribute to the hysteria. Most often the oversimplification element is operative as well. Life is complex, and most phenomena are multidetermined. Accordingly, simple solutions are much more attractive than complicated ones. When the mob's goal is to remove a particular person or group—and thereby solve all of its problems—the movement

becomes particularly attractive. Joining such a movement enhances self-esteem in that one surrounds oneself with others who
share – often to a fanatic degree – one's convictions. Feelings of
power may also be gratified in that the mob has much more
power than any single individual. Although each outbreak has its
own special factors, the aforementioned are often operative.

Some of the more well known examples: In the Middle Ages,
processions of flagellants (people who whipped themselves and
others) traveled throughout Europe convinced that their lashings
were punishments decreed by God and served, therefore, to
assuage the guilt they felt because of their sins. During the
Middle Ages we witnessed throughout central Europe waves of
dancing hysteria, referred to as St. Vitus's dance. Men and
women, usually peasants, would form circles and dance freneti-
cally, as if possessed, until they fell to the ground while foaming
at the mouth. The Children's Crusade (Lyons and Petrucelli,
1978) is now generally considered to be another example of mass
hysteria. In the second decade of the 13th century, an estimated
30,000 children from all parts of France streamed into Marseilles
with the plan of conquering the Holy Land from the Muslims.
They fell victim to disreputable merchants who shipped them to
slave markets in North Africa. During the same period an
estimated group of approximately 20,000 German children
crossed the Alps into various parts of Italy with the hope of
reaching the Holy Land via Italian ports on the Mediterranean.
Many of these children, like the French group, ultimately ended
up as slaves in the Middle East (*Encyclopaedia Britannica*, 1982).

Menninger (1957) describes an epidemic of hysteria that took
place in Lancashire, England, in 1787. It all began when a
working girl, as a prank, placed a mouse into the bosom of
another girl who was quite fearful of mice. The victim of this
prank immediately developed convulsions that lasted 24 hours.
This episode served as the nidus of an outbreak of mass hysteria
that ultimately involved 300 fellow employees. The main symptoms were anxiety, feelings of being strangled, and convulsions.
The convulsions lasted from 15 minutes to 24 hours and involved
tearing of hair, dashing of the head, and falling against walls and

floors. Interestingly, all of the afflicted were cured with an alcoholic beverage and the suggestion that they join in a dance.

Kanner (1935) describes an outbreak that took place in 1892 in Bieberach, Germany, in which 13 girls had attacks that began with headaches and then consisted of dancing movements, hallucinations, delirium, and finally profound sleep. In 1892 in the village of Gross-Tinz in Silesia, a ten-year-old girl exhibited tremors of the hand, which spread over her whole body. Next, several other girls were similarly afflicted. Within a few weeks 20 girls had similar attacks. All this stopped with the summer vacation but, on return to school in the autumn, the wave of hysteria continued with the girls exhibiting convulsions, astasia-abasia (the psychological inability to stand combined with the psychological inability to walk), delirium, arc de cercle (psychologically caused bending of the body anteriorally or posteriorally), profuse perspiration, and barking like dogs. Interestingly, only girls were afflicted during this epidemic, and not one "victim" was a boy. Kanner describes other epidemics of hysteria, mainly in Europe.

It is of interest that in the late-nineteenth century, in both the United States and England, we witnessed a period of excessive preoccupation with and Draconian condemnation of childhood masturbation. Unfortunately, physicians (who should have known better) were actively involved in this campaign of denunciation and attempts to obliterate entirely this nefarious practice. Doctors considered it to be the cause of a wide variety of illnesses, e.g., blindness, insanity, and muscle spasms. Various kinds of restraints were devised in order to prevent children from engaging in this dangerous practice. Some girls were even subjected to clitorectomies, so dangerous was the practice considered to be. Parents were given a long list of symptoms that were considered to be concomitants of masturbation. Some of the alerting signs: temper tantrums, bedwetting, sleep disturbances, appetite changes, mood fluctuations, and withdrawal. Obviously, in the hundred years since those sad times, we seem to have gone back full circle. The same list of symptoms that were indicators of masturbation are now considered to be indicators of sex abuse. Legrand et al. (1989) have written a fascinating article describing the similarities between the masturbation hysteria of the late-nineteenth century and the sex-abuse hysteria of the late-twentieth century, with a comparison of the lists of "indicators."

The Salem witch trial hysteria was not unique to the United States. Actually, belief in witches was pervasive in Europe throughout the Middle Ages, and there have been many episodes of persecution of witches throughout Europe since that time. And the Salem witch trial episode can be considered a derivative of the European episodes, with additional contributing factors particular to the Massachussetts Colony in the late seventeenth century. But the Salem witch trial hysteria was not the only example of mass hysteria in our country's history. Probably the next most well known were the McCarthy hearings in the 1950s. In the course of this wave of hysteria, threats of Communist infiltration and takeover of our government were exaggerated enormously, and Draconian punishments were administered to those who had any sympathies for the movement. Even those who had involved themselves in the Communist party earlier in life did not escape. Blacklists were drawn up, people were fired, and a whole network of investigators and informers served to promulgate the belief in Communism's formidable dangers to the U.S. government. Many of those unfortunate enough to have been subjected to the abominations of McCarthy's committee became social outcasts, and some were even incarcerated. Although thousands certainly suffered during the hysteria of that era, I believe that their numbers are small compared to those whose lives have been destroyed by the sex-abuse hysteria that has been prevalent in the United States since the early 1980s.

The event that is often considered to have laid the foundation for the hysteria was the *The Child Abuse Prevention and Treatment Act* (The Mondale Act), which was passed by the United States Congress in 1973. Congress was certainly well intentioned in its desire to protect abused children. However, the results have been disastrous. The law mandated child-abuse reporting laws in all 50 states, laws in which civil immunity to lawsuits would be provided for anyone reporting the abuse of a child. Furthermore, individuals aware of such crimes—who did not report such abuse—were subject to criminal prosecution. This has resulted in a philosophy of "when in doubt, report." Federal funding was provided for district attorneys to set up special units for the prosecution of child sex abuse; but no funding was provided for defendants. The result of this has been the development of a nationwide army of zealous prosecutors and a sense of impotence for those (the defendants) who are not wealthy enough to finance their own defense (Clancy and Firpo, 1991).

A central cornerstone of our constitutional system is the principle that a man is innocent until proven guilty. This is often stated as the dictum, "Rather 10 (or 100 or 1,000) guilty men go free than one innocent man be falsely convicted of a crime he did not commit." In the service of this principle, civil courts generally require a *preponderance of evidence* before concluding that the defendant is guilty of the alleged crime. In criminal cases, the requirements are even more stringent in that the jury must conclude *beyond reasonable doubt* that the defendant did indeed commit the crime. These traditional constitutional safeguards are now being ignored. Rather, judges now subscribe to the philosophy, "I'd rather be on the safe side," and find defendants guilty with minimal evidence, even "evidence" provided by a three-year-old child who has been unrelentlessly programmed by her vengeful divorced mother to allege that she was sexually abused by her father. One judge said to me, "If there is a scintilla of evidence that this man sexually abused this child, I will send him to jail for as many years as the law will allow." Although juries in criminal cases have been instructed to subscribe to the beyond-reasonable-doubt principle, the instructions of many judges and the ambient hysteria have encouraged them to ignore this factor in their deliberations. Elsewhere (Gardner, 1991a) I have described in detail the ways in which the current sex-abuse hysteria has been promulgated.

BACKGROUND OF MY OWN INVOLVEMENT IN THE FIELD OF CHILD SEX ABUSE

My involvement in child sex abuse derives from my experiences in forensic psychiatry, which date back to my military service in

Germany from 1960 to 1962. It was then that I first became involved in doing forensic evaluations, both in military and German civilian courts. American military dependents were not under the jurisdiction of military courts; accordingly, any crimes they committed were considered to have been perpetrated on German soil and so they were under the jurisdictions of German courts. However, as military dependents, they were entitled to military medical care, which included psychiatric care.

Following my discharge from the service I went into private practice and, in the mid-1960s, in association with the burgeoning divorce rate, I began getting referrals in child custody disputes. My earlier experiences in forensic psychiatry served well as a foundation for such involvement. Over the years, I became increasingly involved in testifying in child custody cases. As a result of these experiences, I gradually became appreciative of the phenomenon that I ultimately termed the *parental alienation syndrome (PAS)* (Gardner, 1985, 1986, 1987, 1989, 1992a). This disorder, which arises almost exclusively in the context of child custody disputes, involves the combination of one parent programming the child against the other parent *and* the child's own contributions, which usually complement those of the programming parent. Accordingly, we are not dealing here simply with brainwashing, but with a *combination* of the parent's and the child's contributions. Generally, the programming serves the purpose of enhancing the brainwashing parent's position in the child custody dispute.

In the early 1980s I began seeing a new development, namely, the incorporation of a sex-abuse accusation as part of the PAS child's scenario of denigration of the allegedly hated parent. It soon became apparent that most (but certainly not all) of these accusations were false. They were particularly attractive to an angry parent because they served as very effective vengeance and exclusionary maneuvers. During that period, when I brought this observation to the attention of mental health professionals, I was met with outcries of rage and derision. "Children never lie when they make accusations of sex abuse," I was told, and I should "believe the children." I was also warned that public statements of this kind were dangerous because my comments would be used by defense attorneys to exonerate known and well-documented sex-abuse perpetrators. My response was this:

> I am 100 percent convinced that *some* of these accusations are false. I am not denying that bona fide sex abuse is widespread and an ancient tradition. What I am saying is that *some* of these accusations are false and that we are seeing more of them in association with the burgeoning child custody disputes. Rather than deny this reality, we have to develop criteria for differentiating between true and false sex-abuse accusations. It is only in this way that we will be able to deal properly with those who have actually abused children and protect those who have been falsely accused. Obviously, this is an extremely important area to which we should devote ourselves.

During the next few years, in spite of significant antagonism, I continued to devote my efforts to the development of differentiating criteria, and these ultimately resulted in my *Sex-Abuse Legitimacy Scale (SAL Scale)*, which was described in my book, *The Parental Alienation Syndrome and the Differentiation Between Fabricated and Genuine Child Sex Abuse* (Gardner, 1987).

When publishing the book, I described the dilemma that I had. On the one hand, I recognized that the *SAL Scale* was a *first* offering and that, ideally, before publishing such an instrument, one should work 15 or 20 years on its development and pull together the findings of many groups of investigators. On the other hand, there was an urgency in that people were being jailed then and we could not wait until "all the data was in" before formulating an objective scale. Although I clearly described these concerns and the scale's drawbacks in the book, there was significant criticism of the scale—especially because I could claim only face validity for many of the criteria (although others certainly had some substantiation in the scientific literature). Over the next few years, with increasing knowledge and experience, I was able to add to my list differentiating criteria. Not only did I devise more criteria, but I was able to improve upon the sensitivity of many of them for differentiating between true and false sex-abuse accusations. Furthermore, I found that my attempts to give a point score (from 1 to 3) to each of the criteria introduced a subjective element to the scoring. In many cases (especially criminal cases), I was not able to satisfy the proviso that all three parties (accuser, accused, and the alleged child victim) be interviewed. Without this proviso being satisfied, the scale could not be used. It was because of these and other considerations that I decided to dispense entirely with the *SAL Scale,* but to use the criteria themselves – without quantification – as well as additional ones that I have formulated in the ensuing years.

Accordingly, in this book I have included the original criteria plus the additional ones that I have developed. I have also dropped a few criteria, especially *recantation,* which in my experience is of little differentiating value because it is seen with both true and false accusations. I do not assign any point scores to the criteria, nor are there any kinds of total point scores that are designed to help differentiate between the true and false sex-abuse accusation. Rather, the examiner is merely asked to come to a decision with regard to whether each of the criteria is satisfied. Then, at the end, the examiner is advised to make a statement along these lines: "Of the 30 criteria applicable for the child, 25 are satisfied. Accordingly, there is a very high likelihood that this child has been sexually abused." Although this format is often less convincing to a court – which often prefers numbers and "scientific" documentation – in reality it is probably a better format at this point, considering the difficulties one has in differentiating between true and false sex-abuse accusations. However, I am convinced that the *proper* utilization of these criteria will place an examiner in a strong position to make a decision regarding whether the accusation is true or false. I am not claiming 100 percent accuracy, because no one can ever know in certain situations whether the sex abuse did indeed occur. I am only claiming that the criteria that I present here, if *properly* utilized, will place an examiner in a good position to come to a meaningful conclusion regarding the likelihood of whether the sex abuse did indeed take place.

The reader may note that I have emphasized the word *proper.* My reason for this is that my experiences with the *SAL Scale* have been that many examiners did not follow the instructions, although they were clearly stated in many places throughout the book and on the cover sheet of the scoring manual. Many did not see fit to interview all three parties and felt comfortable coming to conclusions on the basis of interviewing two and even one of the three. I also noted a significant amount of subjectivity regarding whether a particular criterion was satisfied, even though I believe that I provided clear guidelines for scoring.

In the mid-1980s I began getting invitations to involve myself in doing evaluations in the context of nursery school and day-care center sex-abuse accusations. At first, I refused such invitations because of my insistence that I be allowed to see all three parties, namely, the accuser, the accused, and the alleged child victims. Although strict adherence to this position worked well in civil cases, especially divorce disputes, it was practically impossible to achieve this goal in criminal cases (down which track the nursery school cases were going). Accordingly, after reading and learning about what I consider to be terrible miscarriages of justice—with the incarceration of parties whom I considered to be innocent—I decided to take a less stringent position and agreed to involve myself in such cases. However, I still made every attempt to evaluate all three parties. In addition, I made no promises beforehand that I would serve as an advocate, but only agreed to do so if, after interviewing available parties and reviewing documents, I concluded that I could do so with conviction. In most cases, this could be accomplished in a few hours. In some cases it took longer, and in one case it was not until 40 hours of interviewing and reviewing materials that I came to the conclusion that I could support the position of the defense.

I was surprised to find (although in retrospect I should not have been) that, with rare exception, the same criteria that proved useful in custody cases were also applicable (with minor alterations) to the nursery-school situation. What was originally surprising became less so when I came to appreciate that the very same "validators" were involved, and they were using the same misguided techniques for "validation." One of the differences between the two situations (i.e., the divorce and nursery school situation) related to the hysteria element. We can say that one person is hysterical, and we can say that a large group of people exhibit mass hysteria. No one can reasonably answer the question, "How many people do you have to have before you can use the term *mass hysteria?*" It certainly can be used for 20 or 30. One can possibly use it for 10-20 people. Is the term applicable for five people, or three people, or even two? The question, however, is not too meaningful. What is important is that the greater the number of people who are hysterical at the same time, the greater the likelihood that the mass-hysteria phenomenon will operate. And this is what, I am certain, has taken place in many (I am not saying all) of the nursery schools and day-care centers where sex abuse has been alleged. One hysterical mother is far less likely to bring about the rapid intensification and the fanciful elaborations that one sees in the mass-hysteria situation. One hysterical mother is far less likely to bring the satanic-ritual element into the sex-abuse scenario. The mass-hysteria element increases the likelihood of cross-fertilization, in which one child's scenario – via transmission through parents, therapists, validators, police investigators, etc. – is likely to end up in another child's sex-abuse scenario. By the early 1990s I had accumulated enough experience in the nursery school and day-care center realms to write meaningfully on differentiating between true and false accusations in this realm.

In 1991 I had enough experience with sex abuse hysteria to pull together my ideas in my book, *Sex Abuse Hysteria: Salem Witch Trials Revisited.* The book goes beyond the single hysterical mother in a divorce situation, and even beyond the groups of hysterical parents in nursery school and day-care centers. It describes the network of social, political, and financial factors that fuel the hysteria and contribute thereby to its spread.

More recently, I have had experiences with situations in which adult women are accusing their fathers of having sexually abused them in childhood, especially early childhood. The experiences I had in the divorce and nursery school situations proved useful for developing criteria for differentiating between true and false accusations in this situation. Although a more recent phenomenon, I had enough experience to be able to write with conviction on this subject and have included it as a final chapter in this book. Some of my differentiating criteria for such accusations have been derived from my experiences with children, especially because the accusation usually involves experiences that took place in childhood. However, different criteria have to be utilized, as well, because there are certainly differences in the two situations.

This book is primarily directed to making differentiations in the family situation, especially the child custody dispute and the nursery school and day-care center situations. However, the criteria are still applicable in other situations in which there may be a sex-abuse accusation, e.g., babysitter, scoutmaster, teacher, neighbor, relative, and stranger.

At this point, most people (both professional and lay) place themselves in one of two camps. One group believes that the vast majority of sex-abuse accusations are true, regardless of the situation in which they arise. Another group holds that the mass-hysteria element is so widespread that most (if not all) of the accusations are false. It comes as a surprise to me that most individuals have difficulty accepting the reality that one can have *two* epidemics coexisting, namely, an epidemic of sex-abuse hysteria surrounding true accusations, and a separate epidemic of sex-abuse hysteria related to false accusations. Most agree that we can have simultaneous epidemics of AIDS, hepatitis B, cholera, herpes, and a wide variety of other diseases. Somehow the coexistence of two separate epidemics of hysteria does not sit well with many people. Most also do not consider the various situations in which a sex-abuse accusation arises. Some situations (like the intrafamilial setting and the boarding school) are at quite high risk for sex abuse, whereas others (such as the vicious custody dispute and the nursery school) are low-risk situations. Such considerations are *crucial* to make *at the outset* if one is to make a judicious decision regarding whether a sex-abuse accusation is true or false. I believe that this book presents a balanced view of sex-abuse risks and, when used judiciously, can be extremely valuable for examiners who are being asked to assess such risks. My hope, as well, is that it will play a role in reducing sex-abuse hysteria, because it provides objective and judicious differentiating criteria that can serve as antidotes to the kinds of hyper-emotionalism and loss of subjectivity seen in hysteria.

☐ ONE
A THEORY ABOUT THE VARIETY
OF HUMAN SEXUAL BEHAVIOR

Be fruitful and multiply and fill the earth . . .

Genesis: 1:28

I have found the missing link between the higher ape and civilized man: It is we.

Konrad Lorenz

Man becomes civilized when his animal impulses are tamed, subdued, and transcended by his social nature.

Abba Eban

INTRODUCTION

I have never felt completely comfortable with the terms *natural* and *unnatural* when they apply to human sexual behavior. In a sense, one could say that any form of sexual behavior that can be exhibited by a human being must be considered natural in that it is part of the human repertoire. Generally, the term *unnatural* has been applied to those variations that have been considered unacceptable to a particular social group. In a somewhat grandiose fashion, each society considers natural (in compliance with God's [or nature's] purposes) those particular forms of sexual behavior that are widely practiced and accepted and deems

1

unnatural (at variance with nature's [or God's] purposes) those forms of sexual behavior that are atypical and/or by social convention "wrong," "bad," "disgusting," etc. Sometimes sexual behavior that does not lead directly to procreation has been subsumed under the unnatural rubric. As I hope to demonstrate, even those forms of sexual behavior that do not lead immediately to procreation may still serve nature's purposes and thereby not warrant being excluded from the list of the so-called natural forms of human sexual behavior.

GENDER DIFFERENCES IN MATING PATTERNS

In order to appreciate fully the theory I propose, it is important first for the reader to understand my concept of the origins of gender differences in mating patterns. I believe that there is genetic programming for women to be more passive, coy, and seductive, and for men to be more assertive and aggressive in the courtship process. Although social influences certainly play a role in such patterns, I believe that the genetic factors are the more important. I recognize that this is an unpopular thing to say at a time when male/female egalitarianism is very much in vogue; yet, I believe that I have good arguments to support my position. No one can deny that up until the 20th century men were primarily the hunters and fighters (protectors and warriors). Women, in contrast, were primarily the child rearers. I am making no judgments here regarding whether this was good or bad or right or wrong, only that it was the reality of the world up until the 20th century for the vast majority of people. Of course, there were and still are occasional societies in which this principle did not hold, but these exceptions do not in any way detract from the validity of my generalization. (There is always an island in the South Pacific that will demonstrate any point — in support or in refutation.)

It is reasonable to state that those men who were genetically strong in the hunting/fighting functions were more likely to survive than those who were not. Those who were weaker in these functions were less likely to have food for survival and/or the capacity to protect themselves from their enemies. Consequently, their genes were not as likely to have been passed down to subsequent generations. Also, those who were weak in these areas were less likely to attract women, in that women tend (then and now) to consider as desirable mates men who exhibit a high capacity for providing food, clothing, and shelter for themselves and their children and high capability for protecting the potential family from enemies. This is another reason why the genes of men who were weaker in these areas were less likely to survive in the genetic pool. Similarly, women who were stronger in the child-rearing realm were more likely to be viewed by men as desirable mates and their genes, as well, were more likely to be passed down to their progeny. The greater aggressiveness of the male was not, I believe, simply confined to hunting and warring; it was also utilized in the service of mating. More aggressive men, then, were more likely to be successful in acquiring mates. And so we have another factor favoring the selective survival of more aggressive men.

Youngsters today of both sexes carry within them these genetic programs. Although we human beings are less beholden to our instinctual drives than are lower animals, we are still affected by them. A bird, for example, during the mating season, may have no choice other than to go through the mating ritual of its species. We humans have procreative urges, but we are not required to mate in any particular season, nor are we compelled to follow rigid mating patterns of behavior. However, this does not preclude our being programmed for such mating patterns with the resultant pressure for their expression.

There is another factor operative in what I believe to be gender differences in mating patterns. This relates more directly to reproductive capacity. It is a principle of Darwin's theory of natural selection and survival of the fittest that each species generally produces far more offspring than can possibly survive. Those particular forms that are most adaptable to the environment in which they have been born are more likely to survive and perpetuate the species. Those that are less adaptable to the particular environment will generally die off. This is the central element in the Darwinian theory. If one examines this further, one finds that there are two factors operative here: *quantity* and *quality*.

With regard to *quantity*, the number of offspring produced is far greater than can possibly survive in a particular environment. With regard to *quality*, the quality or type of offspring that is most adaptable to the specific environment is most likely to survive. Accordingly, one must consider both quantity control and quality control. Furthermore, with regard to quantity, the general thrust is for an organism to produce as many offspring as possible, i.e., the greatest quantity possible—most often far more than can possibly survive. With regard to quality, the general thrust is to select, narrow down, and restrict survival to those forms that will adapt best to and survive in a particular environment. The two processes of control, then, are antagonistic. The quantity control factors work toward the survival of the greatest number of offspring. The quality control factors operate to reduce and/or limit the number of offspring that will survive. Those forms that ultimately survive represent a balance of these two antagonistic forces.

In many forms of life, one of the sexes is specifically designated to provide quantity and the other quality. Often, it is not difficult to determine which sex is primarily involved in which function. This is certainly the case for the human being. Men are clearly the ones involved in producing the greatest quantity of offspring, whereas women are the quality controllers. If one were to simply view human beings as baby factories, whose main purpose is to perpetuate the species (a not absurd view), and if one were to ask which sex is more likely to produce a high quantity of offspring, it is clearly the male. If a man were to devote his whole life to the procreative process, it is reasonable that he could father one to two babies a day, providing, of course, he was provided with women who were in the fertile stages of their menstrual cycles. Accordingly, the male is reasonably capable of fathering 500 babies a year. We know that we could start using males for this purpose at about the age of 13 or 14, but we do not know the upper age at which such utilization would no longer be possible. There are men in their 90s who have viable sperm. But let us, more practically, end the male's fecund period at 75, because most men do not live beyond that age, and older men are less likely to father 500 babies a year. Accordingly, it is reasonable to say that the average male has a fecund period of 60 years. Fathering 500 babies a year for 60 years would enable a man to father 30,000 babies. (I am not addressing myself here to practicality, only to the issue of maximum possible reproductive capacity if one were to make use of men and women for this purpose.) In contrast, if a woman were to devote her fecund life to being a baby factory, she could reasonably reproduce one child a year from age 13 to about 56 (the oldest "proven" age at which a woman has been demonstrated to give birth). This will give her approximately 40 to 45 babies. Accordingly, it is reasonable to conclude that the male is very much the one capable of producing the greatest quantity of offspring.

What I have said thus far relates purely to biological capacity. The next question relates to the actual behavior of each of the sexes regarding the procreative process. The *potential* for being a reproductive factory is there, but in practice individuals generally have other things to do with their lives besides fornicating and propagating. And probably the most important of these other functions is child rearing. If no concern is given to the protection of the young, then babies will not survive and there would be no point to devoting one's life solely to manufacturing them. This brings us to quality control, the second step necessary for species survival. It is here that women have played the more formidable role. In order to carry out this function, it behooved women to be more circumspect with regard to mate selection. Those who were so, were more likely to be chosen as mates and more likely to pass their stronger child-rearing genes down to their offspring.

Men, I believe, have been programmed to crave sex indiscriminately with large numbers of women, i.e., to impregnate as many women as possible. From the roving bands of men in perpetual heat, a woman must select the man who is most likely to remain around after impregnation and serve the role of food gatherer and protector. In order to realize this important goal, women do best to be less impulsive with regard to gratifying indiscriminately their sexual urges—in order that they assess more objectively a potential father of their children. Women who were slower in sexual arousal were more likely to be judicious in mate selection and, therefore, more likely to survive. They were more likely to select men who would provide food, clothing, shelter, and protection. Accordingly, I believe that the *average* (I did not say all) present-day woman is slower in sexual arousal than the average man. Once aroused, however, a woman is more likely to attempt to maintain an ongoing relationship with her mate. In contrast, the average (I did not say all) present-day man is quicker in sexual arousal than the average woman. Once gratified, he is less likely to be desirous of maintaining the relationship. I believe that most women would confirm this statement in that the most common complaint single women have is that men are less interested in "commitment" (the in-vogue word for this phenomenon) than women are.

The old saying is applicable here: "Men are looking for girls, and girls are looking for husbands." Men are on the prowl. They are not only out hunting for prey to kill and eat, but hunting for female prey to serve as sexual companions. I believe that if one were able to create a printout of the average adult male's sexual thoughts throughout the course of the day, they would be formidable, especially printouts associated with day-to-day experiences in which the individual is not fully preoccupied with work. I believe that one would find that sexual thoughts would be associated with a large percentage of the man's encounters with females from the teen period and upward. These would involve some kind of sexual encounter. Secretaries, stewardesses, nurses, receptionists, waitresses, and the wide variety of other women that men inevitably encounter in the course of their day become stimuli for such sexual fantasies. Some confirmation of this "fantasy" of mine is to be found in Shanor's study (1978) in which he found that men between ages 12 and 40 think of sex an average of six times per hour. But the distribution over age ranges is not even. Between ages 12 and 19 the frequency is *20 times per hour* (approximately once every three minutes). Things slow down somewhat after that, so that between ages 30 and 39 it is four times an hour.

In short, most men are extremely promiscuous (if not physically, at least psychologically). The main difference between those to whom this label is applied and those to whom it is not, relates to the degree to which the man overtly tries to gain gratification for these urges. From the roving bands of men in heat, the woman must reject the large majority or else she will find herself impregnated by a man who has already gone on to the next cave or condo. She is much more concerned with relationships. I believe that this phenomenon is one of the factors involved in women having greater orgastic capacity than men. Although the woman is more likely to need caressing and tender overtures to be aroused, once aroused she is more likely to remain aroused longer. The male reaches his orgasm and immediately goes into a refractory period ("zonks out," falls asleep). The majority of women have the potential for multiple orgasms. This serves, I believe, the purpose of enhancing procreative capacity. Her multiple orgasmic capacity enables her to "hang in there longer" and ensure that the male who is slow to ejaculation is likely to be sustained in his interest and involvement.

Last, I believe that what I have said here is one explanation for the fact that men are generally more likely to be sexually excited by visual stimuli, whereas women are more likely to respond to tactile stimuli. The roving bands of men spot their prey at a distance and can get excited merely at the sight of a woman. This is in part a derivative of their hunting functions and it also serves to enlarge the potential population of sexual partners. Women, in contrast, need caressing, tenderness, and reassurance that the man will remain around for supplying food and protection for herself and her children. This is one of the reasons why men are more likely than women to be sexually aroused by visual pornographic material.

DAWKINS'S THEORY OF GENE SURVIVAL AND TRANSMISSION

I wish to emphasize that the theory proposed below may very well have been thought of previously by others. Although I have not either read about nor heard about it from others, it rests heavily on one proposed by Dawkins (1976). In fact, one might consider my theory an extension of Dawkins's applied specifically to the various forms of human sexual behavior. This theory, as is true of Dawkins's, rests heavily on Darwinian theory – especially the concepts of natural selection and the survival of the fittest. My theory, like Darwin's and Dawkins's, does not address itself to such ultimate questions as those related to the forces (entities, God, etc.) that created these principles and might very well be involved in their implementation. It does not concern itself with how atoms and molecules got to be here, nor does it concern itself with the origin of the principles that govern their interactions, both simple and complex. Rather, it concerns itself with the implementation of these entities and principles and the physical manifestations of their interactions – from the simplest to the most complex levels, from the earliest to the most recent. Nor does it concern itself with the ultimate purpose(s) of all of this, considering the fact, for example, that all life on earth will ultimately perish and that all forms of sexual behavior – both the "natural" and the "unnatural" varieties – will no longer serve any purpose, at least on this sphere, which we call Earth.

It is well to begin at the beginning, which (as Maria in *The Sound of Music* said) is a very good place to start. This sphere, like many other celestial bodies in the universe, began with its complement of elements, among which were to be found carbon, hydrogen, oxygen, and nitrogen – the fundamental building blocks of life. Under the influence of environmental conditions (both influences emanating from the sun as well as those in the intervening space), simple molecules formed by atomic union. Most important for the purposes of this discussion were water (H_2O), carbon dioxide (CO_2), methane (CH_4), and ammonia (NH_4). After exposure to ultraviolet light and electric currents (probably related to primordial lightning), more complex molecules were formed – especially amino acids, the building blocks of proteins. Scientists have been able to reproduce such transformations in a flask by subjecting the aforementioned simple molecules to ultraviolet radiation and electric currents. Laboratory simulations of the chemical conditions on earth before the beginning of life (as we know it) have produced organic substances such as purines and pyrimidines, which are the building blocks of the genetic molecule DNA. One can readily envision, then, a primordial "soup" in which the simpler and more complex molecules floated. The main method of production (or "creation") of the more complex molecules was the exposure of the simpler ones to the environmental conditions conducive to their formation. This method of formation of complex molecules depends upon the influence of external forces and, presumably, without their presence there would be no creation of the more complex forms.

The next step was the one in which certain molecules exhibited the capacity to reproduce themselves, a process that Dawkins (and others certainly) refer to as *replication.* The method that appears to have been most successful (in fact, it appears to be the only one on earth that we know of) was the one utilized by the DNA molecule. This molecule, made of segments that are to be found floating around in the primordial soup, reproduces itself by absorbing onto itself from the surrounding mixture those particular building blocks that correspond to those already strung on its helical (spiral) chain. The original molecule serves as a mold or template. It attracts corresponding smaller molecules from the soup, each free molecule attached to its own kind on the original model. Ultimately, this results in the formation of a clone of the original DNA molecule. In the next step the two strands separate: *Voilà,* reproduction! Each new strand then becomes a model for further replications, thus producing geometric growth in population.

If all the DNA molecules were cloned from the *original,* there would be few errors. However, with this kind of geometric progression, in which each *new* DNA molecule becomes a template for the reproduction of itself, there is a greater likelihood that "errors" or alternative forms may result, each of which may also survive. We have, then, the introduction of *variety.* Some of the forms have a greater likelihood of survival than others, depending upon the internal stability of the molecular chain.

Ultimately, the free-floating smaller molecules in the primordial soup become scarce as they are utilized ("eaten up") in the formation of the larger DNA molecules. Some sort of competition, then, arises as the DNA molecules compete with one another for the ever scarcer simpler radicals. The next step, according to Dawkins, was basically the phase of cannibalism. Because of the scarcity of free-floating smaller molecules in the primordial mixture, the DNA strands began breaking off segments of their neighbors in order to be provided with "food" for the replication process. The next step—and this was an extremely important one—was the formation by DNA molecules of protective coatings, a physical wall that served as a kind of armor that protected the DNA strand from being cannibalized by its neighbors. These entities (DNA strands, surrounded by protective shells) are basically what we are talking about when we discuss viruses. The protective shell is necessary for the survival of the internal core of DNA. Dawkins refers to this entity as a "survival machine," and this is the term he uses for all subsequent living forms, the function of which is to provide a housing for DNA molecules, especially with regard to their protection.

The next step involved the union of different types of DNA strands (which I will now call genes) to combine their efforts in the service of enhancing the likelihood of survival of the protective coating. Each could serve a different function and thereby increase the likelihood of survival over those with less complex mechanisms for adaptation in the primordial soup. We see, then, the formation of the simplest cells in which the genes are clustered together in the nucleus and the survival wall being represented by the surrounding cytoplasm and cell membrane (for animals) or cell wall (for plants). Obviously, we are describing here one-cell animals and plants. The next step in the evolution of living forms was the bringing together of individual cells into colonies. Here different parts of the colonies could perform different functions—enhancing, thereby, the chances of the DNA surviving. Those cells that were able to live together as colonies, each performing separate but unifying functions, would be at an advantage over those cells that floated about in isolation.

Dawkins then continues:

> A major branch of survival machines, now called plants, started to use sunlight directly themselves to build up complex molecules from simple ones, reenacting at much higher speed the synthetic processes of the original soup. Another branch, now known as animals, "discovered" how to exploit the chemical labors of the plants, either by eating them, or by eating other animals. Both main branches of survival machines evolved more and more ingenious tricks to increase their efficiency in their various ways of life, and new ways of life were continually being opened up. Subbranches and sub-subbranches of survival machines evolved more and more ingenious tricks to increase their efficiency in their various ways of life, and new ways of life were continually being opened up. Subbranches and sub-subbranches evolved, each one excelling in a particular specialized way of making a living: in the sea, on the ground, in the air, underground, up trees, inside other living bodies. This subbranching has given rise to the immense diversity of animals and plants which so impresses us today.

Every survival machine, then, can be viewed as a colony of DNA strands surrounded by successive layers of protective mechanisms. Its purpose, however, is not simply to protect the genes from cannibalistic destruction, but to provide mechanisms for the reproduction of the DNA strands. Here we are talking about the methods by which the particular form of life enables the DNA strands to pass down from generation to generation, each time ridding itself of the housing in which it temporarily resides and providing itself with a new and temporary survival machine. Dawkins states:

> Another aspect of the particulateness(sic) of the gene is that it does not grow senile; it is no more likely to die when it is a million years old than when it is only a hundred. It leaps from body to body down the generations, manipulating body after body in its own way and for its own ends, abandoning a succession of mortal bodies before they sink in senility and death.

Although the gene itself is in a constant state of equilibrium with surrounding atoms and smaller molecules available for its replication, its basic structure and appearance is always the same. It can be compared to a skyscraper that periodically and continually replaces its bricks with others provided externally. Both new bricks and old bricks are essentially immutable in that atoms do not "grow old."

Each cell has the information necessary to re-create the whole survival machine. Furthermore, it has the power to influence various parts of the survival machine, especially with regard to the protective mechanisms necessary for survival and the mechanisms necessary for reproduction, i.e., transmission of DNA replications from one temporary survival machine to the next and so on down the generations.

The millions of different kinds of plants and animals are testimony to the wide variety of survival machines that have evolved over eons. All the cells, all the tissues, all the organ systems, and all the plants and animals that incorporate DNA molecules share in common this one principle: the protection of the genes and their transmission to the next generation. The human brain is but one example of such a system. It is one of the latest and most complex examples of a part of the housing machine that serves to protect the DNA as well as enhance the likelihood that it will be transmitted to the next generation. Although designed by and in a sense controlled by DNA, it has a certain autonomy of its own in that it exerts some influence over the automatic control that genes have over the survival machine, especially with regard to the time of expression of the protective and procreative forces. For example, lower animals appear to have no choice but to perform their specific mating patterns at prescribed times and places. We have the ability to suppress somewhat these cravings, but still are often obsessed with and sometimes even enslaved by them.

As mentioned, Dawkins's theory could be considered the inevitable extension of the Darwinian theory. The major determinant as to whether a particular survival machine will indeed perform its functions is related to the efficiency of the mechanisms devised for protecting DNA and enabling it to transmit its replications down to form the next generation of survival machines. There is selective survival of those machines that are most likely to perform these functions in a particular environment, and there is selective failure to survive (and thereby destruction of DNA) of those housings that are less capable of survival in the particular environment in which the genes find themselves.

THE APPLICATION OF DAWKINS'S THEORY TO HUMAN SEXUAL VARIETY

Introduction

There is no problem applying Dawkins's theory to adult heterosexuality. We can view the human body as the survival machine for our sperm and ova, which are basically housings for our DNA. The sexual act is the step by which DNA replications are transmitted to the next generation of housing machines (our children). All the things we do in our lives can be viewed as steps toward this end. Just about every activity of our daily lives, throughout the 24-hour cycle, can be viewed as attempts to either protect and preserve our DNA or as a step toward its transmission. Every meal we eat, every breath we breathe, every penny we earn, every bit of work we do, can easily be considered part of this grand plan. When we sleep, we are recouping and saving up our energy for the next day's round of survival activities. Other activities, which might initially be considered exceptions to this principle, on careful inquiry may very well be found to be related.

Everything we learn has the potential to serve us in the enhancement of our capacity to survive, either immediately or remotely. Purely scientific inquiry, although initially unrelated, might ultimately find practical applications that serve human survival. What about art and music? Here again they might not initially appear to fit this scheme. However, art is used to enhance female and male attractiveness (in clothing styles and cosmetics) and the artist, in part, wants to impress the lady of his choosing. ("You must come up to my place sometime and view my etchings.") Or, the artist may wish to earn money, again in the service of providing himself (herself) with food, clothing, and shelter—which all serve in the survival of the temporary machine in which his (her) genes are housed. Music can serve similar purposes, for both musician ("She will certainly love me when she hears the music I have created") and the listener ("I love him for the music he has created"). Pleasure, like sleep, is necessary for us when we need to recoup our energies. When I try to think of examples of human endeavor that might not fit under this grand rubric, I am unable to do so. Accordingly, I will stop giving examples that support the theory and go on to a discussion of the forms of sexuality that do not initially appear to do so.

With regard to the atypical forms of sexuality, those that may not initially appear to serve the purposes of procreation, I wish to state at the outset that each of these has, I believe, a genetic and an environmental contribution. The genetic contribution may very well be the result of "gene error," the kind of error that brings about a form of atypical sexual behavior. If a mutation is not of survival value, it is not maintained for long in the genetic pool and the housing in which it is incorporated is destroyed by natural processes (both the housing and the DNA within decompose and in many cases are "eaten by worms"). The kinds of atypical human sexuality discussed here are not in this category because the human beings who exhibit these variations have definitely survived. One does well, also, to view the combination of genetic predisposition and environmental influences as varying. Accordingly, in some individuals the genetic loading may be very high, so much so that little if any environmental contribution may be necessary for the quality to become exhibited. In others the genetic contribution may be low, or even nonexistent; however, environmental (especially family) influences are so formidable that the sexual pattern becomes the primary mode of expression for that individual. One does well, also, to view these two examples as the extremes and to view all individuals who exhibit the particular sexual behavior as lying at some point in between these two extremes.

I am in full agreement with Freud's (1905) theory of the "polymorphous perversity" of the human infant. The infant will exhibit every form of sexual activity known to humanity. Society suppresses those forms that it considers unacceptable and allows expression of those that it considers acceptable. However, residua of the unacceptable variations often press for expression and may be found in various aspects of adult sexuality, both typical and atypical. All, however, are *natural* if one is defining the word as a sexual form of behavior that exists in human beings, regardless of the particular society's attitude toward that specific mode of sexual expression.

There is good reason to believe that most, if not all, children have the capacity to reach orgasm at the time they are born. (I am not recommending that we conduct any scientific studies to prove or disprove what I have just said.) Certainly, infants in the first few months of life may rub their genitals as they lie on their abdomens and their associated facial expressions are strongly suggestive of orgasm. There are people who claim that they cannot remember a time when they did not masturbate. And not all of these people have been sexually abused as children. Like all things in this world, there is a bell-shaped curve, and the age at which people first experienced orgasms also lies on a bell-shaped curve. Most people would date their first orgasm to the pubertal period, but there are many who can go much further back. It is reasonable to assume that there is a small fraction of the population who, without any particular external stimulation (sexual molestation or otherwise), normally experienced such high sexual urges in early infancy and found relief through masturbation. (Recently, sonograms have shown baby boys holding their penises in utero.) This, too, is "natural" and this, too, lends credibility to my belief that children are not only naturally sexual but that they may be the initiators of sexual activities. Although these overtures do not initially serve procreative purposes, they ultimately do because the child who is sexually active at an early age is more likely to be sexually active in adolescence and thereby provide his (her) DNA for the next generation of survival machines.

The common childhood game, aptly called "You-Show-Me-Yours-and-I'll-Show-You-Mine" is yet another example of childhood sexuality. Certainly curiosity plays a role in such games.

Parents begin teaching children, at a very early age, that certain parts of their bodies are to be strictly covered up and not to be exposed to others. Such prohibitions, of course, engender enormous curiosity, a curiosity that can be satisfied by voyeuristic/exhibitionistic games. But the games often go beyond the visual level and frequently involve touching, even with sexual excitation and intent. We see here the influence of DNA already at work. I suspect (but I am not certain) that boys are more interested than girls in these games because of the aforementioned high visual loading to their sexual interest.

Some further examples. A common practice for little children is to play with their genitals, even to the point of orgasm. Furthermore, it is also common for little girls to smell their fingers after such play and they will often find the odors enjoyable to sniff. Commonly, they will be taught by their mothers that such a practice is unacceptable. Boys smelling their fingers after touching their genitals is less common, but is the analogous practice. This olfactory gratification is much more highly developed in lower animals for whom scents play an important role in sexual activity. Residua of this phenomenon certainly exist in adults. We recognize it as "normal" for men to enjoy cunnilingus, a part of which pleasure comes from the olfactory stimulation that such activity provides. And women as well (again, in many segments of our society) enjoy immensely this activity. Here again, we see the residua of a childhood form of sexuality expressing itself in adult heterosexual behavior.

Moreover, orgastic pleasure may very well be the most intense known to the human being. The craving for this gratification is extremely strong and, of course, is the driving force behind the procreative process. The reduction of high sexual tensions and the craving for orgastic gratification is DNA's main method of bringing about reproductive activity and, by extension, its passage to the next generation. This phenomenon also serves to explain the fact that it is the men who stand around peering lasciviously at women, whereas it is far less common for women to do this as obviously and exhibitionistically as men. Many years ago there was a popular song entitled, "Standing on the Corner,

Watching the Girls Go By." And it was not women who were standing on the corner, but men!

Another example. All agree that infants enjoy immensely the breastfeeding experience. Mothers in our society are encouraged to express deep involvement in this practice and are permitted to speak about how psychologically and physically pleasurable breastfeeding is. However, few women will speak openly about orgasmic gratifications associated with the breastfeeding of their infants. It is more acceptable to describe breast stimulation pleasure as part of adult heterosexual activities. It is also acceptable to describe physical pleasure in association with a male partner's breastsucking as part of foreplay. I am not claiming that most women experience orgasms when breastfeeding their infants. I am only claiming that some women do, and that more probably would if they were to overcome the social inhibitions against such gratification.

Women's potential for pleasurable response to breastfeeding serves important biological purposes. It increases the likelihood that she will breastfeed her child, increasing thereby the likelihood that her progeny will survive. It increases the likelihood that she will want to breastfeed subsequent babies, either her own or those of others. It produces in general a heightened level of sexuality, keeps the sexual juices flowing (not only the milk), and increases thereby the likelihood that she will have heterosexual sexual encounters. It increases also the likelihood that she will enjoy her breasts being sucked by adult males during heterosexual encounters. Her pleasure, which is a residuum of both her own breastfeeding in her own infancy (via projective identification with her breastfeeding infant) and the pleasurable sensation provided by the sucking of her breasts, serves to enhance the man's pleasure (via her excitation). Residua of the man's breastfeeding gratifications in his own infancy also contribute to the pleasure experienced by the man when engaging in breastsucking during the heterosexual encounter. These residua, one in each of the parties, enhance the likelihood of copulation and thereby the passage of DNA to the next generation.

It is important for the reader to appreciate that I am making no value judgments on any of these sexual activities. Each society does this and our society is no exception. My purpose here is to present a valueless explanation of these activities. The reader should recognize that I, as a product of the society in which I live, have my biases, prejudices, etc., but these are irrelevant to my presentation here.

The Paraphilias of *DSM-III-R*

At this point I address myself to each of the forms of atypical sexuality described in *DSM-III-R* (1987). These are the forms of atypical sexuality that are considered by the DSM-III-R nomenclature committee to be manifestations of psychiatric disorder. It would be a naive reader who is not appreciative of the fact that there is not a disorder here that was not considered the norm in some other society at some time and some place. This list, therefore, represents the beliefs and even the biases of the nomenclature committee. One confirmation of this point is the fact that homosexuality was considered a bona fide disease in *DSM-II* (1968) and the previous *DSM* (1952) (which has no number and is now retrospectively sometimes referred to as *DSM-I*). The authors of *DSM-III* (1980) took the position that if a person is homosexual and wishes to change his (her) orientation, then the individual might then be considered to be suffering with a psychiatric disorder and might thereby be justifiably treated for such. To the best of my knowledge, this is the first time in the history of medicine that patients themselves make the decision regarding whether or not they have a disease. The homosexual person, then, who was seeking treatment under *DSM-III* criteria had to "enter through the back door" to qualify for a diagnosis under this system.

In *DSM-III-R* (1987) homosexuality is not even listed as a disorder per se. However, if one looks up the word in the index, there is a reference under the very last of the list of sexual disorders: "302.90 Sexual Disorder Not Otherwise Specified." Here are listed sexual disorders that are not to be found listed in any of the previous categories. Three examples are given, the third of which is: "Persistent and marked distress about one's sexual orientation." It is only here that a homosexual person—who is distressed about his (her) sexual orientation—can justifiably be considered to have a disorder. It is of interest that the just quoted lines are the very last ones in the section on sexual disorders. To carry the back door analogy further, the homosexual person who is entering treatment under the *DSM-III-R* provisions must creep through a little trap door that is cut into the back door (the kind that a dog might use). Enough said about the vicissitudes, biases, and unreliability of *DSM-III-R*. I suspect strongly that *DSM-IV* (which is scheduled for publication in 1993) will have yet another set of theories regarding atypical sexuality.

A paraphilia is defined as a form of sexual expression that is atypical or "off the beaten track." It is a sexual activity that is found on a parallel track (thus the prefix "para" [Greek: besides]), but is still a form of lovemaking (thus the word "philia" [Greek: love]). *DSM-III-R* considers the paraphilias to be "sexual disorders," which is a more recent term for "diseases." I will address myself to each of the paraphilias, in the order in which they appear in *DSM-III-R*, and comment on each, especially with regard to the aforementioned theory. I will give particular attention to the issue of the "justification" for such atypical sexuality, especially with regard to the question of its function and purpose if it does not serve the immediate aims of reproduction and species survival. *DSM-III-R* emphasizes that the paraphilic label is justified when the activity is the primary or one of the primary sources of sexual gratification of the individual. The label might not be justified if it exhibits itself only rarely and is a minor part of the person's sexual repertoire. The committee uses the six-month cut-off point for a duration that justifies the diagnosis but, I am certain, recognizes this as somewhat artificial.

Furthermore (and this is important), for each of the paraphilias there is included an important diagnostic proviso: "The person has acted on these urges, or is markedly distressed by them." Accordingly, if an individual is preoccupied with such urges, but has not acted on them, then they would not be considered manifestations of a disorder. This too presents us with problems, especially from the point of view of a therapist who may be consulted regarding treatment. These are strange kinds of disorders indeed. They are disorders if acted on, but not disorders if not acted on. Most would agree that a person who is preoccupied with suicidal thoughts, but who has not acted them out warrants a diagnosis and treatment. For the paraphilias, however, there appears to be an exception to this principle. Also, the issue of distress presents problems for the consultant who is being asked to make a decision whether or not a disease is present. Most would agree that a person who is not distressed by homicidal thoughts is still suffering with a disease. Here again we have the problem attendant to the patients making the decision regarding whether or not a disease is present. I mention these problems because they lend confirmation to my belief that the nomenclature committee has had significant difficulties with the paraphilias, especially with regard to the question of whether or not they are indeed diseases (or, to use the committee's euphemism, "disorders"). Such ambivalence is relevant to my theory about the etiology and purposes of the paraphilias.

The main point I will be making with regard to each of the paraphilias is that they do, in a way, serve the purposes of species survival and are therefore part of the natural repertoire of humanity. They serve this end by their ability to enhance the general level of sexual excitation in society and thereby increase the likelihood that people will involve themselves in activities that are more directly contributory to the reproductive (and, by extension, species survival) process. I recognize that for each of the paraphilias there are a wide variety of psychodynamic mechanisms that may be operative in producing the behavior. However, it is not my purpose here to discuss these in detail. Rather, I will only discuss those psychodynamic aspects that pertain to the aforementioned theory.

Exhibitionism is defined as:

> Over a period of at least six months, recurrent intense sexual urges and sexually arousing fantasies involving the exposure of one's genitals to an unsuspecting stranger.

Although exhibitionism is primarily a male characteristic in its "raw form" (that is, as exhibited by "flashers"), it certainly does exist in women in more subtle form. Seductive gesturing, provocative dancing (not necessarily by burlesque queens and go-go girls), and hysterical behavior generally involve some degree of exhibitionistic sexuality. Accordingly, when one considers these common forms of female exhibitionism, the behavior is much more common among women than men. Although the flasher may wish to startle and gain a sense of power and importance, much more than arouse sexuality, there is still that element operative in this clearly sexual act. And although the exhibitionistic woman may want flattery and attention, more than sexual gratification, the activity is still a form of foreplay and may very well lead to more overt sexual activity. For both sexes the behavior is designed (at least in part) to produce sexual hormone secretions into the bloodstream of the observer and enhance thereby the likelihood of sexual activity and reproduction.

We have strict rules in our society regarding when and where one can be sexually exhibitionistic. Furthermore, exhibitionism is more acceptable in women than in men. The principle is well demonstrated by the old observation: If a woman undresses in front of a window, a man in the street looking at her may be charged with being a voyeur ("peeping Tom"). In contrast, if a man undresses in front of a window and a woman in the street looks at him, he may be charged with exhibitionism (indecent exposure). These differences in social attitude notwithstanding, exhibitionism serves survival value in that it provides visual stimuli that result in the kinds of hormonal secretions that may result in procreation.

Fetishism   is defined as:

> Over a period of at least six months, recurrent intense sexual urges and sexually arousing fantasies involving the use of non-living objects by themselves (e.g., female undergarments).
>
> The fetishes are not only articles of female clothing used in cross-dressing (Transvestic Fetishism) or devices designed for the purpose of tactile genital stimulation (e.g., vibrator).

Here, too, the same principles hold. Often the object may be used in place of "the real thing" when sexual encounters with humans are not available. The fetishistic object may become the symbol of the human sexual object and bring about the same degree of excitation. Fetishism not only serves the purposes of sexual release, but also lessens the likelihood of the sexual organs "drying up." The practice thereby keeps sexual cravings alive and increases the possibility of reproduction. Even the person who may fear sexual encounters at that point, and uses the fetishistic object as a substitute, is keeping himself (herself) in the pool of sexually craving individuals and thereby increases the likelihood of species survival. Here again we see the principle that some of the fetishistic objects (such as vibrators) are borrowed from normal sexuality but are considered pathological when they are used in preference to the interpersonal type of sexual experience. I trust that the *DSM-III-R* committee did not consider the use of vibrators per se to warrant the diagnosis of fetishism and recognized that their use as a "sexual aid" is "normal."

Frotteurism   is defined as:

> Over a period of at least six months, recurrent intense sexual urges and sexually arousing fantasies involving touching and rubbing against a nonconsenting person. It is the touching, not the coercive nature of the act, that is sexually exciting.

These are the people who rub up against others in subways, buses, elevators, and other crowded places. They are people who are considered to be getting their "cheap thrills" in a socially unacceptable way. Once again, men are far more likely than women to be involved in this paraphilia and, once again, they are most often the initiators. This is consistent with what I have said previously about the male being genetically programmed to play the more aggressive role in mating pattern rituals. Women, however, cannot be considered to be completely free of this disorder. As every frotteur knows, there are a certain fraction of women who will not immediately recoil and withdraw, and thereby get across the message that they have no wish to participate in this activity. In spite of "rejections" by the majority of women, there are still enough around who will go along with the secret game and thereby gratify their own frotteuristic cravings without suffering social stigma.

I once interviewed a man who was a frotteur and who claimed that approximately 25 percent of all the women against whom he rubbed his penis responded. Most allowed him to masturbate himself against them, using the motions of the moving vehicle as the cover-up for their own more active participation in the process. Some even rubbed their vulvas against him, thereby gratifying themselves as well. On a few occasions the activity ultimately resulted in their going off together for a sexual encounter. Frotteurism also serves survival purposes. It increases the general level of sexual excitation and thereby increases the likelihood of sexual reproduction.

Pedophilia   is defined as:

> Over a period of at least six months, recurrent intense sexual urges and sexually arousing fantasies involving sexual activity with a prepubescent child or children (generally age 13 or younger).
> The person is at least 16 years old and at least 5 years older than the child or children in A.
> **Note:** Do not include a late adolescent involved in an ongoing sexual relationship with a 12- or 13-year-old.

It is obvious that the *DSM-III-R* nomenclature committee had great difficulty with this definition. The requirement that the person be "at least 16 years old" presents problems if a 15-1/2-year-old boy has a sexual experience with a five-year-old girl. Although he has satisfied the requirement that there be at least a five-year age difference between the two, he would not be considered a pedophile by this definition. In contrast, the jury before whom he is tried for this act (and for which he might get life imprisonment) might very well consider him to be a pedophile. Actually, the *DSM-III-R* committee is not alone here. There is no good definition of pedophilia.

Whatever definition one uses, there are loopholes. One must make exceptions, such as the *DSM-III-R* committee did. If one uses the dictionary definition, i.e., a sexual act between an adult and a child, one is immediately confronted with the problem of what constitutes an adult and what constitutes a child. Does adulthood begin at puberty, at 16, at 18, at 21? All of these ages (and others) have been used at various times by different societies (and even within the same society) as a cutoff point for the definition of adulthood. If one wants to use puberty as the point of differentiation, there are still difficulties. If a *post*pubertal 13-year-old has sex with a *pre*pubertal 11-year-old, is that pedophilia? Most would say no. If a *post*pubertal 11-year-old has a sexual activity with a *pre*pubertal 13-year-old, is the younger one then considered to have sexually molested the older? Again, we see that there is no end to the complications with any of these definitions. All of them attempt to define the parameters of unacceptability (whether psychiatric/diagnostic or legal/criminal) and all fail. Basically, the definition of a pedophile for a psychiatrist is what the nomenclature committee of the American Psychiatric Association considers to be a pedophile for that particular edition of DSM. And the definition by the legal system is not only the one recorded in the statutes of the particular state (and there is great variation), but what the jury decides is pedophilia on the basis of the evidence presented at the accused's trial.

Pertinent to my theory here is that pedophilia also serves procreative purposes. Obviously, it does not serve such purposes on the immediate level in that children cannot become pregnant nor can they make others pregnant. However, the child who is drawn into sexual encounters at an early age is likely to become highly sexualized and crave sexual experiences during the prepubertal years. Such a "charged up child" is more likely to become sexually active after puberty and more likely, therefore, to transmit his (her) genes to his (her) progeny at an early age. (I will have more to say about pedophilia in the next chapter because of its central importance to this book.)

The younger the survival machine at the time sexual urges

appear, the longer will be the span of procreative capacity, and the greater the likelihood the individual will create more survival machines in the next generation. The ideal then—from DNA's point of view—is for the child to be sexually active very early, to have a highly sexualized childhood, and begin procreating at the time of puberty. This increases the likelihood that more survival machines will be produced for the next generation.

Sexual Masochism is defined as:

> Over a period of at least six months, recurrent intense sexual urges and sexually arousing fantasies involving the act (real, not simulated) of being humiliated, beaten, bound, or otherwise made to suffer.

Sexual Sadism Sexual masochism is intrinsically associated with sexual sadism. In fact, the two together are often referred to as "sadomasochism." Accordingly, I will present here the *DSM-III-R* definition of sexual sadism and then discuss both together.

> Over a period of at least six months, recurrent intense sexual urges and sexually arousing fantasies involving acts (real, not simulated) in which the psychological or physical suffering (including humiliation) of the victim is sexually exciting to the person.

Clearly, sadomasochism allows gratification of hostile impulses for the sadist. The motives for the masochist are not so obvious, but from the psychological point of view the individual is gaining some kind of gratification. For some people masochism serves to alleviate their guilt over sexual expression. Punishment can assuage guilt. Some people need the punishment afterward, and some before, and some at the time of the guilt-provoking act. Masochism may relate to identification with masochistic models, the feeling that this is the best that one can get, that more benevolent relationships would not be possible, and other psychological mechanisms that are beyond my purposes here.

Sadomasochism may also serve survival value. Sexual courtship patterns in our society have often been compared to a "hunt." The man, traditionally more assertive (as mentioned, I believe there is some genetic programming here, although environmental factors are certainly operative), seeks his "prey," the woman. If successful, he may consider himself to have made a "conquest." The woman's role is generally one of passivity, coyness, and seductivity in which she lures the man to approach her and make sexual advances. (Here, again, I believe genetic factors play an important role, although environmental ones are certainly operative.) Domination enters here and, in extreme cases, rape. Accordingly, we see a continuum from the normal courting pattern of female passivity and male aggressivity to the more aggressive forms of sexual approach and domination, with a culmination in rape—the extreme example of domination. Every point on this continuum increases the likelihood that the woman will engage in a sexual act and thereby procreate.

Our society encourages women to be seductive, coy, and enticing and encourages men to be forthright, aggressive, and pursuing. The more coercive elements enter into the male's behavior, the greater the likelihood our society will condemn him. The theme of pursuit and domination, however, is widespread. A number of years ago I read a survey in which women were asked about their favorite movie scene. The one that took first place was a scene from "Gone with the Wind" in which Rhett Butler, overcome with sexual passion and frustration, grabs Scarlett O'Hara, picks her up in his arms, and runs up the stairs into the house and presumably up to the bedroom. We accept this as normal, but we will not accept more coercive elements. This reflects society's repression of the animal within us: a male animal who has the potential for rape and a female animal who, by merely a small extension of permissible attitudes, may become masochistic—thereby gaining sexual pleasure from being beaten, bound, and otherwise made to suffer.

It may very well be that for some masochistic women, allowing themselves to be beaten into submission is the price they are willing to pay for gaining the gratification of receiving the sperm. When less aggressive partners are not available, partners who don't take the domination factor too far, they will accept sperm from a sadistic individual, rather than not have any sperm at all.

I wish to emphasize again that I am placing no value judgments on these behaviors at this point. Rather, I am trying to explain the purposes of certain forms of sexual behavior which are found in every society and which are dealt with differently by each society, and even by the same society at different times. Their ubiquity is a testament to the fact that they are natural, i.e., they are part of the human repertoire. We should not let our revulsion and condemnation of them interfere with our ability to understand them. In fact, it is through such understanding that we will be in a better position to decide how to deal with these atypical forms, both from the psychiatric and legal points of view.

Transvestic Fetishism   is defined as:

> Over a period of at least six months, in a heterosexual male, recurrent intense sexual urges and sexually arousing fantasies involving cross-dressing.

The comments I have made previously about fetishism are applicable to transvestic fetishism. In this form of fetishism the objects that cause the sexual arousal are not only female clothing, but cross-dressing, a particular utilization of female clothing. As noted in the *DSM-III-R* definition, these men are usually heterosexual, are sexually aroused by wearing female attire, and are thereby more likely to engage in heterosexual activities—increasing thereby the likelihood of procreation and the passage of their DNA down to the next generation.

It may come as a surprise to the reader to learn that the majority of transvestic fetishists are heterosexual. Certainly, there are homosexuals who wear female clothing as a way of attracting men for sexual purposes. However, these people are different from transvestic fetishists. Female impersonators are probably the most well-known examples of transvestic fetishists. With rare exception, they are heterosexual. It is of interest that *DSM-III-R* does not have a pathological category for homosexual men who cross-dress, but only heterosexual men. This is just one of the paradoxes that is to be found in *DSM-III-R,* a paradox that derives from the diagnostic problems attendant to removing homosexuality from the list of psychiatric disorders.

Voyeurism is defined as:

> Over a period of at least six months, recurrent intense sexual urges and sexually arousing fantasies involving the act of observing an unsuspecting person who is naked, in the process of disrobing, or engaging in sexual activity.

Voyeurism is much more common in men than women. This is not surprising considering the fact that men are much more likely to be excited by visual stimuli than women. It is the men who stand on the street corner jeering at the women passersby. It is men who are much more likely to be sexually excited by pin-up magazines, pornographic movies, and videotapes. As mentioned, I believe this phenomenon relates to the hunter qualities that are much more apparent in males than females. Traditionally, men were the hunters and protectors. It was they who went out to kill animal prey and thereby provide food for their families. Hunting involves (and even requires) visual surveillance. And hunting animals for food is akin to hunting women for procreative purposes. Similar male attributes are involved. It is reasonable to speculate that there was a selective survival of men who were visually powerful and who were good at hunting prey for food and females for procreative purposes. We see here, then, an overlap with the domination element applicable to the understanding of sado-masochism.

DSM-III-R then lists seven other paraphelias that are not only less common, but would probably be considered more pathological than the aforementioned. They all share in common, however, their capacity to enhance sexual arousal and to increase, thereby, the likelihood of heterosexual experience.

Telephone Scatologia (Lewdness)

The man who involves himself in telephone scatologia (lewdness) is clearly trying to arouse a woman. (It is rare for women to involve themselves in this kind of activity.) Although one may claim that the man so involved is basically afraid of women (and this is probably the case), he is still getting sexually aroused by the practice, even though the arousal often culminates only in masturbation. There are occasions, I am certain, in which the woman is receptive and the overture ultimately results in heterosexual activities and therefore procreation. But even when this aim is not realized (certainly more often the case), the man is still keeping his "juices flowing" and preventing them from drying up and thereby removing himself from the heterosexual potentially procreative scene.

Necrophilia (Corpses)

One could argue that necrophilia cannot possibly serve pro-creative purposes. I am in agreement that a dead woman is not going to conceive a child, but this is only half the story. Obviously, a man who must resort to having sexual intercourse with dead bodies has serious difficulties in his ability to relate well to live human beings. (Again, it is not my purpose here to discuss in detail the many possible psychological factors that are operative in each of these activities.) Yet, the necrophiliac is still keeping his juices flowing and increasing, thereby, the likelihood of heterosexual involvement with a person who is more likely to conceive. (For obvious reasons, necrophilia is almost unknown in females.)

Partialism (Exclusive Focus on Part of Body)

The factors operative here are very similar to those operative in fetishism. For reasons peculiar to that individual, a particular part of the body becomes the primary source of gratification. However, this symptom is not a strange one, considering the fact that all men (and to a lesser extent women) engage in it to a certain degree. Men's breast fetish is probably the most well known example of this phenomenon. This preoccupation stems, in part, from the fact that the breast is the first "sex object" of the male (at least according to Freudian theory) and we live in a society in which breasts are indeed worshiped. Furthermore, we enhance the importance of these organs (which are basically bags of fatty tissue intermingled with milk ducts) by social conditioning. Covering them, under most circumstances, makes them more alluring, seductive, and therefore objects of interest. There are men who are similarly turned on by buttocks and vulvas. Interestingly, women are far less likely to exhibit this symptom. This is in part related to their being less aroused by visual stimuli and more aroused by caressing, cuddling, and activities that ensure the kind of depth relationship that will increase the likelihood that the lover will stay around after conception and provide protection for themselves and their children.

Zoophilia (Animals)

Zoophilia, which is reputed to be a traditional activity among farm boys, also provides for sexual release when other outlets are not available. It may also be attractive to those who may have fears and inhibitions regarding overtures to females who are more unpredictable than animals regarding their sexual receptivity. Contrary to popular opinion, zoophilics do not generally have sexual intercourse with animals; rather, their main source of gratification comes from hugging, cuddling, and talking—in a manner similar to a child with a pet. The zoophilia then represents a fixation at an earlier level of psychosexual development. Although progeny are obviously not possible from such relationships, the individuals engaged in such zoophilic activities might be considered to be getting practice for more appropriate partners for the purposes of evolutionary survival.

Coprophilia (Feces)

Once again, one cannot ascribe immediate survival value to this practice. It is a derivative, however, of the polymorphous perversity of children who have to learn that touching their fecal eliminations and then putting their fingers (or feces) in their mouths is generally viewed in our society as a disgusting practice. Here, too, this enhancement of sexual stimulation increases the likelihood that the individual may turn to others and thereby contribute to the procreative process.

To the best of my knowledge, most people who are involved in coprophilic activities do not actually engage in putting feces into their mouths (although a small percentage do); rather, the activities most often involve defecating on one's "loved one." The term also refers to the partner who becomes sexually excited by being defecated upon. Coprophilia is also related to sadomasochism in that the person who enjoys this activity is often involved in a sadomasochistic act with domination/submission and hostile release ("shitting on someone").

Klismaphilia (Enemas)

Anal stimulation in itself can provide sexual pleasure. Most people enjoy the gratification of a "good bowel movement," although it is not considered proper to talk about it in most circles. Furthermore, deep anal penetration, beyond the anus, can produce stimulation of the pubococcygeal muscles, which play an active role in orgasm for both males and females. Hence, an enema can be to the anus what the vibrator is to the vagina. Association of the enema with mothers who provided them in childhood may play a role in producing this type of sexual behavior. What is important for my presentation here is the fact that this kind of stimulation may serve as a prelude to heterosexual intercourse and thereby contribute to procreative purposes.

Urophilia (Urine)

One could argue that urophilia cannot possibly serve procreative purposes. There are children who continue wetting their beds – beyond the time when they should be "trained" – because they like the warm feeling the urine gives them when first passed. Of course, when it gets cold, they change their attitude about this practice. Here, again, the most common activity is not drinking urine (but a small percentage do), but urinating on the "lover." And there are those who become sexually excited by being urinated upon. This practice is analogous to coprophilia and relates to sadomasochism. Once again, the arousal may serve as a part of foreplay and ultimately result in procreative sexual acts.

Further Comments on the Paraphilias

It would be an error for the reader to conclude here that I view the paraphilias to be primarily, if not exclusively, genetically determined biological variants. Although I believe there to be a genetic loading for the paraphilias, I also believe that environmental factors are extremely important in bringing about such behavior. In fact, I consider environmental factors to be playing a more important role in the development of the paraphilias than I do in the development of homosexuality, which, as I will describe below, I also believe warrants being listed as one of the paraphilias. I say this because of the bizarreness of many of the paraphilias, a bizarreness which is akin to the kinds of "craziness" that justifies placement in *DSM-III-R*. Many of the paraphilias are developed in an attempt to avoid intimacy, e.g., fetishism, telephone scatologia, partialism, zoophilia, and necrophilia. Others clearly allow for the release of hostility, which may be a more important factor than the sexual act that is serving as a vehicle for such gratification, e.g., sexual sadism, coprophilia, urophilia, and klismaphilia. Others derive from severe feelings of inadequacy, e.g., voyeurism, exhibitionism, sexual sadism, and pedophilia. Obviously, the psychodynamic factors operative in each of the paraphilias are quite complex and it goes beyond the scope of this book to discuss these in detail. Even the aforementioned outline is an oversimplification in that there is much overlap and complexity to the many psychodynamic factors operative in each of the paraphilias.

One could argue that psychodynamically determined sexual

inhibitions (which may contribute to the development of paraphilias) result from psychological problems that work against the expression of the primary sexual goals of DNA. Accordingly, one could claim that the very existence of the paraphilias weakens my theory. My response is this: Each of the paraphilias may be viewed as an atypical variant, as a mutant that does not primarily serve the purposes of procreation, but that may survive anyway because it can contribute (admittedly in an inefficient way) to the primary DNA goals. Similarly, the psychological inhibitions that interfere with DNA's primary expression also work against its goals, but not completely so. The fact that some forms fail to live up to the high standards put down in the optimum configuration of genetic programming does not negate the theory. My reasoning here is similar to that which holds for the sexual dysfunctions (see below) in which there are failures of genital functioning, which may then interfere with the procreative process. The presence of these weaknesses or abnormalities does not negate the theory.

Sexual Dysfunctions

The sexual dysfunctions are essentially forms of pathology in which there is some inhibition and/or impairment in the individual's capacity to engage in heterosexual intercourse. A psychogenic component is considered to be important in bringing about such disorders, but physiological factors may also be operative, especially in the presence of physical disease. These include: impairments in sexual desire, aversion to sexuality, impairment in the ability of a man to attain or maintain an erection, a man or a woman's inability to achieve orgasm, premature ejaculation, dyspareunia (pain on sexual intercourse), and vaginismus (vaginal spasm on penile entry). Clearly, all of these difficulties interfere with the likelihood of procreation and thereby warrant being included as disorders or "diseases." Obviously, they do represent a failure in the fulfillment of the individual's capacity to achieve this important goal. The presence of these disorders in no way weakens my theory that there is no biological function (all of which have survival value) that may not be compromised by some disease process.

SHOULD HOMOSEXUALITY BE LISTED AMONG THE PARAPHILIAS?

As mentioned, the last *DSM-III-R* section on the sexual disorders allows for the diagnosis of homosexuality (as a sexual disorder) through the "little doggie door," a subsection of the "back door" of the sexual diagnoses. I, myself, would include homosexuality as one of the paraphilias, whether or not one considers any or all of them to warrant placement in *DSM-III-R*. (I believe that political factors, much more than scientific, determined its strange and somewhat confusing placement in the manual.) The argument that homosexuality is "unnatural" because it does not serve procreative purposes is not valid. It certainly is a natural variant, is within the potential of all human beings, and to the best of my knowledge has appeared in every society. Furthermore, as I will elaborate below, it also serves the procreative aims of the species, although not directly.

There are some who claim that the purpose of homosexuality is similar to that of nonreproductive variants that are to be found in many species. Worker ants would be an example. They play an important role in the survival of the ant colony, but are not actively involved in the reproductive process. The argument is also proposed that homosexuals serve artistic purposes in that they are traditionally more artistically sensitive (art, literature, dance, theater, etc.). This theory never rang true for me in that these activities are very recent developments in the history of the human race and would not explain the existence of homosexuality at earlier times and the survival of genes that may very well predispose people to this type of sexual variation.

Although the homosexual genetic loading may very well have arisen as a mutation (as may have been the case for other paraphilias for which there is a high genetic loading), it has survived. There is great variation among mutations with regard to their survival capacity. Some mutants are incompatible with life and the particular form dies in utero. And there are a wide variety of diseases that are manifestations of mutations that can be lethal at any age and at any stage of life. If the mutation allows survival beyond puberty, then the individual is likely to transmit the mutant genes down to the next generation. Medical science may contribute to this process by allowing for the survival of certain mutations that in earlier centuries might not have survived to the pubertal level of development but, as the result of modern medical techniques, are doing so. This is just another example of the fact that medical progress may often be a mixed blessing.

Another theory to justify homosexuality is that it serves the purposes of population control. Although I believe that this theory has more to justify it than the one that holds that homosexuals serve artistic purposes, it also does not set well with me. Nonreproductive variants usually serve some purpose, a purpose that is readily recognized. This does not appear to be the case for homosexuals. We are certainly witnessing a population explosion that is becoming ever more serious, and even dangerous. There is no question that we will ultimately have to provide more effective methods of population control than exist at this point. The longer we allow population to grow geometrically, the greater the weight one will have to give to this theory of the purpose of homosexuality. Perhaps at this point, when the dangers are not as grave, it is a less compelling theory. But acceptance of it must presuppose considerations (by DNA or some master planner) that go very much into the future. And this does not appear to be the way DNA works. It is very much oriented to the here-and-now for the purposes of immediate transmission to the next survival machine. Impulsivity and pleasure-of-the-moment considerations appear to be much more pertinent factors in its behavior than considerations of some remote future event. It is for these reasons, as well, that I am not significantly enthusiastic about the population-control theory of homosexuality.

Homosexual genetic programming has survived not only because we have not routinely killed all homosexuals (although certain societies have attempted to do so), but because homosexuals have not confined themselves sexually to people of their own sex, but have engaged in heterosexual activities as well. In fact, it is safe to say that the vast majority of homosexuals have had some heterosexual experiences. It is also a fact that male homosexuals are typically highly sexualized individuals, much more so than the average male heterosexual, and are well known for their "promiscuity," i.e., their strong need for frequent sex with a large number of sexual partners. Male homosexuals also will typically date the onset of their strong sexual urges to earlier periods of life than heterosexuals (Kinsey et al. 1948; Tripp, 1987). Homosexuality, then, if my theory is correct, serves the purpose of heightening the general level of sexual activity and increases the chances, thereby, that such individuals may involve themselves in heterosexual activities as well.

Homosexuality also increases the likelihood that children will become involved earlier in sexual activities, increasing thereby the likelihood of their becoming actively sexual in the postpubertal period. I am referring here to the homosexual who is also a pedophile (again, much more common in males than females). Like his heterosexual pedophilic counterpart, both contribute to the likelihood that children will become active heterosexual adults.

When I presented the above theory to a colleague of mine, Dr. Jonathan Greene, he suggested that homophobia may also have survival value. Homophobes are revolted by homosexuality and may actively attempt to constrain their behavior. In extreme cases they may even attempt to eliminate homosexuals entirely. One traditional explanation for homophobia given by psychoanalysts is that homophobes are basically uncomfortable with their own unconscious or dimly conscious homosexual urges. By eliminating homosexuality they protect themselves from the stimulation of their own "latent homosexual impulses." I do not deny that this may certainly be a mechanism in some (if not many) homophobic individuals. And, I do not deny that there are probably other psychological mechanisms operative in this aversion. Nor do I deny social influences that teach that homosexuality is an undesirable and even disgusting form of sexual expression. However, Greene has a good point in that homophobia has survival value in that a society cannot tolerate ubiquitous homosexuality. To do so would threaten its very survival. On a very primitive level, then, the battle between homosexuals and heterosexuals is a battle for DNA survival, even though homosexuality—in a more indirect way—does ultimately contribute to DNA survival. It is an inefficient method, however, and a society has to limit the degree to which it can tolerate inefficient methods of reproduction. And all paraphilias are inefficient when compared to the traditional heterosexual reproductive modes.

One could argue, then, that homosexuality justifiably belongs among the paraphilias. It certainly satisfies the basic requirement for such inclusion, namely, that the sexual behavior is atypical (practiced only by a minority of individuals in our society) and that it does not directly serve procreative purposes.

One could argue that all of the paraphilias (whether or not one wants to include in them homosexuality) should not be included in *DSM-III-R* because the manual is devoted primarily to diseases. Although the term *disorder* is used, insurance companies still consider these variations *diseases* or *illnesses*. Exclusion of the paraphilias might deprive paraphilic individuals of the opportunity for insurance coverage if they want treatment for them. Should we therefore consider the insurance companies to be the final arbiters with regard to whether or not a behavioral manifestation warrants inclusion in *DSM-III-R? DSM-III-R* deals with this question somewhat obliquely by stating that in addition to the paraphilic behavioral manifestation, the individual must be "markedly distressed" by the desire to engage in the sexual practice. This, then, brings us back to the problem of patients making the decision whether or not the disease in fact exists. As a physician I would like to believe that a disease exists in its own right, separate from whether or not the patient considers it to exist and separate from whether or not an insurance company decides to provide coverage.

One could argue that something must be seriously deranged in a man who would prefer to have intercourse with a dead body in comparison to a beautiful young woman. One could argue that there must be something seriously wrong with a man who would spurn sexual intercourse with an attractive and receptive young woman and, in preference, put his penis into the anus of another man. When we say that "something is wrong with" a person who engages in certain activities, we are basically saying that the individual is suffering with a psychiatric disorder. One could argue also that the probable genetic predisposition factor, a factor related to a mutation, also argues for the paraphilias to be considered psychiatric disorders. There are other psychiatric disorders that are considered to have a genetic basis, e.g., bipolar disorder and obsessive compulsive disorder (OCD). These certainly are "natural" in that they are to be found in nature, yet they are still considered to be diseases (or, euphemistically, "disorders").

It is a strange paradox that pedophilia is included as a paraphilia, but not homosexuality. Accordingly, if an adult's primary source of sexual gratification is an individual of the same sex, the behavior is not considered to warrant inclusion among the paraphilias (or anywhere else in *DSM-III-R*). However, if the adult desires sex with a child (whether of the same or opposite sex), that behavior is considered to warrant inclusion among the paraphilias. This paradox lends confirmation to my aforementioned statement that the exclusion of homosexuality from *DSM-III-R* has much more to do with political than psychiatric considerations.

Another paradox derives from *DSM-III-R's* exclusion of homosexuality, namely, its considering cross-dressing among heterosexuals to be a disorder (Transvestic Fetishism) but not a disorder if the individual is homosexual. Accordingly, if a homosexual cross-dresses to entice and excite another homosexual, that is normal. If a heterosexual engages in such behavior he (she) has a disorder. An even more important paradox is the inclusion of the Gender Identity Disorder of Childhood. There is an enormous body of research that demonstrates compellingly the high correlation between childhood gender identity disorder and homosexuality during adulthood. Some of the more well known of such studies include those of Bell and Weinberg (1978); Bell, Weinberg, and Hammersmith (1981); Bieber et al. (1962); Green (1985, 1987); Money and Russo (1979); and Zuger (1970, 1976, 1984). Friedman (1988) provides an excellent review of these studies and states, "At present, I believe that this is the only correlation between psychopathology and homosexuality that may be taken as an established fact." We see here a strange inconsistency in *DSM-III-R*. An effeminate boy would be considered by *DSM-III-R* to be suffering with a disorder. Yet, when this same boy becomes an adult homosexual (a highly likely outcome), he no longer is considered to have a disorder; rather, his atypicality is viewed as a normal human variant. Again, I believe that political considerations, far more than psychiatric, have brought those who have made this decision to this inexplicable and even absurd inconsistency.

Although I could argue both ways, my preference would be that all the paraphilias (including homosexuality) be included in *DSM-III-R* as paraphilias and, like bipolar depression and OCD, be considered diseases (or disorders) per se. I would exclude the proviso that the individual has to have distress in order to justify the diagnosis. The fact is that the person is not going to go into treatment if he (she) does not suffer distress, the *DSM-III-R* statement notwithstanding. Atypicality, per se, has traditionally been a justification for inclusion in a list of psychiatric disturbances. There are societies in which paranoia and hallucinations are the norm. There are others in which catatonic people may be worshiped and/or considered to be invested by divine spirits. As Shakespeare's Hamlet put it: "There's nothing either good or bad, but thinking makes it so." Because atypical sexuality is "bad" in our society and because people who exhibit such behavior are going to have difficulties in our society, even though often (but not always) unjustified, we must make special provisions for dealing with them, both in the legal and psychiatric professions.

CONCLUDING COMMENTS

I present here a theory that attempts to bring together a wide variety of human sexual phenomena and provide a common explanation for what may initially appear to be different disorders. Although each of these types of human sexual activity has its own set of causes (both genetic and environmental), they share in common the thread that they all potentially serve the ends of procreation (directly or indirectly), and therefore specifically the transmission of DNA down to the next survival machine.

Freud (1930) in his *Civilization and Its Discontents* points out that society must suppress and repress sexuality if any constructive work is to be done. If all individuals were free to indulge themselves in any form of sexual encounter, we would have little time to involve ourselves in the constructive work necessary for the survival of society. Gibbon (1776-1788) considers widespread licentiousness to have been an important factor in the decline of the Roman Empire. The biblical story of God's destruction of the cities of Sodom and Gomorrah is certainly (at least) a metaphor for the same phenomenon. It may very well be true, as well, that intrafamilial sex, especially, had to be suppressed because of the rivalries that it engendered. Certainly most people in our society (sexual revolution notwithstanding) view sex as a special kind of relationship. This is especially true of women, who are much more oriented to the emotional relationship element in sex. Women are much more oriented toward sexual exclusivity. The opposite side of the exclusivity coin is jealousy. Men, too, are not free from such jealous feelings, especially when another man has sexual opportunities with a woman with whom they are enamored. If it is true that such feelings are of ancient tradition and may have even existed in primitive times, then taboos against incest might have arisen in order to protect people from the devastating effects on the family of such jealous rivalries. Inhibitions have a way of spreading, often to areas that were not part of the central focus at the time of their origin, and this is what might have happened with regard to the widespread sexual inhibitions that we observe in Western society today.

I do not believe it is likely that inhibitions against incest arose from the appreciation that inbreeding may bring about the clinical expression of recessive genes and thereby produce an increase in maladaptive forms. First, I believe that this is a relatively late development in our understanding. In fact, it is probable that the relationship between sexual intercourse and pregnancy has only recently become understood, and this is especially likely to have been the case in societies in which a wide variety of sexual practices were engaged in at all ages. Furthermore, when a family is relatively free of undesirable genes, inbreeding can be beneficial in that it preserves the "purity" of the strain. I am certain that a wide variety of other factors have been involved in the development of sexual inhibitions, but it is beyond the purposes of this book to discuss them.

Mention has already been made of the fact that the paraphilias are much more common in males than females. I believe that the main reason for this difference relates to the aforementioned theory in which I consider men to be primarily involved in the quantity-control aspect of reproduction and women in the quality-control aspect. The biologically programmed "promiscuity" of men easily spreads to their being far less discriminating with regard to the receptacle in which they are willing to deposit their sperm. Accordingly, receptacles that may not immediately bring about an increase in the population may still be utilized, so pervasive and compelling are the urges. The obsessive-compulsive nature of the male sexual drive and the overrepresentation of males in the paraphilic population enhances, I believe, the credibility of my theory.

The presentation of my theory would not be complete without some discussion of masturbation. One could argue that it does not support the theory because this widespread practice serves absolutely no procreative function. In fact, it can be viewed as a "waste" of sexual urges because it does not lead to the transmission of DNA into the next generation of survival machines. I could argue even further that it defeats DNA's purposes in that it allows for a reduction in sexual drive and therefore lessens the likelihood of the immediate quest for procreation. These arguments notwithstanding, I believe that masturbation also serves DNA's purposes. It keeps the juices flowing and thereby contributes to the prevention of disuse atrophy of the reproductive apparatus. More importantly, it serves DNA survival in another way. It allows for the release and gratification of sexual tensions and cravings so that the individual may be then free to direct attention to other survival considerations such as the acquisition of food, clothing, and shelter. Without this form of release, individuals might be continually in a state of excitation and frustration and thereby not be able to provide proper attention to other activities necessary for the survival of the temporary housing machines. The genitals do not exist in isolation from the rest of the body. They require nourishment and protection. The survival machine cannot merely focus on providing opportunities for the copulatory organs to perform their function. Rather, it must also direct itself to other necessary matters that keep the genital organs in good health, functioning properly, and protected from danger. Such activities are not likely to be accomplished effectively and efficiently if the housing machine is distracted significantly by unsatisfied sexual cravings.

As mentioned, I have been particularly careful to avoid making any judgments about these atypical forms of human behavior. I believe, however, that many societies have been unjustifiably punitive to those who exhibit these paraphilic variations and have not been giving proper respect to the genetic factors that may very well be operative. Such considerations might result in greater tolerance for those who exhibit these atypical sexual proclivities. My hope is that this theory will play a role (admittedly small) in bringing about greater sympathy and respect for those individuals who exhibit these variations of sexual behavior. Recognizing that they do play a role in species survival may contribute to some alteration in this unfortunate attitude.

It would be an error for the reader to conclude that I am condoning all of these forms of sexual behavior. I think each one must be considered in its own right with regard to the judgments that one passes on them. An important determinant of my own judgments relates to the coercive element, especially when the coerced person is weaker and/or younger. Although pedophilia may ultimately serve nature's purposes, it is still a form of exploitation of an innocent party. Sadomasochism may also serve the purposes of the survival of the human species, but it is basically a form of cruelty that we could well do without. I have mentioned that we differ from lower animals with regard to the development of the human brain, which has the capacity to suppress and repress those forces that press for indiscriminate reproduction of DNA and its passage down the generations from one survival machine to another. Also, consideration must be given to the social attitude toward a particular variation. It is a disservice to guide children along an atypical developmental track (especially when there is no evidence that their genes are propelling them along that path), because they will predictably suffer for their atypicality. I am not suggesting that we submit to every social prejudice. What I am suggesting is that we try to educate society to be less prejudiced and to be less condemning of those with paraphilias (especially those that do not cause harm to younger and/or weaker individuals).

 **TWO**

THE ACCUSED

INTRODUCTORY COMMENTS

I use the word *pedophilia* to refer to a sexual act between an adult and a child. Although there are some who would restrict the use of this term to certain subcategories of adult-child sexual encounters, I prefer (as do many workers in the field) to use the term in a broader sense, namely, to refer to any kind of sexual behavior between an adult and a child—regardless of the setting and regardless of the nature of the relationship. Actually, there is no good definition of the word *pedophilia* and I try to avoid using it. If one defines pedophilia as a sexual act between an adult and a child, then one has to define what is meant by *adult* and *child*. In some situations an adult is defined as someone over 21 years of age. In other situations an adult is considered to be a person over 18 years old, and in others an adult is someone over 16 (and even 15, 14, and 13). And the same holds true regarding the age at which one is no longer considered a child. In some situations the ages 12, 13, and 14 are considered to be the upper levels of childhood. In other situations the ages 16, 18, and 21 may be used.

It might appear that this problem can be circumvented—with

regard to the definition of pedophilia—if one defines pedophilia as a sexual act between a postpubertal person and a prepubertal person. One problem with this definition is the age gap between the two participants. If a postpubertal 13-year-old boy has a sexual encounter with a prepubertal 11-year-old girl, should we consider that act to warrant the term *pedophilia? DSM-III-R* (which also subscribes to the postpubertal/prepubertal definition) requires there to be a five-year difference between the abuser and victim. Would *DSM-III-R,* then, consider the diagnosis of pedophilia warranted if there were only a four-year difference between the two individuals? And what about a three-year difference? What about the situation in which a *pre*pubertal 13-year-old has a sexual encounter with a *post*pubertal 11-year-old, i.e., the younger child is the more sexually mature and is the "molester." Obviously, the prepubertal/postpubertal definition has its limitations as well.

State statutes generally provide definitions that also easily prove faulty. My final position on this matter is this: a *pedophile* is the name given to a person whom the judge and/or jury decides they want to put away. It is for these reasons that I try to avoid using the term. However, if I substitute the term *adult-child sexual encounters,* I run into the aforementioned problems related to the definitions of *adult* and *child.* I have no solution to the problem and so, on occasion, in order to facilitate communication, still use the term *pedophilia*—but the reader should know my reservations.

It is extremely important that the evaluator appreciate that sexual activities between an adult and a child are an ancient tradition and have been found to exist to a significant degree in just about every society in history that has been studied in depth. The reader who is somewhat incredulous about what I have just said does well to read the very enlightening and well-researched article by Demause (1991), which documents the ubiquity of adult-child sexual activities in the United States, Canada, Latin America, Puerto Rico, Mexico, Scandinavia, Great Britain, Germany, Italy, India, China, Japan, Thailand, and the Middle East. His review covers the wide span of history from ancient times to the present. Demause's 41-page article has 200 footnotes, each of which cites a list of further references supporting the statements made in the main body of the article. It provides compelling evidence that sexual activities between adults and children have been a worldwide phenomenon, the main difference between cultures being the attitudes toward this universal practice.

It is of interest that of all the ancient peoples it may very well be that the Jews were the only ones who were punitive toward pedophiles. According to Kahr (1991):

> The Hebrews of yore seem to have maintained a somewhat more progressive attitude toward pedophilia, and, according to the ancient Jews, anybody who engaged in sexual activity with a boy older than nine years of age would be stoned to death; however, those who copulated with boys *under* the age of nine received only a whipping, because the Jews did not consider boys under nine as sexual beings (p. 201).

Early Christian proscriptions against pedophilia appear to have been derived from the earlier teachings of the Jews, and our present overreaction to pedophilia represents an exaggeration of Judeo-Christian principles and is a significant factor operative in Western society's atypicality with regard to such activities.

The reader would also do well to refer to the excellent article by Kahr (1991), which provides further documentation of the ubiquity of child sex abuse, in the past as well as the present, with particular focus on ancient Greece, ancient Rome, ancient Egypt, and modern Western society—especially Europe and the United States. Kahr divides Western society's attitudes toward adult-child sexuality into four stages:

> 1. The Ancient Period (comprising the times of the Greeks and the Romans). Adults seduced and violated their children in an unashamed and socially acceptable manner.
> 2. The Medieval Period (from the rise of Christianity through the Renaissance). Under the influence of Christianity, parents were made to feel guilty over their sexual inclinations toward their children and could not abuse them with impunity. A prominent feature during this period was the phenomenon of adults pro-

jecting their own sexual impulses onto children and assuming, thereby, that the children were the initiators of sexual activity.

3. The Early Modern Period (the 18th-early 20th centuries). The enhancement even further of guilt and shame over adult-child sexuality. Pedophilic impulses are gratified pornographically, and sub rosa.

4. The Late Modern Period (latter half of the 20th century). Progressive increase in the awareness of the ubiquity of the problem. Practically no social sanction. Abused children viewed as victims.

Konker (1992) also provides an extensive review of the literature on a wide variety of cultural attitudes toward adult-child sexuality. She provides compelling evidence for the conclusion that adult-child sexual behavior is ubiquitous and has been present in just about every society studied, both past and present. For example, she states:

> In a variety of contemporary cultures it appears that adults may affectionately sniff, kiss, blow upon, fondle, and praise the genitals of young male and female children....Valued adult-child sexual contact routinely occurs as part of initiation activities in at least twenty countries throughout the world. (p. 148)

Among contemporary indigenous groups in New Guinea there are some conscious cultural contraints on father-son incestuous relationships, but male children are traditionally sexually initiated by other adult males. Sexual sadistic practices are also widespread.

Again, in New Guinea, Konker (1992) states:

> Various adult's initiation practices may include sexual insults and threats, fellatio, sodomy, urethral piercing and bloodletting, and men rubbing semen on young boys....Also, at initiation, Arapesh girls may have stinging needles rubbed on their bodies and thrust up their vulvas. (p. 148)

No knowledgeable individual seriously believes that the Judaic practice of circumcision (also practiced by Muslims and, interestingly, more recently by Christians) arose from the appreciation that such a procedure would protect an individual from the acquisition of certain diseases. Even now, most recognize this as a retrospective rationalization. I am convinced that the ritual is basically sexual-sadistic and that it is close enough to the obvious sexual-sadistic rituals described in detail by Demause, Kahr, and Konker to warrant this conclusion. The act is sexual in that it involves the penis. It is sadistic in that it involves a mutilation. To this day, certain Orthodox Jews require the circumciser to suck directly the blood from the circumcised penis. I myself personally observed this ritual when I was about 5 or 6 years of age and still remember it clearly. This too is sex in that it is clearly fellatio. And this too is sadistic in that the material being sucked from the penis is blood.

Accordingly, the view that pedophilia is a sickness and a crime is a reflection of Western society's present position on this subject. I am a product of my culture and I am affected by the mores of the society in which I have grown up. I too have come to believe that sexual activity between an adult and a child is a reprehensible act. However, I do not believe that it is intrinsically so; in other societies and in other times it may not be psychologically detrimental. However, I live in my society and it is my job to help people who come my way to adjust—to a reasonable degree—to the society in which they live. I am not claiming that it is my job to make them rubber stamps of the prevailing mores of the majority, only to recognize what these mores are and to appreciate that if they are ignored the individual may be in deep trouble. The indicators listed here, then, are only applicable to our society, at this point, and are in no way presented as applicable to other societies, now and in the past.

I wish to emphasize the point that there is no such thing as "the typical personality" of the adult male pedophile. There are many kinds of individuals who engage in pedophilic behavior, and they cover a broad spectrum of personality types, with much overlap regarding personality qualities. Furthermore, it is rare to find a person who is exclusively pedophilic. Most pedophiles engage in other forms of sexual behavior, especially atypical behavior (Abel et al., 1988). Also, there are varying degrees of exclusivity, ranging from those whose sexual practices include a very high percentage of pedophilic acts and those whose pedophilia may be transient and circumstantial. And this is especially the case for female pedophiles.

Those whose pedophilia appears to be a lifelong pattern are generally referred to as "fixated pedophiles" (Groth, 1979b). These are people who generally never marry and present with a history of ongoing pedophilic acts extending back into adolescence and sometimes even earlier. At the other end of the continuum are individuals who are sometimes referred to as "regressed pedophiles" (Groth, 1979b). They are individuals who may have engaged in pedophilic behavior on one, or only a few, occasions. Often they are married and do not present with a history of significant involvement in a variety of atypical sexual behaviors. The closer the individual is to the fixated end of the continuum, the greater the likelihood the term *pedophile* would be warranted; in contrast, the closer the individual is to the regressed end of the continuum, the less the likelihood one could justifiably apply this label.

In this chapter I will be discussing individuals whose history more justifiably would place them at the fixated end of the continuum. There are certain behavioral manifestations that are more commonly found in pedophiles than in those who do not engage in such behavior. I will refer to these behaviors as *indicators*. The greater the number of indicators present, the greater the likelihood the party has engaged in pedophilia. It is important for the evaluator to appreciate that some of the criteria may be contradictory, so much so that a particular individual cannot possibly satisfy all criteria. For example, the "Coercive-Dominating Behavior" indicator may be satisfied by some individuals, but these same people cannot possibly satisfy, at the same time, the "Passivity and Impaired Self-Assertion" criterion. Clearly, it is unrealistic to expect any individual to satisfy all of the criteria. Rather, one should follow the principle that the greater the number of criteria satisfied, the greater the likelihood the individual has committed pedophilic acts.

The examiner must consider the *quality* and the *quantity* of the criteria satisfied. A man who has a large collection of child pornographic materials may not satisfy many other criteria, but the evidence for pedophilia is still very compelling when this criterion is satisfied. The *conclusion* that the accused has indeed engaged in pedophilic behavior should *not* be based on these criteria alone, but on the broader picture and additional data obtained during the evaluation, especially data obtained from the accuser and the alleged victim(s).

No claim is made that all these criteria have solid scientific validity, proven by exhaustive statistical studies. Rather, they are the behavioral manifestations commonly seen in known pedophiles that are frequently described in the psychological and psychiatric literature. Some of these criteria are supported by extensive scientific study and others by less impressive data. However, none of them are considered invalid criteria by the majority of most competent workers in the field. Because the vast majority of pedophiles are male, most studies of the characteristics of pedophiles are usually conducted with male pedophiles (Alter-Reid et al., 1986; Finkelhor, 1979; Lechmann, 1987).

INDICATORS OF PEDOPHILIA IN THE MALE

1. History of Family Influences Conducive to the Development of Significant Psychopathology

Besides the emotional deprivation described above, there is a wide variety of other forms of family dysfunction that may contribute to the development of psychiatric disturbances in the children growing up in such families. Some examples: family history of violence, alcoholism, drug abuse, psychopathy, serious psychiatric disturbance, and suicide. The more serious the family history of dysfunction, the more seriously disturbed an individual is likely to become, and pedophilia is one type of such disturbance.

2. Longstanding History of Emotional Deprivation

Pedophiles often have a longstanding history of emotional deprivation, especially in early family life. They may have been abandoned by one or both parents, or grown up in homes where they were rejected, humiliated, or exposed to other privations. And such privations may have been suffered subsequently in their relationships with others. Many authors have described this relationship between pedophiles and a family background of emotional neglect. Ayalon (1984) considers emotional neglect to be a factor in the nonviolent type of incest perpetrator. Weinberg (1962) considers emotional deprivation in childhood to have been present in just about all of the incest offenders he studied. Gebhard and Gagnon (1964) also found that the vast majority of incestuous fathers were products of emotionally depriving homes. Money (1990) describes indifference and neglect to be part of the family background of many pedophiles.

3. Intellectual Impairment

Whether or not the average pedophile is of lower intelligence than those who do not engage in this practice is a controversial subject. It seems reasonable that people of low intelligence are less likely to appreciate the consequences of their atypical and even illegal behavior and so are more likely to indulge themselves in the expression of latent pedophilic impulses. Furthermore, their poor judgment increases the likelihood that their behavior will be disclosed to others because they are not intelligent enough to engage in pedophilic acts under circumstances where they will not be discovered or divulged.

Peters (1976) found pedophiles to be of average or below average intelligence. Gebhard and Gagnon (1964) also considered pedophiles to be uneducated and "somewhat simpleminded." In contrast, Weiner (1962) found fathers who involve themselves in incestuous relationships with their daughters to be of high intelligence. History provides us with many examples of highly intelligent pedophiles. Lewis Carroll (1832-1898) (see below in my discussion of the child pornography indicator #16) is one such example. James M. Barrie (1860-1937), the author of *Peter Pan* (clearly an effeminate boy who is often played by girls), was another well-known pedophile (Birkin, 1979). Another famous writer of children's books, Horatio Alger (1834-1899), was also attracted to young boys, and it was this attraction that resulted in his enforced retirement from the Unitarian Ministry (Hoyt, 1974). Money (1990) provides further comments on the pedophilia of Lewis Carroll and James Barrie, especially with regard to the issue of pedophilia and its relationship to high intelligence.

My own guess is that—in 20th-century Western society—pedophiles, on the average, are less likely to be of high intelligence; rather, they are more likely to be of average or below-average intelligence because of their lack of appreciation of the consequences of their activities. Barrie and Dodgson lived in 19th-century England at a time when pedophilia was much more socially acceptable. It was not until the end of that century that there were many exposés of the practice in the public media, exposés that resulted in far more punitive action being taken against pedophiles. I do not claim, however, that this is an important indicator.

4. Childhood History of Sex Abuse

Pedophiles are more likely to have been sexually abused in childhood than those who do not exhibit such behavior. It is part of the family pattern, and the pedophile may be the latest in a long line of sexually abused children, extending back many generations. Finkelhor (1986) states that "this [sexual abuse in childhood] is one of the most consistent findings of recent research." Money (1990) also describes this phenomenon, with particular emphasis on the feelings of entrapment and dilemma that such youngsters experience. When this occurs, it may result in the eroticization of parental love (Eibl-Eibesfeldt, 1990). Longo (1982) reported that approximately half of his adolescent sex offenders had been sexually molested in the prepubertal years. Becker et al. (1986) found that 23 percent of adolescent sex offenders had been the subject of pedophilic experiences. Frisbie (1969) found that 24 percent of a group of sex offenders of children reported childhood histories of sexual contact with an adult. Groth (1979a) found that 25 percent of sex offenders of children had childhood sexual experiences with adults. Condy et al. (1987) found that 37 percent of sexual offenders in his study had childhood sexual experiences with an adult at least five years older than themselves.

5. Longstanding History of Very Strong Sexual Urges

Although there are certainly normal, healthy people who have strong sexual urges and who date back their strong sexual drive to childhood, pedophiles are much more likely to provide such a history. Most (but certainly not all) adults date the onset of strong sexual urges to the pubertal period; pedophiles are more likely to date their sexual urges back even further. In fact, there are some who claim that they cannot remember a time when they did not have strong sexual desires. Some will date the onset of their sexual urges to their own childhood sexual encounters with adults, and these experiences, of course, will serve as a model for their own subsequent pedophilic behavior. The age at which masturbation first began can provide important information in this regard. This abnormally strong sexual drive is one of the reasons why the pedophile may be aroused by children of both sexes and even adults of both sexes.

6. Impulsivity

Pedophiles are often impulsive. In order to perpetrate a pedophilic act, an individual must break through internal barriers to such behavior (guilt and the anticipation of shame if the acts are disclosed) as well as external deterrents (such as the anticipation of punishment). They frequently exhibit impulsive behavior in other areas of their lives, unrelated to their pedophilia. Inquiry into school and work history of pedophiles will often reveal inability to stick to tasks over long periods, with the result that their academic and work histories reveal frequent shifts, temper outbursts, and other manifestations of their impulsivity. Finkelhor (1984) makes reference to impulsivity as one of the preconditions for pedophilia: "The potential offender had to overcome internal inhibitions against acting on that [pedophilic] motivation." Hauggaard and Reppucci (1988), in their review of the literature, found poor impulse control to be one of the hallmarks of the male child sex abuser.

7. Feelings of Inadequacy and Compensatory Narcissism

Many pedophiles are inadequate individuals. They often have few if any accomplishments to point to. They commonly present with a history of poor school and work performance, unsuccessful marriages, and significant impairments in their ability to form age-appropriate friendships. They do not have the ego-strength to tolerate the inevitable rejections associated with age-appropriate heterosexual pursuit, and they may therefore approach children for sexual gratification. The narcissism so frequently seen in pedophiles is compensatory for the underlying feelings of inadequacy. They have a strong craving to be loved and will gravitate toward children because children will so predictably be adoring of an adult who treats them kindly. Leahy (1991) states, "The most common diagnosis of the child abuser is that of narcissistic personality disorder. It is thought that these individuals are seeking from their intimate encounters with children some affirmation that they are both loved and desired." Kohut (1977) also comments on the narcissism of pedophiles as a mechanism for compensating for their fragile sense of self-worth and their frequent experience of self-fragmentation. Crewdson (1988) considers the narcissism to be a direct result of the childhood sexual abuse to which many pedophiles have been subjected. Overholser and Beck (1986) found the pedophiles they studied to be socially inept, which is yet another source of feelings of inadequacy and often a result of it. Children are somewhat indiscriminate in their affection for and even admiration of adults. Accordingly, they are more likely to provide pedophiles with those responses that can serve to compensate for the pedophile's feelings of inadequacy.

Peters (1976) found the offenders he studied to be suffering with deep feelings of inferiority and inadequacy. Medicus and Hopf (1990) state:

> Because of their small size, lack of experience, and sense of insecurity, children and adolescents of either sex do not arouse feelings of inferiority, fear, and anxiety in adult males. Thus, children and adolescents can become "sexual objects" for males who in sociosexual relations with adults feel inferior or anxious (p. 141).

Therefore, because children are so craving for affection, they may seek the affection of children, who are less likely to reject them and are more easily seduced into providing affection. In a more complex way, they may project themselves psychologically onto the children, who are the objects of their affection. By observing the child's pleasure, they satisfy vicariously their own need to be provided love by an adult. In this way they are reenacting and satisfying a childhood frustration. They identify themselves with a loving adult (something they had little experience with in childhood) and identify themselves with the recipient of their affections by projecting themselves simultaneously into the position of the child to whom they are providing affection.

8. Coercive-Dominating Behavior

Some pedophiles are very aggressive individuals, to the point where they will impose themselves physically on others. Sometimes, such behavior is exhibited in the context of antisocial acts, e.g., stealing, mugging, assault and battery, and quickness to engage in physical altercations. Cohen et al. (1969) consider the aggressive offender to be one of three types of pedophiles. They describe such individuals as having a history of antisocial behavior to the point where they are considered aggressive psycho-paths. (The other two types are the immature and the regressed.) This category of pedophiles manifests the domination factor in human sexuality described in detail in Chapter One. The genetically programmed value of domination in human survival can easily extend down to children, who are much more easily dominated than adults. Eibl-Eibersfeldt (1990) considers this to be a particularly important element in pedophilia and describes its derivatives in our evolution from lower animals, as well as its manifestations in a variety of other cultures. Ayalon (1984) considers the domineering type to be one of two types of pedophiles (the other, the nonviolent type, will be described below). The domination factor that may be found in pedophilia is not simply a manifestation of species survival domination derived from lower forms (as described in Chapter One). It may also serve the purposes of ego-enhancement and compensation for feelings of inferiority. An excellent example of this is the report by Roumajon (1960) [quoted by Eibl-Eibersfeldt (1990)] that the initiation rites of certain French youth gangs involve the leaders having anal intercourse with the aspirants. Hauggaard and Reppucci (1988), on the basis of their review of the literature of sexually abusing fathers, found that domination over their wives was a frequently seen characteristic.

There is often a family history of antisocial and even psychopathic behavior, and these family members serve as models for the pedophiles. This same tendency to manipulate and coerce others into submitting to one's will may be an important ingredient in the pedophilic act. Some pedophiles are not so dominating that they physically overpower others in order to force them to submit to their desires; rather, they use psychological and verbal methods of getting others to submit to their wills. A father, for example, who requires the family's rigid adherence to his commands and is excessively punitive regarding the imposition of disciplinary measures on his children would be an example of this kind of behavior. These men's wives also are required to submit to their domination.

9. Passivity and Impaired Self-assertion

In contrast to the kinds of aggressive and domineering behaviors described above, there are some pedophiles who exhibit the opposite kind of behavior, that is, they are passive and inhibited in their capacity to assert themselves. Reference has been made to the nonviolent type of sex-abuse perpetrator described by Ayalon (1984). Peters (1976) also describes sex offenders as being characteristically passive and emotionally dependent. Overholser and Beck (1986) also found many of the offenders he studied to be unassertive. Sometimes individuals of this type have intellectual impairments or serious psychiatric disturbance and are willing to engage in a wide variety of atypical and even illegal behaviors into which they are coerced by more dominant individuals (such as gang or group leaders). Or, they may be so inhibited and passive that their pent-up impulses occasionally break out as the barriers become weakened by the strength of their primitive desires.

10. History of Substance Abuse

Pedophiles are more likely to present with a history of alcohol and/or drug abuse. Sometimes, the pedophilic act is committed under the influence of such substances. It is then that barriers (both internal and external) that suppress pedophilic impulses are weakened and the individual engages in such behavior. These substances can also produce a state of amnesia for the pedophilic act(s), thereby lessening the guilt the individual might otherwise feel for having engaged in such behavior.

Wakefield and Underwager (1988) report the findings of the Minneapolis Family Renewal Center (1979), in which it was found that alcoholism among incest fathers and sex abusers range from 25 to 80 percent. They also quote the studies of Sgroi et al. (1982), in which the authors state, "We are beginning only dimly to appreciate the causal role played by alcohol when the perpetrator of child sexual assault is the father or a father figure." Peters (1976) found that in over half of the pedophiles he studied, the assault occurred while the offender was drinking. Hauggaard and

Reppucci (1988), on the basis of their review of the literature on fathers who had abused their children, found problems with drugs or alcohol to be common.

11. Poor Judgment

Mention has already been made of the poor judgment of people with intellectual impairments and psychosis. However, there are individuals who do not fall into either of these categories who exhibit poor judgment. For example, there are people who have masochistic tendencies that drive them to place themselves in situations where they may be rejected and punished. Some grew up in homes where they just didn't learn good judgment. Even small amounts of drug utilization (such as alcohol and marijuana) — not to the point of intoxication — can impair judgment. When judgment is impaired, latent pedophilic impulses may break through internal (and even external) barriers.

12. Impaired Sexual Interest in Age-appropriate Women

Many pedophiles do not feel competent enough to pursue successfully heterosexual involvement with women their own age. They may not be able to tolerate the inevitable rejections that such pursuit involves. Therefore, they may be attracted to children, who will be more receptive and with whom there will be less of a likelihood of rejection. The longer the past history of inadequate or impaired age-appropriate sexual involvement with women their own age, the greater the likelihood this criterion will be satisfied. Many studies indicate that pedophiles manifest this kind of anxiety with age-appropriate adult females (Johnston and Johnston, 1986; Panton, 1979; Segal and Marshall, 1985). It is important to appreciate, however, that the regressed pedophile may have a past history of interest in age-appropriate women but, in response to stresses, regress to an interest in children. But even these individuals are likely to have a past history of sexual dysfunction and/or involvement in atypical sexual practices.

13. Presence of Other Sexual Deviations

Individuals who are pedophiles generally do not exhibit their pedophilia in isolation from other sexual deviations. One rarely, if ever, sees a well-adjusted adult heterosexual patient who exhibits an isolated sexual deviation such as pedophilia. Rather, other deviations are usually present, e.g., voyeurism, exhibitionism, frotteurism, sadomasochism, rape, or fetishism. Abel et al. (1988) found there to be a wide variety of paraphilic sexual activities practiced by pedophiles, e.g., rape, exhibitionism, voyeurism, frottage, obscene mail, transsexualism, transvestism, fetishism, sadism, masochism, homosexuality, obscene phone calling, public masturbation, bestiality, urolagnia, and coprophilia.

It is of interest that Abel et al. (1988) include homosexuality among the paraphilias. Although this article was written in 1988, one year after the appearance of *DSM-III-R,* the authors still considered homosexuality to warrant inclusion as a paraphilia. As mentioned in Chapter One, I am in complete agreement on this point. Furthermore, Silva (1990), a jailed physician who wrote an autobiographical account of his pedophilia, describes a wide variety of paraphilic behaviors dating back to age nine.

14. Psychosis

Although psychotic behavior can result from early childhood rejections, abandonments, and other forms of psychological trauma, many forms of psychosis have a genetic loading. There are many psychotic manifestations that might be associated with pedophilia. The individual may hear voices that encourage and even command the pedophilic behavior. Psychotic individuals are more likely to entertain a wide variety of primitive sexual fantasies, fantasies that include pedophilia. The judgment of psychotics is often impaired, again increasing the risk of discovery and revelation. Their thought disorders (illogical and bizarre thinking) may result in their believing that what they are doing is benevolent, God-commanded, or worthy of the highest praise.

15. Immaturity and/or Regression

Many pedophiles are more comfortable relating to children because psychologically they are either fixated at or have regressed to earlier levels of development. There may be generalized manifestations of immaturity, or they may regress to such immature levels in response to stress. Some examples of such immature behavior would be bedwetting, failure to live up to day-to-day responsibilities, insensitivity to the feelings of others, selfishness, and low frustration tolerance. Cohen et al. (1969) consider the immature offender to be one of the three types they have found and the regressed offender to be another type. When attempting to differentiate between bona fide offenders and those who have been falsely accused, one will generally find that the falsely accused, who is more likely to have greater ego-strength, is less likely to decompensate under the stresses of the interrogations.

The term *regressed pedophile* is sometimes used to refer to a type of pedophile who has exhibited a reasonably normal heterosexual pattern and then, under certain circumstances of stress, regresses to involvement in pedophilic behavior. In such cases, the pedophilic acts begin relatively late in the individual's life (even in old age) and are not present earlier. Obviously, in such individuals the pedophilia is not a deep-seated pattern, is far more likely to be suppressed or repressed, and is far more amenable to psychotherapy.

16. Large Collection of Child Pornographic Materials

The majority of pedophiles have large collections of child pornographic materials. They are often obsessed with their collections, and many have what can only be described as an insatiable desire to collect such materials. Many not only have trunks full of such materials, but rooms full, attics full, and even trucks full. In recent years videotapes have been added to their collections of printed materials. Postal officials know them well for the kinds of mail they receive, legally or illegally. Kinsey et al.

(1948) found collections of pornographic materials to be the most characteristic finding in his studies of known pedophiles.

Men who involve themselves significantly with taking photographs (and more recently videotapes) of children are highly suspect. This is especially the case if they are particularly interested in photographing children in various degrees of nudity, not necessarily complete. Although the pedophile may not involve himself any further with the children, the photographs are frequently used for masturbatory purposes. Probably one of the most famous pedophiles who combined pedophilia with photographing naked children was the Reverend Charles Dodgson (1832-1898), also known as Lewis Carroll, the author of *Alice's Adventures in Wonderland* and *Through the Looking Glass.* Carroll was an avid photographer, befriended the mothers of young girls, and obtained their permission to make photographic images of their naked daughters (Bullough, 1983; Cohen, 1978). It is of interest that both of Carroll's books were written for one of the young girls to whom he was attracted. Police investigators are familiar with this phenomenon and will often search the home of the alleged pedophile for child pornographic materials.

17. Career Choice That Brings Him In Contact with Children

Some (but certainly not all) pedophiles enter careers that bring them into close contact with children, thereby providing them with opportunities to indulge their pedophilic impulses, for example, nursery school and elementary school teacher, school bus driver, scout master, camp director, music teacher, physical education teacher, children's choir master, and pediatrician. People who are not pedophiles are less likely to involve themselves in these careers (although they certainly might).

18. Recent Rejection by a Female Peer or Dysfunctional Heterosexual Relationship

Some pedophiles will embark upon pedophilic behavior after rejection by an age-appropriate female companion. And this is especially the case if there was a series of such rejections. The greater the number of such rejections, the greater the likelihood that dormant pedophilic impulses will break through the barriers to such behavior. Men with no pedophilic tendencies will not resort to such behavior, no matter how many rejections they suffer. In the divorce situation, this criterion might be satisfied if the involvement in pedophilic behavior takes place very shortly after the separation, especially if the separation is at the initiation of the wife. This criterion is not satisfied if there has been a long time gap between the separation and the accusation. This is especially the case if there has been custody litigation and/or a series of exclusionary maneuvers by the wife.

Tollison and Adams (1979) found that 50 percent of the pedophiles they studied turned to children after unsatisfactory relationships and conflicts with their age-appropriate sexual partners. Some of the pedophiles who satisfy this criterion would be considered "regressed" because of their previously adequate heterosexual adjustment. It is reasonable to assume that pedophilic tendencies were present earlier.

19. Unconvincing Denial

People who have been falsely accused of pedophilia often suffer with a sense of impotent rage. They feel helpless and they may suffer terribly because of the accusation, suffering that may include long jail sentences and destruction of their lives. Accordingly, their professions of innocence are convincing and do not have an artificial quality. In contrast, bona fide pedophiles often exhibit weak and/or obviously feigned denials that are not particularly convincing.

20. Use of Rationalizations and Cognitive Distortions That Justify Pedophilia

Many pedophiles rationalize their behavior, e.g., "I'm a survivor of child abuse myself, so I'm entitled to abuse children," "She enjoyed it, so what's wrong with it," "She's a little Lolita. You just wait until she grows up" (Fuller, 1989; Spelman, 1985).

Some subscribe to the dictum that having sex with a child is a good way to introduce the child to sexual education. Others believe that the adult-child relationship is enhanced by the sexual activities. Some hold that a child who does not physically resist really wants to have sex. Abel et al. (1988) and Groth et al. (1982) describe in detail these and other rationalizations commonly provided by pedophiles. Leahy (1991) states, "The pedophile often has grandiose notions of being at the forefront of a cultural revolution in the liberation of child sexuality." It may be that intellectual weakness may enable the individual to subscribe to these dicta or utilize these rationalizations. The ability to believe such patently absurd rationalizations is another reason why I consider it likely that the average pedophile is of lower than average intelligence.

In contrast, individuals who have not engaged in pedophilic acts, when asked what they think about sex between an adult and a child, will profess the usual attitudes present in our society regarding such acts, e.g., "It's a disgusting act," "It's good they have laws to protect children from such characters," "It's one of the worst things that an adult can do to a child."

21. Resistance to Taking a Lie Detector Test

Bona fide perpetrators will generally refuse to take a lie detector test and often provide a wide variety of justifications for not doing so—such as the test may have false positives or that their lawyer advised them against it. In contrast, people falsely accused of pedophilia are often (but not always) eager to undergo such an examination, even when they recognize that it is not foolproof. People who are knowledgeable about the polygraph know well that psychopaths, delusional individuals, and people under the influence of certain relaxing drugs will lie without concomitant physiological responses, will lie "smoothly and cooly" without concomitant physiological reactions. Thus they can "fool" the instrument. They take the position that they will take their chances with it because they are so confident that they will do well. It is important to note that this criterion has nothing to do with the *findings* on the lie detector test, but rather the person's *attitude* toward taking the test.

22. Lack of Cooperation in the Evaluative Examination

Individuals who have involved themselves in pedophilia recognize that they have perpetrated a criminal act and are likely to be reluctant to reveal themselves fully to a mental health examiner because they recognize that their simple denial may not be enough to convince the interviewer of their innocence. They recognize that other things they may say in the course of an evaluation may reveal their pedophilia—either directly or indirectly. Accordingly, they may be uncooperative and obstructionistic, and they may find excuses to circumvent the interviewer's efforts to learn about them. They may even find excuses (sometimes legal) to avoid being interviewed at all. In contrast, people who are innocent welcome interviews by qualified examiners, even if they have legal sanction for not involving themselves in the evaluation (such as the Fifth Amendment).

23. Duplicity Unrelated to the Sex-abuse Denial and Psychopathic Tendencies

Pedophiles generally present with a longstanding history of deceit. Most recognize the revulsion of society to their deviant behavior as well as the fact that it is a criminal act. Accordingly, they usually exhibit a longstanding pattern of misrepresentation, minimization, denial, and conscious deception about their deviant sexuality (Fuller, 1989). Furthermore, many are psychopathic. This is not surprising because child sex abuse is a form of exploitation and those who indulge in it also show little sensitivity to the effect of their behavior on their child victims. Hauggaard and Reppucci's (1988) review of the literature concluded that many pedophiles exhibit a high *Minnesota Multiphasic Personality Inventory* (MMPI) psychopathic deviant score.

Bona fide perpetrators are not only being deceitful when they deny the pedophilia but will generally exhibit *other* deceits in the course of the evaluation—deceits not directly related to the allegation of pedophilia. The greater the number of such deceptions, the greater the likelihood the individual has perpetrated the pedophilic act. The ancient legal principle is applicable here: *Falsus in uno, falsus in omnibus* (false in one [area], false in all [areas]). In contrast, those who have not committed such acts are less likely to reveal duplicities in other aspects of the evaluation.

24. Excessively Moralistic Attitudes

Some bona fide pedophiles are rigidly moralistic and exhibit significant condemnation of those who "stray from the narrow path"—especially in the sexual realm. They may be proselytizers and "hell, fire, and damnation" preachers (ordained or not). Their preoccupation with the condemnation of those who might "stray" serves as a vehicle for them to suppress their own inner impulses in the sexual realm. They demonstrate well the psychological principle of reaction formation. This is a process in which individuals vehemently condemn in others behavior that they themselves might secretly (and often unconsciously) wish to engage in themselves, but cannot permit themselves to do, or even recognize that they have the exact same inclinations. Not surprisingly, these pent-up impulses become strong, and when they break through they might result in a pedophilic act. People who are not pedophiles are less likely to exhibit this personality trait.

Concluding Comments

When utilizing these criteria for ascertaining whether a suspect has indeed sexually molested a child, the evaluator does well to appreciate that some of the items on this list of indicators are mutually contradictory (e.g., there is an item on passivity and another on aggressivity). Accordingly, it is not likely that an individual will be "clean free," that is, not satisfy any of the criteria. However, this factor notwithstanding, a person who is a pedophile is likely to satisfy many of the criteria, and a person who has not committed a pedophilic act is likely to satisfy few if any of them. There is no formal cut-off point and I have studiously avoided providing any numbers here. Furthermore, it is important that the information derived from this list of indicators be considered along with information provided from other sources, especially from the interviews with the alleged child victim and the accuser(s).

THE CAUSES OF MALE PEDOPHILIA

As mentioned in Chapter One, I believe that there are genetic factors that predispose many individuals toward pedophilia. And these factors vary from being an insignificant or nonexistent contribution to being highly important. In this section I will focus on the environmental and psychological factors that I also consider to be operative to a greater or lesser degree, depending upon the genetic predisposition. Again, I wish to emphasize that I am referring only to pedophiles in Western society at this time.

The Imprinting Factor

Early experiences play an important role in determining later patterns of behavior. This is especially the case if the early experience is an extremely powerful and gratifying one. Take for example a prepubertal child who has never experienced an orgasm, or may not have even experienced strong sexual urges. Imagine, then, this child being seduced into a relationship in which there is not only enormous flattery, enjoyable caressing, but orgastic gratification as well. It is easy to see how a child might become "hooked" by such an experience and crave for frequent gratifications of the same kind. It is easy to see also how this particular pattern may become the model for subsequent sexuality when the child grows older. Furthermore, the older the child becomes, the more autonomy and the greater the likelihood that he (she) can be the initiator of such encounters. Even when the encounters may not be particularly gratifying, and even when there may be a fear element associated with threats regarding disclosure, the child may still become accustomed to this pattern and it may still become deeply ingrained. Even when associated with fear and pain, such early experiences may still become imprinted as the primary pattern of sexual encounter, so powerful are these early influences. When repeated, it may become the only pattern the child knows. We see here a similarity to sadomasochistic individuals who are brought up in homes in which that is the primary form of interaction between people, both in and out of the bedroom scene.

There are homosexuals who date the onset of their homosexuality to just such a childhood seduction. Years later, they may still recall it as one of the most dramatic and memorable experiences of their lives. It is easy to imagine how a youngster, who never previously had an orgasm, is not only introduced to this experience at that time, but the orgasm occurs in association with adoration and flattery unlike that ever previously received. For the youngster it may be a "mind-blowing" experience (the reader will please excuse the pun), one that may affect the future course of the child's life. And, if such seduction occurs on a few occasions, the likelihood of the youngster's going down the homosexual path may be even greater. Some of these youngsters go on to become homosexuals who confine themselves to adult relationships; others become pedophiles, their own pedophilic experience having played a role in that choice (more unconscious than conscious). There are many types of individuals who cause such imprinting in children. Sometimes the seducer is the child's father (far less often the mother), uncle, grandparent, or other relative. It may have been a babysitter, teacher, neighbor, or lover of a parent. There are pedophiles for whom the imprinting process took place in the context of their serving as juvenile prostitutes. In some cases their families were living at poverty levels and relied upon their children's proceeds from prostitution to contribute to the family's support (Reeves, 1981; Phongpaichit, 1982).

It is important for the reader to appreciate that the imprinting factor is not so compelling that the child who is sexually abused will automatically and inevitably become a pedophile.

Throughout Melanesia and New Guinea, childhood pedophilia is a common practice, yet most of the children involved in such activities do not become pedophiles as adults (Herdt, 1981). A very dramatic example of this is to be found among the Sambia tribes of New Guinea. In that tribe, as is so true of other Melanesian societies, the ejaculate is viewed as a powerful vehicle for transmission of masculine power. It is not hard to see how it could symbolize such power, considering the ubiquity of the penis as a symbol of power, even in Western society. In the Zambia tribes boys live with their parents until the age of 8, at which time they move to a men's longhouse, where they live only in the company of males. From ages 8 to 13 they engage in fellatio with adolescent boys in order to enhance their masculinity. Then, at around the time of puberty, they switch roles and become the providers of semen to the younger boys. Then, at age 19, they marry and pedophilic practices cease entirely.

The Domination Factor

In Chapter One I mentioned the importance of the role of domination in species survival and how domination is an extension of the aggression and assertiveness that the male exhibits in the courting pattern. Children, because they are weaker than females, are more easily dominated and so are even more likely to be subdued by an aggressive male. Furthermore, in our social structure, children and females are generally viewed to be of lower status. This contributes to their attractiveness as objects for pedophiles for whom the domination factor is important. And this is one of the factors, as well, explaining why pedophilia is much more common in males than females, so much so that one could say that it is a male form of behavior. Demause (1991) states, "As an adult, the pedophile must have sex with children in order to maintain the illusion of being loved, while at the same time dominating the children as they themselves once experienced domination, repeating actively their own caretakers' sadism."

Similarities Between Children and Females

Children are much more like females than males. This is not only true with regard to their appearances, but their personalities as well. Children and females have less hair than males. The skin of the child is smooth, much more like that of a female than a male (Medicus and Hopf, 1990). The behavioral patterns that women exhibit in the courting process are much more like those of the normal patterns of children than those patterns exhibited by males in the courtship process. Flirting, cuteness, coyness, and seductive smiles are all part of the average child's repertoire. Such patterns are reflected in many of the comments men make to women in lovemaking, e.g., "You're my baby," "You're my sex kitten," and "You're very cute."

Furthermore, children are more like females than males in their desire for affection, intimacy, security, and trust in their relationships (Strassmann, 1981). Moreover, the adoration that the child has for the adult is similar to that which men strive for in their relationships with women. Such adoration is much more easily acquired from a child than an adult—thus the attraction of pedophilia. Of particular importance here is the esteem-enhancement element in such adoration, and this is one of the reasons why (as described above) pedophilia is particularly attractive to men with profound feelings of low self-worth. Also related is the eroticization of the parent-child love relationship. This, too, easily derives from the aforementioned factors (D'Udine, 1990; Garland and Dougher, 1990; Money, 1990). Pedophilia, then, may be viewed (at least in part) as a natural downward extension of the male's attraction to the female. It may be viewed as a generalization of the male's sexual courting pattern beyond what our society considers proper. The love/tenderness factor may be one of the reasons why a sexual encounter between an adult and a child is not necessarily psychologically traumatic.

Compensation for Feelings of Emotional Deprivation

Mention has been made above of the fact that pedophiles often come from homes in which they grew up emotionally

deprived and, in many cases, homes in which there was significant family dysfunction. An adoring child can provide a pedophile with compensation for feelings of deprivation that may have
persisted from the pedophile's childhood. And if the child
involved is also the product of a home in which he (she) is
suffering privation, then sexual involvement with an adoring
adult may become even more attractive. Mention has been made
previously of the somewhat complex psychological mechanism
that may be operative here, namely, the one in which the
pedophile projects himself psychologically onto the child who is
the object of his ministrations and thereby satisfies vicariously his
own need to be the object of intense affection. He thereby
provides his projected self with the love that was not obtained
during his own childhood. Furthermore, the boundaries between
parental love and romantic love may become blurred. This not
only contributes to the gratification provided by the projected
self, but also the adoration provided the pedophile by the loving
child (Eibl-Eibesfeldt, 1990).

Identification with the Aggressor

Stoller (1975, 1979, 1985) considers the identification with the
aggressor factor to be an important one driving pedophiles to
involve themselves in pedophilic behavior. Specifically, many
pedophiles have had childhood experiences in which they were
sexually abused—experiences that were traumatic. (As mentioned, sexual activities with children need not be traumatic for
the child.) One way of dealing with this trauma is to reenact it as
an adult, with another victim. In this way the individual symbolically attempts to gain mastery over a childhood sexual trauma in
which the individual was helpless. By reenacting the sexual
activity as an adult, the individual temporarily turns a passively
endured childhood trauma into an actively controlled adult
triumph (Garland and Dougher, 1990). In addition, the pedophilic act may also serve to enable the individual to gain a feeling
of revenge for having been subjected to the trauma, the built-up
anger vented now on the abused child. Some confirmation for

this theory is provided by the fact that pedophiles often reenact in great detail the same kinds of pedophilic activities that they were subjected to as children. Of course, one could attribute this simply to learning and the modeling effect, but it does provide some confirmation for the aforementioned theory. Longo (1982) and Groth (1979a) studied incarcerated pedophiles and found that they frequently recapitulated in great detail their own childhood sexual experiences. Sometimes the identification is with an adult who has not sexually traumatized the child in the course of the pedophilic act. In such circumstances, the concept of identification with the aggressor is not applicable. Here one might refer to it as "identification with the lover" and need not invoke the aforementioned more complex mechanisms.

Masochistic Factors

Involving oneself in pedophilic behavior in a society that condemns it vehemently and punishes it terribly, often providing mandatory life sentences for a first offense, makes one wonder about the motivations of individuals who involve themselves in this form of behavior. Mention has already been made of the poor judgment often exhibited by pedophiles, as well as my belief that people of lower than average intelligence are probably overrepresented in the pedophilic population. I suspect, also, that a strongly masochistic trend may exist in many pedophiles. After all, the risk of discovery is very great in that children are not famous for their ability to keep secrets. The threat of severe punishment does not seem to deter many pedophiles. Silva (1990), the incarcerated physician who wrote his autobiography from jail, describes himself to have continued to involve himself in pedophilic behavior even when he was out on bail for previous offenses.

Social and Cultural Factors

We live in a youth-oriented society. Younger women are generally considered much more attractive and desirable than older women. One factor in pedophilia may very well be the result of the downward extension and expansion of our youth-worshiping culture. A recent contribution may very well relate to the AIDS epidemic. Since the early 1980s, when AIDS was first described, there has been a growing expansion of the disease into the adult population. Children, having less sexual experience, may be viewed as safer sexual companions. Perhaps the "sexual revolution" that began in the '60s is playing a role. The more permissive attitude toward all forms of sexual behavior may very well increase the prevalence of pedophilia. Perhaps the increasing psychopathy of our society in the last quarter century has played a role. Previously, people were more reluctant to indulge themselves in unacceptable and antisocial impulses; perhaps indulging in child sex abuse is yet another manifestation of the basic psychopathy that has been increasing in recent years.

Concluding Comments

I am certain that other psychological factors are operative. I have delineated here those that I consider to be the most important. The reader does well to approach each patient without preconceived notions regarding which particular factors may have been operative in bringing about the particular patient's pedophilia. Although it is likely that one or more of the aforementioned factors may have been operative, it is also likely that the individual will have reasons that have not been included here.

INDICATORS OF PEDOPHILIA IN THE FEMALE

Until recently, the general consensus among most workers in the field was that female pedophilia was relatively rare, representing perhaps no more than two to three percent of all perpetrators. More recent work, however, suggests strongly that this figure is probably too low; however, all agree that pedophilia is still much more common in males than females. Because of the fact that attention to female pedophilia is more recent and because there are so few such perpetrators, it is even more difficult than for males to list the common indicators of female pedophilia. Accordingly, one must consider the indicators presented here as being even more tentative than those presented for the male. Once again, for each of the indicators I will provide my sources of information as well as arguments both for and against the utilization of the particular indicator. Wakefield and Underwager (1991), in an excellent review of the literature on female pedophilia, describe some of the common methodological problems that make many of the studies suspect. One problem relates to the varying definitions of sex abuse and sexual molestation. Some studies include approaches without contact, whereas other studies consider only contact to justify the term *molestation*. Different examiners utilize different age discrepancies when defining sexual abuse. Many of the studies are retrospective and this, of course, introduces the element of memory distortions which inevitably creep in over time. Some studies include as subjects the children who were allegedly molested in some of the well-known nursery and day-care center scandals, such as the McMartin case in California. Many studies do not specify the criteria by which the decision was made that the accusations were true, and this, of course, introduces errors that result from the inclusion of false accusations in the sample.

Rowan et al. (1990) reviewed the literature on the incidence of sexual abuse of children by females. Most of the studies they reviewed revealed an incidence of one to two percent. Attempts to make generalizations regarding personality types or indicators of female sex abusers were hampered by the attempt to make such generalizations from relatively small numbers, most often under fifteen offenders. The indicators that we have at this point are for the most part based on case reports of individuals.

Most of the studies indicate that female perpetrators tend to be less "pure" pedophiles than male perpetrators in that they have a broader history of a wider variety of heterosexual activities with men their own age. Although male pedophiles certainly provide a history of atypical behavior, the obsession with pedophilia appears to be much more a male than a female characteristic.

One of the problems attendant to collecting statistics on the incidence of female sex abuse relates to the population being studied. Some of the studies involve college students (the group most conveniently available to academicians). The studies involve asking them whether they were sexually abused as children; if so, then more questions are asked about the sex of the abuser, etc. Other studies involve prison inmates, both sexual perpetrators and those who had not committed sexual crimes. The studies derived from prison groups generally yield a higher percentage in which there is a history of child sex abuse. This is not surprising, considering the fact that the prisoners are more likely than college students to have come from dysfunctional homes. Condy et al. (1987) studied 359 male college students and 212 inmates. Some of the inmates had been convicted of sexual crimes (rape and child molestation), and others had been convicted of nonsex crimes. The total number of male subjects in the study was 571. He also studied 797 female subjects (625 college students and 172 female inmates who had been convicted of a variety of crimes). In every category the prisoners, both male and female, reported much more sexual molestation than the college students. Condy et al. (1987) also found that the educational levels of sexually abused men was inversely associated with a childhood history of sexual contact.

CATEGORIES OF FEMALE PEDOPHILES

Most examiners find that the vast majority of female pedophiles fall into one of four categories.

1. Intrafamilial Setting

Not surprisingly, the home appears to be the most common setting in which female pedophilia takes place. Obviously, this is the situation in which the pedophile has the greatest opportunity to be alone with the child. Furthermore, having a relationship with the child (often the pedophile's own child) increases the likelihood of receptivity and seduction. Russell (1986) found that 96 percent of all acts of female pedophilia occurred within the intrafamilial setting. Rowan et al. (1990) describe the incestuous type as the most common form of female pedophilia and consider the molestation to be an aberration of the normal mother-child relationship in which tactile contact and caressing is commonplace. Approximately 75 percent of 40 female sex-abuse perpetrators studied by Faller (1987) were involved in incestuous sex abuse. Eighty-five percent of the women were mothers to at least one of the victims. In addition, 72.5 percent of the women were classified as polyincestuous, that is, there were at least two perpetrators in the family and generally two or more victims. Characteristically, these families involved themselves in group sex with children of both sexes.

2. Adolescent Babysitter

This is a very common situation in which female pedophilia takes place. Here the child is often not a relative of the pedophile, but may very well be. Risin and Koss (1987) found that half of the female perpetrators of the victim population he studied were adolescent babysitters. Margolin (1991) studied the frequency of male and female sex abuse in a variety of situations and found that the babysitting situation was the one in which the female participation had the highest frequency (36 percent). He also found that they were the youngest abusers of the various categories of female abusers (mean age, 6.9 years). Risin and Koss (1987) found that almost half of the female perpetrators were babysitters between ages 14 and 17.

3. Male Coercion

Often the female perpetrates pedophilic acts in association with a male lover with whom she has a dependent relationship. Often she does not get any particular pleasure out of the pedophilic act, but engages in it in order to satisfy her dominant partner. Mathews et al. (1989) and Matthews et al. (1991) found that the women in this category may initially be unreceptive to involving themselves in the abuse, but may subsequently start initiating sexual abuse themselves.

Rowan et al. (1990) found that in five of the nine cases of female pedophiles studied, the abuse took place in association with a dominant male partner. Most of the female sexual offenders studied by O'Connor (1987) were assisting a male offender in the course of their molestation of children. Often the woman is coerced by the male companion into assisting in the molestation, for example, by holding down the victim. Often she is threatened that if she does not assist in this manner, she herself will be beaten, raped, etc. However, not all participation with males is coerced. Often a woman will voluntarily engage in sex with children, either with her husband or a man friend. And such activities take place either with her own children and/or the male friend's children.

In Faller's (1987) study of 46 female sexual offenders, outside men (stepfathers, grandfathers, and male friends of the female perpetrators) were frequently involved in the polyincestuous types of sex abuse, that is, group sexual activities within the family. These males were generally the inciters and the instigators, with the females playing a passive role. Nine of the 29 mothers who involved themselves in incestuous relationships reported by McCarty (1986) describe the offense taking place with a male partner.

Women who engage in sex abuse in compliance with the wishes of their male friends generally have an extremely dependent relationship with these men and are extremely loyal to them. They are willing to subject their children to the abuses of these men and use their children as bait in order to keep the men involved. None of the female co-offenders studied by McCarty (1986) separated voluntarily from these partners; even when the offenders were in prison, the women vowed to wait for them permanently. Mathews et al. (1989) also emphasized the extreme dependency relationship that female abusers have with their male coerced cohorts. Eight of the sixteen female offenders studied by Mathews et al. (1989) began sexually abusing children with a dominant partner. The women in this study, as is true of the women in many other studies, were sexually abused themselves as children and went on to perpetuate as adults the same kinds of abuse. It is as if the pattern laid down in childhood becomes the sexual pattern utilized in adulthood. Fifteen of the 16 female sex offenders studied by Mathews et al. (1989) were sexually abused as children, and one was sexually abused as an adolescent.

4. Teacher/Lover

In this category, the pedophilic act takes place in an educational setting. Not surprisingly, people with pedophilic tendencies are likely to gravitate toward teaching in nursery schools, where they may gain opportunities for pedophilic gratification. However, most often such gratification is either voyeuristic or satisfied in socially acceptable ways. After all, in a nursery school one routinely takes children to the bathroom and can gain visual-sexual gratifications from such activities. In addition, helping children dress and wipe themselves can also provide such gratifications. For most potential pedophiles this degree of satisfaction is enough. There are, however, pedophiles who may take advantage of their opportunities in the nursery school situation and enjoy more overt forms of pedophilic behavior without being disclosed by their young victims. We are living at a time, however, when hysteria regarding sex abuse in nursery schools is widespread. In this atmosphere there is an exaggeration of the risks and ubiquity of this practice, an exaggeration that may make it difficult to determine whether a particular child has indeed been sexually abused. This is an important point because of the widespread attention being given to alleged sexual molestation of younger children in these centers. As I will describe in greater detail in Chapter Nine, the evaluator does well to be familiar with the criteria by which one can differentiate true from false accusations of sex abuse in this category. Yet, partially as a result of the sex-abuse hysteria that we are witnessing at this time (Gardner, 1991a), there are many people who believe that sex abusers (especially males) are potentially lurking behind every tree and beneath every stone, and that they gravitate toward nursery schools like iron to a magnet. These people warn that children must be ever vigilant.

Sometimes women in this category are teachers who involve themselves with prepubescent and adolescent males with whom they relate as a peer. Mathews et al. (1989) state that the teacher/ lover type of female pedophile is generally involved with prepubescent and adolescent males with whom she relates as a peer. Women in the category of teacher/lover pedophile are less commonly involved with children in the day-care and nursery-school levels.

5. Other Categories

This category includes neighbors, friends of the family, and strangers. Most of the literature would support the conclusion that this category is relatively small compared to the others.

INDICATORS OF PEDOPHILIA IN THE ADULT FEMALE

1. History of Dysfunctional Family

Commonly, the female pedophile comes from a dysfunctional home in which have existed a wide variety of unhealthy psychological influences, including alcoholism, drug and/or alcohol abuse, multiple divorces, violence, psychopathy, psychosis, suicide, and other manifestations of family instability. The more serious the family history of dysfunction, the more psychologically disturbed the children will be, the more seriously disturbed these children are likely to become as adults, and the greater the likelihood that they will develop pedophilia—one type of psychiatric disturbance. Wakefield et al. (1990) describe four case histories of women who had sexual contact with their children. All of them had a history of significant losses in childhood, and the sexual activities were viewed as an attempt to gain some emotional gratification. McCarty (1986), in a study of 29 women who had sexually molested their children, found that only two described a good relationship with their parents, although one of these was probably exhibiting reaction formation. Twenty-nine percent of the 29 incestuous mothers studied by McCarty (1986) described alcoholism in their parents, and 29 percent described multiple caretakers. Forty-one percent described traumatic breakup of their parents' marriages. Of 29 female incest offenders studied by McCarty (1986), 26 described a lack of nurturance in their family of origin. Eighty-five percent were married as teenagers and 31 percent were 15 years or younger at the time of their marriage. All of the 16 female sexual offenders studied by Mathews et al. (1989) reported significant family difficulties. They describe family rigidity, inconsistency, or abuse, and they described their childhoods as lonely and isolated. None of them reported a strong sense of involvement with parents or caregivers. Five described themselves as family scapegoats. Twelve of the 16 described discipline within the family as harsh and arbitrary. Ten described an early history of promiscuity.

2. Emotional Deprivation

Pedophiles often have a longstanding history of emotional deprivation, especially in early family life. They may have been abandoned by one or both parents, or have grown up in homes where they were rejected, humiliated, or exposed to other privations. And such privations may have been present subsequently in their relationships with others. Therefore, they seek the affection of children, who are less likely to reject them and more easily seduced into providing affection.

Many female pedophiles are significantly lonely women who are craving for affection. Included in this category are single parents, noncustodial divorced parents, widows, divorcees, women in extremely dysfunctional marriages, and a wide variety of other isolated and lonely women who are craving for affection. A child can provide these women with some compensation for their emotional privations. Chasnoff et al. (1986) reported three cases of sexual abuse involving mothers and their infants. All three women were isolated, and the authors concluded that the sex abuse was motivated by the mother's loneliness. Goodwin and DiVasto (1989), in their report of six cases of mother-daughter incest, concluded that the need for nurturance in the setting of deteriorating marriages was an important factor contributing to the incest. Krug (1989), in a study of eight men who were sexually abused by their mothers, found that the mothers were either divorced or had troubled marriages and were trying to compensate for their emotional privation by incestuous relationships with their sons.

Lukianowicz (1972) concluded that social isolation was a very important etiological factor in female pedophilia. Whereas male pedophiles are less likely to have strong interest in traditional adult heterosexual relationships, female pedophiles are more likely to regress to pedophilia after rejection and/or disappointment in adult heterosexual relationships. None of the 21 female offenders studied by McCarty (1986) preferred sexual relationships with children. About half of the incestuous mothers studied by McCarty (1986) had a history of sexual promiscuity and/or prostitution. Mathews et al. (1989) state that women who involve themselves in incestuous relationships with their children generally are looking to achieve nonthreatening emotional intimacy.

3. Intellectual Impairment

People of low intelligence are less likely to appreciate the consequences of their atypical and even illegal behavior and so are more likely to indulge themselves in the expression of latent pedophilic impulses. Furthermore, their poor judgment increases the likelihood that their behavior will be disclosed to others because they are not intelligent enough to engage in pedophilic acts under circumstances where they will not be discovered or divulged.

Although not a consistent finding, some studies conclude that intellectual impairment is one of the indicators of female pedophilia. As mentioned earlier in my discussion of male pedophilia, there is a significant segment of the pedophilic population that must exhibit poor judgment in order to trust children not to reveal their sexual activities. Faller (1987), in a study of 40 female sexual abusers, found that about half were retarded. Rowan et al. (1990) found that all nine of the female perpetrators he studied had psychological problems or limited intelligence. In Larson et al.'s (1987) study of 12 female convicted sex offenders, none was found to be mentally retarded. Of the nine women studied by Rowan et al. (1990), one was mildly retarded and five tested at the borderline level of intelligence. In Faller's (1987) study of 40 female perpetrators, 32.5 percent were considered mentally retarded or brain damaged, conditions that gravely affected their judgment and impulse control. In Mc-Carty's (1986) study of sexually abusive mothers, about 40 percent were of borderline intelligence. Fifty-six percent of the co-offenders studied by McCarty (1986), that is, those who committed incest in association with a male cohort, were considered to be of borderline intelligence.

4. Childhood History of Sex Abuse

Pedophiles are more likely to have been sexually abused themselves in childhood than those who do not exhibit such behavior. It is part of the family pattern, and the pedophile may be the latest in a long line of sexually abused children, extending back many generations.

Such a history is commonly seen in female pedophiles. In addition, not only have they been subjected to sex abuse, but physical and psychological abuse as well. Mathews et al. (1989) and Matthews et al. (1991) found that 15 of 16 female sexual offenders studied were victims of childhood sexual abuse, and many were also victims of physical abuse. Travin et al. (1990) concluded that most female offenders have a history of physical and sexual victimization. Of the nine women studied by Rowan et al. (1990), four had been sexually abused as children. In Faller's (1987) study of 40 sexually abusive women, 47.5 percent reported being sexually abused in childhood. Russell (1986) found that 54 percent of her group of women had been sexually abused as children. Wyatt (1985) reports that 62 percent of the sexually abusive women that she studied had themselves been sexually abused as children. McCarty (1986) studied 29 mothers who had sexually abused their children. Ninety-five percent of them described sexual and/or physical abuse in their own childhood. Groth (1979a) believes that the former incest victim who becomes an offender does so in an effort to resolve the unresolved sexual trauma the individual experienced as a child. Of course, there is also the element of modeling with one's parents.

5. Psychosis, Psychopathy, and Other Forms of Severe Psychopathology

Although psychotic behavior can result from early childhood rejections, abandonments, and other forms of psychological trauma, many forms of psychosis have a genetic loading. There are many psychotic manifestations that might be associated with pedophilia. The individual may hear voices that encourage and even command the pedophilic behavior. Psychotic individuals are more likely to entertain a wide variety of primitive sexual fantasies, fantasies that include pedophilia. The judgment of psychotics is often impaired, increasing the risk of discovery and revelation. Their thought disorders (illogical and bizarre thinking) may result in their believing that what they are doing is benevolent, God-commanded, or worthy of the highest praise.

This phenomenon is not simply a residuum of earlier beliefs that the vast majority of female pedophiles must be psychotic if they engage in such a socially unacceptable and "perverted" act. There are a number of studies that report a disproportionately high percentage of psychotics in the female pedophilic population. Krug (1989) found no psychotics among the mothers of the eight men who were sexually abused by them as children. Travin et al. (1990) found that most of the female sexual offenders they studied had a longstanding history of psychiatric disorder. Four of nine had a history of psychosis. Of the nine women studied by Rowan et al. (1990), all suffered with serious psychiatric disturbances, including schizophrenia, borderline personality disorder, and psychopathic personality disorder. Condy et al. (1987) administered MMPIs to women inmates, some of whom were child molesters and some of whom were not. The scores of the sexually involved women were significantly higher than the nonsexually on the *schizophrenia* and *hypomania* scales, but significantly lower on the *lie* scale. Seventy-five percent of the 40 female sex offenders studied by Faller (1987) were overtly psychotic. These women developed delusional systems that provided justification for the sex abuse. In addition, ten percent of her group provided a history of psychotic episodes but were not overtly psychotic at the time of the abuse. Four of the nine female perpetrators studied by Travin et al. (1990) were psychotic, and the authors considered the sex abuse to serve as an attempt to stave off further psychotic disintegration. Five of the seven independent female defenders (without a male cohort) (77 percent) suffered serious emotional disturbances, as documented by psychological testing or a history of psychiatric hospitalization.

6. History of Substance Abuse

Pedophiles are likely to present with a history of alcohol and/or drug abuse. Sometimes, the pedophilic act is committed under the influence of such substances. It is then that barriers (both internal and external) that suppress pedophilic impulses are weakened and the individual engages in such behavior. These substances can also produce a state of amnesia for the pedophilic act(s), thereby lessening the guilt the individual might otherwise feel for having engaged in such behavior.

Chemical dependency problems, including drugs and alcohol, are commonly seen among female pedophiles. Faller (1987), in a study of 40 female sexual offenders, found that about half had substance abuse problems. Travin et al. (1990) conclude that female sexual offenders typically have a history of chronic substance abuse. Often the molestation takes place under the influence of alcohol or drugs. Faller (1987), in her study of 40 female sex abusers, found that 55 percent of them gave a history of substance abuse of alcohol or drugs, alone or in combination. Bess and Janssen (1982) state that 40 percent of the incest victims they studied reported alcoholism in their incestuous parents. Nine of the sixteen female sex offenders studied by Mathews et al. (1989) described a history of chemical abuse.

7. Use of Persuasion Rather Than Force

Unlike male pedophiles, it is rare for female pedophiles to coerce or rape their victims. It is not that coercions are never seen, only that they are extremely rare. This is one of the important differences between male and female pedophiles. Accordingly, the victims of female pedophiles are less likely to feel victimized or raped, and this is especially the case for boys. In fact, the older the boy, the greater the likelihood he will feel that the molestation was an opportunity for sexual initiation. Most women in our society perceive pedophilia as sexual violation, whereas men are more likely to view the experience as sexual initiation. Fromuth and Burkhart (1987) found that men who, as children, had sexual encounters with adult women were less likely than women who were similarly molested to perceive childhood sexual experiences as abusive. Faller's (1989) studies reached similar conclusions. Johnson and Shrier (1987) found that all but one of the female molesters used persuasion rather than physical force or threats. Lew (1990) states, "Sexual activity between older women and young boys is rarely treated as abusive."

In Condy et al.'s (1987) study, men who as boys had sexual relations with women were far less likely to feel that they were traumatized than women who had been sexually molested as children. Condy et al. studied both college men and prison inmates who, as children, had been sexually abused by women. Fifty-one percent of the college men had good feelings about the experience and 24 percent had bad feelings. Of the total prison population (rapists, child molesters, and nonsex offenders), 66 percent had good feelings about the experience and 6 percent had bad feelings. Thirty-seven percent of the college men claimed that the experience had a good effect on their sex life, whereas 16 percent claimed that it had a bad effect on their sex life. Forty-three percent of the total prison men described the early experience as having a good effect, whereas 22 percent claimed that it had a bad effect on their sex life. Risin and Koss (1987) found that 24 percent of boys who were sexually abused by a woman, where the sexual abuse involved penetration, were proud of the experience.

All the aforementioned studies, although not directly designed to focus on the question of whether the female pedophile is or is not coercive, lend confirmation to the conclusion that women pedophiles are less likely to be coercive than male pedophiles. These studies provide this confirmation via the reports of male victims, who are far less likely than females to view the sexual experiences as traumatic and are far more likely than females to have positive recollections of their experiences. I believe this in part relates to social attitudes in which women are likely to view the experience as a rape and men as an initiation. Obviously, physical factors are operative here as well. The female is more likely to be physically traumatized than the male by such encounters. Another factor operative here is that women, in general, are less likely than men to be aggressive and physically coercive. This difference, which I consider to have strong biological loading, also contributes to the frequent observation that the female pedophile is far less likely to be coercive than her male counterpart. As a result, their victims are less likely to feel victimized.

8. Physical and Emotional Abuse of the Victims in Addition to Sexual Abuse

This criterion would appear to contradict criterion #7, "Use of Persuasion Rather Than Force." This is not necessarily the case. There are many female pedophiles who subject their victims to physical and emotional abuse and yet will use seductive and noncoercive methods to engage the children in sexual activities. There are, however, females who do use force with their victims, but these represent the minority. We see here, then, confirmation of my statement made previously that some of these criteria may be contradictory and it is therefore rare for all of them to be satisfied by a particular individual.

Faller (1987), in her study of 40 women who had sexually abused children, found that approximately 75 percent of the perpetrators had significantly maltreated their victims in ways other than sexual abuse. She found that 52.5 percent physically neglected the children, 32.5 physically abused them, and 15 percent subjected the children to emotional abuse. Stoller (1975) considers aggressive acts to be a reasonable part of the package of atypical sexuality. He sees it as a reparative experience by which the individual "reverses" the positions of the actors in the drama and also reverses their affects. One moves from victim to victor, from passive object of others' hostility and power to the director or ruler; one's tormentors in turn will be one's "victims."

9. Feelings of Inadequacy

Many female pedophiles suffer with deep-seated feelings of inadequacy or are actually very inadequate in their ability to function in life when compared with the majority of other women. They may have few, if any, accomplishments to provide feelings of self-worth. Often, there is a longstanding history of poor school and work performance, unsuccessful marriages, and significant impairments in their ability to relate successfully with others. They may not have the ego-strength to tolerate the inevitable rejections associated with age-appropriate heterosexual involvement. Accordingly, they may gravitate toward children for sexual gratification. They have a strong craving to be loved and will engage children because children will so predictably be adoring of an adult who treats them kindly. Accordingly, children are more likely to provide these women with those responses that can serve to compensate for their feelings of inadequacy.

Women who satisfy this criterion are likely to fall into the aforementioned "male-coercion" category of female pedophile. These are the women who perpetrate pedophilic acts in association with a domineering male lover upon whom they are dependent. Such a woman may not get any pleasure out of the pedophilic act, but engages in it in order to satisfy her dominant partner. She may even fear that if she refuses to comply with his demands, she may lose him. Because of her feelings of inadequacy, she does not have the confidence that she can attract another man if he were to leave her. Such anticipations may be unrealistic, in that the woman is indeed an attractive and competent person, but feels that she cannot attract a substitute. In many cases, however, the feelings are justified because she is not the kind of person who would attract other men so readily.

10. Presence of Other Sexual Deviations

Women who engage in pedophilic acts generally do not exhibit their pedophilia in isolation from other sexual deviations. It is not likely that a well-adjusted heterosexual female will exhibit an isolated sexual deviation like pedophilia. Rather, other deviations are usually present, such as promiscuity, sadomasochism, homosexuality, and exhibitionism. The sadomasochism may be especially apparent in the aforementioned "male-coercion" type of pedophilic female wherein the pedophilic acts occur in association with submission to a dominant male lover. Because paraphilias are much more common in males than females, the presence of other sexual deviations is more likely to be found in the male than the female pedophile.

11. Unconvincing Denial

Women who have been falsely accused of pedophilic acts are likely to suffer with feelings of impotent rage. The consequences, in our society, of being found guilty of perpetrating such an act are formidable. In the intrafamilial category of female pedophilia, being found guilty may result in loss of one's children. Destruction of one's reputation and even jail sentences are possible. Accordingly, their professions of innocence are convincing and do not have an artificial quality. In contrast, women who have actually involved themselves in pedophilic acts often exhibit weak and/or obviously feigned denials that are not particularly convincing.

12. Use of Rationalizations and Cognitive Distortions That Justify Pedophilia

Many pedophiles rationalize their pedophilic behavior, e.g., "She liked it, so what could be wrong with it?" "I was sexually abused myself so it's okay for me to abuse children," and "I knew she wanted it anyway, so there's nothing wrong with it." Some will justify their activities with the rationalization that sex is a wonderful thing and that people of all ages should not be deprived of its gratifications. Some would like to believe that they are at the forefront of a social revolution in which children become liberated to express their sexuality.

In contrast, women who have not engaged in pedophilic acts, when asked what they think about sex between an adult and a child, will profess the usual attitudes present in our society regarding such acts, e.g., "It's a disgusting act," "It's good they have laws to protect children from such characters," and "It's one of the worst things that an adult can do to a child."

13. Resistance to Taking a Lie Detector Test

Women who have engaged in sexual molestation of children will generally refuse to take a lie detector test and provide a wide variety of justifications, e.g., "My lawyer says I shouldn't take it" and "I don't believe in them." Although the instrument is certainly not foolproof and although many courts do not allow polygraph findings to be introduced as evidence, the person who is genuinely innocent will be enthusiastic about taking the test with the recognition that it is not foolproof and that there may be false positive findings. I wish to emphasize that this criterion has absolutely nothing to do with the *findings* on the lie detector test, but rather the woman's *attitude toward* taking the test.

14. Lack of Cooperation in the Evaluative Examination

Women who have engaged in pedophilic behavior recognize that they have perpetrated a criminal act and are therefore reluctant to reveal themselves to an evaluator. Accordingly, they may be obstructionistic and uncooperative in the course of an evaluation, e.g., they may be late for appointments, forget them, and find other excuses to circumvent the interviewer's efforts. But even prior to the evaluation they may do everything possible to avoid being interviewed. In the course of the evaluation they may be arrogant, passive-aggressive, and resist significantly the interviewer's attempts to learn about them. In contrast, women who are innocent welcome interviews by qualified examiners and will be fully cooperative. They will overcome any inhibitions they have about talking about their personal sexual lives because they recognize that such information is crucial for the evaluator to have, and they appreciate, as well, that their sexual activities are in the normal range.

15. Duplicities Unrelated to the Sex-abuse Denial

Women pedophiles who deny their sexual activities are not only being deceitful when they deny the pedophilia but will generally exhibit *other* deceits during the course of the evaluation – deceits not directly related to the allegation of pedophilia. Accordingly, the examiner does well to be alerted to the presence of such deceits because the greater their number, the greater the likelihood the individual is lying regarding the pedophilic behavior. In contrast, women who have not perpetrated such acts are less likely to reveal duplicities in other aspects of the examination.

CONCLUDING COMMENTS

Because of the paucity of literature on female sex offenders, fewer generalizations can be made about them. It is for this reason that I am unable to provide here a section on the causes of pedophilia in the female, a presentation I was able to provide earlier in this chapter for the male. However, certain statements can tentatively be made that can be useful for examiners in assessing alleged perpetrators. First, it is important for the examiner to avoid utilizing criteria applicable to male perpetrators because there are significant differences in the two populations. For example, male perpetrators most often work alone, whereas it is quite common for female sex abusers to work along with a male cohort, especially one on whom she is significantly dependent. The female perpetrator is more likely to be working as a babysitter and perpetrate the abuse in the context of services for which she is being paid. She is much more likely to use persuasion than force, which is very much a male perpetrator characteristic. Her victims are less likely than the victims of the male perpetrator to feel victimized. And she is more likely than her male pedophilic counterpart to have had a past history of strong heterosexual relationships.

She shares, however, with the male perpetrator a history of sexual, physical, and emotional abuse in childhood, a dysfunctional family history, possibly lower intelligence than average, a greater likelihood of severe psychopathology (including psychosis, borderline personality, and psychopathy), and a history of substance abuse.

THREE
THE CHILD

INTRODUCTION

In this chapter I focus on the psychological and behavioral signs and symptoms that can be useful for the examiner in differentiating true from false sex-abuse accusations. I refer to these manifestations as *indicators* of child sex abuse. In Chapter Five I will focus on the medical signs and symptoms. It is important for the reader to appreciate that there is no such thing as the "typical" signs and symptoms of the sexually abused child. There are some sexually abused children who exhibit absolutely no symptoms at all, and there are others who exhibit such severe symptoms that they could be considered to be psychotic. And, of course, there are children who exhibit symptoms at all points on the continuum between these two extremes. Because of this there is no such thing as a "child sex-abuse syndrome." A syndrome, by definition, is a cluster of symptoms that warrants being considered together because of a common etiology. Although sex abuse may be considered an etiology, the symptoms that such children exhibit are of such great variety that they do not lend themselves to being placed into the kinds of clusters that warrant the syndrome label. I suspect that this is one of the reasons the nomenclature committee of *DSM-III-R* did not include such a syndrome.

I emphasize this point at the beginning of this chapter because one sees reference to this alleged syndrome in many legal documents, and hundreds of hours on the witness stand have been devoted to testimony about this alleged syndrome. Evaluators who tend to see sex abuse in practically every child they examine are not only likely to subscribe to the view that such a syndrome exists, but will include under this rubric just about every psychogenic symptom known to psychiatry. There is not a psychogenic disorder listed in *DSM-III-R* that they will not consider to be a possible manifestation of sex abuse.

A pamphlet (Spelman, 1985) published by an organization that refers to itself as "The National Committee for Prevention of Child Abuse" lists, among others, the following behavioral manifestations that should alert parents that a child has been sexually abused:

1. Clinging, anxious, irritable behavior
2. Regression to babyish habits, such as thumbsucking
3. Nightmares, bedwetting, fear of dark, difficulty falling asleep, new fears
4. Increase or decrease in appetite

The list does include other symptoms related to sexualization and exaggerated interest in sex. However, the aforementioned are certainly not specific for sex abuse and may have a wide variety of other causes, causes not related to sexual molestation. The publication, however, gives no indication that this may be the case. And this is typical of the information provided to the general public and even examiners.

Renshaw (1987) also deplores this state of affairs. She states:

> In addition, there are numerous lay and professional articles now that erroneously list every "generic" symptom of childhood distress as pathognomonic of sex abuse, for example, bedwetting after a weekend visit with a divorced father, withdrawal, daydreaming, sleeping in class, gym refusal, aggression, reading porn

magazines, scratching genitals, masturbation, using obscene language, poor grades, etc. These have been frequent causes for
referral from schools for a child evaluation for possible sexual
abuse.

Furthermore, a formidable problem confronting anyone who
is trying to assess studies on differentiating true from false
sex-abuse accusations is that of knowing with certainty that
children in the allegedly nonabused group were genuinely not
abused and those in the allegedly abused group were indeed
abused. Certainly, in some cases of abuse the group placement is
not difficult. Sperm may have been found in the vagina and the
child may have contracted one or more sexually transmitted
diseases. In other cases there is clear-cut medical evidence for
such abuse. However, there are many allegedly abused children
included in such studies who may not actually have been abused.
For example, Finkelhor et al. (1989) discuss 270 cases of alleged
sexual abuse in day-care centers. They claim all of these cases
were "substantiated" before inclusion in their book. The method
used to "verify" that the children were indeed abused was to call
individuals who were involved in the case and who believed that
the abuse occurred. They state, "If at least one of the local
investigating agencies had decided that abuse had occurred . . .
then we considered the case substantiated." This is a very weak—
and even dangerous—criterion to utilize, especially because of the
hysteria that is widespread in certain settings in which sex abuse
is alleged. It appears that some of the children used in the
Finkelhor et al. study were those who alleged sex abuse in the
McMartin case, a case in which the children appear (at least to
me) to satisfy most of the criteria applicable to the false sex-abuse
accusation.

Kiser et al. (1988) studied ten young children, ages two to
six, who were allegedly suffering with a post-traumatic stress
disorder (PTSD). They were children who were allegedly abused
in a day-care setting. At no point in the article do the authors
mention any consideration of the possibility that the abuse may
not have taken place and that they were dealing with children
who might have been subjected to mass hysteria. The day-care

center was church related and, as I have described elsewhere (Gardner, 1991a), child-care facilities associated with church groups are more likely to be exhibiting this phenomenon than child-care centers that are not church affiliated. The authors state (unashamedly), "The accounts of the families were accepted at face value, just as the complaints and problems of most patients are accepted." Throughout the paper it is clear that these children satisfy many of the criteria of the false sex-abuse accusation. For example, the "disclosures" did not take place until four to six months after the alleged events. This is typical of sex-abuse hysteria in a nursery school setting. And the children's nightmares did not begin until after the disclosure, again a common occurrence in such situations. In a true PTSD, it is rare for there to be such a hiatus. One would think that the presence of this hiatus in all 12 children might lead the examiners to question whether all were indeed sexually abused. It is unfortunate that this article was published in the United States' most prestigious child psychiatry journal because it cannot but lend credibility to the view that such outbreaks are more likely to be true than false.

Another problem that such studies have to deal with is that of knowing with certainty that children in the nonabused group have indeed not been abused. Critics of such studies often claim that the investigators did not take proper precautions to ensure that all of the children in the nonabused group were indeed not abused. This is a criticism that can always be directed, and one can never be completely certain that it is not justified. No matter how carefully the investigators try to screen out such children, they can never be completely certain that they have been successful. Obviously, it is impossible to prove that something did *not* happen. And this is especially the case for child sex abuse, because there are many children who are sexually abused who do not view it as a trauma, and may even consider it part of normal child development. Some who do indeed consider it a trauma may only be mildly traumatized and may, either voluntarily or under pressure by the abuser, not divulge their sexual experiences. Accordingly, even in those studies in which the examiners appear to have taken great pains to screen out sexually abused children from the nonabused group, it may very well be that some of the subjects were indeed abused and this, of course, compromises the validity of the study.

The problem of differentiation is further compounded by the fact that an interrogation may very well provide a child with suggestions about symptoms that may not have previously existed. And these may be incorporated into the child's scenario. As will be mentioned in greater detail in Chapters Six and Nine, this is especially the case for children who have been evaluated by zealous examiners who sometimes refer to themselves as "validators." Moreover, the stress of coercive interviews may very well enhance psychogenic symptoms and, if the investigations are being made in the context of nursery school or day-care center hysteria, then it is inevitable that even more symptoms will result. As will be discussed in Chapter Ten, the so-called treatment for sex abuse of children who were not sexually abused is also likely to produce symptoms that may be considered by the naive examiner to be the derivative results of sex abuse. Under these circumstances they are actually the result of the "therapy." As a result, there are many children who have never been sexually abused and were initially asymptomatic, exhibiting nothing more than the usual behavioral manifestations and fluctuations of the normal child, who end up with a wide variety of symptoms, each of which was picked up along the evaluative and therapeutic trail. There are children who may exhibit lifelong psychotic symptomatology as a result of ongoing "treatment" under the aforementioned circumstances. More will be said about these children in Chapter Ten.

Accordingly, examiners must have a thorough knowledge of the child's previous experiences, especially in the realm of interviews and treatment before the present assessment; otherwise, the examiner is likely to come to false conclusions regarding whether or not the child was indeed abused. Obviously, the examiner who is the first one to evaluate the child will be in the best position to determine whether or not the symptoms described in this chapter are present. The greater the number of previous interviews, the greater the likelihood that specious symptoms of sex abuse will be found. Examiners should conduct a detailed inquiry regarding the sequence of the development of such symptoms, and much can be learned about their appearance from the accuser and sometimes even the accused. Often the records will describe the dates of onset, especially with regard to whether they appeared before or after the interrogations.

Children and/or adults who provide false accusations of sex abuse lie on a continuum with regard to their degree of conscious awareness of a fabrication. On the one extreme are those who are completely aware that the allegation is a lie. At the other extreme are those who are delusional, that is, they actually believe that the abuse took place even though it may not in fact have occurred. Of course, there are false accusations that are combinations of both, at any point along the continuum between accusations that have a high fabrication loading to fabrications that have a high delusional loading. Furthermore, there are many false accusations that begin as fabrications but then develop into delusions. This is especially the case when the allegation has resulted in a series of examinations by many examiners and protracted litigation. I will use the term *false accusation* to refer to the wide variety of accusations that fall at any point along this continuum. I will use the term *fabrication* when the conscious deceit element is predominant and the term *delusion* when this word is more appropriate.

One problem with which I was confronted when devising this list of indicators relates to the fact that there is a wide variety of situations in which sex abuse may occur, with the result that some of the indicators are more applicable to certain situations and not to others. For example, many of the indicators apply primarily to the home situation, where the abuse is perpetrated by a father, mother, or relative. Others apply more specifically to the divorce situation, where the vengeance or exclusionary element may be operative. Some of the indicators might be more applicable when the abuser is a stranger, or babysitter, or teacher. Obviously, it is impractical to cover all of these situations with any single list of indicators. The list here is an attempt to fuse most of the situations, but I have devoted a special chapter (Chapter Nine) to the indicators that are applicable to the nursery school and day-care center situation. In this chapter I make particular reference to incest abuse, abuse as it takes place in the context of divorce and, on occasion, abuse in other situations. Because in the incest situation the abuser is most often the father, I will refer to the father as the abuser in order to avoid unnecessarily complicating the discussion. Similarly, in the divorce situation the accused person is usually the father, and so I will use him as the example. However, the reader should note that in many situations the mother would be the applicable person being discussed.

The bulk of this chapter is devoted to a description of the differentiating criteria that the examiner can utilize to ascertain whether a child's sex-abuse accusation is true or false. Consistent with what I have said above, there is no particular profile that characterizes the sexually abused child. When a characteristic is positive, i.e., when it supports the argument for bona fide sex abuse, then it might be referred to as an *indicator*. However, the examiner should be careful to avoid using the term *typical indicator* because there is none. One can say, however, that the greater the number of indicators for sex abuse, the greater the likelihood the child has been genuinely abused. In contrast, the greater the number of indicators not found to be present that the accusation is false, the greater the likelihood that no abuse took place.

CHILDREN'S MEMORY AND SUGGESTIBILITY

Introduction

It is important for examiners to appreciate the degree to which children are suggestible and how faulty their memories can be about experiences they have. No one can claim perfect recall and all of us forget. Furthermore, one does well to appreciate that memories do not remain unaltered over time; rather, they become restructured. The alterations are not only the result of the influences of our wishes, desire to avoid unpleasant affects, denial mechanisms, etc., but the simple erosion that takes place over time, erosion that may not be related to any particular psychological mechanisms. Events are not stored in the brain like a photograph. Rather, they may be altered in the process of storage because of inattention or psychological distortion. The storage process is not a stagnant one; rather, there is often reconstruction and restructuring. Nor should the retrieval process be viewed as simple reproduction of what is stored, but a process by which there is filtering, censorship, and the introduction of further distortions. In the process of retrieval, missing details may be filled in in order to give the memory a coherence and logic that may be satisfying to the individual's sense of balance and aesthetics, but may introduce further distortions. In his discussion of dreams, Freud referred to this process as "secondary elaboration," the process by which the dreamer provides the dream with a sense of continuity and organization that was not present in the actual dream material. Retrieved memories, then, are best viewed as an integration of the residual images of the stored event with subsequent desires, fears, fantasies, and attitudes toward the revelation. These subsequent embellishments may make us more comfortable, but they widen significantly the gap between the reality and our renditions of reality.

It is also important to appreciate that the human brain does not have a very effective mechanism for distinguishing between imagery derived from events that really happened and imagery related to imagination. We do not have a foolproof alerting mechanism that says to us, "That image is fact" or "That image is fantasy." This might be viewed as a weakness in our memory system because it interferes with our ability to differentiate between reality and fantasy. In short, our thoughts and feelings about what we would like to believe happened often have the same status as the memory traces of what really occurred. These principles are applicable to adults and are even more applicable to children, whose mechanisms for such differentiations are even less efficient. No wonder, then, that children are so suggestible. No wonder, then, that they can be made to believe just about anything.

Studies on Children's Memory
and Suggestibility

Myles-Worsley (1986) studied preschool children's recollection of school events. They found that the children tended to fill in gaps in their memory by providing information from their general knowledge of school events. Brainerd and Ornstein (1991) also studied the incorporation of pre-existing knowledge into verbalizations of retrieved memories. Their conclusion was, "One implication of the literature on children's knowledge is that with the passage of time, information in memory can be altered and interpreted more consistently in the light of prior knowledge. Memory, in short, may become more reconstructive and less reproductive."

All the aforementioned processes are present in adults who, presumably, we expect to be more accurate than children regarding their recollection of events. It is reasonable to view young children (under the age of four and five) to be particularly unreliable with regard to the accuracy of their recollection of events. And the longer the time gap between the actual early childhood event and the time when the child is asked to recall the event, the greater the likelihood there will be distortions. There is general agreement among those who study human memory that anyone (regardless of age) who claims recall of events prior to the age of one is probably fantasizing. Children in that age bracket do not have the cognitive ability to understand how events relate to one another, and so are not capable of storing accurate recollections of things that go on around them. Rather, their memories are much more general impressions that are highly distorted by strong emotional reactions. If this is true (and I believe it is), then the recent rash of public announcements of recollections of sex abuse prior to the age of one should be highly suspect. Most people cannot remember events before the ages of four and five. It is reasonable to conclude that before that age range, memories are primarily primitive pictures without significant coherence. It is reasonable to conclude that individuals who claim accurate recollections before ages four to five may very well be fantasizing, or they have come to believe what they have been told by parents and others about experiences that occurred to them during the two-to-four/five age range.

If one adds children's suggestibility, we have even further difficulty regarding the trustworthiness of children's memories. Children are ever trying to ingratiate themselves to adult authorities and will predictably alter their comments to gain such affection and/or to avoid the withdrawal of it. Although they may initially appreciate that they are altering the truth in the service of maintaining a good relationship with the interrogator, the alteration may become repeated and thereby change the initially stored impression. They are no different from adults in this regard; they are just more likely to exhibit these changes more quickly.

Memory is likely to be particularly faulty for events experienced during times of extreme stress. In fact, under such circumstances amnesia (partial and even complete) is not uncommon. But even events that are recalled may be distorted. The whole body has been mobilized to deal with the danger (most often by fight or flight) and the individual's absorption in survival may preclude accurate recall of events. Under such circumstances, attention may be diverted from a wide variety of minor and, at that moment, irrelevant aspects of the event in order to focus on those elements necessary to attend to for the purposes of survival. A good example of this phenomenon is the experience of soldiers in combat who, following return from a combat zone, may note certain injuries for the first time, injuries that only then are noticed as extremely painful. Attending to the pain at the time of injury might have resulted in loss of life. Ceci (1991) describes just such a situation for the child who is a victim of sex abuse—which generally occurs "in the context of high levels of arousal; personal embarrassment; and a web of motives, threats, inducements, and suggestions that might tilt the odds one way or another that the victim will tell others what happened and tell them accurately or inaccurately." The absence of these elements in traditional laboratory studies cannot but compromise the reliability of the results. Flin (1991) also comments on the differences in the conditions of laboratory studies on memory and actual sexual abuse events. She states, "Reporting a list of unrelated words is somewhat lacking in the emotional intensity of relating the intimate details of a sexual assault."

It is important to appreciate that loss of memory is not always undesirable. In fact, as Toglia (1991) points out, it is adaptive. If we were to remember everything it might drive us insane. This, apparently, was the situation for a patient of Luria (1968). Loftus and her colleagues have conducted many experiments that provide powerful verification for the position that the introduction of misleading post-event information competes with original information in such a way that it transforms an underlying memory and produces changes in the recollection of the event. The original memory is thereby altered, erased, or destroyed (Loftus, 1975; Loftus and Davies, 1984; Loftus et al., 1978; Loftus and Palmer, 1974; Loftus et al., 1985). In a typical experiment (original test procedure) the children first view a series of pictures depicting some event. They are then divided into two groups, those who are asked leading questions and those who are asked misleading questions about specific aspects of the original event. Last, they are tested on their memory for the originally observed details. In one variation the children view a series of slides depicting a little girl playing with a toy rabbit. Later, children in the misled group are told incorrectly that the girl had been playing with a toy dog, whereas subjects in the control group are not provided with any misinformation about the stuffed animal. In the final questioning period they are required to state whether it was a rabbit or a dog that they saw in the original pictures. Typically, the children in the misled group performed more poorly than those in the control (nonmisled group), because subjects in the misled group are more likely to report the misinformation (Zaragoza, 1991). It is important to appreciate that in these studies, although the children in the experimental (misled) group did more poorly than the control (nonmisled) group, there were still some children in the misled group who were not misled and recalled correctly the original animal. Accordingly, the introduction of misinformation does not necessarily result in memory impairment. To translate this into the realm of sexually abused children who may be providing false accusations (such as is often the case in nursery-school and day-care center hysteria), there are still some children in these settings who deny they were abused, in spite of the parental and examiner coercions and introduction of misinformation.

Lindberg (1991) conducted a study in which three groups of children (third graders, sixth graders, and college students) were presented with a five-minute film about "a group of students who were taking a test." One group of subjects in each age group was told beforehand that the students in the film taking the test were a group of known cheaters. The other half were merely told that these were students taking a test. Subsequently, the students in the group that had been told that the film depicted cheaters were asked leading questions about cheating they observed in the film. In contrast, those who were not given this information beforehand were not asked misleading questions about cheating afterward. The third graders in the misled group said that 4.1 people cheated, and the college students in the misled group said that 2.52 people cheated. In contrast, both third graders and college students in the nonmisled group held that less than 2.0 people cheated. We see here yet another study confirming the effect of suggestion on children's memory. Interestingly, the youngest group remembered more of the incidental details than the oldest. Specifically, all subjects were asked to focus on the children, and no mention was made of focus on the teacher who gave the children instructions. The main recall levels for the third graders was 3.63, for the sixth graders, 3.08, and for the college students, 2.23. Accordingly, one cannot automatically state that memory improves with age and that younger subjects will remember more than older subjects for certain memory categories, in this case peripheral memory. However, these findings also confirm the well-known observation that younger children are less likely to pay attention to central issues, issues they are asked to focus on by adult authorities, than older children.

Another question that must be considered when studying the relationship between memory and suggestibility is the presence of stress. Clearly, most children who are being sexually molested are being subjected to a psychological stress, and the question raised is whether their memory for the event is thereby affected. Peters (1991) studied two groups of children: one group was exposed to a fire-alarm situation while interacting with an examiner, and the other group was involved in a similar interaction, but without the fire-alarm condition. Not only did the children in the nonfire-alarm condition recall more accurately, but they were more susceptible to the influence of misleading questions. The author also concludes, "Heightened arousal never increased the recognition or recall accuracy of our subjects."

Goodman (1991) provides a good review of some of the more important articles on the relationship between stress, suggestibility, and memory. The research findings are mixed, with some examiners reporting stress as having a positive effect on memory and other examiners reporting just the opposite. Goodman emphasizes the importance of studies that are designed to be ecologically valid, i.e., that attempt to reproduce the reality conditions "out there in the real world," as opposed to the laboratory. One problem with such research is the ethical one, namely, subjecting children to stress for the purposes of scientific research. Goodman also refers to her research on children's reactions to misleading questions and claims that children are particularly resistant to such questions, especially after the age of four. This has not been my experience. Furthermore, Goodman does not refer to children under the age of four, the ages of children involved in most nursery school and day-care center group-sex accusations. Also, in the divorce situation, many of the allegedly abused children are under four. My experience has been that children between three and four are the best subjects for programming a false sex-abuse accusation. Two-year-olds do not make reliable informants and five-year-olds are less readily brainwashed, although they are certainly not immune. Last, the examiners in her study do not subject the children to *repeated* misleading questions over weeks, months, and even years. Ethical researchers would not subject children to the unrelenting barrage of misleading questions to which children are frequently exposed in sex-abuse evaluations and interrogations. This is the true ecological validity that is not taken into consideration in Goodman's studies.

Warren-Leubecker (1991) points out that studies on the relationship between stress and memory often fail to make proper differentiation between low, moderate, and high degrees of stress and that memory for events that take place under these three separate conditions might differ from one another, i.e., high degrees of stress might have different effects on memory than low degrees of stress.

Goodman and Clarke-Stewart (1991) point out the formidable difficulties in studying the effects of suggestibility on children's memories for sex abuse. The authors recognize that it is almost impossible to provide ecological validity for such studies because the examiners cannot actually observe sexual abuse taking place and then document children's memories for their experiences. Nor could the examiners actively abuse or threaten children for experimental purposes, nor could they pose as social workers or police about to remove children from their homes. Accordingly, the studies reported in this article focus on the suggestibility of nonabused children and their propensity to make false reports when nothing sexual or traumatic occurred. In their studies, such children are exposed to nonabusive events and then interviewed in ways that mimic important features of child abuse investigations. In the first study discussed in this article, four- and seven-year-old children were asked to recall an observation made 10-12 days previously of a confederate playing a clown game with a child. The seven-year-olds were 93 percent accurate and the four-year-olds 83 percent accurate regarding questions about potentially abusive actions that did not take place. With regard to responses to misleading abuse questions, e.g., "He took your clothes off, didn't he?" "Did he kiss you?" no participant children and only one four-year-old bystander made a commission error. The authors conclude from this study that normal children are not suggestible with regard to misleading questions that imply sex abuse when it did not occur. The main flaw here is that the authors did not use two- and three-year-olds, the more common age range in which false sex-abuse accusations are most commonly seen. More importantly, they did not subject these children to the *barrage* of misleading questions that such children traditionally are exposed to by a *parade* of investigators over a long period.

In other studies described in this article, Goodman and Clarke-Stewart (1991) admit that a small percentage of children will indeed alter their memories in response to leading questions, but the authors come to the conclusion that because the average or *most* nonabused children resist suggestibility, children in general are not suggestible. From the point of view of the scientist, these findings may very well be useful. However, from the point of view of a person who is being falsely accused by this small percentage of suggestible children, the effects are devastating.

In another study reported in this article, children were asked four years later to recall a nonabuse interaction with an unfamiliar male confederate (subjects then seven and ten years old). Clarke-Stewart states, "Some of the children's errors might lead to suspicion of abuse. For example, one child falsely affirmed that she had been given a bath, five children agreed to having been both hugged and kissed, and two children said 'yes' when asked if their picture had been taken in the bathtub. Nevertheless, the children were more resistant to abuse-related than to nonabuse-related suggestions." It is to be noted here that the total number of children in this study was 30: 15 seven-year-olds and 15 ten-year-olds. Accordingly, five children (17 percent) falsely claimed they had been hugged and kissed. This is typical of such studies, namely, that often as many as 20 percent of the children will give false-positive responses. Goodman is providing support here for her critics.

Goodman and Clarke-Stewart (1991) then discuss the studies of Clarke-Stewart et al. (1989). They focus here on their well-known study in which children observed a research confederate, "a janitor," either cleaning up and arranging toys (including dolls) or playing with the dolls in a rough and suggestive manner. The children were subsequently interrogated in different ways; however, misleading questions were introduced with varying degrees of pressure. The examiners were either neutral or incriminating regarding the behavior of the janitor, and in some cases they became progressively stronger and more accusatory. Goodman and Clarke-Stewart (1991) state, "Although all children who heard interrogations that were inconsistent with what they had observed eventually converted to the interrogators' view, some did so more rapidly." The authors' final summary:

> In sum, the children's interpretation of a somewhat ambiguous event was easily manipulated by an opinionated adult interviewer. In considering the implications of this research to sexual abuse investigations, however, the most important caveat to keep in mind is that the study did not involve allegations of sexual abuse but rather whether a janitor cleaned or played. Children may be more resistant to manipulation when the suggestions are about abusive acts, especially against the child himself or herself. (p. 102)

First, the statement is not valid. Some of the misleading questions were indeed of the type one sees in sex-abuse investigations. For example, the janitor did indeed look at and even clean the dolls' genital areas, and questions about this activity were asked. One of the misleading questions was, "Did he kiss the doll?" Some of the questions related to the janitor's "guilt" regarding whether he was doing his job or just "playing." And this in itself may suggest sexuality. In closing Goodman and Clarke-Stewart state, "The studies did not include the numerous interviews, examinations, and cross-examinations children often experience in actual cases. We did not imply to the children that our confederates were criminals, and we did not pose as legal authorities."

Steller (1991) is in agreement with me regarding the weaknesses of the aforementioned Goodman and Clarke-Stewart studies and supports those critical of their conclusions. He points out that in one such study, in which eight percent of the children made commission errors implying sex abuse, "This means 8% of the subjects of this condition made errors. Extrapolating this finding to forensic contexts produces an alarmingly high number of false accusations. It is reasonable to assume that the danger for analogous errors in real-life situations would be much greater than in the experimental setting."

Steller (1991) then continues:

> Goodman and Clarke-Stewart seem to have ignored their own findings in concluding that "it seems unlikely that normal children will easily yield to an interviewer's suggestion that something sexual occurred when in fact it did not." The dramatic finding was that one girl not only acquiesced to suggestions by nodding like others did, but also she "falsely claimed that the doctor had placed a stick in her rectum." The fact that the majority of children did resist overtly misleading questions is not an exciting finding; this would only be the case if one would make the assumption that all children are stupid. The finding that an erroneous allegation of extreme severity could be provoked in an experimental setting with a small sample of children is of striking importance for forensic investigations.
>
> Nobody with forensic experience would expect high frequencies of fictitious allegations of sexual abuse. In practice, the difficult detection task is to identify the false alarms, which apparently do occur to an unknown and probably low degree. According to the findings obtained by Goodman and Clarke-Stewart, they occur even under experimental conditions in which less powerful suggestive influences can be expected than under the conditions of real-life interviews conducted by parents, laypersons, and poorly trained professionals. (p. 108)

McGough (1991a) states the following about the aforementioned research of Goodman and Clarke-Stewart:

> The current legal system does little to recreate the kinds of conditions conducive to the elicitation of a reliable account by the child. In an adversarial system of justice, there are few neutral players. Given an authoritarian interviewer (police officer, criminal investigator, parent, or defense counsel), who may be consciously or subconsciously motivated to influence the child's memory; given multiple pretrial interviews; given a child's increased memory-fade over time; and given substantial intervals between the observed events and testimony at trial, substantial impairment of a child's memories seems inevitable. (p. 116)

McGough (1991a) suggests, with regard to Goodman's studies:

> Both series of experiments converge to underscore the impor-
> tance of the initial interview for the elicitation of an unbiased
> account, for the preservation of that version against later potential
> contamination, and perhaps to inoculate the child against predict-
> able subsequent attempts to interfere with his or her autonomous
> memory. The recording of an unbiased initial interview of the child
> is the keystone to reform of the current processes. If a solid record
> were required to be made in any case involving a child witness,
> then no matter what pressures were thereafter brought to bear
> upon the child, the child and the legal system would have a
> benchmark against which subsequent changes could be evaluated
> for improper suggestiveness. (p. 117)

I am in full agreement with this recommendation. Of course, those who are staunchly convinced that "children never lie" would interpret such a nonrevealing interview to indicate that the child was too frightened and/or embarrassed to reveal all the details and that one could only expect such divulgences to take place in the context of a series of interviews with a known interviewer. This is again an example of the no-win situation in which many people accused of sex abuse find themselves.

Davies et al. (1988) compared seven-to-eight-year-olds with nine-to-ten-year-olds and eleven-to-twelve-year-olds regarding their memory, two weeks later, about a visitor to their school, with whom each of the children had been asked to help set up equipment for a talk on road safety. Two weeks later each child was questioned about the visitor and was asked to identify the visitor's picture from a 12-picture array. When the array did not contain a picture of the visitor, children in each category made false identifications. The rate was 88 percent for the seven-to-eight-year-olds and 60 percent for the older children. Once again we see the enormous effect of suggestibility on children's memory. And once again we see demonstrated that younger children are more likely to provide false information than older ones.

Dent (1991) points out that an important variable when comparing studies about the relationship between children's suggestibility and memory is the time interval between the event being recalled and the request for such recollection. Studies vary enormously on this point. Considering the universal agreement that memory fades with time, the failure to standardize this factor makes it very difficult to compare one study with another. Dent's studies also indicate that recall is greater when children are provided with specific closed-ended questions, e.g., "What color was the man's hair?" than when asked open-ended questions like, "Can you tell me what the man looked like?"

Raskin and Esplin (1991) emphasize the motivational element in the distortion of memory for events. For example, a disinterested witness to a crime is likely to have very different motivation for recollection than a person who has been the subject of the criminal act. Raskin and Esplin describe a technique for assessing credibility, namely, a technique that they refer to as *criteria-based content analysis* (CBCA) (Raskin and Steller, 1989; Raskin and Esplin, 1991). This technique is based on the work of Undeutsch (1989), who referred to the procedure as *statement reality analysis.* The technique is based on the assumption that the substantive content of a true statement will be different from that of a false (fabricated or delusional) statement. Undeutsch uses as his foundation data the statements made by tens of thousands of sexually abused children in Germany. When utilizing the method, it is important that the interviewer see the child as soon after the abuse as possible and not introduce contaminating elements in the course of the interview. When utilizing the criteria it is necessary to consider the age, experience, and cognitive ability of the witness. The examiner must be familiar with the typical kinds of statements that would be made at the various age levels. There are 19 areas of criteria related to such considerations as the logical relationship between the components, the degree of organization, the presence of specific details, the nature of conversations, the presence of unusual details, the nature of the child's subjective mental state, changes and corrections in the description, the similarity of the general account to that of bona fide situations.

McGough (1991b) is critical of Raskin's system because it

goes against a basic tenet of the Anglo-American legal system, which is that the court and the juries are the ones who are responsible for ascertaining a witness's credibility; experts, no matter how great their expertise, are not as reliable to accomplish this goal. McGough is reflecting here the traditional legal view. I believe that we in psychiatry and psychology have developed special techniques in recent years to enable us to assess credibility in ways superior to that of the traditional legal system, especially because we have the opportunity to interview directly—in a noncontrived setting—all three parties involved in an accusation: the accuser, the accused, and the alleged victim. I personally believe that Undeutsch, Raskin, Esplin, and others who work with CBCA are making important contributions. My only criticism is that they give too much weight to the child's statements and not enough focus on the interviews of the accuser and the accused, even though they certainly recognize the importance of such assessments.

Wells and Loftus (1991) are somewhat dubious about a scorer's capacity to properly take into consideration the different developmental levels that the examiner is required to appreciate if one is to properly assess a child's scores on the CBCA. The simple instruction that the examiner "consider" age is not, in their opinion, sufficient. Even were the examiner to use formalized standardized tests that might give some assessment of the child's developmental-cognitive level, it would still be difficult to apply these findings to the CBCA. She further criticizes the CBCA on the grounds that studies have not yet been done on its interevaluator reliability. Davies (1991) makes reference to a previous study (Davies et al., 1989), in which groups of children interacted with strangers playing the role of a public health official. A week later the children were questioned about the incident and asked to compile a composite picture of the stranger's face. One child was particularly unsure about the meeting but, after being reminded about it, proceeded to create the composite face. The investigators considered his composite to be in the average-to-poor range. They subsequently learned that this child had not been included in the previous study, but had the same name as a child who was a participant and had inadvertently been brought back a week later under the assumption that he had originally been involved in the study. We see here a good example of a child's suggestibility and the desire to ingratiate himself to adult authority.

King and Yuille (1987) conducted a study in which children in four age groups (6, 9, 11, and 16-17) were seated alone in a room when a stranger entered with plant-care equipment and tended some plants. Before leaving, the stranger noted the time, indicated that it was late, and had to leave. During the subsequent interview each child was asked, "On which arm did the man wear his watch?" In reality, the man had not worn a watch. Each child was also asked whether a scissors had been used to remove a leaf. Actually, a leaf had been removed, but by hand, and scissors, which were in clear view, were not used. The younger children tended to agree with the misleading suggestions whereas the older children did not. The authors also concluded that "the less a child remembers about the event the more he can be misled, and the younger the child the less he will remember." This comment has particular relevance to sex-abuse evaluations because the child who is falsely accusing will have no actual memory of the event and so is more likely to provide "fill-ins" via misleading information provided by interrogators.

Goleman (1988) describes a study conducted by M. Lewis. In this study three-year-olds were asked to remain alone in a room and the examiner, before leaving, set up an attractive toy behind the child's back and told him (her) not to look at it while the examiner was out of the room. The children were observed through a one-way mirror. Only ten percent of the children didn't peek while the examiner was gone. Of the rest, a third admitted they had peeked, a third lied and denied that they had done so, and a third refused to say one way or the other. In short, about two-thirds of the children were deceitful, in that they either lied by omission or lied by commission. This study has less bearing on suggestibility than it has on children's susceptibility to fabrication. Saywitz (1987) states that children are apt to add material when they do not remember. Accordingly, when one asks a child for elaborations with questions such as "What else?" the child is likely to add extraneous and contradictory information.

PSYCHODYNAMIC FACTORS OPERATIVE IN CHILDREN'S FALSE ACCUSATIONS OF SEX ABUSE

Introduction

There are no "typical" psychodynamic patterns in children who provide false sex-abuse accusations. This is especially the case because there are a variety of settings in which such accusations may be seen. Here, I focus on the two most common settings for such accusations, namely, the day-care center and the child custody dispute. Although there are certainly differences in the psychodynamic patterns that may operate in these two situations, there is significant overlap. In addition, factors that may be operative for older children may be less applicable to younger ones. Here I will focus on those psychological factors that are more likely to be operative in younger children, especially those between ages three and five, the most common age bracket in which one sees such false accusations. As mentioned, two-year-olds are too young to be reliable subjects for such inculcation, and children over five are less likely to distort reality. These are the children who are the most suggestible and whose memories can be "expanded" in such a way that they may predictably provide false sex-abuse accusations.

Ingratiation to Adult Authorities

Children are constantly trying to ingratiate themselves to adults, especially to adults in authority, like parents, teachers, and professionals such as physicians, lawyers, and judges. Like all of us, they want to be liked. If lying will serve this end, they are likely to do so. In divorce situations children predictably lie and say to each parent what that parent wants to hear, especially regarding criticisms of the other. This is the most common way they deal with the loyalty conflicts that emerge from divorce and especially from custody disputes. Children embroiled in a custody dispute know where their "bread is buttered." They know that when with parent A, if they express affection for parent B, they may alienate parent A. In contrast, if they join in with parent A, provide criticisms of parent B (new or more ammunition), they will ingratiate themselves to parent A. And the same procedure is used with parent B. The same principle holds when children are being interviewed by validators. They want to ingratiate themselves to them and get the "right answers." If the validator starts with the position that the sex abuse did indeed take place, the child is likely to pick this up quite early in the interview and provide just the responses that the evaluator wants to hear. This tendency of children makes it easy for evaluators to get them to say anything they want. It is almost like taking candy from a baby. Because of the child's naiveté, cognitive immaturity, and suggestibility, the job is made even easier and the child may not realize how preposterous the elicited statements and testimonials are.

The Keeping-up-with-the-Joneses Phenomenon

The examiner must appreciate that children in the nursery-school setting who allege sex abuse may be doing so as a manifestation of what I refer to as the keeping-up-with-the-Joneses phenomenon. After all, if all the other kids are professing sex abuse, why be the only one who doesn't? The others claim that they were at the party where everyone got undressed. The child certainly does not want to admit that he (she) was the only one not invited to that party. The child may initially recognize that there was no such "party," but, after a series of the kinds of coercive interviews frequently conducted in sex-abuse investigations, may actually come to believe that he (she) did attend. And this is another important point. What originally may have been a fabrication or an idea introduced by another comes to be believed by the child. The fabrication then becomes a delusion. This is a common phenomenon. And these false beliefs may become so deeply entrenched that the child may accept them as valid throughout the course of life. I recall seeing one child whose class was given a presentation on sex-abuse prevention. At the end of the presentation the children were asked if anyone had ever touched them in "bad places." First, no child responded. The presenter then asked, "Are you sure?" Then, very hesitantly, one girl raised her hand and pointed to her vaginal area and whispered, "My daddy touches me there." Within a minute two other little girls imitated the exact same gesture and claimed that their daddys too had touched them "down there." All three fathers were reported to Child Protection Services. I myself was involved in one of the cases and found absolutely no evidence that the child had ever been sexually abused.

In another case a four-year-old girl was watching a "Mr. Belvedere" television program devoted to child sex abuse. Near the end of the program Mr. Belvedere himself asked the viewers directly if they themselves had ever been touched in "bad places." He instructed those who had been subjected to such touching to inform the appropriate parent or proper authority. The parents of the child I was seeing were involved in a custody dispute. The child reported the "bad touches" to her mother, who immediately called her lawyer and the social worker whom she was seeing for therapy. Both immediately instructed her to contact Child Protection Services. Again, by the time I saw this child, the father and the child—and even the mother—were psychological "basket cases," and I saw absolutely no evidence that this child had ever been sexually molested.

In another case two sisters, ages two and four, had spent two weeks in a shelter with their mother, who had fled from her husband because of "physical abuse." Actually, the husband had not ever touched the mother, but she was going to use the sojourn in the shelter as confirmatory evidence that her husband had indeed abused her. She was planning to leave him and anticipated that this would support her allegations in a forthcoming child custody dispute. In the shelter were many children who had indeed been sexually abused. In fact, the social worker who was assigned to the children's mother said, "Just about every child who comes here has been sexually abused. At first, they don't talk about it, but after a few days here it all comes out." Not once did it ever enter her head that the children might be picking up "stories" from others in the shelter. Not surprisingly, the two little girls I am discussing here picked up some of the ambient accusations and, not surprisingly again, the mother attempted to use these as well as ammunition in her custody dispute. What is saddest here is that the mother actually believed that her children had been sexually abused by her husband and did not appreciate the obvious fact that they were manifesting the "keeping-up-with-the-Joneses" phenomenon.

Enhanced Attention and Notoriety

Then there is the element of enhanced attention and even notoriety. Many of these children are surrounded by an army of people who provide them with significant attention. Mother may be listening to the child with a degree of concentration never before enjoyed by the child. She is ever walking around with pencil and paper, ready to note down what to the child may be the most meaningless and absurd comments. But soon the child picks up the particular areas that are most likely to attract attention and "stop people in their tracks." The child learns those comments that will distract the mother from other activities, like attending to other siblings or spending time with friends and neighbors. Then there are the child protection workers, the lawyers, the psychologists and psychiatrists, the prosecutors, and the judges. Neighborhood people are constantly "buzzing" about the sex-abuse scandal that took place in the child's nursery school. The children are pointed to by friends and neighbors as the ones who attend "that" nursery school that we all heard about. Many of these cases are given significant coverage by the public media. Reporters, TV announcers, and even appearances on television are possible. All this attention can be enormously gratifying to the child, who may recognize, at some level, that if nothing ever happened, then all these people would evaporate and the notoriety would come to an end.

Mappan (1980) considered the attention-getting factor to be

an important one operative for the children in the Salem Witch Trials. Mappan quotes from the account given by Charles Upham (1802-1875) in his book, *Salem Witchcraft* (1867):

> At this point, if Mr. Parris [father of one of the accusing girls], the ministers, and magistrates had done their duty, the mischief might have been stopped. The girls ought to have been rebuked for their dangerous and forbidden sorceries and divinations, their meetings broken up, and all such tamperings with alleged super-naturalism and spiritualism frowned upon. Instead of this, the neighboring ministers were summoned to meet at Mr. Parris's house to witness the extraordinary doings of the girls, and all they did was to endorse, and pray over, them. Countenance was thus given to their pretensions and the public confidence in the reality of their statements established. Magistrates from the town, church-members, leading people, and people of all sorts, flocked to witness the awful power of Satan, as displayed in the tortures and contortions of the "afflicted children" who became objects of wonder, so far as their feats were regarded, and of pity in view of their agonies and convulsions. (p. 38)

Here we see how the girls, instead of being rebuked and ignored, were surrounded by an army of "ministers . . . magistrates from the town, church members, leading people, and people of all sorts." Replace these individuals with validators, psychologists, prosecutors, lawyers, friends and relatives, newspaper reporters, and television coverage and we see a repetition of the same phenomenon. In both cases the children become "objects of wonder."

Release of Hostility

All human beings must learn to deal with frustration. After all, we can only have a small fraction of all those things in life we would like to possess and so frustration is an inevitable part of the human condition. And frustration, when it persists, ultimately leads to anger. We cannot release our anger whenever and wherever we want. To do so would result in significant rejection and retaliation by significant figures around us. In early childhood we must first learn various techniques for dealing with anger, techniques that suppress, repress, and/or allow for its expression in a wide variety of ways, both healthy and pathological. A socially acceptable scapegoat provides one such mechanism of release.

In the divorce situation the child may have much to be angry about. The parent who leaves the home (usually the father) is generally viewed as an abandoner. Even though he may claim that he no longer loves the mother—but he still loves the children—from their vantage point he has abandoned the household and his reasons and justifications have little meaning for them. Their general position is, "If you really loved us you would stay. If you really loved us you would tolerate all the indignities, frustrations, and abominations you claim you are subjected to at the hands of our mother." Having little if any ability to place themselves in the position of the father, they can more comfortably subscribe to this somewhat egocentric position. There may be financial privations that engender even more anger. And when one adds to these predictable sources of hostility a parent's programming the children to view the other party as the incarnation of all the evil that ever existed in the history of the world, then even more anger is generated. And this situation, of course, leads to the development of a parental alienation syndrome (Gardner, 1992a), a disorder in which the child is programmed into a campaign of vilification and deprecation of a father. It is not difficult to see how a false sex-abuse accusation can develop under these circumstances because it predictably allows for the expression of hostility in a way that is being sanctioned by the programming parent.

In the nursery-school situation the accused teachers and other day-care personnel serve as useful scapegoats for the pent-up angers of the parents and, subsequently, the children. It is almost as if most of the anger that inevitably derives from other sources is funneled into the diatribes against the alleged abusers. It is almost as if nothing other than the accused perpetrators bothers these people. What is striking in these cases is the degree of sadism that many of these children may exhibit. In many of these cases I have been impressed by what I consider to be the innate cruelty of children, a cruelty that lies just beneath the surface and is not significantly suppressed or repressed by the adult authorities who are bringing them up and educating them. These children also become used by women who harbor within themselves significant animosity toward all men. I am referring here to zealous feminists and/or women who were sexually abused as children, as well as others who, for whatever reason, harbor enormous rage toward men. They help fuel the rage that these children exhibit toward the accused. Once again, Mappan (1980) quotes Upham (1867):

> They [the accusing children] appeared as the prosecutors of every poor creature that was tried, and seemed ready to bear testimony against any one upon whom suspicion might happen to fall. It is dreadful to reflect upon the enormity of their wickedness, if they were conscious of imposture throughout. It seems to transcend the capabilities of human crime. There is, perhaps, a slumbering element in the heart of man that sleeps for ever in the bosom of the innocent and good, and requires the perpetration of a great sin to wake it into action, but which, when once aroused, impels the transgressor onward with increasing momentum, as the descending ball is accelerated in its course. It may be that crime begets an appetite for crime, which, like all other appetites, is not quieted but inflamed by gratification. (p. 37)

Infectiousness of Emotions

Then there is what I refer to as the vibrating-tuning-fork principle. This relates to the infectiousness of emotions. Emotions have a way of transmitting themselves from one individual to another, often in very rapid fashion. Walk into a room in which people are grieving for the death of a loved one. The visitor may not even know the deceased but, in a few minutes, may find himself (herself) crying or at least depressed. Comedians know well that they are far less likely to be successful with small audiences than large audiences. The large audience provides him the opportunity for spreading the laughter to those who initially might not have been swept up. The same phenomenon is operative in mass hysteria (Gardner, 1991a). All of these examples operate like vibrating tuning forks: take two tuning forks of the same fixed intrinsic frequency of vibration. Strike one and hold the second (unstruck) close by. Almost immediately the second one will start to vibrate in unison with the first. Children living in a home with an enraged parent who is preoccupied with anger and who may in addition have hysterical outbursts of rage are likely to "vibrate" with such a parent and join in with similar emotions. Without knowing the exact reasons why they are so swept up, they may provide the kinds of rationalizations that result in the preposterous scenarios already described.

Reactions to Normal Childhood Sexuality

Sigmund Freud (1905) referred to children as "polymorphous perverse." I am in full agreement with Freud on this point. Children normally exhibit just about any kind of sexual behavior imaginable: heterosexual, homosexual, bisexual, and autosexual. Infants have no problem caressing any part of anyone's body, whether it be a private part or a public part. And they have absolutely no concern for the gender of the possessor of the target part. Nor do they concern themselves with that person's sexual orientation. They will put into their mouths any object that will fit, whether it be their own or someone else's. They touch all parts of their own bodies and attempt to touch all parts of other people's bodies. In short, they touch, suck, insert, smell, and feel all of their own parts as well as of other human beings and make no particular discriminations regarding the age, sex, or relationship to them of the object of their "sexual" advances. Each society has its own list (most often quite specific) regarding which types of sexual behavior are acceptable and which are prohibited. Generally, parents provide this information in the early years of the child's life and react quite strongly when the child attempts to engage in one of the unacceptable forms of sexual behavior, that is, unacceptable in accordance with the consensus of individuals in the particular society in which the child has been born.

In our society we generally attempt to lead the child down

the heterosexual track, but even here we suppress heterosexual behaviors to varying degrees up until the time of marriage and even afterward. Even in the marital bed, most subscribe to a particular "list" of behaviors that are acceptable and may exhibit strong revulsion when a spouse requests a sexual encounter that is not on the "list." But even when social suppression and repression have been successful (regarding overt behavior), residua of the early primitive polymorphous perversity persist. These suppressed impulses can be gratified in fantasy, symbolism, or vicariously by thinking about others who engage in these activities. Psychiatrists refer to those whose primary orientation is a residuum of the unacceptable and/or atypical as psychopathological or symptomatic. The man in the street will refer to these individuals as perverted. Many years ago, during my residency training, I came to this conclusion: We label as perverts those who engage in sexual behaviors that we personally find disgusting. Because their behavior disgusts us, it is probable that we are suppressing and/or repressing our own unconscious desires to engage in the very behavior we so detest.

Some examples: A three-year-old boy is playing with his penis. Many parents would hold that masturbation is a perfectly natural act, but tell the child that what he is doing is a personal matter and should not be done in front of other people. The child might also be told that if he wishes to engage in that behavior, he should do so in the privacy of his own room. This is the kind of comment that many educated parents would tell their children at this time. However, even this comment communicates certain socially induced restrictions and prohibitions. The boy would not be told that it is improper in public to stick his finger in his ear, to scratch his head, or to rub his knee. It is just the genital area that requires seclusion if there is to be any kind of hand contact. Other parents might react differently. Some would do everything possible to stop the child from engaging in the activity. They might use physical restraints (quite common in the late 19th century) or threaten the boy that they will take him to the doctor and have his penis cut off. (This is what happened to Freud's famous patient, Little Hans [Freud, 1909].) The first child grows up "normal" with regard to masturbation, confining himself to doing it only in private places and not publicly. The second child might develop inhibitions in this area, and even "castration anxiety," as did Little Hans.

A little girl rubs her vulva and clitoris and then enjoys smelling the vaginal secretions on her fingers. Again, there is a wide variety of parental responses. However, in our society, even those who approve of masturbation might not approve of the olfactory sequela. Because cunnilingus is generally acceptable behavior in male/female heterosexuality (in our society at this time), it is acceptable for men to enjoy smelling these female secretions—but not women. We have a double standard here—a double standard that may contribute to a woman's feeling of disgust over the odors of her own genitals.

It is acceptable for male and female infants to enjoy sucking breasts. After the weaning period, children learn that breast sucking is only for infants. Men are allowed to engage in this "infantile" behavior as part of normal foreplay, but women who maintain a desire for such activity might be labeled as having "lesbianic tendencies"—without any connotation that this might be part of the normal female repertoire.

A three-year-old girl and her four-year-old brother are taking a shower with their father. In the course of the frolicking, each child might entertain a transient fantasy of putting the father's penis in his (her) mouth. Considering the relative heights of the three individuals, and considering the proximity of the children's mouths to the father's penis under these circumstances, it is not surprising that such a fantasy might enter each of the children's minds. It might even be expressed in the form of the children's saying laughingly, "I'm going to bite off your penis." Being so close at the time of their lives when they insert everything in sight into their mouths, it is not surprising that this fellatio fantasy is evoked in the shower. In this setting, they may both learn that this is unacceptable behavior. However, residua of these fantasies and drives may very well persist into adult life. The woman is freer to express these in a heterosexual encounter with a man (who is likely to derive great pleasure from the act). However, the boy who exhibits a continued interest in such behavior will at best be considered to have "homosexual tendencies" and may very well be considered a homosexual. Again, we see the very specific selection process and the special gender requirements for each of the sexes.

Anal functions are probably subjected to the most vigorous prohibitions. It is acceptable to say (under certain very restricted and specific circumstances) that one has had a good bowel movement and that one has enjoyed a sense of relief and pleasure. Men (especially adolescent boys) in our society are much freer to make such comments than women, but I cannot imagine that women do not enjoy the same sensations. In old-age homes, however, there appears to be gender-blind permissiveness with regard to a discussion of this topic. Anal stimulation in sexual encounters, however, is generally frowned upon and is viewed as "disgusting" and "perverted." Infants, before they have learned about these social attitudes, have no problem playing with their (or anyone else's) anus or feces—smelling, licking, and even putting such waste in their mouths.

Our attitudes toward flatus is a good example of the power of the social influence on the selective process. It is reasonable to assume that the odor of flatus is approximately the same for all individuals (within a relatively narrow range). The metabolic processes that result in the formation of these gases is quite similar in all physically healthy human beings. Yet, we generally are disgusted by the flatus of other people, but not by our own. We are generally disgusted with the sounds that other people emit when they pass gas, but we do not feel such revulsion when we ourselves create identical sounds. And this distinction (the reader will please excuse this very subtle pun) is socially learned.

My main point, for the purposes of this book, is that the *normal* child exhibits a wide variety of sexual fantasies and behaviors, many of which would be labeled as "sick" or "perverted" if exhibited by adults. I am not claiming that every child fantasizes about every type of sexual activity in the human repertoire. Each child is likely to have a "favorite" list of sexual activities that provide interest and pleasure. Those who claim that children who verbalize such fantasies or exhibit such behaviors could not have had any actual experiences in these areas have little understanding (or memory) of normal child sexuality. Those who have gone further and have considered such manifestations as "proof" that a child has been sexually abused have caused many truly innocent individuals an enormous amount of harm, even to the point of long prison sentences.

A four-year-old girl, for example, may harbor, among her collection of polymorphous perverse fantasies, thoughts about some kinds of sexual encounters with her father. Freud referred to these as oedipal fantasies. Although I am in agreement with Freud that such fantasies are quite common, I am not in agreement with him that they are at the root of most, if not all, childhood and adult psychoneurotic processes. The fantasies do not necessarily involve sexual intercourse; in fact, the younger the child, the less the likelihood she is going to envision the particular sexual act. Rather, the fantasies are a more general and primitive type involving various kinds of contact with various parts of each other's bodies. Expressing these fantasies in the last part of the 20th century may be quite dangerous. In the middle third of this century the child might be brought into deep psychoanalysis (four to five times a week, for example). In contrast, at the end of the century, the mother may call a lawyer and drag the child through a series of interrogations described in detail throughout the course of this book.

Shakespeare was right: "Lord, what fools these mortals be!" (*A Midsummer Night's Dream*). When a child expresses such a fantasy at this time in our history, everyone's ears prick up. Immediately the child senses that she has "dropped a bomb." Immediately the child senses that what she has said is "wrong" or "bad" or "dangerous." Immediately the child recognizes that she must defend herself and exonerate herself. Sometimes she is given a hint regarding how to respond by the parent who angrily inquires, "Who taught you that?" or "Where did you hear about that?" If the parents are involved in a vicious custody dispute and the child recognizes full well that the mother relishes any information critical of the father, the child is likely to blurt out, "My daddy." With lightning speed the mother calls her lawyer. If a child is going to nursery school and there is an opportunity to sue, again with lightning speed the mother calls a lawyer. If the child is found touching herself (which, in the view of some fanatic validators is only done by sexually abused children), the child may also be asked, "Who taught you that?" The idea that no one taught her *that* – and that she taught herself – is not given consideration at all. Sometimes the child will provide another universal response, "My daddy made me do it" (that is, touch herself). Sometimes the routes to the perpetrator are a little more circuitous.

Sometimes the child will point the finger at a sibling as the initiator or the coercer of the sexual activities. But there is little to be gained by an angry mother if the culprit is another child. There are none of the advantages that one can enjoy when the perpetrator is an adult. Immediately, an inquiry is conducted regarding where the *other* child learned to do these terrible things and it is not long before an appropriate "perpetrator" is identified. The notion that the child may have learned additional sexual things (beyond the aforementioned self-learned material) is not given consideration. The idea that the child may have acquired some of the sexual verbalizations from prevention programs, television programs, sex-abuse prevention books and audiotapes, and the ambient saturation with sexuality is not given consideration by such parents and the overzealous evaluators to whom they bring their children.

Psychodynamic Factors Conducive to the Development of a Parental Alienation Syndrome

Some of the aforementioned psychodynamic factors may contribute to the development of a parental alienation syndrome (Gardner, 1992a), especially release of hostility, ingratiation to adult authority, and the infectiousness of emotions. These factors were mentioned above because they may also operate in the sex-abuse hysteria situation. There are other factors that contribute to a false sex-abuse accusation in the context of a child custody dispute, factors that operate in bringing about a parental alienation syndrome, but are not likely to be present in the nursery-school situation. These factors contribute primarily to the development of the parental alienation syndrome, which may serve as a foundation for the sex-abuse accusation. Typically, the sex-abuse accusation comes forth at some point after the development of the syndrome, a point when less punitive and less effective exclusionary maneuvers may not have proven successful.

Maintenance of the Primary Psychological Bond   In most traditional families, the child's psychological bond with the mother is stronger than that which it has with the father. Actually, the child is psychologically bonded to both parents, but there is generally a stronger bonding with the parent who was the primary caretaker in the earliest years of the child's life. In a child custody dispute, there is the threat of rupture of the primary psychological bond, especially in recent years when the court's determinations regarding parental preference are presumably sex blind, and attempts are made to bring about a 50/50 time-sharing arrangement between the parents. The child's campaign of denigration of the father, then, is an attempt to maintain the maternal tie. A sex-abuse accusation may be one of the criticisms directed at the father. The criticism may be generated from the recognition that it pleases the mother and therefore will result in a strengthening of the psychological bond with her.

Fear of Alienating the Preferred Parent   In addition to the aforementioned factor — preservation of the psychological bond with the preferred parent — is the fear of alienation of the preferred parent (again, usually the mother). In the usual divorce situation, it is the father who has left the home. He has thereby created for himself the reputation of being the rejector and the abandoner. No matter how justified his leaving the home, the children will generally view him as an abandoner. Having already been abandoned by one parent, the children are not going to risk abandonment by the second. Accordingly, they fear expressing resentment to the remaining parent (usually the mother) and will automatically take her position in any conflict with the father. By joining forces with her in her campaign of vengeance and vilification of the father, they reduce the risk of her loss of affection. Again, hatching a sex-abuse scenario is likely to have a cohesive effect (admittedly in a sick way) on the relationship with the mother and thereby assuage rejection and abandonment fears.

Reaction Formation   A common factor that contributes to the obsessive hatred of the father is the utilization of the reaction formation mechanism. Obsessive hatred is often a thin disguise for deep love. This is especially the case when there is absolutely no reason to justify the preoccupation with the hated person's defects. True rejection is neutrality, when there is little if any thought of the person. The opposite of love is not hate, but indifference. Each time these children think about how much they hate their fathers, they are still thinking about them. Although the visual imagery may involve hostile fantasies, their fathers are still very much on their minds. The love, however, is expressed as hate in order to assuage the guilt they would feel over overt expression of affection for their fathers, especially in their mothers' presence. This guilt is often coupled with the aforementioned fear of their mothers' rejection if such expressions of affection for their fathers were to be overtly expressed. One boy, when alone with me, stated, "I'm bad for wanting to visit with my father." This was a clear statement of guilt over his wish to visit with his father, his professions of hatred notwithstanding. This child was not born with the idea that it is bad to want to spend time with his father. Rather, he was programmed by his mother to be guilty over such thoughts and feelings.

A sex-abuse accusation may be added to the collection of other indignities that the father has allegedly perpetrated on the child. Previously, in the section on reactions to normal childhood sexuality, in my discussion on the sex-abuse accusation as a derivative of normal childhood sexuality, I mentioned sexual fantasies involving the father. However, I was referring here to pleasant and enjoyable fantasies. By the process of reaction formation one can turn these into unpleasant ones and thereby assuage the guilt that would be experienced if the child were to accept the fact that sexual activities are what she wants. Instead of saying, "I would love to have some sexual involvement with my father," she can say, "I hate having a sexual relationship with my father." Yet, the fantasy in both cases may be very similar if not identical. The child may not fully appreciate the significance of the terms *sexual intercourse* and *rape*, especially the traumatic and coercive elements involved. To the child these are merely acts in which a penis is inserted into her vagina. She may not even appreciate that the attempt to do this would be extremely painful and traumatic. Accordingly, her fantasy "I want him to rape me" can be transformed, by reaction formation, to "I hate the idea of his raping me." And this may be projected out onto the father. The child is essentially saying, "It is not I who want him to rape me, it is he who wants to rape me." This too is guilt assuaging.

Identification with the Aggressor The identification-with-the-aggressor phenomenon may be operative. In identification with the aggressor, a person who is in a weak or impotent position in relation to a more overpowering, threatening individual may deal with the situation by taking on the characteristics of the stronger person. In this way the individual compensates for the feelings of insecurity and the sense of impotency attendant to being weak and vulnerable. The child whose raging mother is incessantly denigrating his father may join forces with her in an attempt to protect himself from being the target of her enormous hostility. He does this from the fear that if he were to join in with his father, he too would be the target of such violent outbursts. The mechanism is operative in the old principle, "If you can't fight 'em, join 'em." Also operative here is the "There-but-for-the-grace-of-God-go-I" mechanism. By joining the mother, the child can say to himself (herself), "If I did not do so I might be in father's position." Also operative here is the mechanism of jumping on the bandwagon of the stronger party in order to share in the joys of victory. In the course of such warfare the child uses any ammunition put into its hands by the aggressor, including a sex-abuse accusation.

Identification with an Idealized Person   Related to the identification-with-the-aggressor phenomenon is the process of identification with an idealized person. In the course of the mother's deprecation, the father becomes viewed as loathsome, worthless, and an individual with few if any admirable qualities. Identification with and emulation of such a person becomes compromised. Deprived of an admirable father for identification, the child may then switch to the mother as the only person to emulate. At the same time that she denigrates the father, she is likely to whitewash herself. The identification, then, is with a perfect individual, and this is viewed as a way of attaining the state of perfection oneself. The psychological fusion that takes place here contributes to the development of the folie-à-deux relationship so commonly seen in the parental alienation syndrome. This contributes to the child's exaggerated reactions to any criticisms the father may have about the mother. Such a child operates on the principle, "I'm like her. When he criticizes her, it's the same as criticizing me." In the course of such identification, the child accepts as gospel everything the mother says, including trumped-up accusations of sex abuse.

Release of Hostility   The development of a parental alienation syndrome can serve as a vehicle for the release of anger, which may have a variety of sources. It is as if it allows for the "sucking in" of a wide variety of anger-evoking experiences and allows for a sanctioned release of them, at least by the mother. If not for the presence of the parental alienation syndrome, such anger might have been suppressed, repressed, or channeled into other modes of release, both healthy and pathological. Mention has already been made of the anger engendered by the father's leaving the home, an act that is viewed as an abandonment. There may be anger at the father for the financial compromises that are most often attendant to divorce—especially a litigated divorce. When parents are swept up in their divorce and custody-dispute hostilities, they pay less attention to their children, and this produces frustration and anger in them. Not only are the children deprived of attention, but even when they are focused on, the parents have little leftover emotion for their children, so drained have they been by the divorce hostilities. There may be anger over the presence of new partners in their parents' lives. These strangers were rarely invited and, in most circumstances, are viewed as unwelcome intruders. However, the children are impotent over their presence and are most often resentful of them. There may be anger over the thwarting of reconciliation preoccupations that, as time goes on, become ever more futile — especially if new persons appear on the scene. Elsewhere (Gardner, 1976, 1979, 1986, 1991b, 1991c), I have discussed in detail these and other sources of anger for children of divorce, especially those involved in custody disputes.

Sexual Rivalry   Sexual factors and sexual rivalry factors are sometimes operative in the alienation. A girl who has a seductive and romanticized relationship with her father (sometimes abetted by the father himself) may find his involvement with a new woman particularly painful. Whereas visitations may have gone somewhat smoothly prior to the father's new relationship, following the new involvement there may be a rapid deterioration in the girl's relationship with her father. Such a girl may say to her father, "You've got to choose between her and me." In such situations there may be no hope for a warm and meaningful relationship between the father's new woman friend and his daughter. Sometimes the mothers of such girls will support the animosity in that it serves well their desire for vengeance. It is not difficult to see how a sex-abuse accusation can easily arise in such a situation. The child's jealousy over the father's sexual involvement with his new woman friend may engender sexual fantasies in her, and this is especially the case in older girls.

Shame over Recanting

There are children, who, when they first allege sex abuse, have not the faintest idea about the implications and consequences of what they are professing. In their wildest dreams they never imagined the rollercoaster effect of their apparently mundane statements. They could not anticipate the avalanche that was unleashed by their seemingly innocuous comments. Some wish to recant, if only to go back to the halcyon days that existed in their lives before the "disclosure." Others may wish to recant because they recognize they have lied, and they wish to reduce the guilt attendant to such recognition. Others may wish to recant because they are ashamed, especially when they have to face the person who is suffering so terribly because of their accusations. Others may wish to recant because, although they believe they were molested, they don't believe that the "punishment fits the crime" and that the abuser should be subjected to such draconian punishments. Children in all of these categories, however, may hesitate to recant because they are ashamed to do so. The prospect of being called a liar by the horde of individuals who have jumped on the child's bandwagon is terrible to behold. The child would rather live with the painful affects associated with continual accusations than face what is considered to be the more painful prospect of standing in the center of a circle of people, all of whom are screaming "liar." And following such public humiliation, they may anticipate further punishment—unknown and possibly too horrendous to even predict with certainty.

Again, there is an uncanny similarity between the children we are seeing today and those accusing witchcraft at the Salem witch trials. On this point, once again, Mappan (1980) quotes Upham (1867):

> A fearful responsibility has been assumed, and they were irretrievably committed to their position. While they adhered to that position, their power was irresistible, and they were sure of the public sympathy and of being cherished by the public favor. If they faltered, they would be the objects of universal execration and the severest penalties of law for the wrongs already done and the falsehoods already sworn to. There was no retracing their steps; and their only safety was in continuing the excitement they had raised. New victims were constantly required to prolong the delusion, fresh fuel to keep up with the conflagration; and they went on to cry out upon others. (p. 39)

And these children fear that, if they recant, they would be "the objects of universal execration and the severest penalties of law for the wrongs already done, and the falsehoods already sworn to."

Concluding Comments

I have delineated above what I consider to be the primary psychodynamic factors operative in the child who provides a false sex-abuse accusation. It is important to appreciate that these psychodynamic factors do not operate in the child in isolation from those operative in the accuser. One does better to view the two as operating in the context of a <u>folie-à-deux</u> relationship. The psychodynamics of the accuser will be elaborated upon in Chapter Four. An understanding of these psychodynamic factors places the reader in a better position to utilize the criteria for differentiating between true and false sex-abuse accusations. By understanding *why* a child might be professing sex abuse enables the examiner to appreciate in greater depth the differentiating criteria and to determine whether or not a particular criterion is satisfied in borderline situations.

THE DIFFERENTIATING CRITERIA

Introductory Comments

It is important to appreciate that the criteria for discriminating between true and false sex-abuse accusations are designed to serve as *guidelines* for making this important and crucial differentiation. They are most applicable in extreme situations, i.e., when there has been severe and chronic sex abuse or when there has been absolutely no sex abuse and the accusation is patently false. Such situations may be relatively easy to assess. Under these circumstances, most of the criteria will readily be applied and one can conclude quite easily that most of the criteria indicate true sex abuse or most of the criteria indicate that the accusation is highly likely to be false.

Application of these criteria, however, may be compromised

and very difficult in certain situations. For example, not all children who have had a sexual encounter with an adult are traumatized by it. The experience may have been an enjoyable one for them, and they may not have recognized that they were being taken advantage of and exploited (abused) until other people informed them that this was the case. Such children, then, may not satisfy some of the criteria, especially those that are applicable when there has been a significant degree of psychological trauma, e.g., fear of retaliation by the accused, depression, withdrawal, and psychosomatic disorders. Another complication relates to the child's experiences with previous interviewers. The greater the number of previous interviews, the greater the likelihood the child's description will become routinized and the greater the likelihood it will resemble the litany typically provided in early interviews by the child who presents a false-accusation scenario. Because of these considerations, the examiner does well to state that a particular criterion could not be utilized because of special considerations pertinent to the particular child being evaluated. However, in most cases it is likely that the examiner will be able to apply the majority of the criteria and thereby come to some conclusion regarding whether or not the sex abuse has taken place.

It is important for the evaluator to appreciate that there is no sharp cut-off point regarding the number of indicators that must be satisfied before coming to the conclusion that sex abuse took place. One can only say that the greater the number of indicators satisfied, the greater the likelihood the sex abuse occurred.

1. Degree of Hesitancy Regarding Divulgence of the Sexual Abuse

Children who have been genuinely abused are often quite hesitant to reveal the abuse. They may feel guilty over or ashamed about their participation in the sexual acts. Or they may have been threatened (see below) with dire consequences if they divulge the abuse. They are fearful of inquiries by professionals and often have vowed to keep the "special secret" about "our little game." Such fear may relate to the threat of the abuser that terrible harm will befall them and their loved ones if they are ever to reveal the sexual activities. Some abused children have been beaten as a warning of what will happen to them if they divulge the secret. Some children are bribed with material goods and money in order to discourage divulgence. Accordingly, it is unlikely that they will discuss the abuse spontaneously. Even when the examiner brings it up peripherally, they may avoid the subject. Some abused children will directly state that they don't wish to talk about their experiences with the accused. For these children, a few interviews may be necessary before the examiner will be able to obtain direct information relating to the abuse.

In contrast, those who are falsely accusing are likely to unashamedly and unhesitatingly describe their sexual experiences. They have no history of a special secret, of threats, or of bribes. In the early phases of their "divulgences" they may not know that such a history is common among children who have been genuinely abused. However, after many interrogations they may *learn* that this is one of the experiences they are expected to describe and so the "secret" may become incorporated into their scenarios. Naive and/or zealous examiners are likely to interpret this new material as yet another divulgence that confirms the abuse, a divulgence that the child was too fearful to talk about earlier.

Children who provide false allegations generally welcome the opportunity to talk about the abuse to mental health professionals, lawyers, judges, etc. And they are often encouraged by the accuser to present their litany to all who will listen. They will often be quite pleased to talk about the terrible indignities they have suffered at the hands of the accused. It is not uncommon for them to begin the interview with their little speeches without any prompting or facilitating comments by the examiner. Often they have been told beforehand by the parent who is programming them that the examiner is a very important person and that it is vital that they provide *all* the details of the abuse. In child custody disputes the child, prior to the interview, may have been coached regarding exactly what to say to the examiner. In day-care center evaluations there may not have been direct coaching, but the child is likely to have been exposed previously to the wave of hysteria in which he (she) is expected to provide "disclosures." Many of the children who are falsely accusing obtain morbid gratification from the attention that they enjoy, attention that they may never have received before. Some of these children are envious of youngsters whose testimonies have been shown on television and reported in the newspapers. They are reminiscent of the children who testified publicly at the Salem witch trials. These children enjoyed a degree of notoriety never previously experienced, and this factor played a role in their providing ever more fantastic elaborations (Mappan, 1980).

It is important for the reader to appreciate that the child who has been genuinely abused, and who has been subjected to a series of evaluations, may become desensitized to them and not reveal the hesitancy that was present during the first (and/or earlier) interviews. This is one of the reasons why the first examiner is in a better position than subsequent examiners to assess a child who claims to have been sexually abused.

2. Degree of Fear of Retaliation by the Accused

Children who falsely allege sex abuse generally make their accusations directly to the accused without any particular fear of retaliation. First, they have not usually been threatened with terrible consequences for divulgence, and second, they are generally reassured by the supporting accuser that they have nothing to fear. They recognize that such divulgences will ingratiate them to the accuser as well as other examiners (such as validators) who are supporting the accusation. Children who have been genuinely abused are often threatened with dire consequences by the abuser and so exhibit significant fear when asked to discuss the abuse, especially in the presence of the alleged offender. Such consequences might include threats of killing the child's mother, killing the child, or the perpetrator's committing suicide. Such a child may exhibit significant fear in the course of the interview—

without any corresponding verbalizations. It may only be after a series of interviews that the child will be comfortable enough to divulge the threat. As a result of such fears, the child might exhibit vehement overreaction when questioned about whether or not he (she) was touched or fondled (Spelman, 1985).

The child who is fabricating sexual abuse generally does not describe fear of the alleged perpetrator and is usually free from tension in the perpetrator's presence. If there is any tension, it relates to fear that the perpetrator will punish the child for the false accusation. The child who has been genuinely abused will be quite fearful of the perpetrator, both inside and outside the examiner's office. In fact, the fear may generalize to others of the same sex, so that the child who was abused by a father may be fearful of being alone with any male figure—including a male examiner. This fear may result in the child's making every attempt to be away from home as much as possible, especially when alone with the offender. In extreme cases these children will run away from home in order to avoid the sexual encounters (I will discuss this indicator later). Fabricators generally have no history of such avoidance, nor are they as likely to have run away from home. In fact, fabricators in custody disputes may even describe tension-free visitations with a divorced father in which setting the alleged abuses are said to have taken place.

3. Degree of Guilt over the Consequences Of the Divulgence to the Accused

I use the word *guilt* to refer to the feeling of lowered self-worth that individuals experience when they entertain thoughts, experience feelings, or commit acts that they have learned are sinful or wrong. Guilt is purely an intrapsychic process in which the individual can feel guilty when alone and unobserved by others. Older children who have been genuinely abused are likely to feel guilt over the divulgence of the sex abuse because of the appreciation of the terrible consequences of the disclosure to the perpetrator. The younger the abused child, the less the capacity to experience such guilt. There is no cut-off point at which children manifest the capacity to experience guilt. Rather, there is a gradually developing capacity that starts in early childhood and, in healthy individuals, reaches a maximum during adulthood. As further confirmation that there is no such cut-off point, there are individuals who go throughout life never experiencing guilt. (We call such people psychopaths.)

Characteristically, young children, both those who are providing false accusations and those who provide true accusations, do not manifest guilt. This relates to their cognitive immaturity, as a result of which they are unable to appreciate that their accusation can literally destroy the life of the accused and can result in such consequences as loss of career, lifelong rejection, incarceration, and suicide. It is in older children that the guilt criterion can be of value for differentiating between the two types of accusation. Older children who provide false sex-abuse accusations may not exhibit guilt over their divulgences because of the morbid gratification they are experiencing over the pain and harm they are causing the alleged abuser. They are acting out the wishes of the coaching parent, are gaining support for their accusations, and are identifying with a person (parent or supporting examiner) who exhibits no guilt over the formidable pains and suffering the accusation causes the accused.

This guiltless disregard is one of the hallmarks of the fabricator. There may be even a morbid or sadistic gratification in the telling of the story. The child may recognize that the accusation is an extremely effective way of hurting the father and may hope thereby to gain the enhanced affection of the accusing mother. I have often been struck by the cruelty of many of the children who provide false accusations. They have received so much support by adults for their false accusations that any guilt they may feel is completely suppressed or ignored. The situation is true testimony to the capacity of the human child to be cruel under certain circumstances. Mappan (1980) notes this phenomenon in his discussion of the Salem witch trials.

Children who have suffered bona fide sexual abuse may feel guilty over their disloyalty and the recognition that the disclosure is going to result in formidable painful consequences for the perpetrator. The perpetrator has often laid the groundwork for such guilt by telling the child never to reveal the secret lest there be terrible consequences. And the commotion that results from the disclosure confirms that terrible consequences have indeed taken place. Children who have been genuinely abused are not often programmed by their mothers to wreak vengeance on the accuser (although they may be). Such children's mothers more often appreciate the importance of the parent-child bond, the abuse notwithstanding.

The child who fabricates may ultimately come to feel guilty over the recognition of the consequences of the accusation, but this is a late-phase development. Accordingly, the examiner does well to find out about the duration of the guilty feelings, especially with regard to their presence or absence at the time of the divulgence. Assessing a child's guilt may be very difficult, especially because there are obviously no objective ways of evaluating it. One must rely primarily on the child's comments and to a lesser extent on intonations and facial expressions. The child's comments may not be particularly useful in this regard, and even when the child uses the word *guilt,* the examiner may not be sure that is the emotion being experienced. Furthermore, there are no specific facial expressions, gestures, or vocal intonations that are exclusively manifestations of guilt; rather, similar behavioral manifestations may be seen in association with other emotions. Often, it is only after a detailed exploration of the child's thoughts and feelings about the alleged perpetrator that the examiner will be in a position to determine whether guilt is present, and whether it relates to the alleged perpetrator.

4. Degree of Guilt over Participation in the Sexual Acts

Children who have been genuinely abused may experience guilt over their participation in the sexual activities—especially if they have been exposed to an environment in which their sexual encounters are viewed as heinous sins or crimes (the more common situation). In contrast, children who provide false sex-abuse allegations do not generally experience such guilt because there were no sexual activities over which to feel guilty. They have not learned that many children who have been sexually abused may feel guilty about their participation. However, if exposed to a series of interrogations in which they pick up the idea that the examiners are desirous of such comments, they will ultimately provide them. Once again, the first examiner is in the best position to decide whether this indicator of sex abuse is present.

The aforementioned guilt over the consequences of the disclosure should be differentiated from guilt over having participated in sexual activities with the perpetrator. The fabricating child generally feels no guilt over the sexual activities allegedly engaged in. The child who has suffered bona fide abuse may very well have enjoyed the experience and will not have appreciated that the behavior was something to feel guilty about. Such a child will often suffer guilt over such pleasure after learning that the act is an unacceptable, sinful, or even a criminal act. And interrogators, although they may try to reassure the child that he (she) was the innocent victim, may still not be successful in assuaging such guilt. The fact that the interrogations are made by individuals such as lawyers, prosecutors, judges, and psychiatrists cannot dispel the notion that some heinous act has been engaged in. Fabricators, not having actually engaged in any act at all, are not likely to feel guilty in association with these interrogations.

A related form of guilt that is derived from the sexual experience relates to the child's having been selected from all the other children as the one for sexual involvement. Often the perpetrator communicates to the child that he (she) should enjoy a special sense of superiority over the siblings for having been so chosen. The abused child gets special attention from the offender at the same time that attention is withdrawn from other siblings. Accordingly, such children may consider themselves participants in activities that involved the exclusion of their beloved siblings. Thus the guilt. This sense of exclusivity may also produce fear of jealous reprisal by the allegedly nonfavored siblings. Children who fabricate do not generally describe guilt over their having been selected or fear of reprisals from siblings because of their allegedly exclusive relationship with the perpetrator. This factor is not generally programmed into their scenarios.

Another form of guilt related to participation in the sexual activities relates to the parents' blaming the child for initiating the sexual activities. The perpetrator will attempt to assuage his (her) own guilt by blaming the child, and the child, because of cognitive immaturity, will accept as valid the accusation. Children who fabricate the sex abuse will not generally describe such parental blaming.

Another related form of guilt arises from the child's need to gain a sense of control in a situation in which he (she) basically feels impotent. Intrinsic to the notion, "It's my fault," is the concept of control. This is the same mechanism that enables children of divorce to believe that a parent's leaving the home was their fault. In such situations the child will often make statements such as, "I know you're leaving because I was bad. I promise I'll never be bad again. I promise that I'll always be good" (Gardner, 1979, 1991b, 1991c). This phenomenon, although it may appear to be a form of guilt because of the child's statement that a transgression has been committed, should not properly be called guilt and is preferably referred to as a *delusion of control* (Gardner, 1970). Again, fabricators are not likely to describe this mechanism.

It is important for the examiner to appreciate that there are some sexually abused children who do not feel guilty over their experiences; this is especially the case when it has been sanctioned by the mother or other adult, either overtly or covertly. Children who fabricate generally do not feel guilty over their alleged sexual acts because there were no actual sexual acts over which to feel guilty. More commonly, children who fabricate sex abuse express feigned anger and artificial indignation over their alleged abuse. They do not feel bad about themselves over what they have allegedly done; they feel angry over what they claim was done to them.

As mentioned with regard to a child's guilt over the consequences of the divulgence to the accused, assessing children's guilt over their participation in the alleged sexual acts may be difficult, if not impossible. Examiners should not feel compelled to utilize this or any other single differentiating criterion. It is far better to skip the criterion of differentiation or to state clearly that one was unable to assess this factor, than to come to a conclusion that may be misleading.

5. Degree of Specificity of the Details of the Sexual Abuse

Children who have been genuinely abused are more likely to be able to provide specific details of the sex abuse because they can refer to an internal visual image related to the abuse experience. When talking about the abuse, the visual image that is brought into mind includes many details that go beyond the imagery directly related to the abuse. This includes details about the place where the abuse occurred, often the approximate time of day (or night), the presence (or absence) of other individuals, and statements made by the abuser, the child, and others who may have been present. When asked about the details of the abuse, the child is capable of providing these corroborative details. In contrast, children whose accusations are false are far less likely to have such an internal visual image because there was no actual experience they can bring into conscious awareness. Accordingly, when asked to describe details of the abuse, e.g., what exactly was said, what was worn, and who was in the vicinity, they have difficulty providing the corroborative details. When asked to provide these details they may say, "I forgot," "I don't remember," or "Ask my mother. She remembers those things better than me." The latter response, of course, "lets the cat out of the bag" and provides strong support that the child has been programmed. Or the child may say, "Ask my mother. She was there watching." When no one else claims that the mother was there (especially the mother), this introduction of a ludicrous element lessens credibility considerably and is a good example of the kind of preposterous additional detail that is the hallmark of the false accusation. Typically, in the earlier interviews nonabused children provide little if any additional details and confine themselves to vague and general statements about the alleged abuse. However, after a series of interviews they may incorporate suggested or fantasized corroborative details, and these may even become fixed in memory.

Children who provide false accusations may refer to the abuse in general terms and even utilize adult terminology, such as "I was sexually molested" or "I was sexually abused." When asked to provide additional details, the youngster is either unable to do so or creates a scenario for the purposes of the interview. This "creation" may not only include the actual abuse but additional details, especially if asked questions about these by the examiner. However, in subsequent interviews a different scenario may be presented. It is common knowledge that no one's memory is good enough to be a good liar and children even less so. In contrast, the child who has suffered bona fide sexual abuse will usually provide specific details, and they will be consistently the same on subsequent interviews. Even though there may be some variations in the story because of the younger child's cognitive limitations and weak reality testing, I still consider this to be a valuable differentiating criterion because children who have been genuinely abused will still provide a much more consistent story than those who are fabricating their abuse. This relates to the aforementioned visual-mental image of the event(s) and the fact that no one's memory is good enough to be a good liar.

Commonly, the false accusation scenario has a nidus of truth related to some realistic experience. But this core of reality will be elaborated upon significantly, especially with the prompting of the accuser. For example: A father may have, indeed, taken his daughter to the bathroom and helped her wipe herself, something that the mother also routinely does. Or, the father may have indeed taken a shower with his two boys, something that fathers commonly do. The inevitable contact between the father's hand and the child's genitalia serves as a nucleus for the sex-abuse allegation, especially after prompting by an adult, such as an accusing parent or a "validator." Additional details are not originally fixed in the child's memory and have to be taught over time. At first, they may be preposterous, ludicrous, and even absurd. After repeated interviews these become sanitized and "corrected." Another example: A father may have, indeed, brushed up against his boys' genitalia in the course of a wrestling match with them. Elaborations provided by mother's prompting may include manual playing with their genitals, erections, and ultimately even ejaculation. They may also include the child's playing with the father's genitalia, again an elaboration of the inevitable body contacts involved in wrestling. Because these elaborations never actually occurred, the child does not have an internal visual image as a reference and so is not likely to be able to provide the specific details. Such details not only relate to the sexual encounter per se, but to details about the places where these encounters allegedly took place and their circumstances.

As will be discussed in Chapter Eight, in a joint interview in which the child and accused are present together, the accused is in an excellent position to "smoke out" the fabricator by pointing out how the corroborative details provided are inaccurate and even preposterous. No matter how astute the cross-examining attorney, no matter how skilled in courtroom inquiries, that attorney is far less capable of questioning the child about these additional details. The accused knows the setting in which the abuse allegedly occurred far better than all the professionals who may be involved in the case, and he is therefore in the best position to conduct the inquiry.

6. Credibility of the Description

Children who have been genuinely abused are likely to provide a credible description of their experiences. In contrast, those who provide false accusations are more likely to provide descriptions that are preposterous and/or ludicrous. Sometimes the fantastic elements are derived from the primitive sexual fantasies of children, those that are manifestations of what Freud (1905) referred to as the child's "polymorphous perversity." Sometimes the absurd fantasies will involve adventures and age-appropriate rescue and superhero fantasies so commonly seen in boys. The inclusion of these in the scenario is one of the hallmarks of the false sex-abuse accusation. Sometimes the fantastic elements are derived from fairy tales and other children's stories. The younger the child, the more likely such absurd elements will be seen in the description. Having no reality experiences to provide, their fantasies run free, and they do not often appreciate the absurdity of what they are saying. In my own experiences, a common theme incorporated into the sex-abuse scenario is the big bad wolf and the three little pigs. In one nursery-school hysteria situation Stromboli from the Pinocchio story was commonly incorporated into many of the children's fantasies.

The examiner does well to consider the description as a whole and decide whether it "hangs together" and whether it is internally consistent. One should determine whether the activities described follow one another logically. This does not preclude the presence of occasional misinterpretations. For example, a child might reasonably consider a perpetrator's moaning to be a reflection of pain and the heavy breathing associated with orgasm to indicate that the person was sick or had a cold at the time. One does well to ask the child about any statements or conversations that took place in the course of the molestation. Again, one wants to assess the credibility of the conversation, especially if it is consistent with the activities being described. A child who has genuinely been abused is likely to provide comments along these lines: "He said that I was his favorite child, and that he loved me more than the others," "He said that he loves me so much that he wants me to feel very good," "He told me that he would give me a piece of candy if I would suck on his penis," "He told me that if I ever told anybody about 'our secret' he would kill my mommy." In contrast, children who are fabricating, having had no such conversations, are more likely to say that, "He said nothing" or "I forget."

Another clue to the credibility of the description is the child's emotional tone while describing the abuse. One is particularly interested in ascertaining whether the affect (emotional tone) is appropriate to the content of what is being said. If the child has been traumatized then one would expect sadness, grief, fear, guilt, and other appropriate emotional reactions to be exhibited at the time the child relates the experiences. In contrast, children who are fabricating will typically present their scenarios in singsong fashion, as if they were reciting a well-memorized poem. It is common for validators to claim that the child's affect was appropriate when relating the details of the alleged abuse. However, when one listens to the audiotapes of their interviews or (better) views a videotape, one sees that this is often not the case. Rather, one may see levity, smiles, and hear the singsong quality of the false-accusation scenario. Obviously, written transcripts are less likely to provide information in this realm. Because the determination as to whether affect is appropriate or inappropriate is often subjective, one may be left in the position of having to trust the word of the evaluator as to whether or not this indicator of credibility was present. It is a common maneuver utilized by validators to provide confirmation for their conclusions, and it is a convenient ploy because parties who are not present at the interview are in a difficult position to decide whether the judgment regarding the appropriateness or inappropriateness of the child's affect is valid.

The child who is fabricating sex abuse will often describe settings that are unlikely for such activities, for example, "He did it to me while my friend went to the bathroom" and "He did it to me while my mommy was in the kitchen." It is reasonable to say that only the most simpleminded or psychotic perpetrator would attempt abuse under these circumstances; but the child is not appreciative of this obvious fact. In contrast, the child who has been genuinely abused sexually will describe settings that are much more likely and reasonable. The story provided by the false accuser is often naive and simplistic. For example, one child stated, "At my father's house he played with my penis and in my mother's house he played with my hiney" and "At my father's house he did it in the daytime and in my mother's house he did it at night." We see here the kind of symmetry that is sometimes found in the false allegation. Small children are attracted to such symmetry in stories, e.g., the good guys and the bad guys, the handsome prince and the beautiful princess, and the cops and the robbers.

In one case I was involved in, the child's false accusation included the following: "My father was running after me to grab my penis. I ran out of the house and hid in the bushes. My mother came out and got me." The mother denied any such occurrence, but (as is often the case) she still held firmly to her belief that the child had indeed been abused. In another case the child stated, "He (the allegedly abusing father) locked me in the closet. But I took the key and unlocked the door." The child insisted that there was a key inside the closet ("I found it on the floor") and unlocked the closet from the inside. Even the child's mother agreed that there was no way that one could unlock the closet from the inside, yet this did not reduce her belief in the validity of the sex-abuse accusation.

One accusing mother had the child in "treatment" six months before the father learned of the existence of the "therapist." Neither the mother nor the therapist contacted the father. Yet, during this six-month period, the child had repeatedly related to the therapist that his father had told him not to tell their "secrets" to the therapist. The therapist knew that the father was not aware of the fact that his child was in treatment with her (and so could not be demanding that the child not tell the therapist about the alleged molestations). Yet she did not consider the child's statement to reflect fantasy or duplicity on the child's part, manifestations that could have led her to question the validity of the sex-abuse allegations. Such "splitting" is common among validators and many who specialize in the diagnosis and treatment of these children. They do not put together facts that might lead to their seriously questioning the scenario.

Questions regarding the ejaculate are common in sex-abuse investigations. Such focus stems from the recognition that the child who has been genuinely abused may be able to provide a credible description of the ejaculate, whereas the child who is fabricating will not be aware of its existence and is likely to become confused by a discussion of this strange substance. Accordingly, it is in the description of the ejaculate, especially, that the nonabused child is likely to provide preposterous explanations. Examiners investigating in this area do well to make certain important differentiations regarding *whose* ejaculate (the offender's or the victim's) and the age of the ejaculator (adult or child). The seminal emission of the adolescent and adult male is generally white, thick, and copious (approximately the liquid volume of a teaspoon). The ejaculate of the prepubertal boy (often referred to as the "stuff" that comes out of the penis) may not be produced at all at the time of orgasm ("the good feeling") or, if present, it is usually clearer (less white) than the adult's and less copious. When interviewing the child, the examiner does well to make a sharp differentiation between the descriptions of the ejaculates of the perpetrator and that of the child, as well as the descriptions of each one's emissions (or lack of such).

The child who has been genuinely abused is usually aware that "stuff" has come out of the offender's penis, but may not be certain about its color. Young children, especially, may believe that it was yellow, confusing it with urine—the only penile emission they are familiar with. Older children may describe the emission as white and sticky. But semen tends to become clearer with the passage of time, at which point the child might easily confuse it with water or urine. Or the child may not know the color because he (she) may not have noticed this particular detail. This is especially the case when the abuse has been coerced and the child has submitted under duress. If the boy himself has been brought to orgasm, he may describe a "good feeling" and either describe no ejaculate or a small quantity of clear or only slightly white fluid.

The child who is fabricating may exhibit initial confusion regarding questions about the "stuff" that came out of the penis of the perpetrator. Although initially unaware of the fact that such emissions exist, the child gets the "hint" implied in the leading question and then is likely to provide fabrications. Yellow is a common response, as a first guess. On further questioning regarding whether the yellow stuff was thick or clear, whether one could easily see through it or not, the child will generally describe a clear liquid like urine—the only penile emission the child is familiar with. If the child senses that this is not the "right" answer, then any color of the rainbow may be provided with any consistency, from clear like water to so thick that one couldn't see through it. Once a programmer has had the opportunity for input, and the educational process has had time to teach, the offender's ejaculate is likely to be described as white.

Children who provide false accusations do not generally appreciate how ridiculous are some of the elaborations they have built into their scenarios. These preposterous and absurd elements are generally not suggested by the brainwashing parent; rather, they are created by the child. The child wants to provide ammunition against the alleged offender and is not sophisticated enough to differentiate between reasonable and unreasonable allegations. Children who are the subject of repeated interrogations, especially by zealous "validators," are likely to provide ever more absurd scenarios. Such evaluators will often accept as valid some of the most preposterous elements, and this only increases the child's desire to provide ever more fantastic elaborations. Ultimately, many of these children move into the realm of satanic fantasies in which the most bizarre elements may be incorporated, e.g., cannibalistic orgies, ritualistic murders of infants, and eating of feces and drinking of urine. I will discuss these further in subsequent chapters.

7. Variations in the Description

Children who have been genuinely abused will most often present a description that does not vary over time. They consistently rely on their memory of actual events. In contrast, children who have not been abused, having no actual experience to bring into memory, are likely to provide different renditions at different times. In order to be a "good" liar, an individual must have a very good memory. And children, because their memories are not very good (in comparison with adults), are generally very poor liars. But even adults do not make good liars in that no one's memory is so good that he (she) can remember the wide variety of versions one may have provided about a particular event or series of events. There are many adults who are now in jail because they were not good liars and therefore provided inconsistent testimony on the witness stand. If this is the case for adults with "mature brains," then it cannot but be more the case for children.

In order to determine whether such variations are present, the examiner does well to conduct at least two (and sometimes more) interviews. Furthermore, the examiner should compare the renditions provided him (her) by the child with those related to previous examiners. Children who have been genuinely abused may not repeatedly relate their experiences with 100 percent accuracy. However, the number of inconsistencies provided by the child who is providing a false accusation is far greater than that which is found in the child who has been genuinely abused. Significant inconsistencies is one of the hallmarks of the false accusation.

It is important for the examiner to appreciate, however, that the younger the child, the weaker this internal display and the greater the likelihood that distortions will creep in— distortions that the child may actually believe. Furthermore, children generally like to please their interviewers, especially if the interviewer is in a position of authority, e.g., a lawyer, judge, prosecutor, or mental health practitioner. This may even result in alterations of the description, even by the child who has genuinely been abused. Furthermore, all of our memories get somewhat blurred over time, and this is especially the case with younger children. Accordingly, the examiner does well to take these factors into consideration when interviewing the child and to recognize that the shorter the time gap between the interview and the alleged abuse, the greater the likelihood this criterion will be a useful one. In contrast, the longer the time gap between the alleged abuse and the interview, the greater the likelihood of variation—especially for younger children. These drawbacks notwithstanding, this item still warrants inclusion among the differentiating criteria because rendition variation is a powerful differentiating criterion in the early phases following the divulgence.

The credibility of the child's statement is obviously an important criterion, and the examiner does well to give serious attention to this factor for discriminating between true and false sex-abuse accusations. Unfortunately, there are some evaluators who place so much emphasis on this particular factor that they do not give proper attention to the multiplicity of other factors that must be considered when making this important differentiation. This is especially the case for those who are committed to the concept of "statement validity analysis" (Raskin and Esplin, 1991; Raskin and Steller, 1989; Raskin and Yuille, 1989; Yuille, 1988; Yuille and Farr, 1987; Yuille et al., 1990). I am in full agreement that a detailed analysis of the child's statements can provide useful information regarding credibility and that the attempts to subcategorize and define the various elements involved in credibility is useful. The problem with this approach, however, is that it is too narrow and does not give enough attention to the wide variety of other factors that must be considered, factors not only in the child, but in the accuser and the accused. The investigatory protocols provided by Yuille, Raskin, and their colleagues focus primarily on the child's statements, and no such analysis is recommended for the accuser (who may be lying) and the accused (who also may be lying.)

8. Advanced Sexual Knowledge for Age

Children who have been genuinely abused often have a sexual vocabulary that is beyond that of other children their age. Even at a time when children are being excessively exposed to sexual information, this criterion may still be valid. I saw one sexually abused five-year-old girl who said, "He kept asking me to give him blow-jobs, and when I wouldn't he would whip me." Furthermore, the same child used the word "blow-jobs" without any hesitation or appreciation of her atypicality regarding the comfort with which she used this term. A seven-year-old said to me, "When he used to kiss me goodnight, he would try to kiss my boobies, and then he used to go down on me. At first I thought it was yuch, but then I started to like it. And then I used to ask him to do it to me." Most seven-year-olds in our society are not aware that the term "go down" refers to cunnilingus. And even those who are familiar with the word do not use it as unselfconsciously as this little girl. When applying this criterion, the examiner does well not simply to consider the *content* of the child's statements with regard to whether or not they reflect age-appropriate knowledge of sexual matters, but the degree of familiarity and comfort that the child has when discussing sexual matters. At a time when sexual knowledge by young people is so ubiquitous, the latter element is more important than the former.

An examiner may have some difficulty differentiating between this criterion and the "borrowed scenario" criterion (#15 below). The *source* of borrowed scenario terminology often suggests a nonsexual origin, whereas the *source* of genuine sex-abuse descriptions suggests actual sexual encounters. Borrowed scenario terminology often suggests a parent or overzealous examiner as the source, whereas the terminology used by children who have been actually abused suggests the abuser as the source. Common borrowed-scenario accusations: "He touched me in my private places," "He touched my private part," "He gave me bad touches." These are the terms commonly used in sex-abuse prevention programs, by validators and overzealous examiners, and are to be found in the mountains of children's books on sex abuse. In contrast, children who are genuinely abused might speak like this: "He taught me how to French kiss," "He put his ding-dong in my butt," "He made me suck him off," and "She used to put vaseline on the vibrator before she stuck it in my hole." The likelihood of such a "vocabulary" being found in the aforementioned parent-teacher sources is almost nil.

When the advanced sexual knowledge criterion (#8) is satisfied, the child is not only comfortable talking about sexual matters that are advanced for the child's age, but does so with a comfort and lack of self-consciousness. Many (but certainly not all) of these children sound "street smart." And some of them talk like "seasoned little whores." Furthermore, these abused children can dwell on these matters at length without hesitation. In contrast, the child who satisfies the borrowed-scenario indicator has only a small repertoire of terms, verbalizes them as part of a litany, and is not likely to speak with comfort, naturalness, and at length like the genuinely abused child who satisfies this criterion.

There are some children who incorporate into a false sex-abuse scenario material derived from observations of others involved in sexual encounters. For example, a child may have observed a babysitter having sexual relations with her boyfriend at a time when she thought the child was sleeping. Or the child may have observed his/her parents involved in sexual encounters, again unbeknownst to the parents. The child may then reenact this observation with anatomical dolls, and the naive evaluator may then conclude that such reenactment "proves" that the child is portraying his (her) own sexual experiences. The child indeed has advanced knowledge of sexual activities, but such advanced knowledge is not related to sexual abuse. Examiners do well, then, when tracing the evolution of the sex-abuse accusation to make inquiries about such potential exposures. In most households children are exposed to parental nudity, dressing and undressing, bathing, showering, and performing toilet functions. These experiences also can be incorporated into a sex-abuse accusation. For example, the father, like most fathers, when bathing the child, washes the crotch area. When the child is asked if her father "touched" her, she is likely to respond affirmatively. Overzealous examiners may not pose more specific questions regarding such "touching" and may impulsively conclude that the child was sexually abused by the father. And this is especially the case if the child has learned that the father's placing his hand in that area has involved him touching her in "bad places." It is for these reasons that I consider a detailed inquiry into the child's sexual exposures—of all types—to be an important part of the inquiry in which the examiner traces the evolution of the sex-abuse accusation.

9. Sexual Excitation

Children who have been genuinely abused are often prematurely brought into a state of adult-level sexual excitation. Children who have not been abused, having had no such excitation, are not likely to exhibit signs and symptoms of sexual arousal. There are, however, some nonabused children who exhibit a high level of sexual excitation, and this may even date back to infancy. This may relate to their being at that point on the bell-shaped distribution curve at which a small percentage of normal children start to exhibit sexual excitation. Or they may be children who resort to masturbation as a tranquilizer, antidepressant, or source of pleasure to counterbalance tensions and frustrations related to family privations and stresses. Accordingly, the examiner does well to get an accurate history about the onset of the sexual excitation, especially with regard to its relation to the onset of the alleged abuse.

Masturbation is one of the most commonly referred to symptoms of sex abuse. Obviously, the child who masturbates might satisfy this criterion for a true accusation of sex abuse. My experience has been that it is extremely uncommon for examiners to get specific information regarding the history of the masturbation, especially regarding whether it antedated the time of the alleged abuse. Equally important, examiners rarely differentiate between the occasional touching (which all normal children exhibit from time to time) and the more intense stimulation that can result in orgasm. The examiner who assumes that the normal child cannot reach orgasm is ignorant about normal child development. Zealous examiners will consider any degree of genital stimulation, no matter how transient and no matter how rare, as an indicator of sex abuse. They ask no questions about the age of onset, the frequency, the intensity, and orgastic response. Examiners who fail to ask these questions are not in a position to determine whether the child has reached a level of excessive sexual stimulation. Furthermore, the excessive sexual excitation seen in the child who has been genuinely abused does not confine itself to masturbation. The child will exhibit other forms of sexualized behavior, such as frequently rubbing his (her) genitals against adults and children.

Sexually abused children may talk frequently about sex, to the point of obsession. Somehow sexual issues seem to come up in many conversations, conversations that would not generally proceed in the sexual direction with other children. They may have an understanding of sexual matters far above and beyond other children their age. Sometimes the precocious sexual knowledge is revealed in the child's drawings and associated stories (Chapter Eight). In the examining room as well, such children may attempt to involve themselves sexually with the examiner by such activities as pulling up the examiner's dress, trying to put their hands in the examiner's pants (or panties), rubbing their genitals against the examiner, etc. At times, the child's genitals have indeed been traumatized by the abuse, especially young girls who have had encounters with abusers who have tried to enter them vaginally, either with fingers or a penis. Sometimes the feeling of damage relates to social reactions regarding physical activities involving the genital area. The child may be obsessed with playing sexual games such as "doctor" and "You show me yours and I'll show you mine." Such abused children may develop an obsessive interest in looking at the genitals of others, male and female, adult and child.

I recall one four-year-old girl whom I subsequently learned was sexually abused by her nursery-school bus driver. The mother noted a relatively sudden onset of obsession with looking at and grabbing the genitals and breasts of women and the genitals of men. She had to stop taking her into the locker room at the YMCA because the child would run around trying to touch other women. At home, as well, she was frequently asking people of both sexes to show her their genitals and let her touch and fondle them. The child appeared to be classical example of Freud's "polymorphous perversity." Or the child may exhibit a knowledge of sexual activities far beyond her (his) age. For example, the child may talk about "French kissing," "humping," and "going down." This premature introduction into sex may result in a heightened state of sexual excitation that frequently seeks relief. Sgroi et al. (1982) described one sexually abused girl who, while watching a television show in which an older man was making advances to a young girl, remarked, "He's a dirty old man, just like grandpoppy."

One of the problems we are currently facing with regard to the issue of the amount of knowledge children should have about sex, especially with regard to its serving as a differentiating criterion, is that sex-abuse prevention programs are providing children with such information. Examiners, then, have to differentiate between the terminology used in such programs (see #15 below, on the borrowed scenario indicator) and idiosyncratic terminology that is more likely related to the child's own personal experiences.

10. Attitude Toward One's Genitals

Children who have suffered genuine sex abuse often consider their genitals, the organs involved in the "crime," to have been damaged. Sometimes the presence of a sexually transmitted disease will contribute to such a feeling. In contrast, children who provide false allegations do not generally describe such feelings of genital deformity, injury, etc. Furthermore, they may not have learned from those who coach them that this is one of the signs of genuine sex abuse.

Some children who have been sexually abused have indeed suffered physical damage to their genitals, and such trauma will generally be verified in medical reports. However, there are children who have been abused who have not suffered any physical damage to their genitals, but still feel that their genitalia have been damaged because of their appreciation of the cultural attitudes toward their sexual activities. Furthermore, the programmers of children who provide false sex-abuse accusations may have brought the child for numerous physical examinations in the hope that the examining physician might provide supporting evidence for sexual abuse. Their hope is that the physician will agree that a minor blemish, a normal rash, inflammation caused by occasional rubbing, etc., is indeed a sign of sexual abuse.

Nonabused children who have been subjected to such repeated examinations may come to believe that their genitals have somehow been damaged. And this will especially be the case if the physician reports the allegation to investigatory authorities, even though he (she) may not have considered the physical signs to indicate sex abuse, but is making the referral on the basis of the accuser's statement and those alleged to have been made by the child. Some children who have been sexually abused will not only feel that their genitals have been damaged, but will be concerned that others will observe the genital deformities as well. Accordingly, they may hesitate to undress in gymnasium locker rooms, resist going to sleep-away camp, or be reluctant to place themselves in any situations in which their genitals may be seen by others. Children who provide false sex-abuse accusations are far less likely to exhibit such concerns. If they do, it may relate to problems having nothing to do with sex abuse.

11. Desensitization Play

Children who have been genuinely abused will often attempt to work through their psychological trauma by repeatedly making reference to it, either directly or in symbolic form, in their play activities. This is a form of natural desensitization that helps them work through the psychological trauma. Each time they reenact the event, they make it a little more bearable. This phenomenon is also referred to as *traumatic reliving* and *spontaneous reenactment*. Such play may also include coping mechanisms in which they provide themselves with maneuvers for protecting themselves from the perpetrator or removing him (her). For example, in doll-house play they may frequently eject the doll that symbolizes the perpetrator and/or refuse to allow that person to enter the house. A common scenario involves protecting oneself from monsters and other malevolent creatures who are trying to harm the child. However, unlike such scenarios in the play of nonabused children, the malevolent figures in these children's stories can often be linked to the perpetrator by specific idiosyncratic details that support the conclusion that the abuse is indeed being symbolized by the malevolent figure. (Overzealous examiners will consider any such fantasy, no matter how common and no matter how unrelated it may be to the abuse, to reflect abuse.) Often the child's fantasies provide symbolic protection from these malevolent creatures.

Sometimes the play will involve a reenactment of the sex-abuse experience, again for the purposes of desensitization. One such boy I saw in treatment insisted upon engaging family members in a game in which they hid themselves in the bathroom, behind the locked door, and waited there until the "bad man" (outside the bathroom door) went away. The child would instruct the adults to peek periodically into the hall in order to reassure the child that the bad person was no longer there. On occasion, the youngster insisted that all participants stand in the shower stall, with the curtains closed, in order to gain further protection from the bad man. Such children will generally exhibit such desensitization play in the evaluative interview. And one may obtain a history of such "games" at home and with relatives.

Children who provide false allegations, not knowing that this is a common phenomenon for sexually abused children, do not introduce such themes into their play. Furthermore, the person who initially programs the child to profess the abuse may not be aware of this phenomenon either and so not instruct the child to participate in such play.

However, the child who has been in "treatment" by an overzealous examiner (regardless of whether or not genuinely abused) is likely to be taught by the therapist to include such themes in the play. Such inclusion is frequently referred to as "empowering." (I will not discuss here the efficacy of such empowering; I will only focus on the presence of such fantasies in the child's play. In Chapters Ten and Eleven I will discuss more about empowering.) Of relevance here is the fact that children who have been in treatment with such therapists will often include these fantasies in their play and thereby deprive the examiner of knowing whether true desensitization play is being manifested or play fantasies that derive from their sessions with their therapists. This is yet another example of the principle mentioned earlier that the examiner who sees the child first is in the best position to make a determination regarding sex abuse and will have a child whose evaluation will be least affected by the input of previous examiners.

12. Threats and Bribes

Children who have been genuinely abused have often been threatened that there will be terrible consequences to themselves and their loved ones if they ever divulge the special "secret." Common threats include murdering the child's mother and/or other loved ones, murdering the child, and the perpetrator's leaving the home or even committing suicide. Others may be bribed to keep quiet. And some children are exposed to both methods of getting them to keep the "secret." Children who are fabricating sex abuse have not been exposed to such threats or bribes and are generally not sophisticated enough to describe them.

It is important for the examiner to appreciate that there are situations in which the offender does not attempt to preserve secrecy. This will be seen in abusers who are very sick psychologically, who may be intellectually impaired, or who may suffer with such disorders as alcoholism or drug abuse. Under the influence of these substances they may not be aware of what they are doing; or, if they are, they have such poor judgment that they do not appreciate the risk of disclosure or consequences of their acts.

Unfortunately, many nonabused children who are subjected to the interrogations of overzealous evaluators learn early that the "secret" is an important part of the scenario. Generally they learn about this from leading questions, which ask them whether the alleged perpetrator either threatened or bribed them to keep "the secret." My experience has been that this is one of the most common contaminants provided by these examiners.

13. Custody/Visitation Disputes

The parental alienation syndrome (Gardner, 1985, 1987, 1989, 1992a) is a disorder that arises in child custody disputes in which a child will view one parent as all good and another as all bad. Most often the mother, who has been the primary child rearer, is viewed as perfect or close to it, and the father, who is disputing for custody, is viewed as a despicable individual. Such children guiltlessly vilify the father and create a variety of malevolent delusions about him, especially with regard to how despicable and heinous he is. Most often, these children have been programmed by their mothers to hate their father and to subject him to a campaign of denigration, but the children themselves often contribute their own scenarios of hostility. It is this *combination* of both the parent's and the child's contributions that warrant the term *parental alienation syndrome*. A sex-abuse allegation can often be part of this package. It is a powerful weapon in the campaign and can be a very attractive accusation for a parent who wishes to wreak vengeance upon and/or exclude a hated spouse. The child complies with the programming parent's coaching and provides the sex-abuse scenarios. When a parental alienation syndrome exhibits itself in full-blown form, it is more likely to support the conclusion that the sex-abuse allegation is false.

Sex-abuse allegations made in the context of a custody/visitation dispute are more likely to be false. This is especially the case if the sex-abuse allegation arose *after* the onset of the dispute. In contrast, a sex-abuse accusation that *brings about* the marital separation—and is the primary reason for the separation—is much more likely to be true. I am not claiming that bona fide sex abuse does not occur at all in the context of a custody/visitation dispute, only that the allegations that arise during such disputes are more likely to be false. An important differentiating criterion is the exact time when the sex-abuse allegation was first made. The examiner does well to conduct a careful inquiry on this point. An allegation made after the child becomes aware of the custody dispute, and especially after parental-alienation-syndrome maneuvers have not proven effective, is more likely to be false. This is one of the reasons why I consider it extremely important for examiners to trace the evolution of a sex-abuse accusation from the very beginning. I will discuss this in greater detail in Chapter Eight.

There are situations in which the parents are embroiled in a vicious child custody dispute in which the child does not develop a full-blown case of parental alienation syndrome. The child may still seize upon a sex-abuse accusation as a convenient weapon in the dispute. Such a child appears to have skipped over the step of the parental alienation syndrome and has seized upon one of the most powerful weapons that he (she) can utilize to assist the supported parent. In contrast, when such a dispute is not present, the allegation is more likely to be genuine. Again, false sex-abuse allegations may certainly be seen in situations in which there is no custody dispute, but they are less common.

Blush and Ross (1987) have given a name to the constellation of behavioral manifestations in which a child fabricates sex abuse in the context of a divorce dispute: the SAID syndrome (Sex Abuse in Divorce syndrome). They describe such children as enjoying significant power in that they are the primary vehicles through which the accuser communicates with the accused, and their sex-abuse accusations can literally destroy and/or remove the accused. Under these circumstances children as young as two or three become "arbitrary dictators" of their families. They describe the borrowed-scenario phenomenon elaborated upon in this chapter (#15, below), as well as the children's spontaneous initiation of the sex-abuse accusation, the litany, the inconsistencies and variations, the exaggerations, and the failure to exhibit bona fide manifestations of having been traumatized.

14. The Litany

Mention has been made of the litany that false accusers may have created for the benefit of the parade of examiners who interview them. This has a rehearsed quality and may include adult terminology such as "Daddy molested me" and "I was sexually abused." At a moment's notice they are ready to "turn on the record" and provide a command performance. This indicator is especially applicable to the term *programming*, which is frequently utilized when referring to the process by which a child develops a parental alienation syndrome. It is as if the brainwashing process imbeds in the child's brain a scenario that can be reproduced when the proper button is pressed. It is analogous to the printout that can be automatically produced by a computer when a proper button is pressed on its keyboard.

Sometimes the child will begin the first interview with a little speech, without the examiner's even providing some introductory and/or facilitating comments. Children who have been genuinely molested will not generally have a litany at the outset, nor are they as likely to use adult terms. Rather, they are hesitant to divulge the abuse and will often speak of it in a fragmented way. However, after repeated inquiries (by the same parade of interrogators), such genuinely abused children may then develop a litany and even incorporate adult terminology (now learned from the interrogators). The longer the time gap between the initial interview and the examiner's own evaluation, the greater the likelihood that the child will have developed a litany. And even the child who has been genuinely abused will become desensitized to the interviews and will ultimately prepare a speech. This differentiating criterion then becomes less useful. Accordingly, examiners do well to learn how many times previously and by whom the child has been interviewed in order to assess properly this differentiating criterion.

Children who have been genuinely abused are not creating any stories. They are telling the truth about an actual experience. Their renditions have the quality of credibility, rather than a rote repetition of a well-rehearsed scenario. In contrast, children who fabricate are creating a tale. In order to be successful when they relate their stories to evaluators, they make sure to "memorize their lines." They may also have been subjected to many rehearsals by the programming parent to ensure that they have learned their lines well. Because children are generally not skilled actors and actresses, their rehearsed presentations have an artificial quality that lessens their credibility. Children who have been involved in criminal trials, who have been "prepared" for testimony before grand juries and juries involved in criminal trials, are also likely to provide litanies, whether or not they have been abused. Sometimes these preparations have gone on for years, increasing thereby the likelihood that the litany will be provided.

15. The Borrowed Scenario

Children who have been genuinely abused describe well the details of their abuse and generally confine sexual discussion to these specific experiences. Those who are providing false accusations, having no such experiences, create their scenarios. Originally, the basic elements and guidelines are provided by the programmer, although he (she) will generally claim that the comments flowed initially from the child without any prompting or coaching. Additional elements in the scenario, however, are inevitably brought in. These are encouraged both by the original programmer and other interrogators, especially "validators." These additional elements may be derived from classroom sex-abuse prevention programs, video- and audiotapes about sex abuse, coloring books about sex abuse, or pornographic movies observed by the child without the parents' awareness. Examiners do well to inquire into the child's experiences with such exposures. This differentiating criterion may become weakened when the child who has indeed been abused also has similar environmental exposures to information about sex abuse.

Parents and validators will sometime claim that the child's talking about sex abuse must relate to real events, because the child has had no exposure to such information. Although this may have been the case in the child's home, the assumption is made that it is also true in the nursery school. Certainly, there was a time when the nursery school was indeed an innocent environment in which the only sexual issues to which the child was exposed was related to bathroom functions. This is no longer the case. Lanning (1992) puts it well:

> The odds are fairly high that in any typical day-care center there might be some children who are victims of incest; victims of

physical abuse; victims of psychological abuse; children of cult members (even satanists); children of parents obsessed with victimization; children of parents obsessed with the evils of satanism; children without conscience; children with a teenage brother or pregnant mother; children with heavy metal music and literature in the home; children with bizarre toys, games, comics, and magazines; children with a VCR and slasher films in their home; children with access to dial-a-porn, party lines, or pornography; or children victimized by a day care center staff member. The possible effects of the interaction of such children prior to the disclosure of the alleged abuse must be evaluated. (p. 26)

I recall one mother who fled to a "shelter for battered women" with the false claim that her husband was beating her. She was involved in a vicious child custody dispute, and I was convinced that her allegation was false. She did not claim any sexual abuse of the children. However, within a few days of being "sheltered," the two little girls, ages two and four, began talking about a variety of sexual activities they claimed they had been engaged in with their father. Not surprisingly, the mother then brought the child's father up on charges of sex abuse. She quoted the social worker at the shelter as having said: "Just about all the kids we have here at this shelter have been sexually abused. They don't talk about it at first, when they first get here, but after a few days it begins to come out. They become more comfortable speaking about it after hearing the other children speak about it." Not once did it enter the social worker's little head that there was an alternative explanation, namely, that the children were merely parroting what they heard from their new friends and that the allegations of sex abuse served to get them the enhanced attention they were observing other children to get when they spoke about such matters. The kinds of borrowed scenarios one sees here are derived from the keeping-up-with-the-Joneses phenomenon described earlier in this chapter.

The child who has been genuinely abused will not generally use adult terminology; rather the child uses descriptive terms appropriate to the idiosyncratic terms used in that child's home, e.g., "He touched my 'gina," "He kissed my pee- pee," and "He put his big pee-pee where my doo-doo comes out." In contrast the child who is falsely accusing sex abuse will often use terms "borrowed" from others, especially the programmer and interrogators who use leading questions. The examiner must be alert to such phraseology, e.g., "I've been sexually molested" and "I've been sexually abused." One five-year-old child said to me, "I've been penetrated." When I asked her what *penetrated* means she replied, "I don't know, my mommy told me that I was penetrated." Sometimes the phraseology of the child fabricator is taken from school programs on sex abuse, e.g., "He touched me in private places," "He touched my private parts," and "He touched me in bad places." Other comments commonly "lifted" from such materials and programs include references to "good touches" and "bad touches," comments about "my body is my own," and "I said no." Commonly, such terminology is also derived from "therapists" who embark upon a treatment program with little if any extensive inquiry regarding whether or not the sex abuse indeed occurred.

16. Depression

Children who have been genuinely sexually abused are often depressed, especially if they have been abused frequently over time, and especially if there have been terrible threats made regarding disclosure of their sexual experiences. The main manifestations of the depression may be depressive affect, loss of appetite, listlessness, loss of enjoyment in play, impaired school curiosity and motivation, poor appetite, and difficulty sleeping. The depression may often be associated with suicidal thoughts, especially if the child is significantly guilty about the sexual experiences. The depression may be related to the feelings of betrayal engendered not only by the offender, but by the passivity and/or failure of others (often the mother) to protect the child and prevent a repetition of the abuse. Depression may be related to pent-up resentment that is not allowed expression, lest the perpetrator carry through with the threats of retaliation.

Those who are falsely accusing are not generally depressed, although they may profess being upset over their alleged sexual experiences. Rather, they appear to be getting a kind of morbid gratification from their accusations, especially when they provide them with a degree of attention and notoriety they never previously enjoyed.

Some sexually abused children become so depressed that they become suicidal. This is much more likely to be the case when the abuse takes place in the home situation and the children feel they cannot escape their abuses. Such children will exhibit the wide variety of symptoms associated with suicidal depression, e.g., sleeplessness, hopelessness, poor appetite, depressed affect, and suicidal preoccupation. Elsewhere (Gardner, 1988b) I have discussed in detail the criteria I utilize to assess the depth of suicidal risk.

17. Withdrawal

Children who have been genuinely abused may often withdraw from involvement with others. They prefer more a fantasy world that is safe and free from the traumas of their real life. Sgroi et al. (1982) state that many sexually abused children will escape their painful reality by withdrawing into fantasy. Frequently, they have a rich fantasy life that provides them with a pleasurable respite from their painful existences. Such withdrawal is observed in the interview and is described as existing in the home, in school, and elsewhere. In school they are described by their teachers as being removed from the others and as having little interest in learning and even socializing with their classmates. They are listless, wan, sad, and pathetic. They have few friends in their neighborhood, and they neither seek nor are sought by peers. Those who falsely accuse are not generally described as withdrawn; they are typically outgoing and outspoken.

Children who have suffered bona fide sex abuse often withdraw from the abuser because of the trauma they anticipate when involved with him. They tend to generalize and assume that others, especially those of the same sex as the abuser, will subject them to sexual indignities as well. They may exhibit fear of going into washrooms, showers, and other places where sex abuse has taken place. The examiner may observe such with-drawal in the interview. And this is especially the case when the examiner is of the same sex as the perpetrator. There is a similarity between the withdrawal of the child who is sexually abused and the flinching of the child who has been physically abused. In both cases the child feels relatively safe when a suspected individual is at a distance. However, the closer an adult figure is, the greater the likelihood the child will be tense. And, if the adult approaches the child, especially in a sudden manner, the child is likely to recoil. Sexually abused children will merely move away for fear that the approach signals a sexual encounter. In contrast, the child who has been physically abused may flinch and exhibit movements of the head suggestive of an attempt to protect oneself from being slapped in the face or even struck in the head. Such flinching is one of the important diagnostic signs of physical abuse. Questioning the child in detail may enable the examiner to ascertain the sources of the child's withdrawal.

Sgroi et al. (1982) describe poor peer relationships as one manifestation of withdrawal. This may relate to the social isola-tion of the abused child's family. Often, a controlling father will not permit his children to get together with others after school and on weekends. Although this may certainly be the case, I would not list peer problems as a useful criterion because it, like school-performance difficulties, is a sensitive indicator of a wide variety of other problems, having little if anything to do with sex abuse. Zealous examiners, especially those who consider Sgroi's book to be their "Bible," will use poor peer relationships as a primary criterion for sex abuse. This is yet another example of how some examiners will consider any symptom, no matter how unrelated to sex abuse, to be indicative.

18. Pathological Compliance

Sexually abused children are often quite compliant. Their experiences with the perpetrator have often been ones in which they have been threatened that noncompliance will result in terrible consequences to themselves and their loved ones. Especially in situations where the perpetrator lives in the home, the child's life is controlled, both body and mind. It is only through compliance that the child may be protected from the realization of the threats. Many develop a cheerful facade that extends to inhibiting themselves from expressing dissatisfaction in any situation and contributes to their compliant behavior. Children who provide false sex-abuse accusations do not generally exhibit such compliant behavior, because they have not had the coercive experiences suffered by the genuinely abused child. What compliance they do exhibit is generally with the request of the programming accuser to provide details about the encounters to anyone and everyone who may ask about them.

Commonly, the abusing father is a very domineering individual who subjects all members of the family to his demands and whims. And the sexual abuse is just one manifestation of such subjugation. These children often develop compliant personalities in association with the fear of invoking the wrath and rejection of the only father they have. And they may be compliant, as well, in imitation of their mothers. Children who falsely accuse are less likely to be compliant. More often they are quite assertive and angrily and vociferously express their vilifications of the accused.

19. Psychosomatic Disorders

Children who have been genuinely abused are more likely to suffer with psychosomatic disorders than those who have not. Their bodies have indeed been traumatized, and they may thereby generalize from the genital trauma to other areas. In addition, such children may develop formidable tensions and anxieties, which may have somatic components such as nausea, vomiting, and stomachaches. Sometimes children who have been forced into oral sex will complain about nausea, vomiting, and stomach aches. Those who falsely accuse do not typically suffer with psychosomatic complaints. Because many are encouraged to express their anger, they tend to externalize it rather than to internalize their emotions. This lessens the likelihood that such children will develop psychosomatic symptoms. However, some false accusers may have such complaints (common in childhood) from other sources. The fact that they are being programmed to provide false accusations of sex abuse is in itself a source of tension.

The younger the child, the less the likelihood the child is going to remember exactly the scenarios being programmed. Not getting the "right" answers for a programming parent and/or "validators" and/or "therapists" can engender significant anxieties. I have seen many cases of falsely accusing children who, in the course of their "therapy," develop psychosomatic complaints. These complaints are considered by their "therapists" to be related to the recent divulgences. They do not consider the possibility that the complaints relate to the tensions and anxieties engendered by their "treatment." The unrelentless sledgehammering that these children are subjected to is not considered the cause of their psychosomatic complaints.

Those children who provide false accusations in the context of a child custody dispute may also suffer tensions related to their sense of betrayal, the loyalty conflict that the divorce hostilities engender, the separation anxieties attendant to the separation, and other tension-engendering exposures attendant to the parental divorce. And such children might also develop somatic complaints as the result of such exposures. These other causes of psychosomatic complaints, causes having nothing to do with sex abuse, weaken this differentiating criterion. However, it still may be a valuable differentiating criterion, especially if the examiner is successful in delineating the factors that are the sources of the child's psychosomatic complaints.

20. Regressive Behavior

Children who have been sexually abused are likely to exhibit regressive behavior such as enuresis, encopresis, thumbsucking, baby talk, and separation anxieties. Having been psychologically traumatized at a higher level of development, they may regress to earlier levels in order to gain the securities attendant to these more primitive states. Children who are falsely accusing are less likely to exhibit such regressive manifestations. However, children who are exposed to the stresses of parental divorce are also likely to regress. And children who have been subjected to sledgehammer interrogations and "therapy" may also regress. A careful history delineating the evolution of the allegation and the time of onset of the regression may shed light on the question of whether the regression is a manifestation of sex abuse or the result of these other factors.

21. Sense of Betrayal

Children who have genuinely been abused may suffer with deep-seated feelings of having been betrayed. They feel betrayed by the offender because of his exploitation of them, and they may feel betrayed by their mothers, especially in situations in which the latter does not provide them with protection from further abuse. Lourie and Blick (1987) describe this phenomenon well:

> Nonetheless, the children still feel betrayed. Someone upon whom the children have relied and in whom was placed a basic sense of trust has taken advantage of this dependency and trust in a destructive way.

The children feel a loss of trust in the parent who has abused them, and the concomitant sense of betrayal may be devastating. Kaufman (1987) states:

> The abuse serves to rob children of the small degree of personal power they may have, leaving them helpless and defenseless in a world in which they have also lost faith in their parents, their primary protectors.

The younger the child, the less specific the child's description of such betrayal. It is only older children who will describe it, especially with regard to the unprotecting mother. Children who provide false accusations of sex abuse in the family situation do not generally complain about the fact that their mothers did not protect them from the indignities they suffered at the hands of their fathers. Rather, they are usually quite laudatory of their mothers and, if a parental alienation syndrome is present, have no complaints at all about them. This factor is lost from consideration by both the mother (who is happy to broadcast the abuse) and the child (who joins her in public denunciation of the father).

Children who fabricate sex abuse in the context of a divorce dispute may describe feelings of betrayal in association with the divorce, but do not generally focus on sex-abuse betrayal. They may describe feelings of betrayal over what they consider an abandonment by the parent who has left the home, and this betrayal is not only of themselves but of the parent who has been left behind. It is important to appreciate that there are many children sexually abused who initially do not feel betrayed by the abusing parent. They may have enjoyed the experience and considered themselves to have been singled out for special favors. It is only later, when they learn about the social attitudes about what has been going on, that they may learn to feel betrayed. It is when they learn that the enjoyable experiences they have been having are considered by society to be sinful and heinous crimes that they begin to feel betrayed. And there are some children who have had sexual encounters with adults who never adopt these social attitudes and therefore never feel betrayed.

May (1991) describes another source of betrayal for the sexually abused child, namely, betrayal by the third party to whom the child has revealed the abuse. That person, sometimes an evaluator from a community agency, promises not to reveal the child's divulgence and then does so. This too may shake the child's confidence and increase his (her) fears. The child who provides false sex-abuse accusations does not exhibit this sense of betrayal by evaluators. In fact, the child is happy to provide the disclosure and welcomes its dissemination by the interviewer.

22. Sleep Disturbances

Because putting the child to bed is commonly used as an opportunity for sexually abusing children, it is not surprising that children who are genuinely abused may fear going to sleep. The tensions and anxieties associated with going to bed may contribute to the development of sleep disturbances. These include refusal to go to bed, insomnia, bedwetting, and nightmares (about which I will say much more below). Children who fabricate sex abuse are not as likely to develop sleep disturbances from the fear of being sexually abused at bedtime. They may, however, develop sleep disturbances in association with other psychological traumas, such as being subjected to a series of interrogations and/or embroilment in their parents' hostilities, especially if the parents are litigating over their custody. Sleep disturbances may also be seen in association with bedwetting and nightmares that may not necessarily relate to sex abuse. It is for this reason that this is a poor differentiating criterion.

Nightmares are commonly considered to be one of the important indicators of sex abuse. There is hardly an article on child sex abuse that does not list nightmares as one of the indicators. My experience has also been that "validators" invariably will list nightmares as one of the important manifestations of child sex abuse. Lawyers, as well, seem to have been swept up in this myth and will often consider the nightmare to be one of the primary indicators of child sex abuse, whether the lawyer is representing the defense or the prosecution. It is rare for any differentiation to be made between nightmares that might relate to the sex abuse and nightmares that may have other sources. It is rare for zealous examiners to ask questions about the *content* of the nightmare in order to try to make some assessment in this regard. But even if one does conduct such an inquiry, one may be hard put to know whether the content relates to sex abuse or to other issues. This problem notwithstanding, the inquiry into content should still be made because there is still the possibility that such an inquiry might enable one to make the differentiation.

A common nightmare of children involves some menacing and malevolent figure coming toward the child, who wakes up just at the time when the figure is about to make contact or engulf him (her). One could argue that the malevolent figure or entity is indeed a symbolic representation of the abuser. However, this is such a common theme in nightmares that one could also argue that it has nothing at all to do with the abuse. I cannot see myself concluding that such a nightmare automatically relates to abuse. It is only when the nightmare involves a direct representation of the abuser or a thin disguise of him (her) that I would be willing to consider it a symptom of sex abuse. It is only when there is something very specific about the malevolent figure, something that is idiosyncratic to the accused, something that provides compelling evidence that the dream figure does indeed represent the alleged perpetrator, that I would consider the dream to be a manifestation of sex abuse. But even then, the view that the alleged perpetrator is malevolent does not necessarily demonstrate that the malevolent act is indeed sex abuse. There are many other things a parent can do to a child that can produce such a dream fantasy, things entirely unrelated to sex abuse. Furthermore, children (like all human beings) tend to project, and dreams sometimes reflect such projections. The anger that is thereby attributed to a hostile figure may reflect the child's own projected anger. Dreams associated with bona fide sex abuse may sometimes reenact fragments of the sexual encounters. This may be part of the desensitization process. And such reenactment may be incorporated into a nightmare. In such cases, obviously, the nightmare is a much stronger indicator that bona fide abuse did indeed take place.

Sgroi et al. (1982) state, "Child-sexual-abuse victims of all ages suffer from nightmares. Surprisingly, the nightmares are usually about falling, kidnappings, or violence, rather than reenactments of the sexual abuse. The children wake up in the night crying and frightened. In young children this type of behavior is frequently known as night terrors." I consider there to be many egregious errors in this statement. First, it leads one to believe that most, if not all, children who have been sexually abused suffer with nightmares. This is not the case. Sexually abused children who have not been subjected to frightening experiences and who believe that they have been singled out to be the recipient of enjoyable experiences will not consider the sexual activities traumatic and are far less likely to have more than the usual number of nightmares.

With regard to Sgroi et al.'s comments about the typical content of the dreams of sexually abused children, falling dreams are very common, so common that they can be considered to be present in just about all people. Obviously, with such ubiquity, they cannot be considered to be a sign of sex abuse. Dreams of being kidnapped are also common, not only in normal children, but those with a wide variety of other disturbances. And dreams of violence are extremely common; in fact, most nightmares involve a violent element in which some malevolent figure is approaching the child in a menacing manner. The child who wakes up at night frightened may be awakening from a nightmare, but is certainly not necessarily exhibiting a night terror, as Sgroi et al. would have us believe. Night terrors are seen in almost all children between the ages of two and four and are *normal*. It appears that Sgroi is not appreciative of the difference and is using the term *night terror* synonymously with *nightmare* or as a term to describe a particularly frightening nightmare. Actually, they are very different entities. Whereas a child having a nightmare can be awakened and reassured, the child who is having a night terror cannot be interrupted in this way. Children will have good memories for nightmares, especially those that occur at the time of awakening. In contrast, the child is usually amnesic for the comments and behaviors exhibited in the course of a night terror. Whereas nightmares may be associated with some degree of twisting and turning and even crying out, night terrors, more typically, are associated with more dramatic body movements including thrusting, seizure-like movements, and even getting out of the bed and running around—all the while with a glassy stare. Night terrors are much more likely a physiological manifestation (akin to seizures), whereas nightmares are more likely psychogenic. Evaluators who zealously subscribe to Sgroi's criteria will frequently consider this normal phenomenon a sign of sex abuse.

Sgroi et al. (1982) also describe other sleep disturbances that may be seen in children who are sexually abused. Because their sleep may have been interrupted or shortened by the abuses, they awake tired and may then find it difficult to cope with school and other activities of the day. Other children sleep long hours as a way of removing themselves from the world. I am in agreement with Sgroi et al. on these manifestations of sleep disturbances that one can see in association with child sex abuse.

23. Chronicity of Abuse

By the time bona fide sex abuse comes to the attention of others, it may have been going on for a long period. This is especially the case because the majority of pedophiles involve themselves in such behavior on a compulsive and frequent basis. Typically, they are highly sexualized people. Raskin and Esplin (1991) state:

> Incestuous relationships typically progress over time, beginning with relatively benign sexual acts and expressions of affection and escalating to more serious sexual acts, such as intercourse and sodomy. Valid accounts of incest usually include a typical progression, whereas fictitious statements often include fully executed, serious sexual acts during the first incident. (pp. 157-158)

False accusers usually describe only one or two experiences initially. In divorce cases this is enough for the purposes of bringing about exclusion of the alleged perpetrator and wreaking vengeance on him (her). However, in the hands of many evaluators and therapists, one can predict an elaboration of the number of times the abuse allegedly took place, to the point where the episodes become countless. One would think that an abuser would be very hesitant to allow such displays in the presence of an examiner, especially an examiner involved in a criminal evaluation. However, the seductive, playful mode of interaction may be so prevalent that it may be the primary mode of relatedness between the two. Accordingly, it may not be easily covered up. This is not a strong differentiating criterion because there certainly are children who have been sexually abused on only one or two occasions before being brought to the attention of authorities. And there are false accusers who have described ongoing sexual encounters over time. This drawback notwithstanding, chronicity still speaks more for the abuse being genuine.

24. Seductive Behavior (Primarily Girls)

The girl who has been sexually abused by her father, and who does not consider her acts to be sinful or bad, may exhibit seductive behavior in the joint interview(s) with him, in the presence of the examiner. She may also develop feelings of sexual excitation when with the abuser, and these may manifest themselves in the joint interview. She may not recognize that such seductive behavior may be a source of embarrassment to him and threaten disclosure of the sexual encounters. Girls who are false accusers, not having developed a sexual tie, are not as likely to be seductive with their fathers. Boys who have been sexually molested are less likely to exhibit seductive behavior with the accused. This criterion provides an excellent example of the value of the joint interview; obviously, it cannot be assessed without such an interview.

When a child who has been genuinely abused is interviewed jointly with the abuser, one may not only see some seductivity on the part of the child, but the behavior may be encouraged by the abuser. When observed together, after an initial period of getting used to the situation, the abuser may relax his guard and slip into a typical pattern of relatedness with the child. There may be giggling, grabbing, and excessive tickling.

25. Pseudomaturity (Primarily Girls)

Some girls who have been sexually abused by their fathers have been prematurely pressured into a pseudomature relationship with him. In some cases the abuse was actually encouraged (overtly or covertly) by the mother in order to use the child as a substitute object for the father's sexual gratification. Such mothers view sexual encounters as odious, and the child is used as a convenient replacement—protecting the mother thereby from exposure to the noxious sexual act. Sometimes this pattern extends itself to the mother's encouraging the daughter to assume other domestic roles such as housekeeping, caring for the other children, serving as the mother's confidante, etc. The result is a pseudomature girl who provides the father with a variety of wifelike gratifications. Girls who are false accusers are less likely to be pseudomature and/or placed in such a situation. However, pseudomaturity can result from other factors—factors having nothing to do with sex abuse—thereby weakening this differentiating criterion. Boys who have been sexually molested are less likely to become pseudomature. If they do exhibit this behavioral pattern, it is more likely the result of other influences.

Sgroi et al. (1982) states, "When the pseudomature exterior is penetrated, a frightened, guilt-ridden, lonely child is revealed." Girls who falsify are less likely to develop this personality pattern.

26. Antisocial Acting Out

Children who have been sexually abused in the home situation have much to be angry about, especially if there has been a coercive element associated with the abuse and they recognize the degree to which they have been exploited. Because of their fear of the perpetrator, they are not capable of expressing their resentments directly to him. Accordingly, they may act out their anger elsewhere. If, in addition, their mothers or other potential protectors refuse to hear their complaints, the pent-up anger becomes even greater. And this may be acted out outside the home, especially in school and in the neighborhood.

In contrast, children who have not been abused are less likely to exhibit such antisocial acting out. However, children whose parents are divorcing, especially parents who are themselves embroiled in vicious battles, are also likely to become angry and are also likely to act out their anger. Accordingly, this criterion is somewhat weakened for children of divorce, and it therefore behooves the evaluator to differentiate between anger derived from exposure to and embroilment in a parent's divorce and anger that may be the result of sexual molestation. Furthermore, there are many other causes of antisocial acting out in children, having nothing to do with parental divorce and/or sex abuse. And these sources of the child's anger must also be investigated before one can come to the conclusion that the antisocial behavior is a manifestation of sex abuse.

27. School Attendance and Performance

Children who are being genuinely abused may often arrive at school early and leave late. Obviously, the school is being used as a refuge from the home. Schools also provide an opportunity for peer contact that may be prohibited by the perpetrator (Sgroi et al., 1982). Of course, this manifestation is only applicable to situations in which the perpetrator is someone who lives in the home, and it is certainly not exhibited by all children who are being molested. Some are so disturbed by their sexual encounters that they have trouble concentrating in school and may thereby find attendance there a source of embarrassment. Such children will not be finding excuses for coming early and staying late. In contrast, children who have not been abused do not demonstrate this particular kind of school attendance problem.

Sgroi et al. (1982) describe many other kinds of school problems that may be exhibited by sexually abused children. These include inability to relate to peers, impaired academic performance, sudden drops in academic performance, and inability to concentrate in school. Because the school situation is the most sensitive indicator of a child's psychopathology, and because it is one of the earliest areas in which psychological difficulties may manifest themselves, impaired school performances is a very poor indicator of sex abuse. Because so many other kinds of problems may result in the same kinds of difficulties, I do not believe that the examiner does well to consider school performance difficulties as an important indicator. I am not saying that children who are sexually abused do not exhibit significant problems in school behavior; I am only saying that the school situation, because it is such a sensitive indicator of a wide variety of other psychological problems, is a poor criterion for differentiating between true and false sex abuse accusations.

28. Fears, Tension, and Anxiety

Children who have been subjected to frequent episodes of sexual abuse may become chronically fearful and tense. Such children exhibit the chronic state of hypervigilance and increased arousal described in *DSM-III-R*. They often present with an expression of what Goodwin (1987) refers to as "frozen watchfulness." These children not only exhibit the previously described fear of people of the same sex as the perpetrator (more often than not, men) but fear of situations similar to those in which the abuse occurred: bedrooms, bathrooms, showers, washrooms, etc. This fear, especially prominent in younger children who are more helpless, relates to their feelings of impotence about being subjected to the sexual abuses. Older children may be fearful primarily of the consequences if they were to disclose any hints of what they have been subjected to. They may fear that they will be murdered, beaten, or abandoned, or that significant individuals in their lives will be subjected to similar consequences. They may fear breakup of the family if they reveal the molestation. Such fears may result in a chronic state of timidity that is observed by friends, relatives, teachers, neighbors, etc. And the examiner, as well, will see this timid and petrified child in the examining room. Of course, I am describing here an extreme example, but such children are seen frequently by those who work intensively with children who have been sexually abused.

In contrast, children who are fabricating sex abuse are far less likely to present with such a picture. There are children, however, who have not been sexually abused but who have been subjected to other traumas that may bring about a similar state. This may be seen in children whose parents have been constantly fighting and who themselves have been subjected to physical and/or severe emotional abuse. Children exposed to and embroiled in ongoing divorce disputes, especially custody disputes, may also present with this picture. However, the child who is providing a false accusation iş far less likely to exhibit such extreme tension.

29. Running Away from Home

Children who have been molested in the home situation may find the home so intolerable that they run away. This is especially the case when the youngster has not been able to obtain help and protection from the other parent (Sgroi et al., 1982). In contrast, children who falsely accuse sex abuse are not as likely to have a history of such behavior.

30. Severe Psychopathology

Occasionally, one sees a child who exhibits severe psychopathology in which there are both psychotic and psychopathic features. Such a child may become involved in indiscriminate accusations of sex abuse involving a wide variety of individuals. No one in sight is immune (therapists included). The accusations are characteristically indiscriminate and often do not have even the nidus of reality, which, as mentioned, is often present in false sex-abuse accusations. Yates and Musty (1988) describe a five-year-old child who fits this picture. He was polymorphous perverse in the Freudian sense, had practically no inhibitions with regard to the expression of his pansexualism, and accused his therapist of molesting him when the therapist helped him out from under a table.

CONCLUDING COMMENTS

It is my hope that the reader will be somewhat overwhelmed by the length of my list of indicators and the problems that beset evaluators who wish to implement them. Evaluators who have a shorter list and evaluators who believe that they can conduct sex-abuse examinations quickly may feel more comfortable, but they are much more likely to make errors when attempting to discriminate between true and false sex-abuse accusations. Obviously, the first evaluator is in the best position to assess for the sex abuse, especially because many of the criteria become blurred over time, especially after the child is subjected to repeated examinations. However, all is not lost for the later evaluator. He (she) is in a good position to trace carefully the evolution of the allegation and to assess for the presence of the kinds of distortions and elaborations that are the hallmarks of the false sex-abuse accusation.

I have provided here 30 indicators that I consider to be useful for differentiating between true and false sex-abuse accusations. My previous attempts to quantify my earlier version of this list (Gardner, 1987) was beset by many problems. Accordingly, I abandoned the attempt to quantify these differentiating criteria. However, a somewhat vaguer (but possibly more useful) quantification may still be useful. One could say, for example, "Of the 30 indicators considered, the evaluation of the child revealed that only two manifested themselves. This makes it highly unlikely that this child was sexually abused, by the accused or anyone else." There is no cut-off point with regard to a number of indicators that should strongly suggest bona fide sexual abuse. Rather, one does well to view these indicators as on a continuum; that the greater the number of indicators present, the greater the likelihood the child was sexually abused. Equally, if not more important that the *quantity* of indicators satisfied is the *quality.* In some cases only a few of the indicators may be satisfied, but each one may provide compelling evidence that the allegation is false. For example, a child may say, "My daddy put the big butcher knife up my wee-wee hole. My mommy saw him do it and she punished him by giving him 'time out'." Although this statement may only satisfy the incredibility criterion (#6), it is compelling evidence that the accusation is false and the examiner should not feel that many more criteria need be satisfied in order to justify this conclusion. This principle is applicable to the criteria utilized when evaluating the accused (Chapter Two) and the accuser (Chapter Four). Of course, these indicators for the child must not be considered in isolation from the indicators of the accuser and the alleged perpetrator. The examiner must consider all three parties and not come to any conclusions before assessing the three.

FOUR
THE ACCUSER

INTRODUCTION

In this chapter I focus primarily on parents who promulgate, both directly and through their children, false sex-abuse accusations in the context of child custody disputes. This type of accuser, in my experience, is the most common at this time. As mentioned, such an accusation provides a rejected parent with an extremely powerful vengeance and exclusionary maneuver that will attract the court's attention and often bring about immediate action by the court. Because mothers, much more commonly than fathers, are likely to initiate such accusations, I will refer to the accuser as the mother. However, it is important to appreciate that fathers may also initiate such accusations, and this has become more common in recent years as a backlash to such mothers' tactics.

In Chapter Nine I will discuss in detail personality characteristics and psychodynamic factors operative in parents who promulgate false accusations in the context of nursery school and day-care situations. These are the circumstances in which the hysterical element prevails and my experience has been that, once again, women are more likely to be involved in such accusations than men, but the female/male ratio is probably not as high.

Support for my observations regarding the sex ratio of false accusers is provided by Wakefield and Underwager (1990), who studied 64 falsely accus*ing* parents whose false accusations occurred in the context of acrimonious child custody disputes. Of this group of 64, 60 were females and 4 were males. Of the 97 falsely accus*ed* parents (again in the context of vicious child custody disputes), 4 were females and 93 males.

There is no such thing as a typical personality pattern of a parent who initiates and promulgates a false sex-abuse accusation. There are, however, *indicators* that may prove useful for examiners attempting to ascertain whether the accusation is true or false. The greater the number of indicators that the accuser is promulgating a false accusation, the greater the likelihood the accusation is false. However, it is important to consider the *quality* of each of the criteria satisfied, not just the *quantity.*

Once again, I cannot emphasize enough the importance of the evaluator tracing in detail the evolution of the sex-abuse accusation. This importance of tracing the evolutionary development of the sex-abuse accusation is reflected in the sequence with which I present the indicators in this chapter. I begin with those early-life experiences that may have served as background and foundation for the false accusation in that their presence, even in the earlier years, increases the likelihood that the individual will subsequently initiate and/or promulgate a false sex-abuse accusation. The sequence then continues through later years, up to the present, and ends with those that may be seen in the course of the evaluation.

With regard to the accuser, one wants to ask *very specific questions* regarding the *very first time* the accuser began to think about the possibility that the child was being sexually abused. One wants to know whether such thoughts were engendered by external or internal events, i.e., whether the thoughts were created in response to actual events that took place in reality or were engendered by internal psychological processes independent of external reality events. If such external occurrences did indeed exist, one wants to know exactly what these events were, especially with regard to the question of the likelihood that such occurrences did indeed represent genuine sexual abuse. If internal events, i.e., internal psychological processes, were the only factors operative in the initiation of the sex-abuse accusation, then there is a high likelihood that a false accusation is being promulgated. Of course, this is only one "piece of the puzzle," but it is an important clue as to whether or not one is dealing with a false accusation.

INDICATORS OF A FALSELY ACCUSING PARENT (USUALLY A MOTHER)

Indicators from Earlier Life

1. Childhood History of Having Been Sexually Abused Herself Mothers of children who have actually been sexually abused are more likely to have been sexually abused themselves in childhood than mothers who provide false accusations. Some (but certainly not all) mothers who have been sexually abused in childhood may create situations that enhance the likelihood that their own children will become sexually abused as well. Sometimes the mother's abuse has resulted in sexual inhibition problems, resulting in their viewing sex as disgusting. They may then facilitate (consciously or unconsciously) their children serving as sexual substitutes in order to protect themselves from involvement in sexual acts. A common complaint made by women who have been sexually abused is that their mothers refused to listen with receptivity to their complaints and even punished them when they complained. One factor operative in such unreceptivity to hearing about the child's abuse is the recognition that interfering with the child's being abused by the father may create a situation in which the father turns to the mother for sexual gratification. Of course, other factors are operative, such as the desire to maintain the marriage, especially the status and economic advantages of such maintenance. Furthermore, sexual abuse tends to repeat itself down the generations, so that a mother who was sexually abused in childhood is more likely to have a child who is sexually abused. It is as if sexual abuse "runs in the family."

It would be an error for the reader to conclude, however, that mothers who have been sexually abused themselves as children may not contribute to a false sex-abuse accusation. For such mothers, sex may be very much on their minds and they may tend to interpret the most frivolous and inconsequential activities as strong indicators of bona fide sex abuse. They may be ever vigilant for signs of sexual molestation and this preoccupation may fuel such misinterpretations. Furthermore, there may be psychological "unfinished business" regarding their reactions to their own childhood sexual experiences. They may still harbor ongoing animosity toward the perpetrator and may readily displace such anger onto any man who provides them justification for such release. And a rejecting husband may serve such a purpose well. Accordingly, the opportunity to wreak vengeance on an abandoning husband can contribute to the formation of a false sex-abuse accusation. The fantasy (or even delusion) of her husband having sex with her child may be a replay, down one generation, of her own experiences. These factors, then, may contribute to the formation of a false sex-abuse accusation by a mother who was herself sexually abused in childhood.

Accordingly, this indicator is a difficult one to apply. What I am basically saying is that of mothers who were sexually abused as children, there is one category whose accusations are more likely to be true, and another category whose accusations are more likely to be false. The mothers in the first category serve as models and facilitators, and the mothers in the second category are projectors and vengeance accusers. It is here that the diagnostic skill of the examiner is crucial. It is here that we see well demonstrated the futility of trying to do a proper sex-abuse evaluation in a short period (a very common situation). It is here where only a very detailed evaluation will enable the examiner to come to any conclusions. If the mother uses the mechanism of projection in other areas, especially if she is paranoid, then this supports the conclusion that the accusation is false. However, there are still paranoid women who were indeed sexually abused as children. However, I still believe that the projection criterion may be useful. If the mother was not sexually abused, then it is more likely that the accusation is false, but one must take into consideration, as well, the subcategory of sexually abused mothers who may foment a false sex-abuse accusation. Because of all of these considerations, this criterion may not prove too useful. Whether or not it is useful, it is still only one of many criteria and, like all of the others, one does not come to a conclusion on the basis of a single indicator. Rather, one must consider all of the indicators and then come to some conclusion as to whether or not the person is likely to be a false accuser.

2. History of Poor Impulse Control Mothers of children who are genuinely abused are not typically impulsive or have a history of such behavior. In contrast, mothers of children who falsely accuse are more likely to have a history of impulsivity, and the false accusation may be one manifestation of such impulsivity. Rather than weighing carefully the pros and cons of the "evidence," they impulsively call in authorities and investigators. Typically, they do not call first the child's father, the person who might give them some information regarding whether or not the abuse took place. Rather, they quickly call a lawyer, child protection services, or other external authority who can be relied upon to take action quickly. Or they may bring their child for an emergency appointment with an examiner who they know (or sense) beforehand will be confirming the abuse. Such a mother is especially likely to seek an examiner who is designated a "validator" or "child advocate."

3. Passivity and/or Inadequacy Mothers of children who are genuinely abused are more likely to be passive and/or inadequate individuals. The passivity and inadequacy may have contributed to a situation in which the perpetrator was allowed to subject the child to the sexual abuse. As described in Chapter Two, many child sex abusers are very domineering individuals whose whole families are subjugated by them. The sexual abuse is just one example of the general emotional and even physical abuse to which the family is subjected. In contrast, mothers who promulgate false accusations are more likely to be self-assertive. They are the ones who are more likely to make a commotion over the alleged abuse and quickly bring it to the attention of a parade of authorities, many (if not all) of whom will be pressured or seduced into supporting the allegation.

4. Social Isolation   Mothers of children who are genuinely abused are more likely to be social isolates than the mothers of those who falsify. Some families in which bona fide abuse occurs are tightly knit units in which the abusing father dominates the family and does everything possible to remove the family members from social involvement. This may serve the purpose of reducing the likelihood of divulgence of the abuse and also may lessen the likelihood that others may similarly gain gratifications from the abused family members. In contrast, mothers of children who provide false accusations are more likely to be outgoing, assertive, and argumentative. They are very independent types who are less likely to have been constrained in their speech or movements by a domineering husband.

**Indicators from Events Preceding
the Evaluation**

5. Exposure of the Child to Sex-Abuse "Educational Material"   We are living at a time when young children are being increasingly exposed to an ever wider variety of sexual materials. Not only do we have sex-abuse prevention programs in schools, but there are videotapes, audiotapes, and coloring books. Parents, as well, have been provided with a wide variety of materials, the purpose of which is to help protect their children from being sexually abused. Validators and other examiners routinely use such books, with rationalizations to be described in greater detail in Chapter Six. These materials teach children about "good touches" and "bad touches." They teach children to beware of strangers and even people who are not strangers, like adult male friends of the family and relatives. The name of the game is "ongoing vigilance." You never know when an innocent and friendly adult male is really a sex pervert in disguise. They would lead children to believe that sex abusers are lurking behind every tree and that any man who offers them candy must be suspect. Not surprisingly, children may incorporate information from these materials into their sex-abuse litanies, and this is one of the sources of the borrowed scenarios described in Chapter Three.

Ostensibly "modern" mothers who are up-to-date with the latest dangers that may befall their children may read children some of these books, ostensibly to help them protect themselves from these ubiquitous perverts. The examiner does well to make inquiries of the accuser regarding exposure of the child to these materials. It should be a routine part of the inquiry devoted to the detailed analysis of the evolution of the sex-abuse accusation. If the child has indeed been subjected to such an exposure, the examiner does well to review the material himself (herself) in order to determine whether any of these messages have been directly incorporated into the child's sex-abuse scenario. One does well to inquire of the accuser as to what exactly were the mother's reasons for reading these materials to the child.

6. Moralism Mothers who provide false sex-abuse accusations may be excessively moralistic. They may condemn vehemently normal and healthy manifestations of childhood sexuality and may even see sexuality in normal encounters that are not basically sexual. They tend to project their own unacceptable sexual impulses onto others and condemn in others what they wish to basically disown in themselves. This is one of the reasons why false accusations are often promulgated by extremely religious fundamentalists who are preoccupied and even obsessed with condemning sexuality. Their obsession with condemning the sexual behavior of others serves to keep repressed and suppressed their own sexuality, over which they feel guilty. Accordingly, we are basically dealing here with the mechanism of reaction formation. This is one of the factors operative in the sex-abuse hysteria seen in nursery schools and day-care centers closely affiliated with such churches. When acting independently, this mechanism may be operative in bringing about a false sex-abuse accusation in the context of an acrimonious child custody dispute. When acting together, such parents may fuel the hysteria that is seen in nursery school and day-care centers in which sexual orgies are alleged to have been perpetrated, especially by personnel. (In this chapter I focus on the former types of mothers, and in Chapter Nine the latter type.)

Sometimes the mothers were not particularly moralistic prior to the divorce, but progressively became so. This is especially the case in situations in which the father has involved himself with a new woman friend. Typically, such mothers begin by vehemently claiming that the children should not be permitted to sleep over at the father's home when the new woman friend is there (even though sleeping behind a locked bedroom door). If this maneuver does not prove successful, they may "up the ante" and claim sexual improprieties (e.g., undressing in front of the children, exposing the children to sexual encounters, etc.) when there is no evidence for such. Such exposures, if they did indeed take place, would generally be considered improprieties and manifestations of injudiciousness. However, in the climate of hysteria in which we are living, they easily become labeled "sexual molestation" and even "sexual abuse." The next step, of course, is direct accusations of parent-child sexual abuse, either by the father or his woman friend.

Mothers of children who are genuinely abused are less likely to exhibit such vehement moralism. An inquiry into their religious background and beliefs does not usually reveal the presence of excessive and/or sexual moralistic attitudes. The proper assessment for the presence of this criterion often requires an inquiry into the religious background and experiences of the accuser. This is sometimes difficult because religion may be a "touchy subject." There are parents who may recognize that the examiner views their religiosity as a manifestation of psychopathology. Such parents may respond very defensively to inquiries in this area with such comments as, "My religious beliefs are none of your business" and "Religion has nothing to do with this. What we are dealing with here is sex abuse." Many parents in this category will select an examiner from the same religious denomination in order to ensure that the fabricated or delusional sex-abuse allegation is not "smoked out." Unfortunately, there are many examiners affiliated with such churches who share with the parents the same excessively moralistic and even delusional attitudes. Under such circumstances, we not only have a folie-à-deux relationship between the mother and child, but a folie-à-trois relationship among the mother, the child, and the examiner. So "touchy" a subject is religion that even *DSM-III-R* has stayed away from it. I am not claiming that all religiosity is psychopathological. I am only claiming that there are millions of people whose religiosity fuels their psychopathology and is part of the psychopathological package. And those who fuse religiosity, excessive moralism, and a false sex-abuse accusation are in this category.

7. The Utilization of Exclusionary Maneuvers   Exclusionary maneuvers are commonly utilized by mothers in the course of programming their children to be alienated from their fathers. These often antedate a child custody dispute and may even antedate the separation. The parental alienation syndrome, then, is often an extension of these earlier exclusionary maneuvers, which then become stepped up and fuel the development and perpetuation of the syndrome. A sex-abuse accusation may represent the final culmination of these maneuvers. It is especially likely to be utilized when earlier exclusionary maneuvers prove inadequate and/or futile. Often these methods of exclusion are part of a program of overprotectiveness, and the mother may consider herself to be more deeply committed to the children than others who are viewed as not taking proper precautions.

It is beyond my purpose here to discuss these maneuvers in detail. I will, however, focus on a few of the common ones. Prior to the separation, the mother may have distrusted the father when assuming a wide variety of normal father involvements, e.g., bathing the children, swimming with them, taking them alone to the park, etc. After the separation she may not tell him about medical appointments, PTA meetings, school recitals, sports events, and other activities involved in the children's lives. Attempts on his part to get information in these areas is viewed as a noxious irritant and, when he persists, he is labeled a "harasser." She may even go to court to protect herself from such "harassments." A favorite exclusionary device is the telephone answering machine that screens all his calls, but allows all other callers to be put through. The greater the number of such maneuvers, the greater the likelihood the sex-abuse accusation is false. After all, such an accusation can result in almost immediate cessation of visitation and, between the time of the accusation and a court hearing (which may take many months and even years), the only contact the father may have with the child is in a public facility in the context of a short, supervised visitation. It is indeed an example of how the law, under the guise of protecting children, falls right into the hands of a mother whose animosity toward the child's father is so great that she blinds herself to the effects of her exclusionary maneuvers on her children. Mothers of children who have been genuinely abused are less likely to provide such a history.

8. The Presence of a Child Custody Dispute and/or Litigation It is extremely important that the examiner ascertain whether the accusation arose in the context of a child custody/visitation dispute. The failure to do so represents a serious deficiency in the evaluator. For those allegations that do take place in the course of a child custody dispute, one wants to find out whether there were previous vengeful and exclusionary maneuvers of which the sex-abuse accusation represents the culmination. The presence of such a history adds strong weight to the conclusion that the sex-abuse accusation is false. Of course, this is still only one indicator and there are certainly children who have been sexually abused while their parents have been disputing for their custody. However, it is likely that the abuse took place before the custody dispute as well. If, however, the divulgence of the abuse was the cause of the separation, then this would be an argument that the accusation is true. We see here, once again, the importance of tracing in detail the evolution of the sex-abuse accusation. Pinpointing exactly when it occurred in the context of events that preceded and succeeded it places the examiner in a better position to determine whether it is true or false.

9. The Presence of a Parental Alienation Syndrome Some children involved in a child custody dispute develop a disorder that I have termed the *parental alienation syndrome.* This is a disorder in which children, programmed by the allegedly "loved" parent, embark upon a campaign of denigration of the allegedly "hated" parent. There is little ambivalence over their hatred, which often spreads to the extended family of the allegedly despised parent. Most often the mothers are involved in such programming, and the fathers are the victims of the campaigns of deprecation. However, we are not dealing here with simple "brainwashing" of the mother against the father. The child's own scenarios of denigration often contribute and complement those promulgated by the mother. Accordingly, I introduced the term *parental alienation syndrome* to refer to *both* of these contributions to the disorder. The reason the children generally prefer to join the mother is that most often their bonding with her is stronger than the bonding with the father, and they fear that if they do not join her side in the divorce warfare, they will be deprived of her affection. Elsewhere (Gardner, 1992a) I have described this disorder in great detail.

Of relevance here is the sex-abuse accusation that may arise in the context of a parental alienation syndrome. Generally, it is a late development. Usually, there is a whole series of previous exclusionary maneuvers that have not proven successful in bringing about removal of the father, and the sex-abuse accusation emerges as a final attempt to remove him entirely from the children's lives. Whereas the presence of a child custody dispute adds weight to the argument that the accusation is false, the presence of a parental alienation syndrome adds even further weight to the conclusion that the sex-abuse accusation is false. However, the examiner should still not lose sight of the fact that we are still dealing here with one criterion—a criterion, however, that should be given great weight.

10. Direct Programming of the Child in the Sex-Abuse Realm The examiner does well to make inquiries that will be helpful for determining whether the mother is programming the child, overtly or covertly, to claim sex abuse. Often one can learn about this in the course of a detailed inquiry into the evolution of the sex-abuse accusation. One does well, then, to find out exactly what the interchanges were between the mother and the child when the first divulgence took place.

On many occasions, mothers have provided me with audio-tapes that, they believe, have captured for all time this initial interchange. Of course, the very presence of such a tape is a clue to the fact that the accusation is false. Unless the mother has been audiotaping everything the child has said since the beginning of life, it is not likely that it was a chance phenomenon that the child just happened to talk about sex abuse at a time when the mother just happened to have the audiotape machine running. The usual scenario is that the mother has elicited some information in the sex-abuse realm and now wants to preserve the comments in order to use them as "proof" that the abuse did indeed occur. Mothers whose children were genuinely abused are not as likely to reach for the audiocassette recorder immediately after the first divul-gence. When listening to such tapes one often will hear the mother make comments such as: "Now I want you to tell me again what you said before about what Daddy did to you in the bathtub" and "No, that's not what you said before. What you said before is that he put his finger in your pee-pee hole. Isn't that what you said?" One can hear here the intonations of support and encouragement for responses that support the sex-abuse accusation, as well as denial and inattentiveness of any comments that would negate it. Such maneuvers, also, are part of the brainwashing process.

As mentioned, three- and four-year-olds are the best subjects for programming a sex-abuse accusation. Two-year-olds are too young to "get the story straight" and so cannot be relied upon to provide the scenario to the various interrogators. Children five and above are less programmable, and there is a risk that they will deny ever having had any of the alleged experiences. However, this problem is not insurmountable. One divorcing mother said to her seven-year-old son, "Let's play a trick on Daddy. Let's go into the police station and you tell them that your daddy put his hand on your penis and made you put your hand on his penis. That will be a real funny trick." The child agreed, the father was arrested, the "validators" (with their anatomical dolls, of course) "validated" these and a whole series of other abuses, and the father's life was destroyed. The child's subsequent recantations were considered to be "proof" that the abuse occurred.

Reminding the child to tell "the truth" before visits with validators and other examiners is yet another part of the programming process. When the child forgets or gives a rendition that does not involve sex abuse, the mother responds, "That's not *really* the truth. The truth is what you told me last time. That's the truth, and I want you to remember that." The child soon learns that the truth is merely the code-term for the sex-abuse scenario litany, a litany that the mother hopes will come forth each time the child is given the cue instruction: "Tell 'the truth'."

Sometimes the child will unwittingly give information regarding this criterion. For example, in the course of an inquiry regarding the alleged sex abuse, the child may make such statements as, "My mother said it happened" and "My mother said my father put his wee-wee into my pee-pee." The young child may not realize that with such a statement the "cat is let out of the bag" and that the mother's programming has been exposed.

In contrast, mothers of children who have been sexually abused do not show evidences for such programming. They recognize that the child can be relied upon to give a credible story and does not need to be reminded and rehearsed before interviews with evaluators and other examiners. Although they may tell the child to tell the truth, they do not do so repeatedly, and they do not get across the message that the truth is the code-word for the sex-abuse litany, which has to be practiced frequently if the child is to "get it right."

11. Initial Denial and/or Downplay of the Abuse Most often, mothers of children who are genuinely abused are very reluctant to admit the abuse—may go for weeks, months, and even years denying it—both to themselves and others. Some are passive-dependent types who are fearful of divulging the abuse lest they be beaten or otherwise subjugated or penalized by their husbands. Others may recognize that disclosure of the sex abuse may destroy the family and even bring about the incarceration of the accused. They would rather live in a situation in which their children are being sexually abused than suffer the breakup of the marriage and the attendant effects on the whole family. There may be a long time-lag, then, between the first disclosures and the bringing of the abuse to the attention of others. In contrast, mothers of children who falsify are very quick to report the abuse, especially to those who can cause pain, embarrassment, and other difficulties for the accused. There is no period of denial or downplaying the abuse. Rather, the opposite is the case: they exaggerate every possible indicator and vociferously describe it in detail to anyone who will listen.

12. Failure to Notify the Father Before Reporting the Alleged Abuse to Outside Authorities Typically, mothers who falsely accuse do not inform the father first in order to get input from him regarding whether or not the abuse occurred. Common reasons given: "He would deny it anyway," "If my child said it happened, it happened, and there was no point wasting time discussing it with him," "I didn't want to waste any time, I wanted to get to an expert immediately in order to find out whether or not it really happened." Such action and its attendant rationalizations is one of the hallmarks of the false accusation. Typically, such mothers will first call an attorney, a "sex abuse expert," or child protection services. Most recognize that once they do this the wheels will start turning quickly, and an army of interrogators will descend upon the child. Many will use state laws to justify their taking immediate action. All 50 states now have laws requiring immediate reporting of sex abuse to proper authorities. These laws notwithstanding, there are millions of mothers who are not reporting their husbands, especially when there is nebulous or inconsequential evidence. Furthermore, there is no law that prevents the mother from first confronting the husband under such circumstances. There is no law that prevents her from discussing the matter with him and deciding not to report if the two together believe that there was no abuse.

Unfortunately, many of the people to whom the mother reports the first "disclosure" will conclude that the abuse did indeed take place, often without getting any input at all from the father. I have been involved in many cases in which the father called the validator in the hope that she would give him some information regarding the nature of the charges. Not surprisingly, such efforts proved futile. Some of the common reasons given: "I will compromise the confidential relationship I have with this child if I were to answer that question," "I have nothing to say to you (validator hangs up)," and "Your wife has requested that I have no communication at all with you and I respect her request." We see here how the folie-à-deux relationship between the mother and the validator serves to keep the father in a state of frustration and ignorance, a situation that provides sadistic gratification for both women and protects them from any information that might cast doubt on the validity of the sex-abuse accusation.

In many cases the father first learns about the fact that he has been accused of sex abuse by the police, who come to his home or place of work to take him to jail in handcuffs. I myself have been involved in a few cases in which this has actually happened. I have been involved in many more in which the father was invited to the police station and first learned about the sex-abuse allegation from the police who were brought in by a child protection service worker who had concluded (without seeing or even calling the father) that the abuse had indeed taken place, and even named him as the abuser. Sometimes such evaluators will justify their actions by such statements as, "He would have denied it anyway" and "My job is just to determine whether or not the child has been sexually abused and not to get involved directly with abusers." Interestingly, evaluators who use the latter rationalization do not generally feel uncomfortable naming the abusers anyway. This is an important criterion. The failure to speak first with the accused is an important criterion and is one of the hallmarks of the false sex-abuse accusation.

Typically, when the father does find out about the charges against him, he finds his wife extremely unreceptive to the idea of confronting him with the details of the sexual abuse. Every possible rationalization for noncommunication is utilized. Sometimes these are borrowed from validators, e.g., "There is no point even discussing it with you, because you'll deny it anyway" and "My attorney has advised me not to discuss it with you." One mother, when the father pleaded with her to give him information about what he was accused of doing, replied, "You tell me. You know it. I'm not going to tell you." Another mother said, "You'll find out in the courtroom." One factor operative in this obstructionism is hostility. It is yet another maneuver designed to torture the father and sadistically enjoy his squirming. Another factor operative is the mother's lack of specific information. She may recognize, at some level, that the accusation is extremely weak, preposterous, and basically a "house of cards." If she were to confront her husband with the information, she might be ashamed of what she is hearing herself say.

13. Enlistment of the Services of a "Hired Gun" Attorney or Mental Health Professional   Mothers of children who falsify are quite likely to engage the services of attorneys and mental health professionals who they know in advance will support their position quite zealously. They generally will resist the appointment of an impartial examiner, because they recognize that such an evaluator may appreciate what they are doing and not provide them with support for their campaign of vilification. In contrast, mothers of children who are genuinely abused are not as likely to be so resistant to the appointment of an impartial evaluator, but they may on occasion be so.

Most examiners consider themselves impartial. My experience has been that only a very small percentage of examiners is truly impartial. A truly impartial examiner will not agree, at the outset, to evaluate only one party. Rather, that examiner insists upon doing everything possible to evaluate all three, namely, the accuser, the accused, and the alleged child victim, before accepting an invitation to do a sex-abuse examination. The truly impartial examiner will make every attempt to serve as a court-appointed impartial *before* embarking upon the evaluation, in order to ensure that all parties will continue with the evaluation and that no one will remove himself (herself) prematurely if the examination appears to move away from the direction they hoped it would take. The truly impartial examiner has gone to court in previous cases and testified both on behalf of the accused and on the behalf of the accuser. Such examiners have a "track record" of having testified on behalf of both sides, not one.

Such examiners have even gone to court and testified on behalf of parties who were initially reluctant to involve themselves in their evaluations. For example, a father proposes a particular examiner to serve as impartial, and the mother initially refuses to involve herself with that examiner, believing that the very fact that the father has proposed him (her) is already a taint and indicates that the examiner must be the father's "hired gun." If, after the mother has been ordered by the court to participate, the evaluator concludes that the mother's position warrants support, a truly impartial evaluator will testify on *her* behalf – the mother's initial reluctance (and even hostility) notwithstanding. A track record of such testimony is strong support that the examiner has been truly impartial. I believe that only a small percentage of evaluators who refer to themselves as impartial will satisfy this important criterion of genuine impartiality. Mothers who are falsely accusing predictably eschew genuinely impartial examiners, whereas those who are confident that their accusation is true will welcome the truly impartial examiner's involvement.

14. History of Attempts to Destroy, Humiliate, or Wreak Vengeance on the Accused Mothers who promulgate false accusations are generally quite desirous of destroying, humiliating, and wreaking vengeance on the accused. They relish the thought of incarcerating the accused, even for years. They are so bent on destroying the accused that they may blind themselves to the fact that such incarceration may cut off permanently all the funds they are receiving. The lengths to which such mothers may go to hurt the accused have no limits. I recall one falsely accusing mother who reported her physician-husband to the state licensing authority. Although a homemaker, and although she had absolutely no significantly marketable skills, the depth of her rage (and delusion) was such that she blinded herself to the severe economic privations she would suffer if her husband's medical license was taken away.

Mothers of children who are genuinely abused are less likely to want to wreak such vengeance on the perpetrator, but they certainly may on occasion. Although mothers of children who have been genuinely abused may on occasion be very vengeful, my experience has been that their retaliatory rage is only a small fraction of that which one sees in the false accuser. They are generally not blind to the economic effects of the accusation. In fact, as mentioned, it is a factor that plays a role in the down-playing of bona fide sexual abuse by many mothers.

15. Attitude Toward Medical Findings Related to the Sex Abuse   Mothers of children who have been genuinely abused are not likely to exaggerate the medical findings, although some may occasionally do so. In contrast, mothers who provide false accusations are likely to exaggerate enormously the most minor medical findings and consider them *proof* of sex abuse. Typically, such mothers bring to their pediatrician's attention the most minor genital lesions with the hopeful expectation that proof of sex abuse will be provided. It is not uncommon for such mothers to make a pilgrimage to a series of doctors in the hope of providing such confirmation. Vaginal rashes and infections are ubiquitous, and there is hardly a little girl who does not suffer with such disorders from time to time. Considering the sensitivity of this area in infant girls, there is probably no child who does not occasionally have such a rash or infection. If a pediatrician reports that the findings are "consistent with" sex abuse (and all such rashes are consistent with sex abuse), such a mother quickly presents the medical findings to a validator, who will predictably consider this finding as "medical proof" of the abuse. We see here how some physicians will play directly into the schemes of a false accuser. I believe that pediatricians are becoming increasingly aware of such mothers and are more likely to record in their charts, "No evidence for sex abuse." In Chapter Five I will discuss medical findings in much greater detail.

16. Failure to Appreciate the Psychological Trauma to the Child of Repeated Interrogations   Mothers of children who falsify sexual abuse are often so enraged that they blind themselves to the psychological trauma to the child of repeated interviews. Typically, they embark on a campaign of interrogations by physicians, psychologists, child protection evaluators, "validators," lawyers, prosecutors, detectives, and any other individual who would be willing to interview the child in order to "validate" the abuse. They appear to be oblivious to the fact that subjecting their children to such a parade of interrogations may bring about formidable psychological disorder. Often, the symptoms that are generated from the interrogations then become "proof" of the abuse. Mothers of children who have been genuinely abused are often more sensitive to such trauma, and they will do everything possible to protect their children from such a parade of interrogations. In Chapter Ten I will describe in detail the psychological problems that can result in children subjected to such a parade of interrogators.

17. The Acquisition of a Coterie of Supporters and Enablers
Typically, mothers who promulgate false sex-abuse accusations collect a coterie of individuals who provide them with support for their accusation. I often refer to these people as "enablers," a term borrowed from Alcoholics Anonymous. These are the people who provide psychological and often financial and physical support to alcoholics and other drug abusers. Although the term is new, the phenomenon is well known in that most forms of psychopathology involve the participation of enablers. Unfortunately, many enablers are therapists, especially women who are "treating" or "counseling" the accusing mother. They will openly state that they are providing her with support and assistance in her "validation" of the abuse. Commonly, these therapists see no need to interview the father and will refuse to meet with him if he requests such an interview. A common rationalization for such refusal: "He'll only deny it anyway, so what's the point of seeing him" or "Children never lie under such circumstances, so there's no point to my wasting time seeing him." Commonly, the sisters, mothers, aunts, and other relatives of the accusing mother will jump on her bandwagon and participate in the campaign of denigration of the father that, of course, filters down to the

children. Because the sex-abuse accusation most often has a very weak foundation, the accuser needs these supporters in order to protect the whole "house of cards" from falling down.

Although mothers of children who have been genuinely abused may need some support from close friends and relatives, they rarely sweep them up in a wave of denigration and ask for their assistance in destroying the father. Nor do they need continual "validation" required by falsely accusing mothers, especially when information comes their way that may make them intermittently question whether the abuse really took place.

18. Deep Commitment to the Opinions of the "Experts"
Conducting child sex-abuse accusations is "open territory" for would-be evaluators. To the best of my knowledge, there are no state certifications for the discipline of "sex-abuse evaluator." Even in the fields of psychiatry and psychology, the fields in which one would think that such evaluations should take place, there is no formal subspecialty specifically designated for such evaluations. At this point sex-abuse evaluations are being conducted by a wide variety of individuals from numerous disciplines. Furthermore, the knowledge, training, and experiences necessary to conduct such examinations have not been clearly defined. Even in my own field, child psychiatry, there is no formal subspecialty for sex abuse, and most of us in the field who do this kind of work are basically self-trained. Older people, like myself, received no training in sex abuse during our residencies because so few of these children were brought to our attention. Younger people are receiving some training, but no formal certification is required to designate oneself as an "expert." However, we at least have training in child psychiatry, child development, child interview techniques, child psychopathology, and the treatment of psychiatric disorders of children. Accordingly, we at least have some kind of a foundation for developing derivative expertise in the sex-abuse area.

There are many individuals, however, who were never trained in any of the formal mental health disciplines and who are self-appointed sex-abuse evaluators, "validators," "child advocates," and "therapists." Typically, those who foster false sex-abuse accusations are quick to designate as "experts" such unqualified individuals and typically do not ask questions about their background and degree of expertise. A typical comment by a falsely accusing mother: "I really didn't know whether it happened. I wanted to keep an open mind. So I went to the experts, and they validated that the abuse took place. They told me that children never lie. They told me that if a child says she was sexually abused, it had to happen." Although such mothers will agree that there are bad doctors and bad lawyers, who may do them more harm than good, they rigidly hold to the belief that their "validator" is an expert, or otherwise she would not have been hired by the local child protection service. The fact that the validator may be 21 years old, had a crash course given by a detective, and is working on her first case does not in any way weaken her "expertise." The fact that the "expert," after a 15-minute interview, was willing to come to the conclusion that the child had been sexually abused does not seem to shake the mother's faith in her expertise. The fact that the expert was willing to write on her chart that the father was the abuser—without even the need to make a telephone call to him (let alone see him)—does not shake the mother's faith in the evaluator's ability.

In situations in which there has been a series of such "experts," these mothers may profess, "All I want to do is to get to the bottom of this. I know that the experts have different opinions. This has been somewhat confusing to me. But I'm not going to drop this. I'm going to do everything possible to find out whether this *really* happened. As long as there is one expert who says that it happened, I'm not going to stop." In today's climate it is easy to find many experts who will say "it happened." Such mothers, therefore, can predictably find support for their false accusation. Another method of "finding out" is to put the child in "treatment." The theory here is that "therapy," as an uncovering process that delves ever more deeply into the remotest recesses of the unconscious mind, will ultimately smoke out "the truth." It may take weeks, it may take months, and it may even take years—because the trauma has been so great that recollection of the events must have been deeply repressed. Inevitably, in the hands of such "therapists," the child provides progressively more elaborate and even bizarre disclosures, which confirm that the abuse did indeed take place. This expert who is the child's *therapist*—and therefore should know better than anyone else—is viewed as the final authority whose opinion is considered to be much more "valid" than other examiners who have less intimate knowledge of the inner workings of the child's mind.

A related phenomenon is to view a court's decision as verification because the judge (another "expert" in such matters) could not possibly have issued a restraining order if the sex abuse had not actually taken place. Interruption of visitation or the requirement that visits be monitored is used as "proof" that the abuse did indeed occur. Even though all these precautions were instituted—pending the court's final decision—they are viewed by such mothers as verification by people in authority who have expertise. The fact that the judge made his (her) decision in five minutes in no way lessens the validity of the decision and this mother's respect for it. And, if the court does decide that the father did indeed sexually abuse the children, then the mother views this as "conclusive proof." She then becomes a strong proponent of the view that the criminal system has no imperfections and that judges are faultless in their wisdom and the conclusions to which they come.

Mothers of children who are genuinely abused do not generally have such commitment to experts, whether they be in the mental health or legal professions. They recognize the reality of the situation, namely, that there is a wide variety of individuals, of varying degrees of expertise, ranging from the most incompetent to the most competent. They are likely to ask questions about the training and experience of those who are examining their children and take a more discriminating attitude with regard to their receptivity to the findings of the professionals who evaluate their children.

Indicators Obtained During the Course Of the Evaluation

19. Shame over Revelation of the Abuse   Mothers of children who are genuinely abused are often very ashamed of the fact that their husbands have sexually abused their children. Such shame will manifest itself early in the course of the interviews with the examiner. They will often say that such abuse reflects negatively on the family's reputation and that they have done everything possible to keep the abuse a secret from friends, relatives, and neighbors.

In contrast, mothers who are angry and support false sex-abuse accusations, because they recognize that it can be a powerful weapon in a custody dispute, generally exhibit little if any shame over revelation of the abuse. For some of these mothers, they would be pleased to accept an invitation to discuss the abuse on nationally syndicated television. Commonly, they call the newspapers in order to publicly humiliate their husbands, and they relish the thought of friends and neighbors reading articles about his depravity. Sometimes the newspapers claim that they learned of the abuse from an "anonymous" caller, and sometimes the newspaper refuses to divulge its source. I have seen a few mothers who deny any knowledge whatsoever of the method by which the newspaper learned of the abuse, but the father is convinced that it was his wife who informed the public media. In such situations, the examiner does well to consider the father's version much more likely and the mother's version yet another example of her deceitfulness.

20. Attitude Toward Taking a Lie Detector Test This indicator does *not* relate to the *results* of a lie detector test. Rather, it relates to the receptivity or lack of receptivity to taking the test. Mothers who genuinely believe that the abuse took place are likely to be receptive to taking the test. Those who are consciously fabricating are often quite reluctant to take the test and may utilize their attorneys to protect them from pressure to do so. They recognize that the test (even though not foolproof) may reveal their duplicity. Mothers who are delusional, however, who actually believe that the abuse took place (when there is absolutely no evidence that it did), may offer to take a lie detector test, so convinced are they that their accusation is a valid one. Unfortunately, such mothers, if they do take a lie detector test, may "pass" because they are so convinced that the abuse occurred that they exhibit none of the physiological changes that manifest lying.

My experience has been that the question of a lie detector test being administered for the accused is quite common. In contrast, it is rare for the question to be raised for the accuser. This is a strange phenomenon. All agree that the tests are not foolproof, and most appreciate that there are many courts in which the findings of such tests will not be admitted into evidence. It would seem, therefore, that these drawbacks of the test would apply equally to both the accused and the accuser. In practice, they do not. Rather, the falsely accused person almost routinely requests the tests, its drawbacks notwithstanding. A person suspected of being a false accuser, however, is rarely asked to take a lie detector test. This should not inhibit the evaluator exploring the accuser's attitude toward the lie detector test. It should not discourage the evaluator from using the *attitude* as an indicator.

21. Appreciation of the Importance of Maintenance of the Child's Relationship with the Accused   Mothers who promulgate false sex-abuse accusations are often so angry that they do not appreciate the importance of the child's relationship with the father. They do everything to sever it (often completely) and may view the sex-abuse allegation as a potent mechanism for attaining this goal. Such mothers see nothing wrong with a therapeutic program that encourages frequent displays of vengeful hostility toward the accused, in the service of helping the child let out the anger that is presumably present as a result of the abuse. Such mothers welcome every legal authority that will support their exclusionary maneuvers. Mothers of children who have been genuinely abused are more likely to be appreciative of the father-child relationship, but at times may very well want to discontinue it. In Chapter Eleven I will discuss in detail the issue of the genuinely abused child's relationship with the parent abuser.

The evaluator does well to look into the mother's family background with regard to exclusionary maneuvers toward men, especially her own father. It is very common for people to reproduce family patterns down the generations. I believe it is reasonable to say that a family pattern—no matter how patholog-ical—is likely to be reproduced, professions of regret, denial, and abhorrence of the pattern notwithstanding. Women whose fa-thers were alcoholics are more likely to marry alcoholics, their abhorrence of the disorder notwithstanding. Women whose fathers beat their mothers are more likely to marry men who will beat them, their vows never to do so notwithstanding. Of course, there are complex psychodynamic factors operative in such choices, but the modeling effect is clearly operative. And the same factor operates in divorce. One of the reasons why the divorce rate is burgeoning is that the increase in the divorce rate has been going on long enough (since the post-World-War-II era) that many people divorcing today are the children of parents who are divorced as well.

Accordingly, if a woman's mother excluded her father, the likelihood that the mother will treat her own husband similarly is increased. Often, the similarities are almost uncanny in that they occur at the same point in the relationship, except separated by one generation. It is almost as if there is a compulsion to repeat the pattern, and a sex-abuse accusation can predictably bring about this result. For example, I have seen a number of cases in which the accusing mother's mother separated from her husband because he was sexually molesting his daughter (then at the prekindergarten level). The daughter grows up, marries, and then she (now the adult accuser) accuses her husband of sexually molesting their prekindergarten-aged daughter. Whereas in her own childhood it may very well have been the case that the accuser's father molested her, in these cases I found no evidence that the husbands were molesting their daughters. Having had the experience of having been sexually abused themselves at that age, they anticipated that the same thing would occur one generation later, an anticipation that served as the nidus of a delusion. The husband had to be driven from the home and the child thereby protected from abuses that never occurred. I am not claiming that this is a frequent phenomenon; I am only claiming that therapists should be alert to its existence.

In other cases I have seen, the general family pattern was

one in which the men were basically viewed by the women as sperm donors; once they had fulfilled this function, their services were dispensed with. Either the women routinely divorced their husbands, or, if they remained married, they lived a life in which they ignored them or removed themselves with every possible excuse. Our present hysteria over sex abuse provides mothers in this category with a very powerful weapon for bringing about a quick and predictably effective method of perpetrating these family patterns.

22. The Use of the Code-Term "The Truth" to Refer to the Sex-Abuse Scenario Mention has already been made of the pilgrimage embarked upon by mothers who promulgate false sex-abuse accusations, a pilgrimage whose purpose is to find out "the truth" regarding whether or not the sex abuse really occurred. Actually, they are not looking so much to find out the truth as they are looking for people to substantiate that the sex abuse took place. Those examiners whose version of the truth is that no sex abuse took place are ignored, and they proclaim fidelity to an ever-growing parade of examiners who will verify that the real truth is that the abuse took place. It is not long before the term *the truth* becomes the code-term for the sex-abuse scenario and the child learns this important meaning of the words *the truth*. Accordingly, prior to her appointment with the examiner or "therapist," the child is reminded by the mother to tell "the truth." After a few sessions with a validator, the child learns well the meaning of this term and can be relied upon to pour forth with the litany. One of the purposes of the child's "therapy" is to entrench the truth in the child's psychic structure and help the child get the story "right" in preparation for its presentation in court or to a grand jury. In addition, the truth involves a progressive elaboration of the sexual abuses in order to strengthen the case. The mother and the validator then work in collusion in order to achieve this important goal. I have seen many evaluations in which the following interchange took place (frequently recorded on audio- and videotape):

Validator: Why are you here?
Patient: I'm here to tell you *the truth?*
Validator: What is the truth?
Patient (in sing-song fashion): The truth is that my daddy put his finger in my doo-doo hole, and he put his wee-wee in my mouth, and he put his wee-wee into my sister's pee-pee hole, and he put his wee-wee into my brother's mouth.
Validator: Where did all this happen?
Patient: It happened in my grandma's house while she wasn't looking.

In contrast, one does not generally get such well-rehearsed scenarios from children who were genuinely abused, especially scenarios in which Grandma was facilitating and even orchestrating the sex orgy between her son and his children. Nor is there the use of the shibboleth *the truth* to refer to the description of the sexual abuses.

23. Hysterical and/or Exhibitionistic Personality Mothers who fabricate a sex-abuse allegation are often hysterical and/or exhibitionistic. They typically exaggerate situations, "make mountains out of molehills," and will take every opportunity to broadcast the abuse. They see danger in situations in which others are not concerned. Accordingly, they are likely to see sexual molestation in situations that others consider a normal activity. The child who touches her vulva is not seen as engaging in normal behavior, but must be doing so because she was sexually abused. Hysterics usually need an audience, and this is one of the factors operative in their acquiring a coterie of enablers. They can be very exhibitionistic and dramatic and may do extremely well on the witness stand. Such skilled actresses have sent many men to jail. Judges are taken in by their tears and their theatrical skills. One of the hallmarks of the hysteric is the quick turnoff when there is no longer an audience. (No actress can possibly play to an empty theater.) Accordingly, once off the witness stand, and in the privacy of a small room off the courtroom, they will gloat over the success of their performances.

Some hysterical women are sexually inhibited and project

their own unacceptable sexual impulses onto others. This factor may be operative in their belief that the sex abuse did indeed take place. In contrast, mothers whose children have been genuinely abused are far less likely to be exhibitionistic or histrionic about the abuse; however, they may be sexually inhibited if they are in that category of mothers who were sexually abused as children and who promulgate the sex abuse in their own children.

24. Paranoia   The presence of paranoia not directly related to (or focused on) the abuse increases the likelihood that the sex abuse has become part of a paranoid system. In such cases the conscious fabrication element is less likely than the delusional in bringing about the sex-abuse allegation. Women who were not paranoid prior to the separation may become so, especially after prolonged exposure to divorce and/or custody litigation. The paranoid system may include only her husband and his extended family, and a sex-abuse accusation may become incorporated into the delusional system that centers on him. As is true of paranoid symptoms, the delusions are not changed by confrontations with reality, no matter how compelling.

One of the factors operative in the difficulty one has in changing the paranoid's mind is the vagueness of the accusations. When one tries to "pin down" the paranoid and get specific facts about exactly what the abuses were, the paranoid responds with vagueness, circumstantiality, and evasive answers. This difficulty in pinning down the individual is one of the hallmarks of paranoia. Even a court decision that the husband is not guilty of sex abuse does not usually change such a mother's paranoid ideation regarding the sex abuse. Rather, she may expand the delusional system in order to rationalize the court's decision, for example, she may believe that the judge was paid off by her husband or that his attorneys were "in cahoots" with the judge. And this is one of the typical manifestations of paranoia, namely, that paranoids divide all individuals into two classes of people: those who are with them and those who are against them. Those who are with them are considered wise, noble, and sensitive individuals, and those who are against them are considered to be evil or corrupt. All those who do not provide unswerving loyalty are placed in the evil and corrupt category. In contrast, mothers of children who are genuinely abused are less likely to be paranoid.

I believe that paranoia is much more common than generally appreciated. And this is especially the case when the paranoia confines itself to a relatively narrow area, such as a delusional accusation of child sex abuse. A hint that paranoia may be operative may be provided in a situation in which the mother refuses to allow previously trusted extended family members to supervise the visitation. She may come to believe that the father can easily convince these friends and relatives to allow, facilitate, or engage themselves in sexual activities with the child(ren). And these may be people who by no stretch of the imagination would involve themselves in such behavior. The *Rorschach Test* (Rorschach, 1921) and *Minnesota Multiphasic Personality Inventory (MMPI-2)* (Hathaway and McKinley, 1989) may detect such paranoia and may provide confirmation that it exists in many cases. However, these instruments are not foolproof, and they do not invariably detect paranoia.

25. Enthusiastic Commitment to the Data-Collection Process
Evaluators, especially "validators," and police investigators generally find mothers who are promulgating a false sex-abuse accusation to be extremely cooperative regarding collecting evidence. When their child is with them, their notebooks are ever at hand to ensure that they will be able to jot down verbatim anything the child says that might provide "proof" that the sex abuse took place. Such children have never enjoyed such attention and have never been taken so seriously. Of course, these maneuvers only entrench in the child's mind the notion that the abuse has taken place and reinforces the expression of comments supporting the allegation. Mothers who have previously been otherwise somewhat relaxed and loose now become obsessive-compulsives with regard to keeping these notebooks. The books are brought to the validator's and/or therapist's office in order to ensure that this material becomes focused on in the course of treatment. The presence of such a notebook is one of the

hallmarks of the false accuser. In contrast, mothers of children who have been genuinely abused are rarely as compulsive with regard to such notetaking. They are usually confident that the child herself (himself) will provide the necessary facts.

26. Corroboration of the Child's Sex-Abuse Description in Joint Interview(s)   Mothers of children who falsify will often provide clues to the child in joint interview in order to ensure that the child provides the "right" story. Similarly the child may "check" with the mother, through side glances and gestures, in order to be sure that he (she) is telling the correct story. Obviously, examiners who do not conduct joint interviews will not be able to avail themselves of this important indicator. Mothers of children who are genuinely abused are less likely to send such messages and their children are less likely to need them in joint interview. In this situation the mothers need not provide clues and reminders; they can rely upon the child to provide a credible description.

In Chapter Three I have spoken about the implications of the child's telling "the truth." For programmed children the truth is basically a detailed description of the sex abuse. The child quickly learns that this is a shibboleth for the sex-abuse scenario. If the truth were simply the fact that no sex abuse occurred, then the child would not be brought to an evaluator or "validator" to make the simple statement that nothing at all happened. However, the *truth* is an elaborate statement that may take many interviews to fully "discover." In joint interview with a corroborating mother, she may simply say to the child, "Just tell the truth. That's all I want you do is tell the truth."

I have seen many situations in which child protection workers will keep the accusing mother in the room with the child during the evaluative interview(s). The rationale here often is, "The child was very young and wouldn't have been comfortable speaking with me alone." I have observed videotapes and/or read clinical notes of such interviews and have seen directly the prompting element that was operative here. The child would turn to the mother for corroboration and, in some cases, the mother even corrected the child when she had forgotten her "script."

Competent evaluators, especially those experienced in working with families in which the children have been embroiled in a child custody dispute, recognize well that children involved in such conflicts have a terrible loyalty conflict. Accordingly, they say to each parent what they suspect that parent wants to hear. In the course of evaluations they will provide that scenario desired by the parent who is either in the room or even in the waiting room. Accordingly, one must conduct multiple interviews in which the child is seen alone, with parent A, and with parent B. And this phenomenon is especially important to appreciate when conducting a sex-abuse evaluation. Seeing the child alone enables one to obtain a "purer" story, one uncontaminated by the parental presence. And seeing the child together with the accuser provides the examiner with an opportunity to observe checking, prompting, and other manifestations of programming.

27. Cooperation During the Course of the Evaluation
Mothers of children who are genuinely abused wish to cooperate fully with an impartial examiner, and they in no way impede his (her) investigations. In contrast, mothers who are supporting false accusations are likely to be obstructionistic because they recognize that the more information the examiner has, the more likely he (she) will conclude that the allegation is false. Such obstructionism may manifest itself by refusal to sign permission slips necessary for the review of reports by other examiners, cancellation of appointments, refusal to participate in joint interviews, lateness, and other maneuvers designed to impede and even bring about a discontinuation of the evaluation. It is for such mothers that the provisions document (Addendum I)—which I require to be signed before serving as an impartial examiner—was designed. It requires a court order—designating me the impartial examiner—before I embark upon an evaluation. It ensures that all parties will be required to cooperate from the awareness that obstructionism will be reported to the court and will compromise significantly the impeding party's position in the subsequent litigation. Occasionally, a mother of a child who has been genuinely abused will also be uncooperative because of the fear that the

examiner might not conclude that abuse did indeed take place. This occasional exception notwithstanding, mothers of children who have been genuinely abused are usually far more cooperative than those who are promoting false sex-abuse accusations.

28. Belief in the Preposterous   Falsely accusing mothers are likely to accept as valid the most preposterous statements made by the child. They are similar to the validators in this regard, and the two together often involve themselves in a folie-à-deux relationship. They utilize as well the wide variety of rationalizations that serve to make credible the incredible. They selectively ignore information that might shed doubt on certain elements in the sex-abuse scenario. They pathologize the normal and utilize the mechanism of retrospective reinterpretation in order to justify the sex-abuse accusation.

Good examples of the degree to which accusers can stretch their imaginations are the rationalizations provided for obstructing the father's visitations with the children. Such mothers will often claim that he is not to be trusted alone—for one minute—so strong is his compulsion to sexually abuse the children. All a supervisor need do is turn his (her) back, and the father is likely to engage in lightning-speed sexual molestation. His parents, who previously may have had a good relationship with the children's mother, are now viewed as unreliable with regard to protecting the children from their son's compulsion to sexually abuse them. Even in some relatively public situations as birthday parties, he is not to be trusted—so skilled and cunning is he regarding quick sex.

Such women do not seem to appreciate that the father, even if so skillful, would have to be retarded and/or psychotic to attempt sexual molestation at a time when he is being carefully scrutinized as a sex abuser and every scintilla of potentially validating data is being collected by a parade of people, most of whom are convinced he sexually abused the children. The realities are that fathers in such situations strictly steer clear of any situation that might be interpreted by zealous evaluators as "proof" of their having sexually abused their children. Even if there is no formal supervision, they generally consider it insane to bathe or undress with their children, even under supervised conditions. Even separated and divorced fathers who have not been accused of sex abuse are becoming increasingly hesitant to bathe or undress with their children, so widespread is the sex-abuse hysteria that we have witnessed since the early 1980s.

29. Expansion of the Sex-Abuse Danger to the Extended Family of the Accused Whereas previously the extended family of the accused father may have had reasonably good relationships with the accusing mother, following the promulgation of a false sex-abuse accusation, the father's parents and other members of his extended family become somehow tainted. On occasion I have seen them to be directly accused as on-site facilitators and/or direct participants in the sexual abuse. More commonly, however, some degree of sanity remains in the minds of these mothers and they do not go so far afield. Rather, they just distance themselves from these people and consider them to have been indirect facilitators of the abuse. In situations in which the court has ordered the father's visitations to be supervised, pending a plenary hearing, the father often proposes his parents as reasonable supervisors. Typically, mothers who falsely accuse quickly reject this proposal. Common reasons: "He's very manipulative, and I can see him talking them into letting him be alone with them" or "They're old people, and I don't trust them to keep an eye on him all the time." Such extension of the danger and such exclusion of the extended family of the father are two of the hallmarks of the false sex-abuse accusation. When there has been genuine sex abuse, the parents of the abusing father are quite sympathetic and may be brought in to be of assistance.

30. Duplicity in Aspects of the Evaluation Not Directly Related to the Sex-Abuse Accusation One way of assessing the honesty of an interviewee regarding the sex-abuse accusation is to determine whether there have been duplicities exhibited in other areas of the evaluation, not directly related to the sex-abuse accusation. A person who is dishonest in one area is more likely to be dishonest in another. This relates to the legal principle: *Falsus in uno, falsus in omnibus* (false in one [thing], false in all). Accordingly, mothers of children who falsely accuse are more likely to exhibit dishonesty in other aspects of the evaluation, whereas mothers of children who are genuinely abused are less likely to exhibit duplicity in areas of the evaluation unrelated to the sex-abuse issue.

I am not referring here to deceits alleged by one party against the other, deceits that manifested themselves prior to or outside of the evaluation. Rather, I am referring to deceits directly observed by the examiner, especially those admitted to by the deceitful person. A common area in which an examiner may directly observe deceit relates to the payment of fees. The party may promise to pay and the payment is not forthcoming. Excuses may be provided: "I forgot" and "It slipped my mind." Or the common, "the-check-is-in-the-mail" maneuver may be used. Somehow the postal service is particularly inefficient with regard to this party's check. Or checks may bounce with the excuse, "Oh, I made an error in calculating my balance." These lower-order deceits may not carry much weight in one's written report, and I may not make reference to them, especially when I have more compelling examples of deceit. My main reason for omitting them is that there is the *possibility* that the excuse or rationalization has validity. One wants "harder-ammunition" arguments that are irrefutable, especially in the course of one's testimony.

A higher-order deceit is one in which the examiner is convinced that he (she) made a certain statement to a parent and the parent denies vehemently that the statement was ever made. Having corroboration from the other parent, who was present in the room at the time, certainly adds weight to the examiner's conclusion that the denying parent is being deceitful. However, even here, it is still a matter of two opinions versus one opinion, and the situation still leaves some room for doubt. An even better example is an *action* (as opposed to a statement) that the examiner has directly observed himself (herself). I remember one situation in which I was seeing a child alone while the mother was in the waiting room. When I opened the door to bring her in, I found her just outside the door, trying to listen. I told her that I would prefer her to sit in the waiting room, because her presence at the door would compromise my evaluation in a number of ways. The woman agreed and sat down in the waiting room. About 15 minutes later, when I went to the door again (I was not checking on her), I found her once again standing at the door. When I once again asked her to please cooperate she replied, "This is a free country and I can stand where I want." We not only see here an example of lack of cooperation, but deceitfulness as well.

Another example: In one case, in my initial conversation with the parents, I learned that the former housekeeper was allegedly an observer to the sex abuse and was therefore an important person for me to interview. I asked both parents to please promise me that they would not say anything to her about the sex abuse prior to my interview. They both promised me that they would not. I also informed them that if either of them did speak with her *substantively* with regard to my interview, it would not only compromise my interview; such lack of cooperation would be indicated in my report to the court. When I interviewed the housekeeper, she told me that the mother had said to her comments along these lines: "I promised Dr. Gardner that I wouldn't speak with you before he spoke with you. So I don't want you to tell him that I am speaking with you. I only want to help *remind* you about what you had seen." The housekeeper then attempted to exonerate her former employer by rationalizing her action as simply an attempt to remind her in order that she might provide me with more accurate information.

When I subsequently confronted the mother with what the housekeeper had said, she was quite upset over the housekeeper's divulgence, admitted that she had promised not to talk with her in this way, and admitted that she had even told the housekeeper not to divulge her preliminary conversations to me. It was clear that she was very upset with the housekeeper's disclosure of the mother's deceit. However, she rationalized her action by stating that it was more important that she get accurate information to me than to keep her promise. We see here a Class-A kind of deceit, one that carries great weight with regard to satisfying this criterion.

Joint interviews are especially useful in "smoking out" such duplicities. No matter how good our memories are, we generally do not recall all the specifics about an evaluation as well as the participants. They have first-hand experience with the issues being discussed and are highly motivated to recall important material. Accordingly, one party may say, "Doctor, what he (she) is saying now is very different from what she (he) told you three weeks ago in our joint interview." Many examiners would not have recalled the inconsistency, and it would have "passed them by." We see here an excellent example of the value of the joint interview and yet another reason why examiners do well to insist upon them—preferably by court order—before agreeing to embark on an evaluation.

COMMON PSYCHODYNAMIC FACTORS OPERATIVE IN MOTHERS WHO PROVIDE FALSE SEX-ABUSE ACCUSATIONS

I present here some of the more common psychodynamic factors operative in mothers who initiate and/or promulgate false sex-abuse accusations. Once again, I focus in this chapter primarily on mothers whose accusations arise in the context of viciously contested child custody disputes. In Chapter Nine I will describe those psychodynamic factors commonly seen in parents whose accusations arise in the context of nursery school and day-care centers. Although there is certainly overlap, there are psychodynamic factors that are unique to each situation.

Rage and Vengeance

There are many factors that may contribute to divorcing women's rage. Many feel abandoned and recognize that their situation after the divorce is likely to be fraught with frustration and humiliation. Their chances of remarriage are less than those of their former husbands. Their economic situation is generally less favorable and this, too, is a source of ongoing frustration. Their spouses may have already been involved with a new woman and this cannot but contribute to a sense of jealous rage, lending justification to the observation that "Hell hath no fury like a woman scorned." Elsewhere (Gardner, 1992a) I have discussed in detail other sources of anger in divorcing women, anger that may contribute to their children's developing a parental alienation syndrome—a disorder from which false sex-abuse accusations often emerge.

As a derivative of the enormous rage engendered by the aforementioned factors, it is not surprising that many of these mothers are extremely vengeful. Depriving their spouses of the children—the fathers' most treasured possessions—is probably the most effective method for wreaking such vengeance. Accordingly, one usually sees a progression of exclusionary maneuvers and obstructive activities, all designed to reduce access of the father to the children. And a sex-abuse accusation probably represents the most powerful maneuver for effecting such exclusion. It is the one that is most likely to bring about quick removal of the father, as well as a significant curtailment, interruption, and even cessation of visitations. It could also reasonably result in his incarceration.

Projection and Paranoia

As mentioned, I believe that paranoia is much more common than is generally appreciated. Furthermore, paranoid decompensation is quite common in association with divorce litigation. Divorce litigation is one of the greatest stresses that people can be subjected to, and it is no surprise that a wide variety of psychiatric disorders can emerge in the context of such psychological trauma. Elsewhere (Gardner, 1986) I have described in detail some of the more common manifestations of such psychiatric deterioration. Paranoid deterioration is especially likely to take place in preparanoid personalities. Such personality problems may very well have played a role in bringing about the divorce because of the oversuspiciousness, constant state of vigilance, and the nitpicking and faultfinding that preparanoid individuals often exhibit.

Once the parties have embarked upon a course of divorce litigation, paranoid features are likely to become elaborated. There are indeed secret meetings between clients and lawyers in which the individuals are literally "plotting strategies" to utilize against one another. Each party may be making detailed notes about the other's statements and activities. There may be little if any corroboration of distortions, corroborations that might lessen the elaboration of paranoid delusions. One could almost say to each parent, "You are not paranoid; he (she) really is plotting against you." And the problem is further compounded if the paranoid parent is represented by a paranoid attorney. Unfortunately, preparanoid and paranoid types tend to gravitate toward the law because it is a field in which people can obtain protection from the various indignities that they may be subjected to in life.

The generalized paranoid thinking engendered and intensified by the litigation may serve as a foundation for a sex-abuse spinoff. This is especially the case if the mother has had sexual problems in the categories already described in this chapter, experiences like having been sexually abused as a child, experiences that engender enormous rage toward men, and the rejections of divorce.

Central to paranoia is the mechanism of projection. Basically, in projection one attributes to others one's own thoughts and feelings that one wishes to disown. The individual is basically saying, "It is not I who harbor within me these terrible thoughts and feelings; it is he (she)." Accordingly, by the process of projection the individual assuages guilt over the unacceptable impulses. A sexually inhibited person, someone who is uncomfortable with his (her) sexual thoughts and feelings, may project them outward onto another party and thereby assuage the guilt that would otherwise be felt in association with conscious awareness of such tendencies. In a more complex way the paranoid projection enables the projector to be a vicarious recipient of such sexual activities.

A mother, for example, who cannot allow herself to accept the fact that she still may harbor the desire for sexual activities with her now-hated spouse, may project these feelings onto her daughter and develop the delusion that her husband has sexually molested the child. It is as if each time she entertains the pedophilic fantasy (of her husband molesting her daughter), she satisfies vicariously (by projecting herself into her daughter's position) her own desire to be the recipient of her spouse's sexual overtures. Sometimes such a fantasy extends to include other molesters such as extended family members and other friends and relatives. This I believe is one of the factors operative in the sexual orgies believed to take place in nursery schools and day-care centers (see Chapter Nine). Or, the projection may involve vicarious identification with the abuser. In this way, the accuser satisfies her own desires to be perpetrating the sexual act herself. This factor may also be operative in nursery school and day-care center situations (in Chapter Nine I discuss this situation in much greater detail).

Green and Schetky (1988) points out that such mothers may have previously accused the hated spouse of sexual misconduct with other family members and other women. The child sex-abuse allegation, then, is an extension of previous jealousy delusions. She describes how these mothers coerce their children into a folie-à-deux relationship in which the paranoid delusion is a central element. Yates and Musty (1988) use the term *projective identification* to refer to this process in false child sex-abuse accusations. They use the term to refer not only to the projective element involved, but in the identification of the accuser with the party who is considered to be perpetrating the abuse. As a result, the accuser tends to dominate, devalue, and/or control the accused. Here again, what is being devalued is the accuser's own sexual impulses. Of the 46 accusing parents studied by Wakefield and Underwager (1990), four were diagnosed as suffering with paranoid personality disorder. I myself would consider the paranoid factor to be more common than found by Wakefield and Underwager.

Hysteria

In the late 19th century Freud considered hysterical symptoms to be related to repressed sexual urges, sexual urges that could not be allowed into conscious awareness because of guilt. Although there are many women who warrant the hysteria label, not all are sexually inhibited. I focus here on that subcategory of hysterical women (those who coincide with Freud's group) who indeed do have sexual inhibition problems. They, like the afore-mentioned paranoids, tend to use the mechanism of projection for assuaging the guilt they feel over their sexual thoughts and feelings. In addition, women who suffer with this disorder exhibit histrionic features and tend to exaggerate in dramatic fashion. These qualities contribute to a false sex-abuse accusation. These women tend to exaggerate the sexual implications of normal genital findings and see sexuality when in fact it does not exist, again by the mechanism of projection. They not only exaggerate the import of the evidence but exhibit exaggerated reactions to the implications of the alleged sexual encounters. They scream, rant, rave, and exhibitionistically elaborate on the suffering they and the child feel over the alleged molestation.

Another contributory factor relates to the ambient hysteria that is widespread at this time (Gardner, 1991a; Wakefield and Underwager, 1990). This ambient hysteria may contribute to the hysteria of some of these women. This is one of the characteristics of the mass-hysteria phenomenon, namely, that mildly hysterical individuals are likely to get swept up in the ambient hysteria, which then has the effect of escalating the hysterical reactions of the predisposed. If, however, the child is part of a group of allegedly sexually molested children, such as is found in the day-care or nursery school situation, then these mothers very early become swept up in that hysterical scene (I will discuss this factor more in Chapter Nine).

Ross and Blush (1990) consider the histrionic personality pattern to be one of the more common patterns seen in mothers who claim sex abuse in the context of a child custody dispute. These mothers manifest symptoms of what they refer to as the SAID syndrome (Sex Abuse In Divorce syndrome). Typically, these mothers are not able to give specific factual information to corroborate their sex-abuse accusations; rather, their descriptions are "vague, circular, and nonspecific responses which emphasize the feeling tone and impressions of the situation." Their interpretations of the child's behavior tend to be extensions of her own feelings. Their exaggeration of the import of the evidence and their feelings of victimization create a situation of ongoing hypervigilance that may result in frequent trips to pediatricians for medical verification and frequent requests for detailed and unnecessary medical procedures without regard for the effects on the child of such examinations. Six of the 46 accusing parents studied by Wakefield and Underwager (1990) had histrionic disorders.

Reproduction of the Family Pattern

Most agree that parents serve as models for their children and thereby play an important role in determining their behavior. The development of language is one of the more obvious examples of this phenomenon. A child born in an American family, where both parents speak only English, is not going to spontaneously start speaking in Chinese. And the opposite is obviously true for the child born in China. What is not often appreciated is that psychopathological processes are similarly copied, even processes that are against the best interests of all concerned. Parents with phobias are likely to have children who are themselves phobic. Even unconscious processes are likely to get transmitted down to children via the children's modeling themselves after behavioral manifestations that are derivatives of the unconscious processes. Paranoid parents are likely to produce paranoid children. Although the psychodynamic mechanisms that produce the paranoia in the parents may be somewhat different from those that produce the paranoia in the children, the symptomatic manifestations may be identical. In a similar way, family patterns and expectations are likely to be transmitted to children. If many individuals in a child's extended family divorce in the course of the child's upbringing, it is likely that the children in such families will divorce when older. A girl who grows up without a father may not have any particular commitment to the notion that fathers play an important role in the upbringing of children. Accordingly, she may not consider her husband to be an important figure in her children's lives and may divorce him for frivolous reasons. His attempts to involve himself may be viewed with suspicion and even anxiety because of the strangeness of such interest. A woman's family pattern may have been one in which men were viewed as useless and extraneous, with the result that a long pattern of exclusionary maneuvers may have been utilized to remove males from the family scene. Such a woman's father and brothers, although in the home, were viewed more like pieces of furniture than active participants in her upbringing. Such a woman may have little ambivalence in situations that bring about considerations of divorce. Divorce is certainly one way of removing a man from the family scene. However, divorce may be costly and time consuming, and it may not always achieve the result of expelling the man from the home. A sex-abuse accusation can achieve this much more quickly and effectively.

A girl may have been sexually abused by her father at age three. She grows up considering that age to be a particularly vulnerable one and hopes that when she has her own child, she will be able to protect her daughter from a similar experience. Accordingly, even before she marries, she may be anticipating that her future child will be sexually abused at that "vulnerable" age. Subsequently, the woman marries and has a daughter. Even at the time of the daughter's birth she may think along these lines: "I wish it was a boy. Girls are more likely to be abused by their fathers. Before long I'm going to have to start keeping an eye on him." And, as the child approaches the age of three, the mother is ever alert for the signs and symptoms of sex abuse. Under those circumstances, it is not surprising that, when the child reaches age three, the mother will conclude that sex abuse has occurred, even with the most absurd and unconvincing "evidence." Her prophecy has been fulfilled; but it has been self-fulfilled. Although other factors may have contributed to the false sex-abuse accusation, the compulsion to repeat the family pattern is certainly operative. This particular factor in producing false sex-abuse accusations has not been given the attention it deserves.

The Sperm-Donor Concept of Males

Related to the reproduction-of-the-family-pattern maneuver is the male-as-sperm-donor concept. There are women who view men primarily as sperm donors and little else. Although many would also want the male to serve as a provider of food, clothing, and shelter, these contributions may be of secondary importance to these women. It is probable that this concept has a genetic foundation. Both men and women certainly have reproductive instincts that are fueled by sexual drives. Although the sexual drives may very well be equal in intensity in the two sexes, the ways in which these instincts are expressed behaviorally are very different. Women are more likely to become sexually aroused in situations that involve emotional bonding in an exclusive relationship with a male. Men, in contrast, are more likely to be promiscuous with regard to their sexual cravings. In short, women want husbands, and men want "girls." Women want marriage and children, and men want to "get laid." (In Chapter One of this book I have described what I consider to be the genetic factors operative in these gender differences.)

Traditionally, women have been most attracted to men who will not only impregnate them and satisfy thereby their maternal instincts, but men who will also be providers and protectors. Although men certainly have gravitated toward women who could provide them with gratification of their paternal instincts, their role as provider and protector has been of significant, if not greater, importance. For women, the craving for emotional bonding that is so important in the sexual situation gets carried down to their emotional bonding with children. And this, of course, enhances the likelihood that she will feed and protect the children and enlist the aid of her mate when they are in trouble. But women are weak and somewhat helpless in the face of enemies. Accordingly, somebody has to "stand guard" and protect the family as well as go out there and find food. If the male's bonding with the children were stronger than his commitment to serving as provider and protector, the children might not survive because of the compromises of the father's commitment to food acquisition and protection.

Residua of this genetic programming exists today, environmental changes notwithstanding. The male as protector is no longer as great a need as it was in the past; he doesn't have to stand guard very much any more. Even his role as provider can be taken over by others: friends, relatives, and even social services (such as welfare). Although his role as sperm donor can also be substituted for by artificial insemination, most women do not go to the trouble and expense of utilizing this alternative method of impregnation (although some certainly do). Besides, for most women it is much more fun to do it in the natural way, which also provides her with the opportunity to select the father of the children. There are many women, then, whose basic concept of the man is that he is the sperm donor; after he has served this purpose, his services can be dispensed with entirely. There are many women who are very overt about this view of males, but there are others who are less so. There are women who will say that they cannot *really* talk with men, and they are much more bonded with women. (This is *one* of the reasons why *some* women become lesbians.) Some women in this category get artificially inseminated. Others select the mate, conceive, and then part ways with the individual. (In some cases the man knows what has gone on; in other cases he does not.) Some women who subscribe to the sperm-donor concept of the male's role do actually marry and then use the man for the purposes of providing food, clothing, and shelter for the children. However, they then have little to do with their husbands. Others marry for a short period and then divorce. Such women may provide a wide variety of reasons for expelling the man, e.g., "I don't love him any more" and "We just went down separate paths in life." However, the real reason that these women are divorcing is that the man has served his purpose—like the fish who deposits sperm on the eggs and then swims away.

For most women, divorce may not be an easy procedure, especially because of its expense and grief. A sex-abuse accusation can solve this problem almost instantaneously. The sperm donor is not only quickly removed from the house, but he may be incarcerated for many years. Accordingly, he will not be coming around the house anymore, "bothering" his wife and their children. I believe that the concept of the male as a walking sperm donor is far more widespread than is commonly appreciated. It is related to the previously described reproduction-of-the-family-

pattern mechanism in that the woman's mother may have operated in accordance with the same principle. Because of its
ubiquity, examiners do well to consider this factor in evaluations
designed to determine whether a sex-abuse accusation is true or
false.

Borderline Personality Disorder

Another subcategory of women who provide false accusations are those who are prepsychotic and/or fall in the category of
borderline personality disorder. Blush and Ross (1987) and Ross
and Blush (1990) consider these women to have impaired reality
testing that interferes significantly with their functioning. They
consider this type to be a degeneration of the aforementioned
hysterical personality disorder, a deterioration that may come
about in response to the stresses of the divorce. Characteristically,
they present with *bizarre* descriptions of historical and anecdotal
evidence. Many peculiarities are to be found in descriptions of
their past history, e.g., "beginning menses at five years of age,
having two children without ever having had intercourse with the
estranged spouse, and having a name entirely different from her
legal birth name." My own experience has been that these
women, under the stresses of the custody dispute, may deterio-
rate into overt psychosis and exhibit, in the context of such
psychosis, psychotic symptoms including paranoia. The rage and
frustration that fuel their deterioration bring about the decompensation and loss of reality testing that contribute to the development of a false sex-abuse accusation.

Naiveté and/or Intellectual Impairment

I am convinced that some of the women who promulgate
false sex-abuse accusations are individuals easily swept up with
the trends that are in vogue at the time and are easily led. Some
are passive-dependent types and so are quite likely to believe
what any authority tells them. They, like many people in this
world (unfortunately), just "go along with the crowd." We are
much more like sheep than we would like to believe, but

politicians and many leaders appreciate this principle quite well. Six of the 46 accusing parents studied by Wakefield and Underwager (1990) were given the diagnosis of dependent personality disorders. These are people who by no stretch of the imagination could be considered to be independent thinkers. Rather, they are quite dependent on any authority who presents himself (herself) as an expert. And these include some of the most incompetent and fanatic individuals, such as are sometimes seen in child protection services and in police investigatory agencies. I suspect that if one were able to get the average IQ of all women in child custody disputes who promulgate a false sex-abuse accusation, and compare them with women in a control group of mothers who are also litigating for custody but who do not allege sex abuse, the average IQ of the false accusers would be lower than that of the average nonaccuser.

As is true of all generalizations, there are exceptions. Although I still hold to my belief that the *average* mother who falsely accuses her husband is of lower IQ than the average nonaccuser, there is a subcategory of false accusers who are much brighter than the average. I have come across a few women of extremely high intelligence (one in the 99.99 level on the WAIS-R). These women are very skillful and cunning. They easily seduce inexperienced and naive examiners and interrogators into believing that the sex abuse occurred. They are very quick to pick up from these examiners the criteria that they are utilizing to differentiate between true and false accusations, and they make sure to feed them the specific information that will bring about the conclusion that the abuse did occur. When providing depositions and when testifying in court, they very skillfully portray themselves as open-minded, as only wanting to find out "the truth," and playact this role in an extremely convincing manner. However, if one separates their actions from their words, it is not difficult to see how they have promulgated the false accusation from the outset. Examiners do well to recognize this category of women who falsely accuse sex abuse and not be seduced by their seemingly irrefutable logic and often clever rationalizations.

CONCLUSIONS

Just as there is no typical profile of the child who is sexually abused, or of the pedophile, there is no typical profile of the false accuser. Even within the context of the child custody dispute—a situation in which false accusations are common—there is still no typical profile. As is true of the other two parties involved in the false sex-abuse accusation (the accused and the alleged child victim), there are indicators that can help the evaluator determine whether the accuser's accusation is true or false. I have listed here 30 such indicators. The greater the number of false indicators present, the greater the likelihood the accusation is false. There is no cutoff point, and it is unlikely that any false accuser is going to get a "perfect score."

Furthermore, I must once again emphasize the importance of the evaluator's doing everything possible to examine all three parties involved: the accuser, the accused, and the alleged child victim. The failure to interview all three compromises significantly the evaluation. Furthermore, the failure to see all three deprives the evaluator of the opportunity for joint interviews, so crucial to the determination of whether the accusation is true or false. After all, the best person to cross-examine the accuser is the accused. The accused knows better than even the most skillful evaluators the signs and symptoms of the accuser's deceitfulness. Utilizing third parties such as lawyers or mental health professionals to conduct such cross-examinations is far less efficient and reliable than allowing the accuser himself (herself) to conduct such an inquiry.

I recognize that the goal of seeing all three parties is much more easily accomplished in civil cases than in criminal cases. For the reader who is not appreciative of this difference, most divorce lawsuits are litigated in civil courts. If the sex-abuse accusation has not been brought to the attention of the police and/or if a decision has been made not to prosecute criminally, the sex-abuse allegation may still be heard in the civil court in association with the custody/visitation proceedings. If, however, the criminal authorities have stepped in, then there may be parallel proceedings in both the civil and criminal courts. For reasons that go far beyond the purposes of this book, it is extremely difficult to achieve the goal of seeing all three parties when working within the criminal justice system. Under such circumstances, the evaluator should still do everything possible to achieve this goal, and when it is not achieved (the usual situation), then utilize whatever other materials may be available, materials such as depositions, trial testimony, videotapes, audiotapes, etc.

In closing, I would like to mention a tactic used by Richard Y. Feder, a family court judge in Dade County, Florida. When a woman embroiled in a vicious child custody dispute brings up a sex-abuse accusation—after a series of other accusations have not proved successful for excluding her hated spouse from the children—he informs her that he is certainly willing to hear the case. However, he warns her in advance that should he conclude that the sex-abuse accusation is false, she will be deprived of primary custodial status. His experience has been that the vast majorities of such accusations are then withdrawn. I believe there is much merit to Judge Feder's approach here. It is an extremely effective way of differentiating—very quickly— between true and false accusations. I have heard of other judges who have instituted this policy as well.

Mental health evaluators, of course, have no such power and so they could not themselves utilize this "differentiating criterion." They can, however, utilize it in a less definitive fashion, namely, including in their report a statement that the false sex-abuse accusation should be considered a serious parental deficiency because it is clearly a form of emotional abuse of children and a manifestation of cruelty and sadistic behavior directed toward a spouse. Accordingly, evaluators should recommend that the court give this deficiency serious consideration when weighing the pros and cons of primary custodial assignment. Although I would not go so far as to consider the utilization of a false accusation to automatically deprive a falsely accusing parent of primary custody, I would certainly consider it a serious parental deficiency in the custodial considerations conducted by both mental health and legal professionals. I think judges would do well to handle such cases like Judge Feder. If more were to do so, there would be fewer false accusations.

☐ FIVE
MEDICAL FINDINGS, THE PENILE PLETHYSMOGRAPH, AND THE POLYGRAPH

MEDICAL FINDINGS

INTRODUCTION

Interestingly, up until a few years ago there was very little published in the medical literature on the physical findings consistent with child sex abuse. Furthermore, there was even less published on normal findings in nonabused children. Moreover, there were no extensive studies on what the normal hymen of the nonabused child looks like. Some claimed that the normal hymen is circular and that *any* irregularity is an indicator of something having been inserted into the vaginal canal. Others claimed that there is a wide variety of irregularities within the normal range. But even those in the latter group were not able to provide specific experimental data regarding the frequency of each of these irregularities. There was even controversy regarding the size of the normal hymenal ring at various ages. Until recently, there were no extensive studies in which measurements were taken. And even the studies that *were* done were flawed by the fact that the investigators did not take into consideration the fact that the hymenal orifice varies in size with the position the child assumes when the examination is being conducted, as well as the degree to which the child's legs are spread by the examiner. Similarly, there was no good information regarding the differences between the normal anus and the anus that has been subjected to sexual abuse.

In spite of our relative ignorance in this realm, physicians have been asked with increasing frequency to provide the definitive "proof" regarding whether or not sexual abuse has taken place. This has been the case even though most people who are knowledgeable about child sex abuse recognize that in many cases there will be no physical findings because the perpetrator has not done anything more than caressed the child. However, the need for such verification has been strong, so strong that the objectivity of both those who make the request and those physicians who have responded has been compromised. In response to this need, pediatricians, pediatric gynecologists, and people from other branches of medicine (such as internal medicine and family practice) have become "experts" on child sex abuse in recent years. Those who confirm sex abuse in the vast majority of cases referred to them are generally attractive to prosecutors, who can rely on them to provide the "definitive medical evidence," that is, the "proof" that sex abuse indeed took place. Those who rarely find sex abuse are likely to be engaged by defense attorneys who invite them to testify that the child is "normal" and that there was "no evidence for sex abuse." Although there are people who claim that they are completely neutral, my experience has been that most people who are doing this kind of work have a reputation (whether warranted or not) for being in either of the two camps.

There are doctors (even pediatricians) who claim that any inflammation of a little girl's vulva is a manifestation of sex abuse. Most, however, claim that this is an extremely common finding and can result from sweat, tight pants, certain kinds of soap, and the occasional mild rubbing (sometimes masturbatory) activity of the normal girl. There are some who hold that the normal hymen is a perfect circle (or close to it), without any irregularities. It follows, then, that if any irregularities are found, these must have been artificially created by the insertion of something, possibly a finger, possibly a penis, or possibly something else (like a crayon or pencil). There are others who claim that the normal hymen is most often not a circle and there are irregularities, tags, and bumps. Others hold that these irregularities (sometimes referred to as serrated hymenal orifices) are within the normal range of hymenal variation. Some claim that a three-year-old girl's vagina can accommodate an adult's fingers and even penis without necessarily showing signs of physical trauma, other than the production of the aforementioned irregularities, tags, and bumps. Others claim that the insertion of an adult male penis into a three-year-old girl's vagina will produce severe pain, significant bleeding, and deep lacerations, and that the insertion of crayons and pencils at that age is extremely rare because of the pain and trauma that such insertion will produce.

There are significant differences of opinion regarding what is the normal size of the hymenal opening, and this, of course, bears directly on the question of abuse. Most agree that there have not been large studies of many children at different ages with regard to what the normal hymen looks like, its size, and whether or not it is indeed circular. Furthermore, all do agree that the older the child, the greater the likelihood the vaginal opening will accommodate a penis without significant trauma. Thus, by the age of nine or ten, one does not get the same degree of trauma that one may get at younger ages. Most agree, as well, that children of nine and ten, whose vaginal orifices are still small, could still be brought to the point of intercourse with an adult by gradual stretching of the vagina in the course of repeated experiences in which progressively larger objects (fingers, and ultimately a penis) are inserted.

There are some who hold that a certain type of dilatation ("winking") of the anal mucosa is pathognomonic of penile penetration into the anus. There are others who claim that such dilatation is normal. (Here I am with the group that holds that such puckering is most often normal and is not a manifestation of sex abuse.)

The net result of this situation is that there may be sharply divided opinions among physicians regarding whether a particular child has been sexually abused. However, this does not stop each side from bringing in a parade of adversary physicians who predictably provide the "proof" that the child was sexually abused or that there is "no evidence" of sexual abuse. Another result of this situation is that many doctors are making a lot of money, especially because providing court testimony can be quite remunerative.

DEFINITION OF TERMS

It goes way beyond the purposes of this chapter to discuss in detail the wide variety of medical terms that may be used in the examination of a child who is being evaluated for sex abuse. I will focus here on certain terms that are frequently seen and warrant understanding by those who read such reports. Because girls are much more frequently subjected to sex abuse than boys, and because controversies regarding the signs of sex abuse are much greater in girls than boys, most of the comments I make here relate to the physical examination of girls. I will make the assumption, also, that the reader has a basic familiarity with the female genitalia and is familiar with such terms as labia majora, labia minora, clitoris, urethral meatus (orifice), hymenal orifice, and vaginal walls.

Examination Positions

Most often there are two positions described for a girl's examination, the supine frog-leg position and the prone knee-chest position. When examined in the supine frog-leg position, the child is on her back and the legs spread apart in "frog-leg" fashion. In the prone knee-chest position, the child's abdomen is close to the table and she is supported by her knees and chest. McCann (1988) emphasizes the importance of the child's chest touching the table and the child's back in a relaxed position. Examination of the vagina and cervix (without the use of a speculum) is more easily accomplished in young children in the prone knee-chest position. Sometimes a third position is utilized, the supine knee-chest position. Here the child lies on her back, puts her legs together, flexes her thighs at her hips, and is asked to hug her knees to her chest. I will make further comments on these positions below. According to Muram (1989a), it is important for the examiner to examine the child within one week of the alleged assault. It is in that period that residual bruises and inflammation are more likely to be present. Beyond that time these associated findings are likely to disappear.

Hymenal Configurations

There are a wide variety of hymenal orifices and configurations. So great is their variation that some orifices do not easily lend themselves into being categorized. Furthermore, there is no strict standardization with regard to the names of the various kinds of openings. Accordingly, different examiners may use different names for the same hymenal configuration. As will be described below, the way in which the child is positioned may affect the hymenal configuration and thereby affect the name used by the examiner. I describe here the most common types of vaginal orifices. Next to each name I have placed in parentheses other terms that are often used for the same configuration.

> **Annular (Circumferential, Cuff-like, Central)** This is the simplest configuration. The hymenal orifice is represented by a relatively even circle. Basically, it is a circular hole that can vary in diameter from almost a pinpoint to an enlarged orifice that leaves practically no hymen at all, only a rim. The cuff-like configuration is also annular, yet there is a thickening at the circumference of the orifice. Most competent examiners agree that the perfect circle type of hymen is not common.
>
> **Crescentic (Horseshoe, U-Shaped, Posterior Rim, Semilunar)** The hymenal orifice is represented by a half-moon or crescent. The bottom of the U-shape, however, is at the posterior position (closest to the anus). The hymenal tissue, then, can appear as if it were hanging down from above (the anterior position).

Redundant (Denticular, Folded, Fimbriated, Serrated) Here the configuration is one in which tooth-like (denticular) tags of varying size project into the hymenal orifice. When these are relatively small, they give a saw-tooth (serrated) appearance. Because they are directed inward from the hymenal rim, they are called fimbriated (fringed).

The redundant configuration is quite common. The hymenal tissue projections are commonly referred to as *tags* and *bumps*. Estrogen has the effect of thickening the hymen and increasing the formation of these redundant projections into the hymenal orifice. Accordingly, the prepubertal girl is likely to have more such redundancies than younger girls. The spaces between these projections are often referred to as *notches* and *clefts*. These are to be differentiated from *tears* and *lacerations*, which suggest the insertion (partial or complete) of some object (animate or inanimate) beyond the hymen into the vaginal cavity. Whereas notches and clefts do not extend outward to the base (or periphery) of the hymen, tears and lacerations frequently do. And this is one of the important differentiating criteria between them. Furthermore, notches and clefts have rounded edges, whereas tears and lacerations have sharp edges.

Vascularity of the tissue around notches and clefts is even, smooth, and continuous with the vascularity and color of the rest of the hymen. Just as estrogen increases redundancy, it also has the effect of thickening the hymen and obscuring thereby the fine lacy vascular pattern typical of younger girls. This thickening also results in a loss of the translucency of the hymenal tissues, and the thickening gives the appearance of rounding of the edge of the hymenal membrane. Tears and lacerations are surrounded by tissue of different color, depending upon the period between the trauma and the time of the examination. The terms *healed tears* and *scars* are used to refer to stages of healing. I will comment further on these terms in the sections below.

Septate A septum is a partition or a dividing wall between two spaces or cavities. A septate hymen with one or more partitions (usually vertical) will result in two or more parallel (but also vertical) orifices.

Slit-like The hymenal orifice is represented by a thin slit, almost completely occluding communication between the vagina and the exterior.

Punctate (Cribriform) In this configuration there are multiple extremely small (pinpoint) orifices.

Imperforate Here there is no hymenal orifice at all. This may not cause difficulties prior to puberty. After the child starts menstruating, however, incision of the hymen is necessary if there is to be proper release of the menstrual flow.

The term *anterior* is used to refer to that part of the hymen that is closest to the front of the body, and the term *posterior* to that part of the hymen that is closest to the back of the child's body. Commonly, the site of a particular observation is described by visualizing the hymenal ring to be like the face of a clock. Accordingly, 12:00 o'clock would be the most anterior position; 3:00 o'clock the position closest to the child's left side (the examiner's right); 6:00 o'clock, the position closest to the child's anus; and 9:00 o'clock the position closest to the child's right side (the examiner's left). There is a widespread belief that attempts to insert an object (animate or inanimate) into the child's vagina is more likely to produce trauma to the posterior rim of the hymen, namely, in the range from the 3:00 to 9:00 o'clock position.

Sometimes examination of the hymen may be compromised by the presence of *labial adhesions*. These cause a sticking together of adjacent parts of the labia minora. Sometimes the attachment is by fibrous bands, and sometimes merely by a sticking together of labial tissue. These are so common that they are generally considered to be in the normal range. Most competent examiners would not consider them, per se, to be a sign of sex abuse.

Additional Terms

Here I define further terms frequently seen in reports by examiners assessing for sex abuse.

Labial adhesions This term refers to the "sticking together" of the labia minora and/or labia majora. Other names for the same phenomenon include *labial agglutination, vulvar fusion, vulvar synechiae, gynatresia, coalescence of the labia minora,* and *occlusion of the vaginal vestibule*. Labial adhesions are usually seen between the ages of two months and seven years. They are generally considered to be the result of poor hygiene, a mild vulvitis, or mechanical irritation along with hypoestrogenism (McCann et al., 1988).

Synechiae This refers to a pathological union of parts. It is synonymous with the word *adhesion*. It is best viewed as a sticking together of parts that should be separate from one another. Infection and irritation can cause synechiae.

Posterior fourchette A fold of mucous membrane just inside the point of posterior conversion of the vulva (labia majora).

Examining Instruments

Because the hymenal structures are so small (the average normal hymenal orifice of a three-year-old is 4-5 mm) and because measurements may be difficult, variable, and somewhat subjective, visualization aids are often utilized. One such aid is the traditional *otoscope*. Although designed for examination of the ears, it has proven useful in the genital examination as well. It is basically a flashlight with a cone-shaped attachment and magnifying glass that, at the same time, focuses a beam of light on the area to be examined and allows the examiner to have a magnified view of what is being seen.

A superior instrument is the *colposcope*. The colposcope is a pair of mounted binoculars which can be mounted on a tripod or suspended from a movable mechanical arm. It generally magnifies from 10 to 20 times. The colposcope allows for visualization of structures that may not be visible to the naked eye. The colposcope is also equipped with an internal light for better visualization. It includes a green filter that assists in the examination of the vascular bed. Finkel (1989) states: "The green light improves visualization of scar tissue and alterations in the vascular pattern of the hymenal membrane and perihymenal tissues." Special cameras can be used to take photographs through the colposcope. The terms *colposcopy* and *colposcopic examination* refer to the procedure in which the colposcope is used. McCann (1990) has written an excellent description of the colposcope and its use. Muram and Elias (1989) have reservations about the colposcopy and do not consider it significantly superior to the unaided eye.

The *vaginal speculum* is an instrument that allows for visualization of the vaginal wall and the cervix. It is best visualized as a split tube with a special handle. The tube is inserted into the vagina and by squeezing the handle the tube expands, thereby widening the vagina and allowing for visualization of the cervix and vaginal wall, especially while the speculum is being removed. Although it comes in various sizes, it is rarely used in the examination of children. The insertion of a vaginal speculum into the vagina of a child would be very painful, and even traumatic, especially to the hymenal ring.

The Tanner Stages

The Tanner stages are used to describe objectively the developmental level of the secondary sexual characteristics in children and adults. The stage levels are divided into three categories: breast, genitals, and pubic hair. In each of these realms there are five or six stages, ranging from the most immature to the most mature. For example, Stage I of pubic hair development is no pubic hair at all. Stage II of breast development is the presence of a breast bud, with elevation of the breast and nipple on a small mound. Stage V of genital development in the male is a penis of adult size and shape. Although the Tanner stage has little if anything to do with sex abuse, I mention it here because the term is frequently seen in the medical reports of children being evaluated for sex abuse.

THE EXAMINATION

Obviously, it goes well beyond the purposes of this book (as well as my degree of expertise) to discuss in detail the physical examination of the child who is suspect for sex abuse. I discuss here some special areas of consideration that are extremely important to focus on if one is to put into proper perspective the significance of such an examination. A common practice is for the physician who conducts the examination to come to a conclusion about sex abuse purely on the basis of the physical examination per se. The argument given here is that others should be responsible for delving into the background information, which can shed light on whether the sex abuse did indeed take place.

The doctor may claim, "I'm a doctor, not a detective. My job is to describe medical findings; others concern themselves with the investigation." I am not in agreement with this position. When examining for the presence of other diseases, that same doctor would certainly ask questions of one or both parents in order to obtain a "history" and thereby get more information about the disease under consideration. Like most things in life, there is a continuum from the zero-to-hundred level of involvement. A physician who confines himself (herself) strictly to the examination alone is at the zero level in terms of getting historical background information. Most physicians who examine for sex abuse will go a little beyond that and get *some* information from the party who brings the child, most often the mother. Usually, such data collection does not occupy more than a minute or two. Accordingly, there is little meaningful inquiry into the details of the allegation and little opportunity to assess its credibility and likelihood. I have never (I repeat *never*) seen a medical report in which the examiner has seen fit to invite the alleged perpetrator (even when that perpetrator is the father [the most common case]) to provide input. Most often the examiner will make a statement that the findings are "consistent with sex abuse." However, I have seen reports in which the alleged perpetrator is named, even though that party was not only not seen but there wasn't even an invitation extended to the party to provide information. Such a practice is unconscionable and is worthy, in my opinion, of a malpractice suit. Such a physician is basically making a diagnosis on a person whom he (she) has never seen. I am certain that the same doctor would be very reluctant to write in his (her) chart any other diagnosis regarding a person who was not directly examined.

The failure to get information from available alleged perpetrators has caused much unnecessary grief. I cannot criticize such physicians strongly enough. Although state laws generally require the physician to report suspected abuse, they do not prevent the physician from speaking with the alleged perpetrator before making a final decision regarding whether or not a referral and investigation are warranted. Furthermore, many of these physicians do not appreciate the degree of ineptitude of the "validators" to whom they are referring their patients. They seem to be operating under the delusion that these people are truly competent in the area of differentiating between true and false sex-abuse accusations. As physicians they are sworn to subscribe to the Hippocratic oath in which they vow that they will "above all do no harm" to their patients. There is no question that many of the children who are referred to child protection services, evaluated by "validators," and others of that ilk are being seriously traumatized and that the physician has played a role in contributing to such trauma. I am not suggesting that physicians break the law. I am only suggesting that they take the time to get more information before making such referrals. I am also pointing out to them the common ineptitude of those people to whom they are referring their patient for the "final decision." They must also appreciate how their "impressions" and statements (for example, "consistent with sex abuse"), although not conclusive in their minds, are viewed by many lay people as the final "proof." Perhaps if physicians appreciated this more, they would be less quick to come to conclusions.

The measurement of the hymenal orifice is considered an important part of the physical examination of girls suspected of being sexually abused. It is important to appreciate how variable this finding can be. Yet, there are people who are in jail because of this one measurement. The horizontal (transverse) diameter of the hymenal orifice is usually measured in the supine frog-leg position. Many factors are operative in determining what this diameter is. If the child is correctly positioned, the heels will be placed just below the buttocks. Clearly, if they are in another position, such as 12 inches below the buttocks, a different measurement will be obtained.

The examiner must be sure that the child's heels are at the same position assumed by those children on whom the normative data were obtained. Then there is the variable of the degree to which the child's legs are spread. Usually, an assistant stands next to the child and slowly spreads the child's legs while distracting and reassuring the child. Obviously, the greater the degree of spread, the wider will be the hymenal orifice. However, even when the legs are extended to the extreme position comfortable, the labia majora are usually still so close to one another that the hymen will not be observable. Accordingly, the assistant generally pulls the labia majora apart laterally and posteriorly in order to allow hymenal visualization. Obviously, there are varying degrees of such posterolateral traction, and the greater the traction, the greater the expansion of the hymenal orifice. Accordingly, the assistant must attempt to apply such traction to the same degree applied by those collecting the normative data. A common standard is for the assistant to apply traction at the mid-point of the labia majora to a point 1-1.5 cm on either side of the midline.

Furthermore, a lag must be allowed between the time of retraction and the time of taking the measurement. There is usually a 1-2-second period during which the hymenal ring must be allowed to dilate. Competent examiners usually allow at least a 3-4-second time lag in order to ensure that the hymenal ring is going to relax into its resting position. McCann (1988) emphasizes that the greater the traction on the labia majora, the greater the width the hymenal diameter will be, and this is one of the explanations why different examiners get different results when measuring hymenal openings. He also points out that the vertical diameter is smaller in the supine frog-leg position than it is in the prone knee-chest position.

A small millimeter ruler is then placed very close to the vaginal opening. Obviously, any squirming by the child is going to compromise the accuracy of this measurement. However, even under optimum conditions, and even with strict reproduction of the positioning utilized by those collecting the normative data, there is bound to be some variability of measurement because of the minuteness of the measurement being considered here. A millimeter is approximately 1/25 of an inch. Although the human eye is capable of discriminating between, let us say, 4 mm and 5 mm, it is obvious we are dealing here with a discrimination that is close to the edge of the capability of the human eye (and brain). One has to consider also that the distance of the examiner's eye from the hymenal orifice and the distance of the ruler from the hymenal orifice can very well affect the measurement perceived by the examiner. I am convinced that if the same examiner were to examine the same child on the following day, even when attempting to reproduce exactly the conditions of the examination, there would be variability. Furthermore, *another* examiner, again under the same circumstances, is also likely to come up with a different measurement. The American Academy of Pediatrics (1991) in its statement, "Guidelines for the Evaluation of Sexual Abuse of Children," emphasizes the aforementioned variability and impresses upon pediatricians the importance of taking these variations into consideration when making decisions regarding the normality or abnormality of the size of the hymenal orifice.

The prone knee-chest position is generally used to measure the vertical diameter of the hymen. Here, too, lateral traction is required if one is to properly visualize the hymen, and here, too, there is great variability regarding the child's positioning and the degree of lateral traction. Here, too, standardization is necessary. McCann (1990) states: "The head is turned to one side with the forearms resting on either side of the head. The knees are separated 6-8 inches and maintained in 90 degrees of flexion. The examiner's thumbs are then placed beneath the leading edge of the gluteous maximus at the level of the vaginal introitus and the posterior portion of the perineum is lifted, revealing the hymenal orifice." Obviously, the examiner who does not follow this procedure exactly will obtain different measurements of the hymenal orifice. Examination in the prone knee-chest position allows the hymenal tissues to fall forward and thereby provides better visualization of the full circumference of the hymenal orifice than is generally possible in the frog-leg position. Horowitz (1987) provides a good general statement of procedures for conducting a pediatric examination for sex abuse, as does the American Academy of Pediatrics, Committee on Child Abuse and Neglect (1991).

WHAT ARE NORMAL GENITAL MEDICAL FINDINGS?

Female Genital Findings

As mentioned, it has only been in recent years that extensive studies have been done to determine normal medical genital findings in children. And this belated interest relates to the rapid increase in reports of sex abuse and the need to obtain accurate data in order to differentiate the normal from the sexually abused child. It is my hope that the reader will now be impressed with the complexity of the problem of obtaining normative data with regard to the hymenal orifice, and that the reader will be even more overwhelmed by the complexity of the problem after a discussion of the wide variety of seemingly pathological config-urations that are found in normal children.

First, with regard to data collection on the size of the normal hymenal orifice, one of the problems attendant to conducting such studies is that of knowing with certainty that the children studied were not abused. As I am sure the reader appreciates, it is impossible to "prove" that "something didn't happen." The greater the number of children included in a study, the greater the likelihood the findings will be credible. However, the greater the number of such child subjects, the less the likelihood that each of them was studied in depth with regard to whether or not they were sexually abused. The fact that children were taken from a "normal population" of youngsters who were not referred for abuse is no guarantee that some of the subjects being studied were not abused. This is one of the criticisms directed at such studies, especially by those who tend to diagnose sex abuse in the vast majority of patients referred to them. These individuals are likely to use as criteria findings that other observers would consider to be in the normal range. This is one of the problems we are dealing with in this field, and it is a significant source of controversy.

Goff et al. (1989) studied 273 prepubertal girls as part of their routine health assessment. They measured horizontal diameters only in the supine knee-chest position and the supine frog-leg position. No measurements were made in the prone knee-chest position. The girls ranged in age from less than one to age seven. This study, as is true of most studies, confirmed that the vaginal orifice increases in size with age. They found that the horizontal hymenal diameter was generally larger when measured in the supine knee-chest position than in the supine frog-leg position. Interestingly, an orifice greater than 4 mm in horizontal diameter was rare. The study is a very good one, especially because the authors describe in great detail the exact positioning of the children prior to measurement. McCann et al. (1990) studied 93 girls between the ages of 10 months and 10 years. Whereas Goff et al. (1989) used direct visual measurements, McCann et al. (1990) used a colposcope. McCann et al. took both vertical and horizontal measurements in the supine position with labial separation, the supine position with labial traction, and the prone knee-chest position. McCann et al's findings are different from those of Goff et al., in that the hymenal orifices were typically larger. There was only one mean measurement below 4.0 mm, and that was the horizontal measurement in the supine labial separation position, namely, 3.9 + 1.4 mm. The largest finding was for the eight-year-old girls in the 8-10-year group in the prone knee-chest position, namely, the vertical diameter of 8.7 + 2.6 mm. Considering these extremes, one can see that the range goes from 3.9 to 8.7 mm. Accordingly, those who hold that any measurement over 4 mm is indicative of sex abuse (which would be suggested by Goff et al.'s studies) would not find support in McCann et al.'s studies. Both are competent examining teams and both have written articles that are very impressive. Yet, they would be quoted by adversaries in a courtroom dispute regarding whether or not sex abuse took place.

Finkel (1989) holds that a transverse hymenal diameter of greater than 5 mm is suggestive of sexual abuse. However, because of the unreliability of such measurements, repeated measurements must be taken before coming to a conclusion. He also emphasizes that the position of the child and the degree of relaxation are important factors in determining the measurement.

Another reliable study was conducted by White et al. (1989). They studied 242 females, ages 1-12. Three groups were studied: (1) sexually abused, (2) no history of sexual contact, but at risk, (3) nonabused. Transverse diameters only were obtained with patients in the supine frog-leg position. Lateral tension was applied to the hymenal opening. Measurements were made by visualization of a measuring tape held over the hymenal orifice or by a cotton-tipped applicator. They found that 88 percent of children who complained of penile/vaginal penetration had a vaginal introital diameter of greater than 4 mm, as compared to 18 percent of children who described no such penetration. Their conclusion: a vaginal introital diameter of greater than 4 mm is highly associated with sexual contact in children less than 13 years of age. It is important for the reader to appreciate that the transverse diameter of the average adult erect penis is approximately 3.5 cm (35 mm) and an index finger is approximately 1.5 cm (15 mm) wide. Accordingly, the insertion of either of these into a hymenal orifice of 5 mm will invariably cause significant widening and, certainly in the younger girl, pain and trauma. Accordingly, when a three-year-old girl claims that an alleged perpetrator inserted his penis into her vagina and the vaginal examination reveals a diameter of, for example, 7-8 mm, it is extremely unlikely that the penetration being described actually took place. The more likely explanation is either examiner error or the hymenal orifice is at the upper end of the normal bell-shaped curve of hymenal diameters.

McCann et al. (1990) describe other observations relevant to the problem of differentiating the nonabused from the sexually abused children. Example: Some claim that rolled hymenal edges are a manifestation of sex abuse. McCann et al. found that the rolled edge is much more commonly seen in the supine positions, but tends to disappear in the knee-chest position. Finkel (1989), in contrast, states that rounded hymenal edges are one of the results of the effects of estrogen in the prepubertal girl and are more likely to be visualized in the knee-chest position. This not only says something about the importance of positioning, but also says something about rolled edges as a sign of sex abuse.

With regard to hymenal configuration, McCann et al. (1990) found crescent (36 percent), concentric [annular] (32 percent), septate (1 percent), cribriform (0 percent), imperforate (2 percent). In 17 percent of the subjects he was unable to determine the exact configuration because of redundancy of hymenal tissues and the failure of the hymenal orifice to open. These findings lend confirmation to those who claim that a perfectly circular hymen is not the only configuration. With regard to the hymenal edge, he found the following: smooth (26 percent), irregular (25 percent), redundant (25 percent), and angular (8 percent). Again, these findings lend support to those who hold that there is great variation in the configuration of the hymenal oriface. In the traction frog-leg position, with regard to some of the "abnormalities" sometimes considered manifestations of sex abuse, he found the following: thickened hymenal edge (53.8 percent), localized roll of the hymenal edge (23.8 percent), hymenal mounds (33.8 percent), hymenal projections (33.3 percent), hymenal tags (24.4 percent), peri-hymenal bands (16 percent), septal remnants (8.6 percent), hymenal septa (2.5 percent), hymenal notches (6.6 percent), hymenal synechiae [adhesion of the hymen to adjacent tissues] (2.4 percent).

Some claim that the normal hymen is regular in its vascularity and any areas of vascular irregularity, areas in which the vascularization is different from surrounding tissues, is strongly suggestive of healed tears and other signs of sex abuse. McCann et al. (1990) found irregular vascularity in 31.3 percent of those children examined in the separation frog-leg position, 30.9 percent in those children examined in the traction frog-leg position, and 28.9 percent of those when examined in the knee-chest position. Aside from areas of irregular vascularity, they found areas of isolated increase in vascularity in 13.9 percent of those examined in the separation frog-leg position, 16.0 percent of those examined in the traction frog-leg position, and 22.8 percent of those examined in the prone knee-chest position. These findings strongly suggest that the vascular irregularity criterion for sex abuse is improper and risky (especially for those being falsely accused).

The McCann et al. study (1990) directs itself, as well, to the frequency of other "abnormalities" sometimes considered manifestations of sex abuse. For example, he found erythema of the vestibule to be present in 56 percent of the children examined. (The vestibule is the portion of the vulva bounded by the labia minora. At the floor of the vestibule are [from anterior to posterior] the clitoris, urethral orifice, and the hymen.) As mentioned, vulval rashes are quite common in children. These relate to poor hygiene, a wide variety of infections (not necessarily related to sexually transmitted diseases), tight panties, certain soaps, rubbing, scratching, and masturbation (to mention the most common). I have been involved in a number of cases in which these more common and likely causes of the erythema were ignored and the examiner concluded that the findings were "consistent" with sex abuse or even manifestations of sex abuse. He found labial adhesions to be present in 38.9 percent of the children studied. He also found periurethral bands in 50.6 percent of the children studied.

I have discussed in some detail the McCann et al. (1990) article because it provides compelling evidence that normal children exhibit a wide variety of variations, many of which have been considered signs of sex abuse. It is of interest that McCann et al.'s original group consisted of 114 girls, but 23 were excluded because of the early onset of puberty and the possibility of undetected sexual abuse. The list of behavioral manifestations that warranted their exclusion from the study included: nightmares, fears, moodiness, change in school performance, truancy, and acting out behaviors (among others). All of these could be seen in normal children (at least on occasion), and many of these behaviors are manifestations of a wide variety of childhood problems completely unrelated to sex abuse. There are sexually abused children, however, who may exhibit one or more of these behavioral manifestations. To the best of my knowledge, McCann et al. (1990) did not conduct a detailed inquiry regarding whether these behavioral manifestations were signs and symptoms of sex abuse, were in the normal range, or related to other causes. On the one hand, the exclusion of all these children, simply on the basis of the presence of one or more of these symptoms, made his sample "purer"—thereby lessening the likelihood that sexually abused children were included. On the other hand, he may have unnecessarily shrunk his patient population, thereby lessening somewhat the credibility of his findings and depriving himself of many subjects who were not molested.

Anal Findings (Male and Female)

Anal and perianal findings are also a source of significant controversy. One of the most widely known such controversies relates to the anal examinations described by Hobbs and Wynne (1986, 1987). These examiners claimed that a pathognomonic sign of child sex abuse was "reflex dilatation and alternate contraction and relaxation of the anal sphincter or 'twitchiness' without dilatation." One finding, also referred to as anal "winking," is considered a pathognomonic sign of anal intercourse. As a result of using this criterion, hundreds of children in England were diagnosed as having been sexually abused, with the result that 121 children were removed from 57 families. It took a government investigation to bring society to its senses and return these children to their families. McCann et al. (1989) studied 267 children (161 girls and 106 boys), ages 2 months to 11 years. They found anal dilatation in 49 percent of the children, and the mean time of the initial dilatation was 65 seconds. The anus opened and closed intermittently in 62 percent of the subjects in which dilatation occurred. Accordingly, about 30 percent of all the children studied exhibited the intermittent dilatation and relaxation of the anal sphincter, which Hobbs and Wynne considered a sign indicative of sex abuse.

McCann et al. (1989) describe other anal findings in normal children that are often considered signs of sex abuse. They found that 41 percent of their group exhibited erythema. There is no question that children who have been sexually molested per anus will exhibit erythema. But in this study, 41 percent of normal children exhibited erythema as well. McCann et al. found increased pigmentation in 30 percent, another finding that is often considered a sign of sex abuse. They found venous engorgement in 52 percent after two minutes in the knee-chest position. Again, venous engorgement has also been considered a sign of sex abuse. Anal tags and folds are also considered by some to be indicative of sex abuse. These were found anterior to the anus in 11 percent of the children studied. No abrasions, hematomas, or fissures (common findings in sex abuse) were found.

WHAT ARE THE GENITAL FINDINGS IN SEXUALLY ABUSED CHILDREN?

Introduction

Studies of the anogenital findings in sex abuse are beset by a number of problems. First, all knowledgeable investigators agree that some children who have been genuinely abused sexually will exhibit no medical findings. This relates to the fact that they were often caressed and touched in a nontraumatic way. Another problem relates to the fact that the investigators can never be sure that all the children in the nonabused group studied were indeed never abused. There is also the risk that some of the children in the abused group were indeed not abused, but this is less likely. A third problem relates to the fact that a wide variety of abnormalities are seen in normal children, and the aforementioned studies of McCann et al. (1990) provide good verification of this. What we are trying to find, then, are *specific* medical findings that are seen only in abused children and not in those who have not been abused. All studies must take these potential contaminants into consideration.

Female Genital Findings

Emans et al. (1987) studied 305 girls. They were divided into three groups: (1) sexually abused (119 girls), (2) normal girls with no genital complaints (127 girls), and (3) girls with other genital complaints (59 girls). The abused group was found more likely to have scars on the hymen or the posterior fourchette (9 percent vs. 1 percent, $p < 0.002$), increased friability (ease of bleeding) of the posterior fourchette (10 percent vs. 1 percent, $p < 0.001$), attenuation (stretching and thinning) of the hymen (18 percent vs. 4 percent, $p < 0.0003$), and synechiae (adhesions) from the hymenal ring to the vagina (8 percent vs. 0 percent, $p < 0.0009$). We see here that we are not dealing with a situation in which a finding is present in the abused group and not present in the nonabused. Rather, we see here a situation in which certain findings are more likely to be present in the abused group than in the nonabused group. The obvious problem with this kind of finding is that its presence then does not necessarily mean that the particular child being examined was abused.

Interestingly, Emans et al. (1987) found a wide variety of symptoms to be present with equal likelihood in both groups, the abused and nonabused. There was no statistical difference between groups 1 and 3 regarding the frequency of abrasions, hymenal tears, intravaginal synechiae, and condyloma acuminata (venereal warts). This study, then, suggests that these particular findings are not of diagnostic significance when attempting to differentiate abused from nonabused children. Interestingly, erythema (reddening) was more common in the nonabused group than in the abused group (68 percent vs. 34 percent, $p < 0.0001$). There was no statistical difference between the dimensions of the hymenal opening of the abused and the nonabused group. One would certainly expect a larger average hymenal opening in the abused group, but this study did not confirm such a difference. Perhaps there were too few girls in the 119 abused who had the kind of sexual molestation that would produce an enlargement of the hymenal ring. However, as Herman-Giddens and Frothingham (1987) point out, "The hymen, contrary to common notion, is often a slack, thick, folded, stretchable tissue which may persist after digital or penile penetration." The same authors hold that "a vaginal opening of greater than 5 mm is not common and may indicate vaginal penetration with a finger, object, or penis."

McCann (1988) states that 85 percent of preadolescent children who are being molested are molested on a chronic, ongoing, and recurring basis. Such molestation should, then, produce changes indicative of chronic trauma. He emphasizes the importance of examination for bruises in *other* parts of the body, in the nongenital area. The mouth is a common site of lesions because the perpetrator may have placed his hand over the child's mouth in order to stop the child from screaming. Grab marks on the arms and inner thighs are also strongly suggestive of sex abuse, especially thumb marks on the inner aspect of the thigh, placed there when the child's legs were forced apart. He also states that labial injury is common at the time of rape because the labia majora are generally closed and the perpetrator pushes his penis repeatedly against closed labia. McCann (1988) holds that the most common area of hymenal injury is between the 4:00 and 7:00 o'clock positions because the penis is forced downward and backward. He emphasizes that children heal quickly and that examinations after the first few days may not confirm the abuse. Because the length of the vagina of four- and five-year-old girls is only 4 cm, trauma to the vagina, cervix, and lower part of the uterus is common.

McCann et al. (1988) studied six sisters, all of whom had been sexually molested by male family members. All of these girls had labial adhesions, and four of the six had changes in the area of the posterior fourchette (a fold of mucus membrane just inside the posterior commissure of the vulva). Furthermore, four of the girls' hymens revealed abnormalities of the hymenal edge (irregular, rolled, or septum) and three revealed irregularities of the hymenal membrane (redundant, thick, scarred). Four exhibited abnormal vascular patterns, and all six exhibited adhesions and/or scars of the posterior fourchette. The labial adhesions in these cases were associated with posterior fourchette changes and other findings consistent with sex abuse. The authors' position is that labial adhesions per se are not indicative of sex abuse. However, if associated with other findings suggestive of sex abuse, such as posterior fourchette trauma, then it should be considered one such manifestation. We see here, then, a situation in which a normal finding is considered a sign of sex abuse under certain circumstances. In these six cases the labial adhesions were associated with other findings indicative of sex abuse. Furthermore, labial adhesions usually occur from ages two to seven. In this case two of the girls were ages eight and nine, beyond the age at which one usually sees labial adhesions.

Muram (1989a) divides the genital findings into four categories:

> 1) Normal-appearing genitalia.
> 2) Nonspecific findings. Abnormalities of the genitalia that could have been caused by sexual abuse, but also are often seen in girls who are not victims of sexual abuse (e.g., inflammation and scratching). These findings may be the sequelae of poor perineal hygiene or nonspecific infection. Included in this category are redness of the external genitalia, increased vascular pattern of the vestibular and labial mucosa, presence of purulent discharge from the vagina, small skin fissures or lacerations in the area of the posterior fourchette, and agglutination of the labia minora.
> 3) Specific findings. The presence of one or more abnormalities strongly suggesting sexual abuse. Such findings include recent or healed lacerations of the hymen and vaginal mucosa, enlarged hymenal opening of 1 cm, proctoepisiotomy (a laceration of the vaginal mucosa extending through the rectovaginal septum to involve the rectal mucosa), and indentations in the skin indicating teeth (bite) marks. This category also includes patients with laboratory confirmation of a venereal disease.
> 4) Definitve findings. Any presence of sperm.

It is of interest that Muram (1989a) considers labial agglutination to be a nonspecific finding, in that it does not necessarily indicate sex abuse. Of importance in the third category, specific findings, are hymenal tears that extend to the base of the hymenal ring as to be differentiated from hymenal clefts which do not extend that peripherally. Muram believes that an astute examiner will do just as well with the unaided eye as with the colposcope.

Muram (1989b) studied 31 girls who were assaulted by 30 individuals, all of whom confessed to having sexually molested them. Both the girls and the perpetrators were in agreement that the sex abuse took place. Obviously, this is a good study sample for ascertaining the physical effects of sex abuse. It circumvents one of the aforementioned problems regarding such studies, namely, the uncertainty regarding whether or not the girl being examined was genuinely abused or was genuinely in the nonabused category. In 18 of the 31 cases the offender admitted to vaginal penetration. However, specific findings were only to be found in 11 of these 18 girls (61 percent). In those girls in which penetration was denied only 3 of 13 (23 percent) provided specific findings. It is to be noted, however, that the girls range in age from 2 to 15. It is not surprising that some of the teenagers who experienced penile penetration would not have findings of abuse. It is of interest that of the 31 girls, inflammation, bruising, and irritation were seen in only 9, all of whom were evaluated within one week of the assault. None of the girls evaluated one week after the abuse had findings suggestive of inflammation. Muram states: "If no tear of the hymen occurred, the examination will fail to detect any abnormalities." This is an important point. According to Muram, the most important specific sign of sexual molestation is hymenal tear, to the base, especially extending into the vaginal canal. Other abnormalities, such as inflammation and bruising, tend to heal within a week.

The most important statement that Muram makes is that the most consistent finding in bona fide sex abuse is laceration or tear of the hymenal ring, down through the base, and extending often into the adjacent vaginal wall. This sign is one of the most important for differentiating genuine from fabricated abuse.

On occasion, a child may sustain significant genital injuries associated with trauma to the perineal area as a result of falls and fence or straddle injuries (Behrman and Vaughn, 1983; Paul, 1977). Here one may see the kinds of lacerations seen in sexual abuse. One may also see abrasions and other forms of injury to the perivaginal area. However, the time of the trauma is generally well known to the child (and usually an adult), and there is nothing else in the history to suggest sexual abuse. Paul (1977) claims that penile penetration in younger children will cause widespread injuries, including lacerations of the hymen, vagina, and labia. There will be profuse bleeding and the child will experience excruciating pain. This is an important point because in many cases of fabricated sex abuse, the child will describe no pain or minimal pain.

Anal Findings

McCann (1988) states that children who have been subjected to anal intercourse on repeated occasions suffer with a relaxation of the external anal sphincter, but not of the internal anal sphincter. Accordingly, there is a typical funnel-like appearance of the anus on physical examination.

Finkel (1989) reported on seven children who had experienced acute genital and anal trauma in association with sexual abuse. Some of the more superficial manifestations of the trauma (abrasions, superficial lacerations, contusions, and bleeding) may not be apparent after four days. In two of Finkel's seven cases, penile-anal penetration was involved. In one case Finkel described "superficial lacerations of the anal verge tissues in anterior and posterior midline positions each measuring 2 mm circumferencially and 3 mm in length." In the second case he described five mucocutaneous superficial lacerations, some of which extended from the external anal mucosa down into the anal canal.

SEXUALLY TRANSMITTED DISEASES

The presence of a sexually transmitted disease (previously referred to as venereal disease) is generally considered definitive evidence for sex abuse. Of the wide variety of such diseases, the most commonly found in sexually abused children are: gonorrhea, syphilis, Chlamydia, condyloma acuminatum, Trichomonas vaginalis, and herpes 1 (genital). However, it is important to appreciate that gonorrhea, syphilis, and Chlamydia can be acquired perinatally from the mother, and this must be given consideration before deciding that the presence of such a disease automatically indicates sex abuse (American Academy of Pediatrics, Committee of Child Abuse and Neglect, 1991). The material for gonorrhea culture is generally obtained from cotton swabs of the vagina, throat, and rectum. The organism may sometimes be grown from cultures of the urine of suspected boys. The urine can also be examined for Trichomonas infection. Tests for syphilis are usually obtained from a blood sample. Vaginal secretions can also be cultured for the presence of Chlamydia, herpes, and Trichomonas. Vaginal secretions can be examined directly (microscopically, with proper staining) for gonorrhea and Trichomonas.

Condyloma acuminatum is also referred to as genital warts and venereal warts. It is caused by a virus called the human papilloma virus (HPV). It is the most common *viral* sexually transmitted disease in the United States and is now more common than herpes (due to the recent rapid increase in its incidence). Because the incubation period is approximately one month (Stewart et al., 1987), the genital warts will not be observable immediately after a child has been abused. The diagnosis is made generally by direct observation, the warts usually appearing like warts on other parts of the body, but they do extend into the vaginal canal, cervix, and rectum. Sometimes the warts are inconspicuous or completely invisible to the naked eye. Horowitz (1987) provides an excellent protocol for the examination for sexually transmitted diseases.

Although the presence of a sexually transmitted disease is strongly suggestive of sex abuse, one must also consider that the disease was acquired by the child in a nonsexual way. The problem in such situations is that the suspect may indeed have the sexually transmitted disease but did not have a sexual encounter with the child. Rather, the disease was transmitted in a nonsexual way. Clearly, an accused who is trying to deny a sexual encounter will give strong support to this theory. And such support can be found in the medical literature, where there are many articles providing instances of just such a method of transmission. For example, Shore and Winklestein (1971) claim that 50 percent of their sample of children contracted their gonococcal infection in the absence of sex abuse. They stated that only one-fifth of their sample acquired the gonorrhea through a sexual experience. Kaplan (1986) claims that the gonococcus can survive outside the human body for up to 24 hours. Kaplan cites a 1929 study in which several newborns in the same hospital nursery were found to have gonococcal infections, and it was believed that the organism was transferred with thermometers. Wakefield and Underwager (1988) refer to studies in which gonorrhea was found to have been transmitted nonsexually among peers, via close physical contact with infected adults or indirect contact through bedclothes or hands. They also refer to the work of DeJong et al. (1982), who report that venereal warts can be transmitted through close nonsexual contact, during delivery, and by sexual encounters.

Sperm in the Vagina And the Pregnancy Test

The presence of sperm in the vagina of a prepubertal child is obvious evidence for sex abuse. It is proof that a postpubertal male has sexually penetrated the prepubertal girl. The presence of sperm in the vagina of a postpubertal girl is not necessarily evidence of sex abuse, in that she may have voluntarily had sexual relations without in any way being abused. Fresh sperm can be examined directly under the microscope. After 24 hours sperm may not be viable enough for such direct examination. Sperm may be visualized with Wood's light, under which it becomes fluorescent. These fluorescent "tear drops" shine dramatically in contrast to other vaginal secretions that are examined under Wood's light (McCann, 1988). The examiner must take care to question the parents regarding whether the child has taken a bath between the time of the alleged abuse and the time of the examination. Obviously, if the sperm has been washed out, the Wood's light test will not be positive. The sperm sample can also be tested for the presence of acid phosphatase, an enzyme that is secreted by the prostate gland and is to be found in the ejaculate. Acid phosphatase is not normally found in the vagina.

In association with the examination for sperm, one must consider the pregnancy test. Obviously, the pregnancy test is not viable for prepubertal children, although there are reports of pregnancy in girls as young as eight and many examiners will routinely do them for children of that age and above. Although conducting a pregnancy test on a prepubertal child may seem unnecessary and even absurd, it is not completely so. There are children who are capable of becoming pregnant who have exhibited few if any signs of sexual maturity. And this is where the Tanner level of sexual development may provide information regarding whether or not the child could indeed be pregnant. An eight- or nine-year-old, exhibiting Tanner II and III levels, may very well be capable of pregnancy.

THE PENILE PLETHYSMOGRAPH

The plethysmograph is an instrument that is enjoying increasing popularity as a method for ascertaining whether a male suspect is indeed a pedophile. It is considered by some to be a definitive examination to determine whether or not sex abuse has taken place. The basic principle of the test is that a man with pedophilic tendencies will become sexually excited when provided with visual and auditory pedophilic stimuli involving adult-child sexual encounters. An appropriately sized ring is placed around the man's penis, a ring which is connected to a computer that records any increases in the circumference of the man's penis while being exposed to the pedophilic auditory and sexual stimuli. The test is administered in a small, darkened room. The man measures the circumference of his flaccid penis and places on his penis a metal ring of the appropriate size. In some models the penis is placed in an airtight sack or covering which can measure total changes in the volume of the penis, rather than just the circumference. The man sits in a reclining chair. Wires from the ring feed into a computer that measures minute changes in the electrical resistance of his penis. He also wears earphones.

A series of pictures is then displayed in front of the reclining man, and he is asked to indicate the approximate age, gender, and activity of the individuals depicted. He is also asked to declare whether he is sexually aroused. Slides may be shown in progressively more provocative stages. For example, in one slide a prepubescent girl is shown clothed, in a second partly clothed, and in a third, nude. The attempt here is to provide progressively arousing stimuli. Nonstimulating slides are interspaced to allow for "recovery." The prepubescent and adolescent boys and girls are generally not engaged in sexual activities. Other slides depict adults, both homosexual and heterosexual, engaging in such activities. Both the degree of arousal to each slide and the length of time it takes the man to return to the flaccid state are indicators of sexual interest. Some examiners present these subjects with audiotapes that would be sexually arousing to pedophiles.

Medlyn (1989) presents some of the arguments, pro and con, for using the plethysmograph. An individual can masturbate or have sex just before taking the test, thereby repressing the level of sexual excitation that would have otherwise taken place at the time of the evaluation. Furthermore, there are individuals who may very well be aroused by these pictures, but who are capable of consciously suppressing their arousal. An accused perpetrator may be so depressed over the prospect of going to jail that sexual excitation will not take place at the time of the testing. I personally believe that the tension and anxiety associated with the testing might very well suppress sexual responses more likely to exhibit themselves in periods of relaxation. Another risk is that the test will be considered by lawyers and judges as the definitive proof of whether or not sexual molestation took place. The quest for a quick, simple test is ubiquitous and dangerous.

Selkin (1991) is basically critical of the plethysmograph, primarily because standards for scoring are not available. Most of those who administer the test are self-taught experts. He quotes the findings of Simon and Schouten (1990) in which they criticize the plethysmograph because the subject can willfully distort the results. Furthermore, there is no clear relationship between the subject's erectile responses and clinical deviant behavior. Also, they suspect that the plethysmograph would be ineffective with impotent subjects.

Wakefield and Underwager (1988) are also critical of the penile plethysmograph. They note the lack of controlled double-blind studies. They also point out that there are many individuals who might have positive findings on the plethysmograph, but who would never act out on these impulses. They quote the studies of Freund et al. (1972), who report that nondeviant volunteers responded with penile engorgement to slides of 8- to 11-year-old girls and to slides of the buttocks of prepubescent boys. Here we see a study providing strong confirmation that nonpedophilic individuals will respond positively to these pictures. We see here the dangers and risks of this instrument being confirmed. Wakefield and Underwager (1988) also quote studies demonstrating that deviant subjects can suppress their sexual responses to stimuli known to be effective in producing sexual excitation (Henson and Rubin, 1971; Laws and Rubin, 1969; Quinsey and Bergerson, 1976). Freund (1963) reports on faking sexual responses. Abel, et al. (1975) report that deviant subjects can suppress sexual responses to stimuli known to be capable of producing excitation in them.

THE POLYGRAPH ("LIE DETECTOR TEST")

In Chapter Two I discussed the *attitude* of the suspected pedophile toward the polygraph as one of the indicators of pedophilia. I discussed there the accused person's *attitude toward* taking the lie detector test as opposed to *the findings* of the lie detector test. I mentioned that those individuals who are genuinely innocent are quite eager to take the test, even though they are aware that it is not foolproof, that there may be false positives, and that they may thereby be found guilty of a crime they did not commit. Generally, they are so sure that they are innocent and so sure that they will be calm, that they are willing to take these risks. In contrast, individuals who are genuine abusers are very reluctant to take the test, rarely volunteer to take it, and, when offered to take it, generally find an excuse along the lines that it is not foolproof or that their lawyer has discouraged them from taking it. I generally do not consider the *findings* of the lie detector test in my evaluation; I leave that to the court. Some courts will admit such findings in evidence and others will not. Polygraphs are very attractive to law enforcement authorities because they hold promise for providing a simple answer to what is clearly a very complex question. And this, of course, is one of the most common problems confronting people who are falsely accused. The desire on the part of investigators to utilize quick and easily administered "tests" often results in false accusations being considered valid.

Wakefield and Underwager (1988), on the basis of their reviews of the literature, do not find enough evidence to support the reliability of the test. They note that The American Psychological Association (Abeles, 1986) considers the validity of the polygraph unsatisfactory. Wakefield and Underwager (1988) also note that the American Medical Association's Council on Scientific Affairs (JAMA, 1986) concluded that the polygraph is of "dubious value" because of the high number of false positives and false negatives. The British Psychological Society (1986) also does not approve the use of the polygraph, considering the false positives to be up to the 50-percent level in some studies. Lykken (1985) states:

> All anyone can determine from the polygraph charts is that the subject was more disturbed by one question than he was by another. One cannot say why the question was disturbing, whether it evoked guilt or fear or indignation, or, indeed, whether the reaction was produced by the question at all—a subject who bites his tongue or constricts his anal sphincter just as the question is asked can produce a response on the polygraph that cannot be distinguished from spontaneous emotional disturbance (p. 101).

Safire (1989) in a *New York Times* essay, written at the time when the Reagan administration was planning to require polygraph tests of CIA employees and thousands of others whose jobs were considered "sensitive" by the government, describes how the CIA had been duped by a small army of Cubans who had allegedly abandoned Fidel Castro and had offered their services to the CIA. Although these individuals "passed" their polygraph tests, they were actually double agents who supplied us with misleading information provided by the KGB. This "disinformation," which we gullibly accepted as valid, played an important role in a number of governmental miscalculations.

I myself am very dubious about the polygraph. I am certain that there are some individuals who are so tense at the time of taking the test that they may very well provide false positive responses. Furthermore, I have personally seen psychopathic patients who have "passed" the polygraph, people who I was convinced were lying. Their psychopathy enabled them to answer falsely without any sense of grief, tension, anxiety, or other reactions that might be physiologically measured. I suspect that an individual on a tranquilizer or who had a drink of alcohol might similarly "pass" the test.

CONCLUSIONS

It is my hope that the reader will have a sense of the complexity of the medical findings in sex-abuse cases. The tendency among many evaluators has been to view the "medical findings" as providing the final definitive answer: the "proof." The more one knows about these findings, the greater the uncertainty one should have. Clearly, there are some findings that are conclusive, e.g., sperm in the vagina and pregnancy. The presence of a sexually transmitted disease is certainly strong evidence, but one must be sure that one is not dealing with a disease that was acquired perinatally or nonsexually. Much controversy still rages about what normal hymenal findings are. At this point, we know that there is enormous variation among normal children regarding hymenal configuration. When an injury is clearly a tear, especially a tear that extends to the edge of the hymen and into the adjacent vaginal wall, then we can be more certain that bona fide abuse has probably taken place. With regard to the polygraph and the plethysmograph, evaluators who take seriously the findings on these instruments are likely to support an inordinately high number of false positives and false negatives. Wakefield and Underwager (1988) provide an excellent discussion of medical findings in sex abuse. Coleman (1989) has also provided a useful review of some of the dilemmas confronting us when we attempt to understand medical findings.

 **SIX**

THE "VALIDATORS" AND OTHER EXAMINERS

COMMENTS ON THE TERM *VALIDATOR*

I recognize that I am extremely critical of many (and probably most) of the people who are doing evaluations in sex-abuse cases. I appreciate that there are some (but I believe they are in the minority) who are conducting skillful evaluations that are balanced and unbiased. My experience, however, has been that the majority of those evaluators whose examinations I have had the opportunity to evaluate in depth exhibit significant deficiencies in their techniques. It is this group that I am referring to in this chapter, and it is this group that is playing a significant role in the present sex-abuse fiasco. One cannot possibly know the exact percentage of evaluators who fall into the category that I am criticizing here. Furthermore, even that division is artificial in that each evaluator falls at some point along a continuum—from those who manifest most, if not all, of the deficiencies described here to the most competent and skilled who exhibit few, if any, of them. Although their percentage is not certain (and probably cannot be known), there is no question that there are enough of these inadequate and incompetent evaluators to warrant the criticisms presented here.

I suspect that those who refer to themselves as "validators" are most likely performing at the levels of incompetence described in this chapter. The very fact that they are comfortable referring to themselves as validators provides strong justification for my placing them in this category. The name implies that their sole purpose is to *validate* or confirm that the abuse took place. It is the equivalent of a criminal court judge referring to himself (herself) as the "convictor" or the "incarcerator." More recently, a new "occupation" has come into vogue: "the child advocate." These individuals sanctimoniously pride themselves on the fact that they defend the rights of children (unlike the rest of us who are "unconcerned"). They, of course, hold that "children never lie about sex abuse," and they accept as valid every statement a child makes that might verify sex abuse and support vigorously the "rights" of their child clients to be protected from the sea of perpetrators who are ever craving to subject them to a wide variety of abuses. What I have to say here about "validators" applies to "child advocates" in that we are basically dealing with the same group.

Examiners who read what I have just said here, and find themselves angry and offended, might give serious consideration to the possibility that there is validity to my criticisms and that rectification of the problem might be warranted. Those who respond to such irritation by not giving any consideration to the possibility that my criticisms are valid are likely to be depriving themselves of the opportunity to learn some useful principles and interviewing techniques.

WHO ARE THESE PEOPLE?

There is no generally recognized training program for sex-abuse evaluators. The field is basically "open territory." Some have training in psychology, some in social work, and many in various aspects of "social service." Many are self-styled "therapists" who have absolutely no training at all, even in related disciplines. It is important for the reader to appreciate that all states have specific requirements for certification in such disciplines as psychiatry, clinical psychology, and clinical social work. States vary, however, regarding their receptivity to providing certification for family counselors, pastoral counselors, nurse practitioners, and other types of mental health professionals. I do not know of a state (and there may be one or more) that provides certification for therapists. In most states (to the best of my knowledge), anyone can hang up a shingle and say that he (she) is a therapist, and one cannot be prevented from practicing because of the failure to have certification or a license. In short, one cannot be penalized for practicing without a license if one does not have to have a license in the first place.

Some of these self-styled therapists have also crept into the sex-abuse field, where they serve not only as evaluators but as therapists. Sex abuse is a "growth industry." Until recently, they tell us, when we were not aware of how widespread the sex-abuse phenomenon was, we did not train many individuals who were qualified to conduct such evaluations and provide appropriate treatment. Now we have come to appreciate how limited are the number of people available to take on the monumental task of processing all these cases. Legislators are bombarded with requests to provide more money to train and recruit such personnel. Because of the great demand for their services and the paucity of highly qualified people, standards are lowered, requirements are ill defined, and a wide variety of obvious incompetents are conducting such evaluations and treatment.

Many of these ill-qualified and incompetent people take "courses" in which they are trained by others of questionable qualifications. What happens then is that the misinformation, ignorance, and gullibility of the teachers get passed on to their students and so on down the generations. Unfortunately, most students (happily not all) take a very passive and receptive view of their instructors. They make the assumption that the teachers must know what they are talking about or otherwise they wouldn't be in their position of authority. Walk into any classroom (even in the most prestigious colleges), and one will see an army of students writing down reflexly what their instructors are saying. The "best" students are those who regurgitate what they have been asked to memorize. Even in the best schools this process takes place. I believe that only a very small percentage of students is actually encouraged to question the authority of their instructors and to genuinely think independently and creatively. It is no surprise, then, that evaluators, who have most often had limited and even inferior educational experiences, are even more prone to accept as gospel what they are taught in these courses. Even I, who have provided expert testimony in courts on this subject, *never* received formal training (during my medical school, internship, and residency days in the 1950s) for differentiating between bona fide and fabricated sex-abuse allegations. However, I have at least had many years of training in related fields — psychiatry, psychology, child development, and medicine — which have served as a foundation for my subsequent three decades of experience in this realm.

Most sex-abuse workers operate in the context of a government agency, referred to in many states as the Child Protection Team (CPT) or Child Protection Service (CPS). Many unashamedly refer to themselves as "validators." Those who utilize this term make no secret of the fact that the vast majority (if not all) of the children they have evaluated have been sexually abused. As implied in their name, they are merely there to "validate" what everybody knows happened anyway. Otherwise, why would the child be brought forth? I am certain that a judge who referred to himself (herself) as a "convictor" would not be considered to have the neutrality that we expect of people in such positions. Yet, we say little about validators and the obvious bias implied in their very title. In their partial (I emphasize the word *partial* here) defense, many of these people have been working in settings where the vast majority of referrals relate to intrafamilial sex abuse, where the prevalence of genuine abuse is quite high. They have had little experience in vicious child custody disputes and day-care center allegations, where the incidence is quite low. They have had little experience with making the differentiations necessary when evaluating referrals in the latter categories. Accordingly, they tend to assume that what was valid in the intrafamilial situation is valid in other situations as well. This could have been a rectifiable problem. Unfortunately, for the reasons provided throughout this book, this problem was not addressed adequately or soon enough, thereby contributing to the prevention of the mass hysteria phenomenon that we are experiencing at this time.

WHAT DO THEY DO?

To date, I have spent about 300 hours viewing and analyzing the videotapes of these examiners, and I have spent about 3,000 hours (my best estimate) reviewing their reports and reading their depositions and testimonies. Although such materials have been sent to me from various parts of the United States, it is amazing how similar the techniques are. Accordingly, I consider myself to be in a good position to describe in detail exactly what these examiners do. In fact, because they work so similarly – regardless of what part of the country they operate in – it is easy to make some generalizations about their techniques.

"Children Never Lie"

In order to justify and advance their prediction that the child will be found to be abused, they espouse the dictum that "children never lie" on all issues related to sex abuse. The reasoning goes that a young child, having had absolutely no exposure to or experience with sexual encounters, must be telling the truth if such an encounter is described. A related slogan is "believe the children." Even those who have had children them-selves, and deal daily with the fabrications and delusions of their own children, have no problem waving these banners. In order to maintain this position they must deny the "polymorphous per-versity" that Freud described almost a hundred years ago and that all parents (if they will only just look and listen) have to accept as a reality of childhood. They have to believe that the sex-abuse prevention programs to which many of their evaluees have already been exposed are in no way a contaminant to their investigatory process. They have to believe, as well, that there has been no coaching or programming (overt or covert, conscious or unconscious) by the parents who bring their children to them, even though a vicious child custody dispute may be taking place or the child is one of many parading out of a nursery school in which there is an atmosphere of mass hysteria. They have to deny, as well, the previously described ubiquity of sexual stimuli in our society.

Early Interview Maneuvers

Typically, the child is brought to the interview by the accusing mother. It is rare for people who refer to themselves as validators to request that the father be present. On those occasions when I have had the opportunity to ask a validator why he (she) did not invite the father, common responses are, "He would deny it anyway so there's no point to my seeing him" and "My job is not to do an investigation; my job is only to interview the child in order to find out whether the child was sexually abused." Also, little time is generally spent with the mother. Usually, the validator merely gets a few bits of information from her about the nature of the sex abuse but, typically, does not spend significant time obtaining more information, especially details of the evolution of the sex-abuse accusation, significant information about the setting in which the sex abuse allegedly occurred, and data that might relate to the mother's credibility. I have seen a number of situations in which the validator, approximately three-quarters of an hour later (by which time the child's initial "evaluation" has been completed), has written on the chart that the child was sexually abused *and* that the father sexually abused the child. In many of these cases, the validator is not even aware of the fact that the parents are involved in a highly acrimonious divorce dispute. The assumption is made, at the outset, that all one need do is interview the child and that one should be able to obtain the information necessary to "validate" the abuse. The assumption is also made that one should be able to obtain this information in the vast majority of cases from children ages two to four and that if one just perseveres long enough, the confirmatory information will ultimately be forthcoming.

My experience has been that in about half of the cases in which I·have been involved, the mother has remained in the interview room with the child throughout most, if not all, of this initial interview. The justification given here is that the child would be uncomfortable alone in the room with a strange examiner. There is often little appreciation of the fact that the mother's presence serves as a serious contaminant and increases formidably the likelihood that a false accusation will be supported by the mother's presence. Often the mother helps the child "remember" what to say and the examiner appreciates her cooperation and input, with little appreciation of the educational and programming process that is transpiring.

Quite early in the interview, the validator considers it important to provide the child with some "guidelines" regarding what her purpose is. The rationale here is to help the child feel comfortable in a strange environment. Typically, the child is told that the validator's job is to help "protect" children and to help keep them "safe." Although the validator usually believes that the use of these words helps relax the child, there is little appreciation of the fact that they accomplish just the opposite. Their implication is that the child is somehow being exposed to some danger and that the validator's job is to provide protection. Such reassurances, then, only serve to entrench – at the outset – the notion that the child has indeed been subjected to some dangerous situation. Although sex abuse is not mentioned at this point, it is clear about the path down which the child is being led.

Many validators do have a short "warm-up" period (five minutes or so), the purpose of which is to help the child become more comfortable. During this period the child may be permitted to play with traditional play-therapy equipment. This initial phase may appear harmless enough and may even appear to be good therapeutic technique. However, typically, the examiner is not really concerned about the fantasies produced by the traditional equipment at this point. I have seen tapes in which very significant material has been elicited during these first few minutes, but the examiner has not appreciated the value of what is being said because she has been merely going through the motions of this "warm-up" period in order to get the *real* material, which is obviously related to sex abuse. Accordingly, this material was not followed up, material that was genuinely related to what was on the child's mind at that point. Had this material been focused on, the examiner might have obtained true data that could have been useful for ascertaining whether the child had been sexually abused. So even here, where good technique is ostensibly being utilized, we already see a serious contaminant. Although some validators' examining rooms do have a traditional assortment of child play equipment, I have seen many (via videotape studies) in which the only equipment visible to the child are the anatomical dolls. Although these dolls are usually dressed, they are the *only* play equipment available to the child. Accordingly, when the child is presumably invited to engage in free play, the only equipment available is guaranteed to elicit material related to sexual issues. Some validators will, however, engage in a period of free play with standard equipment, play that is designed to relax the child and make the child more comfortable and familiar with the examiner.

Ascertaining Whether the Child Can Differentiate Between the Truth and a Lie

Early in the interview these examiners first satisfy themselves that the child can differentiate between the truth and a lie. In many states, the judge, lawyers, and all other investigators are required by statute to submit to this requirement before proceeding with the substantive issues in the interview. For example, when examining children in the three-to-five-year age level, a typical maneuver in the service of satisfying this requirement is for the examiner to point to a red object and say to the child, "This is *red*. Is that the truth or a lie?" If the child answers that the examiner is being truthful ("That's true"), the examiner may then proceed by pointing to something that is green and saying, "This is black. Is that the truth or a lie?" If the child then states that the examiner is then "lying," the examiner may then proceed to a series of other equally asinine questions in order to demonstrate that the child knows the difference between the truth and a lie.

The examples I have given here are the most common types of questions asked to ascertain whether the child knows the difference between the truth and a lie. Examiners who go through this ritual fail to appreciate that for children between the ages of two and five the word *lie* might mean "a naughty word." Between ages five and eight-and-a-half it might merely mean "something that isn't true," including a mistake (Frost, 1986). In these examples just mentioned, the child might be thinking that the examiner has made a mistake. Yet, because the child uses the words *mistake* and *lie* interchangeably, the child might say that the examiner is lying when in actuality the child believes the examiner made a mistake. McIver (1986), in a discussion of the works of Jean Piaget (*The Moral Development of Children*), refers to Piaget's position that "a lie is what an adult says it is." So much for the semantic problems inherent in this simplistic approach to the assessment of the child's credibility.

But there are other problems associated with this line of questioning. The same child is not asked the question, "Santa Claus brings you gifts at Christmas time. Is that the truth or a lie?" "The good fairy left money under your pillow after your tooth fell out. Is that the truth or a lie?" Obviously, asking any question that would be more complex—one that might result in the child's demonstrating confusion between fact and fantasy—would confront the examiner with the obvious fact that young children have great difficulty differentiating between fact and fantasies, between the truth and a lie, in a wide variety of areas. As mentioned previously, we adults are not famous for our capacity to make such differentiations either. Ignoring this obvious fact enables such examiners to proceed with the "validation." Nor do they set up situations in which the child is likely to lie, such as when accused of a transgression. Children traditionally lie under such circumstances, but to demonstrate this in the interview would, of course, raise questions about the child's veracity regarding the sexual abuse issue.

In one sex-abuse case I was involved in, a four-and-a-half-year-old child got all the "right" answers to the simplistic truth-vs.-lie questions of the aforementioned type. The following interchange then took place:

> *Investigator:* Good girl! And what happens to you if you tell a lie?
> *Child:* Your nose gets bigger and bigger and bigger and bigger and bigger and bigger every time you lie!
> *Investigator:* Like who?
> *Child:* Like Pinocchio.
> *Investigator:* (laughs)
> *Child:* (laughs)

Not surprisingly, this examiner had concluded that the child knew the difference between the truth and a lie and totally ignored the implications of the child's subsequent response, namely, that her ability to differentiate between fact and fantasy did not go so far that she recognized as fantasy the nose-growing scenario in the Pinocchio story. The traditional questions select the most obvious and simplistic examples in order to "prove" that the child knows the difference. Examiners who have formulated these questions do not select questions that might truly tax the child's capacity to differentiate between fantasy and reality. It is like giving an intelligence test in which the most difficult questions are "How much is one and one?" and "What color is grass?" It is to be noted here, also, that both the child and the investigator laughed together. We see here one example of the levity that is often present in these interviews. It is often a game that can best be called, "See if you can guess the right answers." I will elaborate on this point below.

It is of interest that later in the same interview, while the child was providing allegedly corroborative details about the alleged sex abuse, she suddenly interrupted the interviewer and the following interchange took place:

> *Child:* Is my nose growing?
> *Investigator:* No. Why?

Child: 'Cause.
Investigator: Does that mean you're lying?
Child: No.
Investigator: Well, then, why would your nose be growing?
Child: (laughs) I don't know, to make a joke.
Investigator: Ohh . . . a joke . . . okay. Have you ever seen your daddy without his clothes on?
Child: Uhh . . . sometimes.

Here, the child clearly recognized that she was lying and feared that the investigator would learn this by seeing her nose grow. The child is clearly fearful that her lying would be revealed and then protected herself from anticipated criticism for lying by claiming that she was only joking. They both laughed together about her "joke." We see here also another typical maneuver of validators, specifically, the selective inattention phenomenon. The examiner did not explore further the obvious possibility that the child was lying about the sex abuse and that her concern about her nose growing was an obvious manifestation of such concern. Rather, she and the child both laughed and then the examiner went back to her sledgehammer leading question regarding the sex abuse: "Have you ever seen your daddy without his clothes on?" Here we see another clear demonstration of the child's inability to differentiate fact from fantasy, at least with regard to the Pinocchio story. Yet this examiner concluded that the child could indeed differentiate between the truth and a lie and that she was indeed being truthful when she claimed sex abuse. Again, we see the levity of the interview, a point that I will comment on below.

What is also ignored by validators is the fact that *knowing the difference* between the truth and a lie is very different from the issue of whether or not the child *will actually* lie. These evaluators make the very naive assumption that because the child knows the difference between the truth and a lie, the child will not lie. The vast majority of people who commit crimes know quite well the difference between the truth and a lie; yet, they still lie, especially in response to questions that might divulge their guilt. The whole inquiry regarding differentiating between the truth and a lie is a mockery, a sham, a ritual that these people go through in order to convince themselves that they are indeed getting to "the truth."

"The Truth" as Code-Term For *Sex Abuse*

In ancient Rome it was generally held that slaves made poor witnesses at trials because they would typically lie. Accordingly, slaves who were called upon to testify were often beaten mercilessly in order to be sure that they were telling the truth. This was the main reason why masters were generally reluctant to allow their slaves to testify—after being subjected to the aforementioned methods for "helping" them recall the truth, they were left basically useless as workers. During the Middle Ages (and beyond) it was quite common to "help" witnesses remember what the truth was by stretching their bodies on a rack, progressively turning thumb screws, and utilizing other methods of recall-engendering torture. And there are many parts of the world today in which torture is still routinely used in order to help prisoners remember "the truth." If the reader believes that such methods were used only by barbarians in the distant past, or only utilized today by sadistic psychopaths in other parts of the world, then the reader is out of touch with what is going on among mothers, validators, and children whom they are unrelentlessly encouraging to tell "the truth." The methods of torture are no longer physical; they are emotional and psychological. But they are methods of torture nevertheless. And there is only one *truth* being extracted: admission of sexual abuse. Once the child is brought down the sex-abuse disclosure track, the child is unrelentlessly programmed to tell "the truth."

At those times when the child describes the sexual molestation, the interrogator is satisfied, and all agree that the child has been telling the truth. When, however, the child recants, does not remember, or exhibits ambivalence regarding whether the molestation did indeed occur, the child is then repeatedly coerced to tell "the truth." Denial of sexual molestation is not the truth. Only a description of molestation is "the truth." It doesn't take much time for the child to learn that the truth is merely a code-term for sexual molestation. Accordingly, before interviews with validators and other interrogators, the mother intermittently (from the sidelines) reminds the child to tell "the truth." In interviews as well (mothers are often present during these interviews), the mother intermittently (from the sidelines) reminds the child to tell "the truth." And the validator knows quite well that there is only one truth. She and the mother speak the same language. They have the same shibboleth for sexual molestation. And the validator will not accept the child's negations and will only ask the child to tell "the truth." The bottom line of this whole scenario is the validator's going to court and claiming that she believes that the child was telling "the truth."

Naming the Body Parts

The next step in a typical evaluation is to bring out some pictures of naked people, the ostensible purpose of which is to find out what names the particular child being interviewed uses for the various organs and orifices that are to be found on the human body. I have not yet seen or heard of an examiner who will ask the mother questions regarding what terms the child uses for these body parts. To do so would deprive the examiner of the opportunity to introduce the subject of sexuality at the outset, which is what the discussion of naming body parts is really all about. Typically, these examiners are oblivious to the importance of the psychological blank screen (like the blank card on the *Thematic Apperception Test [TAT]* [Murray, 1936]) as the most valid way of obtaining information about what's going on in a person's mind. (The TAT is a psychological test in which the patient is presented with a series of cards, each of which depicts a somewhat vague scene, and the patient is asked to describe what is going on. There is no "right" answer, and the projections so elicited provide the examiner with information about the psychological processes that are operative in the patient's mind. The blank card, in which there are no external stimuli, is the most anxiety-provoking—but at the same time the most revealing—of the series of cards.) Sometimes the so-called anatomically correct dolls (see below and Chapter Seven) are brought out at this point to serve the same purpose, namely, to ascertain the names the child uses for the various sexual organs.

These examiners do not seem to appreciate that the anatomical pictures and dolls are different from just about anything the child has previously seen and are likely to produce strong emotional reactions. This serves to obfuscate and suppress other emotions (having nothing to do with sex abuse) that may be at the forefront of the child's mind. Also, they transmit to the child the message that the examiner is interested in discussing matters related to naked bodies, and this serves to draw the child's thoughts, fantasies, and feelings into that path. Whether the examiner uses the pictures or the dolls, a significant contamination has been introduced at the outset, a contamination that already makes it unlikely that the examiner will truly find out whether the child has been genuinely abused. After exposure to these pictures or dolls, one cannot know whether the child's verbalizations about sex abuse were the result of an actual experience or were stimulated by the naked human figures.

The So-called Anatomically Correct Dolls

Anatomically correct dolls (for the reader who does not know about these monstrosities) are dolls that specifically depict genital parts (including pubic hair) and breasts (most often with prominent nipples). Many have gaping orifices (vagina, anus, and mouth). Many cannot be justifiably called "anatomically correct" because of the disproportion between the size of the genitals and the rest of the body. More recently, in order to protect themselves from this criticism, many of these workers have referred to the dolls as "anatomically detailed dolls." No matter what they are called, they are a serious contamination to any meaningful psychiatric interview. Unless the child has been previously evaluated by one of these "validators," it is most likely that the child has never seen such a doll before. The child cannot but be startled and amazed by such a doll. The likelihood of the child's ignoring these unusual genital features is almost at the zero level. Accordingly, the dolls almost demand attention and predictably will bring about the child's talking about sexual issues. Again, the contamination here is so great that the likelihood of differentiating between bona fide and fabricated sex abuse has become reduced considerably by the utilization of these terrible contaminants.

If one gives a child a peg and a hole, the child is going to put the peg in the hole unless the child is retarded or psychotic. Give a child a wooden doughnut; the child will inevitably place his (her) fingers in the hole. Give a child one of these female anatomical dolls with wide open mouth, anus, and vagina, the child will inevitably place one or more fingers in one of these conspicuous orifices. For many of these workers, such an act is "proof" that the child has indeed been sexually abused. The assumption is made that what the child does with these dolls is an exact, point-by-point replication of what has occurred in reality. The argument goes that these dolls "help" the child verbalize what has happened. Presumably, they help the child overcome cognitive and verbal immaturities or psychological tensions and anxieties that interfere with direct discussion of the abuse. And this is a basic premise upon which these people work. All this is crass rationalization. It justifies the use of these materials to verify what the examiner believes in the first place, namely, that the sex abuse did occur. No competent psychologist or psychiatrist believes that the child's projections on the Rorschach, TAT, or doll play necessarily reflect reality. What they do reflect is the child's cognitive processes, wishes, aspirations, and distortions— although they certainly could include reality elements.

These examiners do not consider the obvious alternative that what the child does with these dolls may have nothing at all to do with what has taken place in reality. But, of course, if they consider this possibility, then they have greater difficulty "proving" the sex abuse, which is what they are there to validate. With such a premise, it is no surprise that many of these examiners claim to have seen hundreds of children in succession, all of whom have demonstrated that they have been sexually abused.

In the course of playing with these dolls, it is almost inevitable that the child will take the penis (often erect) and place it in one of the orifices of the female doll. And this, of course, "proves" that the child engaged in the activity depicted by the insertion, namely, fellatio, vaginal intercourse, or anal intercourse.

Even if the child is two years old and even if the insertion of the alleged perpetrator's penis into the child's vagina would produce lacerations, abrasions, contusions, severe bleeding, and pain (inevitably the case when an attempt is made to place an adult male penis into a two-year-old's vagina), the examiner concludes that the sexual intercourse did take place because it was demonstrated during doll play. What is one of the great paradoxes of this field is that some of these examiners are indeed trained clinical psychologists (some even have Ph.D. degrees) and utilize projective instruments as a vehicle for learning about the child's fantasies, wishes, aspirations, and distortions. Yet, in the same report, when the child projects material about sex abuse onto these dolls, the assumption is made that here the child is telling the truth. This cognitive "splitting" on the part of such examiners is testament to the power of the human mind to deceive itself in the service of one's wishes, in this case the wish to see sex abuse.

Sophisticated and sensitive clinicians allow a child to begin a session by scanning and selecting from an array of materials that are available for play evaluation and therapy. They recognize that the child's selection will be determined by the psychological processes that are pressing for expression. They appreciate that the toy so selected will be the one that is most likely to serve as a catalyst for the expression of those thoughts and feelings that are most important for the child to reveal at that moment. Validators have little if any appreciation of this phenomenon. Many of these examiners often have nothing else on their shelves but the anatomical dolls and, even if they do, do not allow the child free play and selection. Rather, validators confront the child with the dolls immediately. Of course, there are some examiners who do indeed allow the free play. However, the actual presence of such dolls is such a significant contaminant that I would consider any examiner who utilizes them to be incompetent. I am not alone in this regard. In the state of California, testimony based on information elicited from such dolls may not be admissible in court. It is my hope that other states will soon follow suit. In Chapter Seven I comment further on these dolls.

I have seen tapes of a few validators who play the game *Doctor* as part of their evaluative procedure. They use dolls that can be undressed and that are part of a doctor game that can be purchased in toy stores. There is a stethoscope, blood pressure cuff, otoscope, and other medical paraphernalia. Of course, the dolls can be undressed. Obviously, the game provides the validator with yet another opportunity to get the child to undress the dolls and to talk about the various parts of the naked body.

Leading Questions

Most of these examiners seem to be oblivious to the value of the open-ended question, the question that has a universe of possible responses. It is not pure chance that competent examiners begin each session with questions such as "So what's on your mind?" and "What would you like to talk about today?" The equivalent opening for young children is to allow the child free play in the playroom in order to choose whatever object is desired. Well-trained examiners appreciate that the best toys for projection are those that have the fewest contaminating stimuli. Accordingly, play objects such as blocks, sand, clay, crayons, and blank paper serve well in this regard because they do not have any intrinsic contaminations to the pure projections. Dolls are less valuable for this purpose but, because they resemble human beings, are more likely to catalyze projections related to human relationships. However, experienced examiners recognize that the fewer details the doll has, the better it will serve as a stimulus for the child's uncontaminated projections.

Validators do not seem to appreciate these well-established principles of child psychological evaluation and treatment. Well-trained examiners recognize also that all play equipment are props and should only be used when the examiner cannot elicit the desired material by using verbal catalysts. They know also that the best verbal catalysts are questions of the aforementioned type, which do not include any specific references to any particular issue. Rather, the questions are designed to facilitate the expression of a universe of possible thoughts and feelings. What the child selects from that universe is therefore highly meaningful and provides the examiner with useful information about what is going on in the child's mind. Even a request like "Tell me about school" is not a good one to begin with because it directs the child to only one of the universe of possible areas that might have been focused upon.

Validators appear to be oblivious to these important techniques in child evaluation and treatment. Many "zero right in" with their leading questions. Almost invariably, these direct the child to talk about sex abuse. Some typical examples: A three-year-old girl has placed her finger in the vagina of the anatomically correct doll. As mentioned, validators almost invariably consider this to be "proof" that some adult perpetrator has placed his (less often her) finger in the child's vagina. The examiner, without any previous discussion about the child's father, says, "Does your daddy put his fingers in you just like that?" The child may not have been sexually abused and may never even have thought about her father doing such a thing. Yet, the question plants a seed in the child's mind that such an event could possibly take place. Another example: While holding up the chart of a naked woman (allegedly to find out what names the child uses for the various body parts), the examiner asks, "Has your teacher ever touched you there?" The child may never have been abused by her teacher or anyone else. The question introduces the visual image of such an encounter and contaminates, thereby, all further inquiry regarding sex abuse, by the teacher or anyone else for that matter. After that, whether the answer is yes or no (see below), one does not really know whether such an event actually occurred. In Chapter Seven I comment further on leading questions.

Belief in the Preposterous

No matter how preposterous the allegation, no matter how absurd, these examiners will believe them. They have no trouble believing that adult males can have sexual intercourse with two-year-old girls with no evidence of pain, bleeding, and trauma. The facts that the adult male penis cannot be accommodated by the vagina of a two-year-old and that insertion will result in the aforementioned consequences are ignored. They would believe that a child can be forced to drink urine and eat feces and yet, minutes later, be perfectly happy and friendly—without any sign or symptom of the indignities suffered only a few minutes earlier. They would believe that one person was able to undress 25 children, engage them simultaneously in a wide variety of sexual activities, and then dress them quickly in order to be picked up by their parents. And yet, not a single child left wearing the wrong sock, underwear, or other article of clothing. They believe that children can have swords inserted up their rectums with no medical evidence. They believe that children can be smeared with feces and yet be so quickly and thoroughly cleaned that not a scintilla of evidence remains to serve as a clue as to what transpired only a few minutes earlier.

They believe that children can witness the barbecuing of babies, the slaughtering of infants and animals, and their burial in cemeteries, without breathing a word of these activities for weeks and even months after exposure to these atrocities. They can believe that dozens of children can be sworn to silence without ever breathing a word to their parents about any of the tortures to which they have been subjected. They believe that children can be stabbed with scissors, knives, and other instruments in their mouths, ears, noses, vaginas, and anuses, and yet not reveal any signs of their trauma (even on medical examination) only minutes after the event. They believe that bands of men wearing masks and costumes (clowns, big bad wolf costumes, cops, firemen) can enter a school, involve the children in a wide variety of the aforementioned rituals and abuses, and then sneak out, completely unobserved by teachers, parents, and school administrators.

They believe that pedophiles are exceedingly clever and cunning in their methods, so much so that even the most experienced detectives and investigators may find no clues or remnants whatsoever of the wide variety of tortures, rituals, and abuses to which these children have been subjected. Even though no one has ever found any of the dead bodies that these children describe having been buried as a part of their abuse rituals, and even though many cemeteries have been dug up in the search for such bodies, they still believe that such sacrifices indeed took place. Many believe that hundreds of babies have been burned, stabbed, cooked, barbecued, and drowned in the service of warning children that this will happen to them if they breathe a word of their experiences to their parents. Even though not one remnant of any of the aforementioned infants has been found, the belief is still strong. It is as if the "common sense" cells and tracks of their brains have been extirpated by a special operation.

Rationalizing as Credible the Incredible

Validators are highly skilled in their ability to utilize rationalization. This is especially the case when they are confronted with material that is absurd and ludicrous. They have devised a series of cognitive maneuvers in the service of this goal. For example, if a child states that the sexual molestation occurred in her (his) own home (something that no one on the scene believes is true), the explanation provided is that the child is fusing two different scenes and that such fusion is common among children of that age. A child may say that the molestation took place in the therapist's office, again something that no one believes is the case. A common explanation is that the child has relocated the abuse in order to place it in a "safe haven," thereby lessening the trauma. Every conceivable distortion that a child might possibly entertain can be given credibility by such rationalizations. When confronted with the fact that shoving a sword up the rectum of a child (or anyone else for that matter) would produce quick and certain death, the examiner will say, "Perhaps it was a toy sword or perhaps the perpetrator *threatened* to shove a sword up the child's rectum and the child is merely creating a fantasy that is a derivative of this threat." The greater the number of such rationalizations, and the more frequently the examiner needs to twist logic and thereby invoke one of these rationalizations, the greater the likelihood one is dealing with a false accusation. In fact, this is one of the hallmarks of the false accusation.

In one of the cases in which I was involved, many of the children claimed that the alleged perpetrator had brought the children to his own home and that he himself had called the police and was then arrested. No one really believed this and no one ever went to the trouble of asking the police whether there was any record of such a call. The therapists and investigators, however, came up with a whole series of rationalizations to justify this aspect of the scenario. Some of the explanations proffered: "He (the alleged perpetrator) dressed as a policeman and made believe that he made the call," "The children misinterpreted someone as being a policeman when he really wasn't," and "Someone else threatened that they would call the police." In the same case, one three-year-old girl claimed that the perpetrator had cut off his penis, put it on his head, and squeezed it to the point where blood dripped on the top of his head. Most of the validators (although I cannot say all) did not believe that this actually happened. Certainly, no one called in a urologist to examine the boy to see if there was any evidence for this "penisectomy" that this boy allegedly performed on himself. One of the rationalization scenarios considered was that the boy put ketchup on his head and that the child somehow considered the ketchup to be blood. (Interestingly, rationalizations were not provided for other aspects of this ludicrous scenario.)

When such rationalizations are utilized, those testifying in support of the defense do well to make comments along these lines: "Every time one utilizes this type of rationalization maneuver—a rationalization that serves to make credible the incredible—one adds to the likelihood that we are dealing here with a false accusation. The most likely things are most likely. The most likely explanation is the one that is more often related to reality. Every time one must do mental gymnastics in order to make credible the incredible, one is providing support for the argument that one is dealing with a false accusation."

Selective Ignoring of the Impossible

The aforementioned activities, although outlandish and preposterous, are still within the realm of possibility (often narrowly so). When examiners are confronted with information that even they recognize as impossible, then other psychological mechanisms must be utilized in order to maintain the delusion that the child has been sexually abused. For example, in the course of describing the abuse, the child says that her mother (the one who brought about the allegation in the first place) was present at the time when the nursery school teacher fed her "doo-doo." Because the examiner does not believe that this was the case, this bit of information will be disregarded with the excuse that "the child was tired at the time." When the child states that the abuse took place in the examiner's office, a common explanation is "That's her way of saying that she views my office as a 'safe haven' and that's why she spoke about the abuse taking place here." When confronted with inconsistencies that are mutually contradictory and would suggest that one of the versions has to be impossible, the examiner might state: "It's not my job to confront the child with inconsistencies or impossible things," or "Of course, that's impossible," or "That's just a product of his imagination. It's not even worth discussing." Sometimes nothing at all is said and when the child makes an impossible comment the examiner just goes on ignoring it as if it were never spoken.

Another way of dealing with the introduction of impossible elements into the scenario is to utilize the mechanism of splitting. Specifically, if the child states, for example, that all four grandparents were there and observed the molestation, the examiner might state, "She's confusing two events, the molestation and the family gathering." In this way the sex-abuse scenario remains "pure" and its contaminants removed.

Sometimes the examiner does not even feel the need to provide a rationalization for ignoring material that might suggest that the story is not valid. One child claimed that her nursery school teacher had picked up a car and had thrown it into a tree. The examiner unashamedly stated that, of course, this could not have happened and then went on to accept as valid all other information that supported the conclusion that sex abuse did indeed occur. This selective inattention to noncorroborating data is one of the hallmarks of these validators' interview techniques.

Another maneuver utilized by these examiners is this: "Her denial proves it's true. That's typical of these children who are sexually abused. They keep denying that it happened. That's because they were threatened with terrible consequences if they were to admit it. I've seen many such cases." Another explanation that is provided when a child denies that anything has happened: "She's repressing it. It's been so traumatic to her that she can't talk about it. It may take months of therapy before she'll be able to admit it, even to herself. That's how powerful these repressive forces are." Obviously, there is no way for accused people to win when the child is interviewed by such validators.

The Utilization of the Yes/No Question

Competent examiners recognize the risks of the yes/no question and generally avoid it. They realize that little information is obtained from such a question. (This is something that attorneys and judges have yet to discover.) When one gets a yes or no answer, one does not know whether the interviewee is lying, telling the truth, or merely providing an answer (yes or no selected at random) to "get the examiner off his (her) back." Spontaneously verbalized sentences and paragraphs are far better sources of information. These essay-type answers are more likely to be revealing of the child's true thoughts and feelings. But these examiners do not appreciate this obvious fact. Generally, they persist in the inquiry until they get the yeses they want. Often the questions are quite confusing to the child, to the point where the child does not even understand what is being asked. In such an altered state of consciousness, the child is likely to say yes to every question in order to get the examiner to come to the end of the unrelentless series of questions. Because children are suggestible and wish to ingratiate themselves to authority, they may provide all the yes answers the examiner wishes (I have discussed children's suggestibility in greater detail in Chapter Three).

The yes/no question is also used in association with the seed-planting phenomenon. On day one the examiner asks the child if she ever had a particular sexual experience—for example, whether her father put his penis in her mouth. (This is a very dangerous thing for an adult male to do to an unreceptive child [unless the child has no teeth].) The child may never have entertained such a fantasy. However, the very question has now planted the seed, and the visual image of such an encounter has now been created in the child's mind. At that point, the child who has never had such an experience will say no. During a subsequent interview, the interviewer (or another examiner) may ask the same question. This time the visual image will be brought out of memory storage and the child may be somewhat confused regarding whether or not such a thing actually happened. A young child may not be able to differentiate between an image that depicts something that actually happened and an image that depicts something that was suggested. In fact, we adults are not immune from such a process either. (Professional brainwashers and propagandists know well that if you tell someone a lie frequently enough, the person will believe it.) If the child then shows some confusion regarding whether such an event actually took place, the examiner is sure to hammer away at the question: "Are you sure?" "Are you sure he didn't do it?" Finally, the child says yes, and that will serve as another nail in the coffin of the accused. This is not only tragic for the falsely accused person, but it is also tragic for the child who is likely to believe for the rest of her (his) life that the event took place.

The So-called Indicators of Sex Abuse

Validators utilize an ever-growing list of "indicators" of sex abuse. These are the behavioral manifestations, which can be observed by parents, that result from sex abuse. These manifestations can be roughly divided into two categories (although there is some overlap). The first is those behaviors that most competent and knowledgeable observers would consider normal. In fact, healthy and knowledgeable parents would also consider these behaviors to be part of the normal child's repertoire. It takes a zealous validator and a gullible parent to share in the delusion that these behavioral patterns are indeed the result of sex abuse.

The second category is psychological symptoms, which are listed in the manual of psychiatric disorders. Most competent evaluators recognize that these disorders have a wide variety of causes, most of which have absolutely nothing to do with sex abuse. The validators would consider most of them to result from sex abuse. Of course, this division into two categories is my own; validators have just one long list of behavioral manifestations, all of which derive from sex abuse. I will now provide a few examples from each of these two categories.

"Indicators" That Would Be Considered Normal by Competent Evaluators *(Pathologizing Normal Behavior)* Examiners who consider the behavioral manifestations in this category as signs of sex abuse must be abysmally ignorant of normal childhood development. Or, if they have received such training, they have to obliterate from memory what they have learned. Furthermore, if they themselves have children, they must deny their own observations (past or present) regarding the presence of these behaviors in their offspring. The frequency with which they are capable of ignoring what they observe is a testament to the power of the human mind to utilize selective inattention, denial, and projection. Some examples: One doesn't have to be a full professor of pediatrics to know that many children are still bedwetting at ages three and four. This does not prevent validators from considering bedwetting at that age to be a sign of sex abuse.

One does not have to be a full professor of child psychiatry to know that normal children exhibit occasional nightmares, especially in early to mid-childhood. Some of these nightmares are the direct result of frightening experiences, such as watching a "scary" movie on television or actually having a frightening experience. Such nightmares are part of the desensitization process that helps children adapt to these frightening exposures. Other nightmares arise sui generis and have complex psychological meanings that are still not completely understood (Gardner, 1988b, 1992b). Validators will typically consider nightmares to be one of the important indicators of sex abuse. Although frequent nightmares of certain types might very well be an indicator of sex abuse, these evaluators typically do not attempt to make any differentiation between normal nightmares and those that might be exhibited by sexually abused children. I have never seen a validator's report in which an inquiry has been made into the frequency and content of nightmares and the relationship between the described nightmares and the alleged abuse. Rather, the presence of a nightmare—any nightmare at all—is used as strong support for the conclusion that the child has been sexually molested. This is not the way the human mind works. If a nightmare is being used for the purposes of desensitization to a trauma (whether it be sex abuse or another kind of trauma), it is likely to serve this function soon after the abuse—even the first night following the abuse—not months or years later. Validators ignore this obvious fact in order to justify the use of the nightmare as an indicator of sex abuse. We see here yet another example of the previously described hiatus phenomenon.

Furthermore, if the nightmare is to be used as an indicator, one would think that the examiner might want to consider the *content*, especially with regard to the likelihood that it relates to sex abuse. Most validators do not seem to have any need to do this. Any nightmare, regardless of content, is used as an indicator. They can justify this with the old psychoanalytic standby that it represents a symbol for the sex abuse. The most common normal nightmare involves some malevolent entity (a point, a shadow, a monster, a bad man, a bogeyman, etc.) coming menacingly toward the child. Typically, the child wakes up just before the malevolent figure reaches the child. Invariably, evaluators consider this malevolent entity to be symbolic of the alleged sex-abuse perpetrator. Whatever the meaning of this nightmare (and my own opinion on its meaning is irrelevant at this point), they do not see the need to explain how the vast majority of nonsexually abused children will have the *same* nightmare. (The reader who is interested in my opinion of the meaning of this common nightmare might wish to refer to my publications on the meaning of children's dreams [Gardner, 1986, 1988b].) In one case in which I was involved, a three-year-old child described how the "big bad wolf" was chasing her in a dream. Predictably, the validator concluded that this dream was proof that the child had been sexually abused. This child was one of many involved in a day-care center sex-abuse "scandal." The parents actively communicated with one another regarding their children's symptoms and, not surprisingly, within a few weeks most of the other children were also reporting big bad wolf nightmares. Rather than consider this to be the result of the mass hysteria phenomenon, all the validators concluded that the big bad wolf represented the alleged perpetrator, an adolescent boy whom I considered to be completely innocent.

The parents are alerted to be on the lookout for any behavioral changes. Predictably, these are considered to be manifestations of sex abuse. In order to utilize this criterion, one must ignore the obvious fact that every child in the history of the world exhibits behavioral changes, often on a day-to-day basis. Normal children exhibit behavioral changes; if they did not, they would not be moving along the developmental track. The one-year-old behaves differently from the newborn infant, the two-year-old differently from the one-year-old, the three-year-old differently from the two-year-old, and so on. Development does not run an even course; rather, it moves in spurts and plateaus. Furthermore, children go ahead three steps and go back two steps, and so it goes. Children have good days and bad days (just like adults). Some of the behavioral changes that validators will consider manifestations of sex abuse are an increase in sibling rivalry, refusal to go to sleep, changing attitudes regarding foods, periods of uncooperative behavior, defiance, and exaggerated reactions to normal disciplinary measures. In one well-publicized case, the parents informed the validator that the child had developed an aversion to tuna fish. The validator quickly concluded that this was yet another proof that the child had been sexually molested. Her reasoning: The human vagina, as everyone knows, smells like fish. This child's aversion to tuna fish must relate to the fact that she had performed cunnilingus on her nursery school teacher, the alleged perpetrator. With the utilization of logic like this, it is easy to see how impotent accused individuals feel when the alleged victims are being evaluated by such sick and/or ignorant examiners.

The list of indicators that is derived from normal childhood behavior is long, and there are many other examples. I usually refer to this practice by validators as *pathologizing normal behavior.* Temper tantrums are normal, especially between the ages of two and four. In fact, it is reasonable to say that all children, at some time or another, exhibit temper tantrums. It is the normal, natural, primitive way in which children express their anger. Predictably, validators consider temper tantrums to be a manifestation of sex abuse, the child allegedly acting out the anger that was built up against the perpetrator. All siblings exhibit frequent rivalry. In fact, it is ubiquitous. The first-born is generally king (queen) of the world. The second-born now requires that the throne be shared, and worse, the time that the parents must devote to the second is greater than that which must be devoted to the first. This produces even greater rivalrous feelings. And when other children come along, there is even greater resentment over the fact that the parental involvement must be shared among all the children. I would go further and say that children who do not exhibit rivalrous feelings toward their siblings have some form of psychopathology, especially in the area of suppression and repression of their thoughts and feelings. Once again, validators ignore this reality and would consider sibling rivalry to be one of the indicators.

And now to masturbation. All normal children explore their bodies from time to time and do not differentiate between the genital area and other parts. They have to learn from others that touching oneself in that particular area is socially unacceptable, especially in public. Children usually learn by themselves that stimulation of that area can provide pleasures different from those derived from touching other areas. Although orgastic capacity is possible at birth, most young children under the age of nine or ten do not stimulate themselves to the point where they reach orgasm. Those who do may very well have been prematurely introduced into the pubital and postpubital levels of sexual arousal. Certainly, such introduction can be the result of sex abuse. But this is not the *only* reason why a younger child might masturbate to orgasm. In some children it is a tension-relieving device, especially when they grow up in homes in which there has been significant privation and/or stress. In some it can serve as an antidepressant. When a knowledgeable evaluator hears that a child is masturbating, the examiner will make detailed inquiry about the frequency, the time of onset, the circumstances under which it occurs, and whether the child masturbates to orgasm. All this information is useful in ascertaining whether the masturbation is related to sex abuse. Typically, validators do not make such inquiries. They hear the word *masturbation* and that is enough to prove that the child has been sexually molested.

In the late nineteenth century, in both the United States and England, we witnessed a period of excessive preoccupation and draconian condemnation of childhood masturbation. Unfortunately, physicians (who should have known better) were actively involved in this campaign of denunciation and attempts to obliterate entirely this nefarious practice. Doctors considered it to be the cause of a wide variety of illnesses, e.g., blindness, insanity, and muscle spasms. Various kinds of restraints were devised in order to prevent children from engaging in this dangerous practice. Some girls were even subjected to clitorectomies, so dangerous was the practice considered to be. Parents were given a long list of symptoms that were considered to be concomitants of masturbation. Some of the alerting signs were temper tantrums, bedwetting, sleep disturbances, appetite changes, mood fluctuations, and withdrawal. Obviously, in the hundred years since those sad times, we seem to have gone back full circle. The same list of symptoms that were indicators of masturbation are now considered to be indicators of sex abuse. Legrand et al. (1989) have written a fascinating article describing the similarities between the masturbation hysteria of the late nineteenth century and the sex-abuse hysteria of the late twentieth century, with a comparison of the lists of "indicators."

It is unfortunate that physicians have played an important role in these crazes. As I have discussed in detail elsewhere

(Gardner, 1991a), it was a doctor (Dr. William Griggs of Salem) who first "diagnosed" the children in the Salem witchcraft trials as being possessed by the devil. Doctors were actively involved in the antimasturbation fanaticism of the late nineteenth century. And, unfortunately, there are "doctors" actively involved in the present fiasco. There are physicians who are diagnosing sex abuse in the vast majority of children they examine, utilizing criteria that are generally considered to be within the normal range (e.g., anal "winking" and hymenal tags). And there are other kinds of doctors (Ph.D. psychologists and M.D. psychiatrists) who are serving as validators and therapists and are perpetrating the abominations described throughout this book.

"Indicators" That Would Be Considered by Competent Observers to Be Symptomatic of Disorders Having Nothing to Do with Sex Abuse   Here I refer to those symptoms that are to be found in the *Diagnostic and Statistical Manual of the American Psychiatric Association (DSM-III-R)*. If we are to believe the validators, just about any symptom in this manual that could possibly have a psychogenic (or environmental) cause can be a manifestation of sex abuse. These would include depression, phobias, tics, obsessive compulsive rituals, conduct disorders, antisocial behavior, hyperactivity, attention deficit disorder, headaches, gastrointestinal complaints (nausea, cramps, diarrhea), musculoskeletal complaints, etc. In short, if there is any possibility of attributing symptoms to sex abuse, the evaluator will do so. It is easier to do this when one is ignorant of the multiplicity of factors that can indeed bring about such disorders. Many validators lack this training and so have no problem with this oversimplified approach to the explanation for these symptoms.

The maneuver utilized here is to assume, often reflexly, that a psychopathological manifestation is the result of sex abuse. In order to do this, the evaluator must make the assumption that the child came from a normal, healthy home and all went well prior to the alleged sex abuse. Typically, these examiners do little if any inquiry into the home situation. Detailed interviews of the parents are quite uncommon; rather, from the outset, the primary (and often exclusive) focus is on the child. Most often the conclusion that the child was sexually abused is made within a few minutes, with absolutely no inquiry into the family background, especially with regard to the presence of factors that might be contributory to the development of psychopathology. Many of the validators would not know how to conduct such an evaluation, so limited has been their training. Obviously, if they were to conduct such inquiries, they might learn that the origin of the symptoms has nothing to do with sex abuse but is more likely to be the result of psychopathology- engendering environmental influences.

Another common maneuver is to attribute to sex abuse the symptoms that arose directly from the series of interrogations conducted by the validators, lawyers, psychologists, psychiatrists, prosecutors, etc. A detailed history (which most of these individuals fail to take) would quickly indicate that the child's symptoms began at around the time of the interrogations, rather than at the time of the alleged sex abuse. Of course, validators would not want to believe for one moment that their allegedly sensitive and nonintrusive investigations could bring about psychopathology. I consider my own interviews to be sophisticated and to be ones in which I avoid the numerous interview pitfalls and errors described in this book. However, I openly admit that even my interviews may be stressful to children and might contribute to the development of psychopathology. However, in my defense, they are limited to a few interviews and I do not conduct "therapy" for sex abuse, unless I am 100 percent convinced that the abuse has indeed taken place. With regard to the stresses related to the few interviews I do conduct during evaluations, I believe that their effects are small as far as their contribution to producing long-term and even permanent psychopathology. Such stresses are a small price to pay when one considers the terrible consequences to a falsely accused person if the court (and often the jury) is not convinced that the allegation is false. We have to weigh here the trauma to the child caused by my inquiry against the psychological trauma suffered by a falsely accused person—whose life may be destroyed and who may even be incarcerated for many years.

"The Sex Abuse Syndrome"

There are some examiners who claim that the child's symptoms are manifestations of "the sex abuse syndrome." When asked what exactly is the sex abuse syndrome, they will describe the particular symptoms that the child exhibits (both normal and abnormal) that are allegedly manifestations of it. As mentioned, there is no symptom that escapes being included under this rubric. The fact that *DSM-III-R* does not recognize such a syndrome and the fact that it is the only syndrome in the history of psychiatry that includes *all* psychological symptoms and behavioral manifestations—both normal and abnormal—does not deter these evaluators from resorting to this meaningless statement. I sometimes have the thought, when reading the reports of such evaluators, that *DSM-III-R* should have as its subtitle: "The Sex Abuse Syndrome."

The Child Sexual Abuse Accommodation Syndrome

The *child sexual abuse accommodation syndrome* (CSAAS) is a term that was introduced by Summit. His first article on this syndrome appeared in 1983. The syndrome consists of a series of reactions that children have to being sexually abused in the intrafamilial situation.

Five stages are described:

1. Secrecy
2. Helplessness
3. Entrapment and accommodation
4. Delayed, unconvincing disclosure
5. Retraction

The primary manifestations of each of these stages will first be presented. Because Summit's cases involved primarily father-daughter incest, the abuser will be referred to as the father (he) and the victim as the daughter (she).

Secrecy   Typically, the child is warned by the abuser never to reveal the molestation because to do so would result in terrible consequences. The threats range from allusion to vague and nonspecific consequences to very specific ones such as "Your mother will kill you," "I'll kill your dog," and "I'll kill you." These threats may be repeated with the result that the child may become terrorized. Often, when the child attempts divulgence to others, they will respond with denial, disbelief, and warnings to the child never to mention such things. These responses tend to communicate to the child that terrible acts have been perpetrated, too terrible to talk about. They also have the effect of discouraging the child from disclosing the molestation and thereby entrenching the secrecy phase.

Helplessness   Because of the disparity in size and power between the child victim and the abuser, the child feels overwhelmed and helpless. In the incestuous situation this feeling of helplessness is even more profound because the child has no escape. Children are generally easily intimidated by an adult molester, and the child's failure to find an adult advocate entrenches the sense of helplessness.

Entrapment and Accommodation   It is rare for the molestation to be a one-time occurrence. Rather, more often it is repeated over months and even years. Most often the adult becomes addicted to the molestation because it is so easily accomplished. Over time, because there is no escape, the child resigns herself to the experiences as part of life's pattern.

A variety of accommodation maneuvers may then develop. Some children lessen their helplessness by developing the delusion that they themselves have been the initiators. Others become receptive and accommodating in the hope of earning the love and acceptance and avoiding the rejection of the abuser. By psychological splitting, the child denies that the abusing father is in any

296 THE "VALIDATORS" AND OTHER EXAMINERS

way "bad" and becomes convinced that he is "good." Another accommodation mechanism is a derivative of the child's being told that if she does not submit, the father will have no choice but to turn to other siblings. In this way the child comes to feel that she is acting nobly. Keeping the secret protects the mother from the devastating effects of disclosure, and this too enables the child to feel good about the maintenance of secrecy. Protecting the father from the disruption of the home, divorce, and even a jail sentence can also serve this purpose. Summit (1983) puts it well: "Maintaining a lie to keep the secret is the ultimate virtue, while telling the truth would be the greatest sin."

The rage engendered in this situation becomes internalized and contributes to the development of a wide variety of psychopathological mechanisms and, when it erupts, it is often released via a wide variety of antisocial behaviors. Males are more likely to act out their anger, whereas females are more likely to internalize it. For adolescents drugs and alcohol may be used to deal with the painful affects attendant to the ongoing state of subjugation.

Other accommodation mechanisms are described by Summit, but to detail them would be beyond the purposes of this summary.

Delayed, Conflicted, and Unconvincing Disclosure In many cases disclosures may never be made. In most, adolescence is the earliest time of disclosure. Even in this period the mother may be disbelieving, especially because of her appreciation of the disruptive consequences to the family of her doing otherwise. Furthermore, child protective agencies, as well, may be incredulous of the child's accusations, and this too contributes to the child's sense of frustration, impotent rage, and ambivalence over disclosure.

Retraction Once the disclosure has been made, many of the predictions of the father come to be true and these contribute to retraction. Summit states:

Her father abandons her and calls her a liar. Her mother does not believe her or decompensates into hysteria and rage. The family is fragmented, and all the children are placed in custody. The father is threatened with disgrace and imprisonment. The girl is blamed for causing the whole mess, and everyone seems to treat her like a freak. She is interrogated about all the tawdry details and encouraged to incriminate her father, yet the father remains unchallenged, remaining at home in the security of the family. She is held in custody with no apparent hope of returning home if the dependency petition is sustained.

The message from the mother is very clear, often explicit. "Why do you insist on telling those awful stories about your father? If you send him to prison, we won't be a family anymore. We'll end up on welfare with no place to stay. Is that what *you* want to do to us?"

Once again, the child bears the responsibility of either preserving or destroying the family. The role reversal continues with the "bad" choice being to tell the truth and the "good" choice being to capitulate and restore a lie for the sake of the family.

DRAWBACKS AND RISKS OF UTILIZING THE CHILD SEXUAL ABUSE ACCOMMODATION SYNDROME AS A DIAGNOSTIC INSTRUMENT

The reader does well to be reminded that Summit's article was published in 1983. Accordingly, the phenomena described therein relate to observations made 10 or more years ago. Levels 4 and 5 presuppose an incredulous mother and a disbelieving community, especially police and child protective services. This is no longer the case. In fact, the opposite is true, namely, mothers are much more likely to believe the child and the police and child protective services err in the opposite direction and are likely to accept as valid even the most frivolous and absurd accusations.

It is also important to appreciate that Summit describes a series of reactions of children who have been sexually molested in the intrafamilial situation. Accordingly, the syndrome's application to other situations, such as nursery schools, molestation by a stranger, molestation by a babysitter, and molestation by a teacher, is inappropriate. In all of these situations the child is not living with the molester and is not as likely therefore to develop the kinds of reactions seen at those levels in which there is a sense of entrapment, especially levels 2 and 3.

This point is worthy of repetition: It is not likely that the progression of symptoms described by Summit in 1983 will be applicable to children in 1992, even those who have been molested in the intrafamilial situation. And this is especially the case for levels 2, 3, 4, and 5.

The CSAAS has enjoyed a significant amount of attention, especially via its utilization as an instrument for diagnosis, i.e., ascertaining whether a child has been sexually abused. And its use in this regard has not been confined only to allegations of sex abuse in the intrafamilial situation, but encompasses other situations as well. Nowhere in Summit's original article does he claim that it should be used for this purpose. Furthermore, on numerous occasions (examples to be cited below) he has specifically stated that such utilization is inappropriate and goes beyond the intentions of his description. *The primary problem has been that overzealous and/or incompetent examiners have used the CSAAS as a diagnostic technique with the result that many innocent individuals have been found to be guilty of sex abuse and some have even been incarcerated.*

The *secrecy* phase has been expanded by overzealous examiners to include *denial*. Accordingly, children who have denied being sexually abused are considered to be in the secrecy phase and therefore exhibiting manifestations of sex abuse. This, of course, puts the accused in a no-win situation. If the child *admits* sexual abuse, then the allegation is considered confirmed. If the child *denies* sexual abuse, then the allegation is *still* considered confirmed by concluding that the denial is merely a manifestation of the child being in the secrecy phase of the CSAAS.

A child's sense of *helplessness* is also utilized to confirm sex abuse. Other sources of feelings of helplessness are not considered. A child, for example, exposed to and embroiled in a vicious child custody dispute may feel like a rope in a tug-of-war. Rather than attribute such feelings of helplessness to the situation causing it, the child's helplessness is viewed as yet another manifestation of the CSAAS, and this is considered to lend support to the validity of the accusation.

The wide variety of symptoms described by Summit (only a few of which I have mentioned above), symptoms that are a derivative of the child's feelings of chronic *entrapment*, have also been utilized by overzealous examiners as confirmation of sex abuse. The causes of such symptoms are myriad and cover the wide variety of situations that could bring about psychogenic psychopathology. For example, Summit refers to the rage engendered in children during this phase. He then talks about the various symptoms that may arise depending upon whether the rage is internalized or externalized. There are hundreds of situations that can engender anger, situations that have absolutely nothing to do with sex abuse. Using such symptoms as an indicator of sex abuse is again a grievous misapplication of the CSAAS.

Ambivalent and *unconvincing disclosure* has also been misapplied. Certainly, children who have been genuinely abused may be conflicted with regard to their disclosures. However, children who are providing false accusations may also be conflicted about disclosures for various reasons. They may feel guilty and ashamed about their false accusations, especially if they are old enough to appreciate the grave consequences of their accusations. They may fear retaliation by the accused, not because they have divulged the secret of true sex abuse, but because they recognize that he has every reason to be incensed over their duplicity. Their divulgence may be unconvincing because the child is confused. The person programming the child and overzealous examiners may be trying to convince the child that the abuse did indeed take place, and the child has no recollection of such. During the process of this educational "programming" process, the child's disclosures may indeed be unconvincing and conflicted. Again, the utilization of this manifestation as a criterion for bona fide sex abuse is a grievous misapplication of the CSAAS.

Last, *retraction* may very well be seen in children who are sexually abused, especially because of their appreciation of the consequences to the accused of the divulgence. However, children who promulgate false accusations may also recant. Here, too, the recantation may stem from guilt, shame, and the appreciation of the terrible consequences to the accused of the accusation. These may not have been appreciated by the child prior to the accusation. When recantation is considered diagnostic of abuse the accused is again placed in a no-win situation because the retraction is not considered of any consequence. The accused is deemed guilty if the child admits it, and he is considered guilty if the child denies it. There are examiners who boldly state, "The fact that the child denies it is proof that it happened." I hope the reader will believe me when I say that this is a common statement and not just one made by some fringe lunatic validators. One mother stated that her child's therapist said to her, with regard to her five-year-old son's denial, "It's not what he didn't say, but *how* he didn't say it, that proves that he was abused." (This statement provides support for those who hold that even people with low IQs can be creative.) Again, such a ludicrous position cannot but leave the accused with a sense of impotent rage.

Other Misapplications of the Child Sexual Abuse Accommodation Syndrome

Mention has already been made of two areas of misapplication of the CSAAS, namely, its misuse as a diagnostic instrument and its use in sex accusations which are not in the intrafamilial setting. Its application in highly volatile divorce disputes has been particularly grievous because of the high incidence of false accusations in that situation. Because a sex-abuse accusation is an extremely powerful vengeance and exclusionary maneuver, such accusations have become increasingly widespread in recent years. In the nursery-school situation as well, where the hysteria element is often operative, there is also good reason to believe that false accusations are widespread. In both of these situations the child is not living with the alleged perpetrator, and so an important factor in bringing about the CSAAS is not present.

Another misapplication of the CSAAS has been its use for preschool children. Summit (1991) states that the population from which he drew conclusions regarding the CSAAS were not "very young children" nor did he focus on "boy victims." Unfortunately, the CSAAS has been used as a diagnostic instrument for preschool children, and this has especially been the case in some of the more highly publicized nursery school cases such as McMartin in California, the Kelly Michaels case in New Jersey, and the Fijnje case in Florida.

Concluding Comments Regarding the Sexual Abuse Accommodation Syndrome

Summit's CSAAS (1983) was not designed to serve as a diagnostic instrument. To utilize it in this way may result in innocent individuals being considered guilty of having sexually abused the alleged victim.

The symptomatic manifestations described by Summit are applicable to children abused in the intrafamilial situation and are far less likely to be applicable to children abused in other situations, such as children embroiled in child custody disputes and children exposed to sex-abuse hysteria in nursery school situations.

The symptoms described by Summit refer to children seen prior to 1983 when child protection services, police, and parents were less alerted to the ubiquity of child sex abuse and were more likely to be disbelieving of children's disclosures. Not only is this no longer the case, but there is good reason to believe that the opposite now is true and that there are many overzealous examiners who are ready to accept as valid any allegation, no matter how frivolous and no matter how preposterous. Accordingly, the CSASS may not even be applicable now to children whose abuse has occurred in the intrafamilial situation.

These drawbacks notwithstanding, the syndrome may have some validity as a "cause of suspicion" for an evaluator. A child who indeed has a history of such manifestations may very well have been abused, and the syndrome can serve to alert the examiner to the *possibility* of abuse. Whether or not the child does exhibit manifestations of the CSAAS, the examiner should be utilizing a much wider variety of investigative medical and psychiatric techniques in order to ascertain whether or not the child has indeed been sexually abused.

Techniques That Reinforce a Positive Sex-Abuse Response

When one views carefully audiotapes and videotapes (especially the latter) of validators' interviews, one frequently observes significant positive reinforcement of any of the child's responses that indicate that the abuse took place and negative reinforcement and even punishment of comments that do not support the conclusion of sex abuse. Quite often the child's mother (the accuser) is in the room and the child's father (the accused) is absent and may not even know that the accusation has been made. And this is especially the case for the first interview, which may serve as a foundation for all subsequent interviews, especially with regard to what is being expected and desired by the interrogators. Some common positively reinforcing comments made after the initial disclosure: "Very good," "That's right!" "You're doing very well!" and "You're doing a very good job!" If the child is reluctant to talk, he (she) may be told that following the interview the child will be taken to an ice cream parlor, a fast-food restaurant, or provided with some similar reward. At the end of the interview the child may be told, "There, you've said it. Don't you feel good now?" When the child doesn't get the "right" answers, the examiner may react with cold stiffness, incredulity, and repeated questions that get across the message of dissatisfaction with negative responses. McIver (1986) made the following comments about a videotaped interview of a four-and-a-half-year-old girl who was accusing a man of molesting her:

> It was clear that the child was being led to say that the defendant had touched her genital area with his hands and his mouth. The worker smiled and hugged her when she made such allegations, and was cold and non-demonstrative when she didn't.

My own experience has been that McIver's observation is typical, so much so that truly neutral questioning is rare, at least among the videotapes of these inquiries that I have observed.

The So-called Disclosure

Prior to the last few years, I had no problem with the word *disclosure*. It produced no particular emotional reactions in me, and I did not react to it differently than to the vast majority of other words in the English language. However, in the last few years I find myself reacting with a combination of nausea and irritation every time I hear the word, especially when used by a validator or when I see it written in a sex-abuse evaluation. I believe that if I were hooked up to a polygraph, I would exhibit strong physiological reactions to that word, even when used in a context having nothing to do with the assessment of whether I was telling the truth. These reactions derive from its use by the vast majority of validators. They use the word *disclosure* to indicate "proof" or "validation" that the child has been sexually abused. When the child states that he (she) has been sexually abused and/or provides a description of such molestation (no matter how fragmentary), the examiner gleefully records that she has "made a disclosure." There is no neutrality here regarding whether the child's statement is truly indicative of actual sex abuse. Rather, the word *disclosure* becomes equated with confirmation that the sex abuse did indeed occur because the child described such an event. The high point of the interview has been reached. The sex abuse of the child has now been "validated." All the preliminary contaminations have proven successful. The first domino has now fallen and the rest can be expected to tumble down, one after the other, with ultimate "justice" being done to the alleged perpetrator (who is no longer the "alleged" abuser but is now merely the sex abuser). At this moment of exultation, many validators have no problem even writing down the name of the accused and stating that the sex abuse by him has been confirmed by this "disclosure."

In the nursery school and day-care-center situations the problem is even worse. Here, a group of validators has been engaged to evaluate a parade of children, many of whom from the outset deny having been sexually abused. Predictably, after a series of interviews in the hands of these people, the inevitable "disclosure" is elicited (or, more accurately, coerced). Telephone calls are made, word gets around, and the message is buzzed: "Did you hear? Gloria made a 'disclosure'." There are many innocent individuals who are rotting in jail because of such "disclosures," and I have no embarrassment describing my strong emotional reaction to the word. In fact, I would go further and say that if I were not to react strongly to this word, it would represent insensitivity on my part as a physician dedicated to the welfare of those who seek my services.

More Direct Coercive Techniques

Although all the aforementioned techniques are, in a sense, coercive, there are some maneuvers that these people utilize that are more obviously so. One is: "I know it happened and I'm going to keep you here until you tell me the truth." Other examples: "Things like this happen to lots of kids. I know many children to whom the same thing happened. Don't worry. I'll protect you." "You can tell me. I'll make sure that he'll never do *that* again." "Now, Bobby, Jamie, Bill, Bob, etc., all told me that it happened to them. Are you going to be the only child in the whole school who is not going to tell me what happened?" The examiner here is appreciative of children's enormous need to conform and not be different from the majority. I refer to this as the "Keeping-up-with-the-Joneses" phenomenon (see Chapter Three). Sigston and White (1975) have studied this phenomenon in depth and provide excellent verification of its existence. It is indeed a powerful method for extracting a false sex-abuse accusation. Other examples: "I don't believe that's the only place he touched you. I want you to tell me about the *other* places. You know there *were* other places." The physical torturing of a witness or an accused party is an ancient tradition. Inflict pain on an individual and you are likely to get a confession. These techniques are the modern-day equivalent of physical torture and, like their ancient antecedents, they also work with a high degree of predictability. Our founding fathers presumably ensured (in our Constitution) protection from such tactics for all Americans. Unfortunately, there appear to be some "loopholes" in that these torture techniques are still being utilized.

The "Inappropriate-Affect" Maneuver

American Psychiatric Glossary (Stone, 1988) defines *affect* as:

> Subjective experience of emotion accompanying an idea or mental representation. The word affect is often used loosely as a generic term for feeling, emotion, or mood. Affect and emotion are commonly used interchangeably.

When I was in my psychiatric residency training, in the late 1950s, *affect* was more strictly defined as the subjective (mental) aspect of an emotion, whereas the term *emotion* referred to both the mental and the physical concomitant. The physical concomitant could sometimes be observed via observation of facial expression, body movements, etc. There are typical facial expressions for fear and rage, and even lower animals exhibit similar changes in facial musculature in situations that might engender such reactions. However, we can say absolutely nothing about the internal mental state of a lower animal when the facial expression suggests fear or rage. We can make speculations, but we cannot know. With human beings we can make speculations and we can learn something about the internal mental concomitants of what the individual is telling us. But even then we cannot know with certainty, and it is a question of our belief in the credibility of the individual who describes the affect. My main point here is that affect, when used in a traditional and purer sense, is not something that another individual can know. It is only something that is known to the individual experiencing that affect.

Commonly, the word *affect* is linked with the terms *appropriate* and *inappropriate*. Psychiatrists commonly say that the individual's affect was "appropriate to ideation" or that the individual's affect was "not appropriate to ideation." This distinction is especially useful when evaluating people who are suspected of being schizophrenic, because schizophrenics typically exhibit a disassociation between affect and ideation, i.e., their affect may be inappropriate to ideation. For example, a schizophrenic may giggle upon learning about the death of a close relative.

The reader may be wondering at this point what all this has to do with the techniques used by validators. It has a lot to do with one of the techniques they use for justifying the conclusion that a child was sexually abused, especially when their conclusion is at variance with what people of common sense consider to be reasonable and highly likely. A common maneuver in such situations, especially in the courtroom, is for the validator to claim that the child's verbalizations about sexual molestation "ring true" because the affect that was associated with these verbalizations was appropriate and consistent. The validator's clinical notes only mention what the child verbalized. On occasion there may even be a notation, "The child's affect was appropriate." However, the reader must take the word of the validator that the affect was indeed appropriate, because the reader was not there to get any sense of whether this statement is true or false. Even when one has a transcript of an audiotape (or videotape), one may not know what the affect of the child was, especially whether it was appropriate or inappropriate. All one has on a transcript are the child's words. The transcript can at least provide verification of the validator's notes, but it cannot say anything about affect.

Although audiotapes can sometimes give the listener information about the child's affect, it is primarily videotapes that enable other examiners to determine whether or not the validator's *subjective impression* of the affect was possibly valid. My experience has been that in the vast majority of cases in which the evidence was strong for a false accusation, the videotapes indicated strongly that the child's affect was *not* appropriate to ideation, in spite of the validator's statement that such was the case. For example, the interview may have a gamelike quality, a quality not in any way suggested by the transcript. It is as if the child and interviewer are playing the game: "Can You Guess What I'm Thinking?" Such interviews are basically an educational process in which the child, by getting a series of "right" answers, learns a certain scenario that is then reproduced for the next interrogator. There is often a levity to such interviews, especially when the child gets many *right* answers. And this is especially the case when the examiner provides the kinds of positive reinforcement described above, e.g., "Good girl" or "That's right." On occasion the videotape will confirm levity suggested by the written transcript (as was the case of the previously described four-and-a-half-year-old girl who believed that her nose would grow like Pinocchio's if she lied to the investigator).

The "Dissociation" Maneuver

Related to and overlapping the inappropriate affect maneuver is the "dissociation" maneuver. *American Psychiatric Glossary* (Stone, 1988) defines dissociation as:

> The splitting off of clusters of mental contents from conscious awareness, a mechanism central to hysterical conversion and dissociative disorders; the separation of an idea from its emotional significance and affect as seen in the inappropriate *affect* of schizophrenic patients. (p. 52)

The term *dissociative disorder* is defined as:

> Category of disorders in *DSM-III-R* in which there is a sudden, temporary alteration in normally integrated functions of *consciousness*, identity, or motor behavior, so that some part of one or more of these functions is lost. It includes psychogenic *amnesia*, psychogenic *fugue, multiple personality*, and *depersonalization disorder*. (p. 52)

As can be seen, a central element in the dissociation mechanism is a "splitting off" of one part of mental life from another. Accordingly, the aforementioned inappropriate affect of schizophrenic patients is one kind of dissociation. People who have been subjected to severe traumas may dissociate the traumatic material (both cognitive and emotional) in order to protect themselves from the psychological pains attendant to full conscious appreciation of the trauma. Not surprisingly, many validators have embraced the concept and have applied it to sexually abused children as part of the validation process. A common situation in which this maneuver is utilized is the one in which a child is continually subjected to an interviewer who is sledgehammering the child into describing the details of the alleged sexual encounter. If the child becomes mute, "spaced out," or otherwise uncommunicative, the validator may indicate that the child has now "dissociated." The implication here is that the interview has touched on the sex-abuse material and the child is "dissociating" this material because of the psychological pain attendant to its being allowed entrance into conscious awareness. I cannot deny that this may be a possible explanation for the observed phenomenon. However, we are most often dealing here with three- and four-year-old children, and the spacing out is generally not accompanied by any verbal statements that might provide the observer with some hint regarding exactly what is going on in the child's mind. Accordingly, one cannot state with certainty that the validator's speculation regarding what is going on is not valid.

However, other explanations are not given serious consideration. For example, one possible explanation relates to the fact that the child feels overwhelmed by the coercive questions and is confused by the failure to have provided the "right" answers. The child's withdrawal, then, serves to protect him (her) from further responses, responses that might again be sensed by the child as incorrect because they do not meet with the examiner's approval. It is almost as if the brain computer has broken down, so overwhelmed has it been with data. Also, there may be a fear element here that plays a role in the child's "freezing up." Not having gotten a series of "right" answers and sensing the examiner's mounting exasperation and/or impatience, the child may become afraid to provide another answer and be met once again with further negative feedback by the examiner. Freezing up protects the child from such unpleasant reactions by the evaluator. I have never yet seen a report in which the examiner has considered these alternative explanations for the child's spacing out. Rather, the examiner simply states that the child has "dissociated," and this is viewed as automatically confirmatory that the sex abuse has taken place.

Involvement with Parents, the Accused, and the Accuser

Typically, these evaluators see little or no need to interview the accused. In fact, I have come across some who actually believe that it is illegal to interview the accused. This requires a delusional misinterpretation of the U.S. Constitution. Although the accused has the right *not* to speak to the accuser (whether in a court of law or under any other circumstances), this does not mean that the accused *cannot* speak to the accuser if he (she) wishes to. Most accused individuals (especially those who are genuinely innocent) are most eager to confront their accusers. Yet these accused individuals are often deprived of this constitutional right. There are validators who, after interviewing only the child, unashamedly write in their reports that the child was abused and *name* the accused without ever having interviewed or even spoken to him (her).

Generally, these evaluators do not even conduct detailed inquiries with the adult accuser (most often the child's mother). They take at face value her accusations and do not consider the possibility that they may be fabricated or delusional. Rather, they do the opposite, namely, take any shred of information that might support the conclusion and use it in the process of "validation." As mentioned, they will consider normal childhood behaviors as manifestations of sexual abuse, e.g., nightmares, bedwetting, temper tantrums, mood swings, and, of course, masturbation. The mother's report of these occurrences serves to confirm that the child was indeed abused. And the validator becomes even more convinced that the abuse took place when the child exhibits in the office what are traditionally considered to be psychopathological manifestations. Rather than look into other possible sources of such problems in family life—sources unrelated to sexual abuse—they immediately come to the conclusion that these behavioral difficulties are the direct result of the sex abuse. (As mentioned, every symptom in the diagnostic manual has been listed as a possible result of sex abuse. Accordingly, everything now fits together and the abuse is "validated.")

When questioned as to why they did not interview, or even contact, the accused, validators will provide a variety of excuses — none of which are justifiable. Some will claim that time just does not permit the kind of intensive investigation that will allow for inquiries with the accused. I cannot imagine a hospital stating publicly that time does not permit the surgeon to spend more than 30 minutes on any operation. I have been told by validators when questioned as to why they didn't contact the accused, "I'm not an investigator." This too is a rationalization. An examiner *is* an investigator. An examiner is investigating whether or not sex abuse took place. Another common rationalization: "He'll lie anyway, so it's a waste of time." I suspect that this is a derivative of the "children never lie" dictum. The whole principle is: "Children never lie and accused individuals never tell the truth." And that wraps it all up. Next case!

Another argument given: "The police don't want us to question the alleged perpetrator until after they have finished with their investigation of him." There are a number of possibilities here. One is that the police never made the request and this is simply a lie being used as a rationalization. But let us, for the sake of argument, accept as valid the statement that the police did indeed make this request. If they did, then it is inappropriate for the evaluating facility to comply with it. The ethical position for such a facility to take is that they — not the police — decide who should be interviewed and who should not and *when* the interview should take place. If the police insist on imposing their interview schedule on the facility, then the facility should consider it unethical to provide such services. I would never agree to involve myself in an evaluation in which the police are telling me when I can see an individual. I assume the police would not be telling a surgeon when he can operate, nor would any competent surgeon agree to this restriction if the police had the gall to make the request. In short, if an evaluating facility is complying with police directives, then it is compromising its evaluative procedures. There is no justification for such compliance.

Obviously, there are many ways in which interviewing the accused could be useful in such evaluations. These not only involve interviewing the accused alone, but also interviewing the accused in joint sessions with the accuser, the alleged victim, and all three together. This is the best method for "smoking out" the truth. Family therapists know this well, but these examiners seem to be oblivious to this obviously useful technique. The argument that the child might be traumatized by such a confrontation is not an excuse to preclude its utilization entirely. First, examiners should have the freedom to decide whether or not such joint interviews would do more good than harm. By automatically precluding involvement with the accused, this option is not utilized. Furthermore, although such confrontations may be psychologically traumatic to the child under certain circumstances, one must also consider the psychological trauma to the person falsely accused. It can result in a completely ruined life and/or years of incarceration. These rights of the accused are rarely considered by these examiners. On many occasions I have been asked to interview a child—and only the child—and then make a decision regarding whether the child has been sexually abused. I have *never* accepted such an invitation. Before involvement in the case I make every attempt to obtain a court order in which all three parties are required to participate (the accuser, the accused, and the alleged victim), individually and in any combination that I consider warranted. This does not automatically involve a joint interview with the alleged victim and the accused, but it often may. In either case, I must be given the freedom to make that decision.

WHY DO THESE PEOPLE FUNCTION IN THIS WAY?

Obviously, there is a wide variety of individuals who serve as validators. Equally obvious is the fact that for each person, there is a multiplicity of factors operative in this career choice. There are also many factors involved if one is to explain why these individuals function as they do. No one person will fit into all of the categories mentioned below; however, I am convinced that each of these explanations is applicable to at least some of the individuals who serve as validators.

Impaired Educational Background

There is no question that we are witnessing a progressive deterioration of educational standards throughout the United States. Although there are certainly areas in which things have improved in recent years, there is no question that there are more areas in which things have degenerated—so that the overall picture is much more in the direction of downhill than uphill. The erosion of standards has occurred at just about every level, from kindergarten to graduate school. No one can deny that there has been a deterioration in the public schools during the last 25 years, certainly in the large cities and probably in suburban and rural communities as well. One compelling verification of this (if one needs it) is the progressive deterioration of Scholastic Aptitude Test (SAT) scores. But the numbers here do not reflect the full story. The test has progressively become easier. Accordingly, if the test were as rigorous as it was in the past, the deterioration would become even more apparent. Here I will discuss what I consider to be some of the important factors operative in bringing about this deplorable situation, factors at the elementary, high school, and college levels.

Elementary Schools

"All Men Are Created Equal"   Ours is seemingly an egalitarian educational system that assumes "all children are created equal" and all children should receive the same educational exposure. This is misguided egalitarianism. The principle blinds itself to the obvious intellectual differences that children exhibit from the time of birth. On the one hand, educators appreciate that every intelligence test has its distribution curve, from the intellectually

impaired to the superior. On the other hand, our educational system in the United States does not properly accommodate these differences. I do not claim that there is no appreciation at all of these differences; I only claim that educators do not exhibit enough appreciation of these differences. Although there are special classes for learning-disabled children and technical high schools for those who are not academically inclined, the main thrust and orientation of our educational system is toward preparing youngsters to enter colleges and universities. The ideal presented is that all children should go to college and those who do not achieve this lofty goal bring shame upon themselves and their families.

Most countries have no problem accepting the fact that not all children should be on a strong academic track. Accordingly, in many countries, somewhere between the ages of nine and eleven, children are divided into three tracks. The highest track ultimately leads to the university. The lowest track ends formal, intense academic training at about age eleven or twelve and then emphasizes various trades and skills. And the middle track is somewhere between the two. Of course, if the child has been placed in the wrong track, there is still a possibility of switching. We would do well in the United States to institute such a system. It would protect many children from significant grief. To say that all people should be *treated* equally before the *law* is certainly reasonable. But to say that all are *created* equal is absurd. What is more reasonable to say, as Orwell did in *Animal Farm*, is that "some are more equal than others." Because public statements of such inegalitarianism are considered undemocratic in our society at this time, it is extremely unlikely that such changes will be introduced into our system in the foreseeable future—certainly not before the end of this century.

Some Causes of School Deterioration   Many factors have contributed to school deterioration in recent years. One relates to teachers' salaries. It is unreasonable to expect that schools can attract high-quality, well-educated individuals when other careers provide much greater pay. In most municipalities garbage men make as much as, if not more than, elementary school teachers. The public sector can generally afford to provide higher salaries than private and parochial schools; yet the public schools seem to be getting the poorest-quality teachers. The more dedicated teachers are willing to take positions for lower salaries in order to work in the more academically stimulating atmosphere of the private and/or parochial schools.

I believe there has been a general diminution in the commitment of teachers to the educational process. I am not claiming that this is true of all teachers, only that the percentage of teachers who are deeply committed to their profession has been sharply reduced in the last 15 to 20 years. One manifestation of this trend is the decreased frequency with which children are required to do homework. Giving children homework most often involves homework for the teacher. And less dedicated teachers are not willing to take on this extra responsibility. In previous years there were many more teachers who were viewed to be somewhat hard-nosed and dictatorial, yet their despotism was benevolent and years later their students were able to look back with gratitude on what they were "forced" to do. These days, "respect" for the child often involves a degree of permissiveness and indulgence that serves children ill in the course of their education. A good educational experience helps the child learn that there are times when one has to do things that may be unpleasant in order to derive future benefits. "Respecting" the child's wish not to endure such discomforts is basically not in the child's best interests. True respect for children involves the *requirement* that they do what is best for them, not the indulgence of their avoidance of reasonable responsibilities. The net result of these unfortunate trends is that children learn less during their primary and secondary school years—with the subsequent result that SAT scores have dropped significantly during the last 15 to 20 years, and many studies have demonstrated that the majority of children are abysmally ignorant of basic facts about history, geography, literature, English, and mathematics.

Another factor operative in the deterioration of the educational system has been the growth of a generation of teachers who themselves have not learned very much during their own educational processes. Often, these are teachers who went to college during the 1960s, when students' self-indulgence may have reached an all-time high. Grammar, punctuation, spelling, and foreign languages were dismissed as "irrelevant." Many other subjects that required self-discipline and hard work were also often viewed as irrelevant. Graduates of this era are now teaching our youngsters. Not only do many of these teachers serve as poor models for their students, due to their impaired commitment to the educational process, but they are compromised as well in what they can teach. I routinely ask parents to bring in my child-patients' report cards. Often I see egregious errors in grammar, punctuation, and spelling. I have had secretaries whom I have had to let go after a week or two because of their ignorance of basic English. They were not people who I felt needed time to adjust to a new job; rather, it might have taken years to get them to reach the point where they could function adequately in a standard secretarial position. They often did not even appreciate how ignorant they were. They did not even recognize that a misspelled word looked misspelled, and so they had no motivation to consult a dictionary for the correct spelling.

High School

In their book *What Do Our 17-Year-Olds Know?* Ravitch and Finn (1987) report a study conducted with approximately 18,000 17-year-olds who were selected to reflect the make-up of the population as a whole regarding region, sex, race, type of school, and type of community. Some of their findings: Thirty percent of the students did not know that Christopher Columbus reached the New World before 1750. More than 35 percent were not aware that the Watergate scandal took place after 1950. More than 30 percent believed that one consequence of the Spanish-American War was the defeat of the Spanish Armada. Approximately half of the students believed that *Nineteen Eighty-Four* dealt with the destruction of the human race in a nuclear war. Over one-third did not know that Aesop wrote fables. Over 42 percent did not know who Senator Joseph McCarthy was nor for what he became infamous. Seventy percent were unable to identify the Magna Carta. And the book goes on and on with many more examples of the abysmal ignorance of the average American teenager. These findings should not be surprising, considering the kinds of educational programs these youngsters are being provided.

Some parents bring their adolescents for treatment because of poor academic motivation. Many of these youngsters attend schools where the educational standards are low and where they are automatically moved ahead every year and then dropped off the edge of the system when they complete the twelfth grade. Some, however, are in more demanding high schools, but they still have little commitment to the educational process. Sometimes the youngster's lack of motivation is indeed related to intrafamilial and intrapsychic problems. At other times, the youngster is merely one of a stream of hundreds of thousands who are moving along an educational track that demands little and provides even less. Their teachers are uncommitted and unmotivated, watch the clock, do not give homework (homework for the student is homework for the teacher), and so do not provide models for their students— models of people who are "turned on" by learning.

College

I believe that *most* (but certainly not *all*) colleges in the United States are not serving primarily as educational institutions; rather, they are serving as what I call "winter camps" that alternate with their students' summer recreational (and sometimes work) programs. Most youngsters attending colleges are not really looking for an education, but for another four years of self-indulgence and prolongation of their dependent state. We have a unique disease in the United States, a disease I call *the college disease*. Millions of parents believe that it is crucial that their children attend college. They actually believe that the schools to which they are sending their children are actually serving educational purposes. When there is a demand for something, there will always be individuals who will be pleased to provide a supply of the item, especially when there is good money to be made in the business. Most college institutions in the United States are basically businesses that cater to a gullible population of parents who believe that it is *crucial* that their children (no matter how simple and/or academically unmotivated) have a college education (no matter how specious and inferior).

These institutions have their academic hierarchy, their assistant professors, associate professors, and full professors. They have their college-style buildings (especially red brick and ivy), their alumni associations, their football teams, and their fund-raising campaigns. And they even offer formal courses; the "students" take examinations; and grades are given. Yet the whole thing does not add up to what can justifiably be referred to as an education. The majority of students are not there to learn; rather they are there primarily to have a good time—which often includes significant indulgence in sex, alcohol, and drugs. What they most often learn are some new sexual techniques, what their tolerance for alcohol is, and perhaps the use of some new drugs that they haven't tried before. They also learn how easy it is to get a college diploma. When the "students" are not engaged in these activities, they go through the motions of attending classes, but little is learned. Grade inflation fosters the delusion that they are learning something and ensures that even those with borderline intelligence will get high grades. Professors are concerned that if they give a student a grade lower than B, then the youngster will have trouble getting into graduate school and the college's reputation and popularity may thereby suffer. It is rare for someone to "flunk out." And why should they fail? Does one kick a good customer out of the store? If a customer's parents are willing to continue to pay for the services provided, it would be self-destructive of the college in this highly competitive market to cut off a predictable supply of money because of the student's failure to consume the product being offered.

I am not claiming that *all* the aforementioned criticisms apply to *all* collegiate institutions and *all* students. If I had to give a percentage of those academic institutions in the United States that fit the above description, I would say that it is in the 75 to 80 percent range. As mentioned, these colleges provide many of their students with gratification of pathological dependency needs. Such colleges also serve as a mechanism for transferring dependency from parents to those who administer these institutions. And thwarting college authorities (especially by antisocial behavior and refusal to study) is often a transfer of rebellion from parents to school authorities—a rebellion in which the dependency-denial element is often operative.

When I attended college, we generally went from nine a.m. to five p.m. Monday through Friday, and a half day on Saturday. Most courses met four or five times a week and laboratory courses two to three afternoons a week. It was expected that one would do four or five hours of homework a night. School began the day following Labor Day and continued right through early June. There was a one-week Christmas vacation, possibly a one-week Easter vacation, and of course national holidays. Otherwise we went to school. This is no longer the case. Even in the so-called best colleges and universities, the formal academic program is far less rigorous. Most students average two or three hours a day of classes, while professors may only have to come in five to ten hours a week and are otherwise unseen. These days, the academic year, although it may start around Labor Day, generally ends in early May. Some institutions use the Christmas and/or Easter season as an excuse for an extended holiday (two to four weeks). Others have long vacations (lasting two to four weeks) between semesters. Many need no other excuse for a long break than the season (spring or winter vacation). When I attended college, professors were on campus throughout the course of the day. Things are vastly changed. Today, it is not uncommon for professors to live at significant distances from the campus and appear only on the days when they teach, and often only during the hours when they teach. Otherwise, they are unavailable. Students at these institutions are being short-changed. "Educations" of this kind may cost $15,000 a year or more. Parents and students are being "ripped off."

Recently, a mother of a patient, who teaches at one of the

public universities in New York City, related to me an incident that demonstrates well the deterioration of our educational systems, even at the highest level. The woman is a highly intelligent, well-trained, scholarly individual with a Ph.D. in a very demanding field. One day her chairman called her into his office and told her that he was having a problem with her, namely, that too many of her students were failing. He informed her that a 40 percent failure rate was unacceptable. She informed him that she was actually being quite generous, and that if she had graded in a more honest way about 60 percent of her students would fail. He told her that he had sat in on a couple of her classes, knew exactly what the problem was, and considered it easily rectifiable. He then went on to explain to her that she was not giving tests in the "correct" manner. What she was doing was to tell students on Friday, for example, that there would be a test on Monday covering the material in certain chapters of the textbook. This he considered "unfair" to the students. Rather, the "correct" way to give a test was to tell the students on Friday exactly what questions would be asked on Monday. Under the new system, the failure rate dropped from 40 to 20 percent, but even then she found herself being quite generous. Such procedures are a manifestation of the bastardization of the educational system. They make a farce of education and, worse, are a terrible disservice to students. The next step, of course, is merely to tell what questions will be asked and give the answers that will be expected. If one extends this further, one might as well give out (or sell) the diplomas in advance and save everybody a lot of trouble.

Things are even worse at some of the two-year colleges. Many of these institutions merely go through the motions of providing an education and are basically a sham. Students are given textbooks that are seemingly rigorous and demanding, yet in actuality the students are only required to learn a small fraction of what is presented therein. Those in charge recognize the travesty but are party to it, even at the highest levels. The net result of all this is that students are not getting a bona fide education and are thereby entering into the workplace ill equipped to handle jobs for which they are ostensibly being trained. Also they are being deprived of the feelings of accomplishment and high self-worth enjoyed by those who have acquired skills and talents through years of hard labor and dedication. The situation thereby contributes to psychopathology, because feelings of low self-worth are an important contributing factor in the development of psychogenic symptoms. In addition, such bogus education contributes to psychopathic trends (I am not saying gross psychopathy) because of the sanctions the youngsters are given for "cutting corners," taking short-cuts, and otherwise doing shabby work.

Yet, at the same time that their education is eroding, the honors that students are receiving become ever easier to acquire. When I graduated from Columbia College in 1952, my recollection is that no more than one percent graduated *summa cum laude,* perhaps another three or four percent *magna cum laude,* and perhaps another five percent *cum laude.* My recollection is that students below the 10 percent level of the class could not hope to acquire any of these honors. In the mid-1980s I attended the Harvard College graduation of one of my children. I noted that the upper 75 percent of the class received one of these honors. In other words, a person could be in the 75th percentile level of the class and would graduate *cum laude.* When I spoke to faculty people about this, I was informed that the school is well aware of its liberal view with regard to bestowing these honors, but that it is justified because it helps graduates get into graduate school and jobs. I am dubious. Those who make these decisions are well aware that *cum laude* may very well indicate the 50th to 75th percentile of the class and will act accordingly. It serves to compromise the respect for the honor and does Harvard (and other schools who do the same) a disservice. It is one example of the intellectual and moral erosion that has taken place, even at the highest levels of education.

The Education of Validators

People who work as validators are products of this eroded educational system, at all levels, and this weakness in their

educational foundation is reflected in their work. A good education, if anything, should provide individuals with "common
sense." Validators, above all, lack common sense. In fact, I
consider that to be the number one item on the list of their
deficiencies. One has to lack common sense if one is to believe the
preposterous things that they accept as valid in order to justify
their conclusions. There was a time when one had to be bright in
order to get into most colleges. As mentioned, this is less often
the case today and there are, without question, many validators
who are not particularly intelligent—even though they may have
a college and/or university education. People who are less intelligent are less likely to have common sense. However, sometimes
this can be rectified (to some extent) by academic work that
focuses on the capacity for logical reasoning. Courses in logic,
mathematics, physics, and chemistry can most likely do this (for
those who are intellectually competent to handle these disciplines). In a less direct way, just about any good college course
(including the arts) should involve a certain amount of logical
thinking. What is clear is that many of these validators lack the
basic intelligence and/or the educational exposure that might
have provided them with common sense.

When I was in medical school, our professors would frequently say to us: "Remember this: The most likely things are
most likely." At first, I thought the warning was both inane and
unnecessary. As time went on, however, I came to appreciate the
great wisdom in this seemingly absurd statement. The admonition was most often applied to situations in which a medical
student would diagnose a patient as having the rare tropical
disease that had just been read about the previous night. This was
often done in a state of exultation associated with the pride at
having made such a brilliant diagnosis. The professor, often
trying to avoid putting the student down, would say something
along these lines: "It looks like common viral gastroenteritis to
me" or "It looks like the garden variety of bacterial pneumonia to
me." The reality of the world is that the most common things *are*
most common and that one does well to remember this. Validators seem to be oblivious to this ancient and obvious wisdom.

Rather, they go in the opposite direction and consider as valid the most unlikely and even preposterous possibilities. One does not need a Ph.D. in advanced mathematics to recognize that the likelihood of a nursery school teacher undressing 50 three-year-old children (in order to involve them when naked in a sex orgy), and then dressing them all quickly, is not very likely to end up with every child wearing the exact same socks, shoes, underwear, dresses, pants, shirts, hats, and coats as they came in with.

Every parent knows that the best way to get a three-year-old child to say something to another person is to preface the message with: "I want to tell you a secret and I want you to promise me that you'll *never* tell anyone." This is the most predictable way to get the message into the pool of public information. Yet, these examiners believe that one can do this with a whole class of children and be confident that they will never breathe a word of their experiences to their parents or anyone else. There are three classes of people who believe that one can accomplish this goal of group secrecy by three- year-olds: (1) psychotics, (2) retardates, and (3) zealous validators. The rest of the world well appreciates that it is unreasonable to expect three-year-old children to involve themselves in conspiracies of silence, especially with regard to dramatic experiences (such as people dressed as clowns, monsters, etc., to engaging the children in sexual intercourse, putting swords up their rectums, and feeding them feces). These examiners do not seem to appreciate that it is not very likely that one can feed feces to a group of children, make them drink their urine, and expose them to a variety of other painful and frightening indignities and yet, only minutes later, get them to skip happily out of the classroom without a speck of feces on their lips or a drop of urine on their tongues. When presented with this argument, validators claim that the children have been frightened into secrecy by threats of body mutilation, murder, etc. This too is an absurd rationalization. Let us forget, for the moment, the failure to find these mutilated bodies with which the children were threatened. The idea that the *whole* group could be frightened into silence is absurd. Perhaps a few, but not *all* of them for the extended period between the alleged abuse and its divulgence. In fact, one could argue that frightened children would be even more likely to reveal quickly what they have been allegedly exposed to.

The "Holier-Than-Thou" Phenomenon

Many readers, I would guess, have seen the common bumper sticker: "I brake for animals." There is a "holier-than-thou" message being transmitted here. The implication here is that the driver of the vehicle bearing this message is a kind of individual who stops for animals and that others are less likely to do so. The message communicates to the reader in the car behind that he (she) should be ever on the alert for a sudden stop by the car ahead and that the driver in front is likely to be stopping short quite frequently. "Keep your foot close to the brakes," it says, "because you never know when you'll have to stop short. You don't have to worry about this when you follow other cars, because they're not driven by the kinds of deeply caring people who are sensitive enough to brake for animals." I have had the thought that, if I had the opportunity, I would ask such individuals if they brake for human beings. The same phenomenon is exhibited by politicians who claim proudly and sanctimoniously that they are fighting for the homeless, the elderly, the poor, and children who are abandoned. The implication is that their opponents are against these individuals.

Validators (and the aforementioned newer breed of "child advocates") often manifest this patronizing attitude. They — unlike the rest of us — are there to protect children. They — unlike the rest of us — "believe the children." The implication here is that those who do not believe the children (like the author) are somehow low-life characters who are exposing children to the sea of abusers, who are ever ready to pounce on their prey. It provides these examiners with a feeling of special importance, which likely serves to compensate for basic feelings of inadequacy. If one basically feels competent about oneself, if one basically has a strong sense of self-worth, one does not have to go around looking down one's nose at others. One does not have to go around putting up signs, waving banners, and exhorting one's superiority over others.

The same phenomenon, in a more subtle way, is exhibited by many clinicians in the mental health professions who pride themselves on their "respect" for children. They, unlike the rest of us, are *really* sensitive to children's thoughts and feelings. They, unlike the rest of us, *listen very carefully* to what children are saying and have the *deepest respect* for their wishes. In the precious atmosphere of their offices, they provide the child with "unconditional positive regard" and reflexly "respect" every thought (no matter how outlandish) and every feeling (no matter how at variance with reality) that teachers, parents, and other insensitive individuals do not provide. These same "therapists" may reflexly support the child's position in any difference he (she) may have with the parents, again in the service of respecting the child's position. When this attitude on the therapist's part is carried into a sex-abuse evaluation, it contributes to the development of false sex-abuse accusations. And, when carried over into the treatment of a child who is not sexually abused, it can contribute to the child's delusion that such an event did occur. Competent and sophisticated therapists know well that true respect for children is not complying with what they say they want but with what they really need.

I suspect that some readers (especially those whom I have criticized) would consider me to have exhibited a "holier-than-thou" attitude throughout the course of this book. I do not deny that one might easily come to this conclusion. However, in my defense, I believe that it is important to differentiate two types of criticism, namely, that which is justified and that which is unjustified. One could argue that every criticizer is exhibiting a "holier- than-thou" attitude toward the person being criticized. Whatever the criticism, no matter how constructive, it has within it the implicit message that the criticizer is superior to the person being criticized. The criticizer is basically saying that he (she) acts in a superior way, knows better, and feels it incumbent upon him (her) to communicate the corrective measures to the criticized individual so that he (she) can mend his (her) ways and be a "better person." And this holds even when the criticism is completely·justified and even when the rectification of the criticized person's deficit(s) would be a boon to the world. It is important, therefore, to differentiate between criticisms that are warranted and those that are unwarranted. People who have bumper stickers saying "I brake for animals," people who wave the banner "Believe the children," and those therapists who proudly proclaim that they "respect" their child patients are in this second category. People in this category more justifiably warrant the "holier-than-thou" epithet. The important question for the reader of this book should not be whether I warrant the holier-than-thou label, but whether the criticisms I am making are valid and whether the changes that could result from their implementation are desirable.

The Erosion of Values

Most would agree that we have witnessed in the last quarter century a progressive erosion of values in the United States (and probably Western society at large). Evidence of this deterioration is to be found everywhere. Crime rates (with isolated exceptions) are ever soaring. Drug abuse is ubiquitous. Prisons in most states are overcrowded and cannot accommodate the ever-increasing flow of convicted criminals. Many are released into the street before the completion of their sentences in order to accommodate the new wave of inmates. In large cities automobile thefts, muggings, and other "minor crimes" are so commonplace that they receive little if any attention by the police, and the perpetrators rarely are meaningfully punished. Church boxes are pilfered, subway turnstiles are jumped over, garbage is strewn on streets, and human beings evacuate in public. Teachers are ever cutting corners, less homework is given, school vacations are longer, college admission (with rare exception) is easier, and handing in other students' written work ever more common. Plagiarism among faculty people (even in the most prestigious universities) is becoming increasingly commonplace. And the probable increase in genuine child sex abuse in the intrafamilial situation is another example of this psychopathy. (The reader does well not to forget that I believe that bona fide sex abuse does indeed take place and is indeed ubiquitous and may even be on the rise.)

One of the many manifestations of this moral erosion has been the progressive insensitivity of people to one another. The Golden Rule has essentially become a quaint anachronism. It is all right for clergymen to tell children in Sunday school that they should treat one another as they themselves would like to be treated, but it is another thing to seriously implement this wisdom in the reality of the adult world. Many factors have been operative in producing this state of affairs. Parental modeling plays an important role in children's development of sympathy and empathy (which are directly related to the ability to put oneself in another person's position). The increasing popularity of day-care centers (their value and justification notwithstanding) deprives children of the kind of intimate involvement with biological parents from which values develop. No matter how dedicated the caretakers at these centers, no matter how educated they may be, they cannot provide the same kind of loving concern as a biological parent. (Elsewhere [Gardner, 1988a] I describe this in greater detail, especially with regard to a solution to this problem that would not involve condemning mothers to return to the home to merely cook and change diapers.) Violence on television and in the cinema is ubiquitous. Most often, little or nothing is portrayed about the pain suffered by the victims of such violence. In the 1960s and 1970s, during the days of the "me generation," books that emphasized the point "think of number one" often became best-sellers.

Evaluators who conclude that the vast majority (if not all) of the children they see have indeed been sexually abused are likely to have a defect in their capacity to place themselves in the positions of those who suffer from their decision. There is an element of psychopathy apparent in a person who would see a three-year-old child for a few minutes and then write a note stating that a particular individual (the father, the stepfather, a nursery school teacher, etc.) sexually abused that child. It takes a defect in the mechanisms of conscience to do such an abominable thing. One must completely ignore the effects of such a statement on the alleged perpetrator, effects that may include psychological devastation, destruction of one's lifestyle, and years of incarceration. This is what the "me generation" has wrought.

Interestingly, religious fundamentalism is most often (but certainly not always) a manifestation of moral erosion. I recognize that this statement may come as a surprise to some readers, but it is nevertheless a reality. The more the religious fundamentalist attempts to impose his (her) religious beliefs on others, the less sensitivity the religious zealot has for the person being converted. The examples are legion: Christ's crucifixion, the annihilation of the anti-church Albigensian sects in the thirteenth century, the Crusades, the Spanish Inquisition, the numerous religious wars in Europe between the Protestants and the Catholics, and (to skip quickly many such wars and bring us up to the present) the conflicts between the Shiite Moslems and the more moderate Islamic sects. When religious fundamentalism ignores the wishes, ideas, and feelings of other human beings, it is psychopathy masked as religiosity. It is no less a manifestation of moral erosion than the more overt examples cited above. The recent upsurge in religious fundamentalism in the United States may very well be a "backlash" to the "sexual revolution" of the 1960s and 1970s. Those in the movement who focus on sex have a convenient vehicle for their condemnation in the form of sex-abuse validation. The goal of publicly humiliating and incarcerating every "pervert" can only be reached if there is a significant defect in conscience and a suspension of the very morality that the religious proselytizers and purifiers proclaim to hold in such high esteem.

Sex-Abuse Victims As Validators

All career choices are determined by psychological factors and even psychopathological factors—and the people who choose sex-abuse work are no exception. I believe that people who have been sexually abused themselves in childhood are much more likely to enter this field than those who have not had such childhood experiences. I believe that if one were to compare the frequency of childhood sexual molestation in a thousand sex-abuse workers with three to four matched groups of workers in unrelated fields, the percentage of sex-abuse workers who were sexually molested as children would be significantly higher than the percentages in the other three to four groups. The sex-abuse field is attractive to those who were molested because it provides them with the opportunity for working through in many complex ways residual and unresolved reactions to their early traumas. I am not claiming that these factors necessarily operate at conscious levels (but they may), nor am I claiming that the processes are necessarily pathological (but they may be).

The phenomenon is no different from the factors that operate in just about any other field. To begin with my own field, many people choose medicine because they have grown up in a home with a parent who has suffered with a chronic illness. They may deal with this childhood trauma by devoting their lives to the treatment of others with that particular disorder or to the search for a cure for the parent's illness. Many choose psychiatry or psychology because they hope to gain understanding and even help for their own problems. People who frequently consider themselves to be put upon or victimized may choose law as a vehicle for protecting themselves and others from such persecutions. People who grew up in poverty may aspire to be (and even become) philanthropists; when they give to others they are basically giving to their projected selves. In all of these examples there is a range from the nonpathological to the pathological psychodynamic factors, and each person's balance lies at some point along the continuum.

Among the sex-abuse workers who have been sexually molested as children, there are many who use their career experience in healthy ways in their work—much to the benefit of abused children and their families. They have been there, they know what it's like, and they can provide a degree of sympathy and empathy not often possible for one who has never had the experience. But there are others in this group for whom pathological factors are clearly operative in their work with patients—

factors that may becloud their objectivity. Some of these individuals harbor significant resentment against the original perpetrator, resentment that may not have been dealt with completely or properly. They vent their pent-up hostility on present-day offenders in a work setting that provides sanctions for such pathological release. And some of these workers operate on the principle that there will never be enough perpetrators to punish, so great is their desire to wreak vengeance on those who sexually molest children. Concluding that an alleged perpetrator is indeed innocent deprives them of their vengeful gratification. It is this subgroup of sex-abuse workers who may work with exaggerated zeal to prosecute alleged abusers and resist strongly the idea that some alleged offenders are indeed innocent. They often adhere tenaciously to the position that children *never* fabricate sex abuse. They must blind themselves to the aforementioned developments in recent years that make this notion an anachronism. Such zeal and denial have contributed significantly to the sex-abuse hysteria that we are witnessing at this time.

Furthermore, when these people "treat" sexually abused children, they can gratify vicariously the desire to treat their projected selves. They are curing themselves of the residua of their sex abuse by curing children who have been so afflicted. Again, this may be a normal, healthy mechanism for some who have been genuinely abused. However, if one has to diagnose normal children as being abused and then subject them to years of "treatment," then much psychological damage is being done and such treatment is an abomination. It can destroy children. It can provide chronic psychological trauma. Unfortunately, there are hundreds (and probably thousands) of children in the United States today who are being subjected to such "therapy."

I recognize that there will be some (especially those who work with sexually abused children) who will conclude that what I have just stated is prejudice on my part and that I have no scientific evidence to support my conclusions. I agree that I have no such studies to support my hypothesis and that my conclusions are based on my own experiences as well as the experiences of colleagues in the mental health professions (some of whom, interestingly, work in the field of sex abuse). My view of people in my own field is no less critical. There is no question that the specialty of psychiatry attracts some of the sickest medical students, and this is no doubt a factor in the reputation we have as being "crazies." This phenomenon also serves as an explanation for the fact that the suicide rate among psychiatrists is the highest of all the medical specialties. Accordingly, if I am prejudiced against sex-abuse workers, I may very well be considered to be prejudiced against people in my own field. However, one might also conclude that I am making accurate statements about both fields.

I am not at all claiming that all (or even the majority) of people involved as validators have been sexually abused as children. I am stating only that they are probably more highly represented than other groups in the population of sex-abuse workers. There are other psychological factors that may be operative. Involvement in this field provides the various kinds of sexual release described earlier in this book, e.g., vicarious gratification, reaction formation, voyeurism, etc. Many can gratify "savior syndrome" personality qualities. They devote themselves to protecting children from perverts who are to be found everywhere: among divorcing fathers, in nursery schools and day-care centers, in the streets, in parks, and in cruising cars and trucks. It's a dangerous world out there for children, with sex perverts hiding under practically every stone and lurking behind practically every tree. There is much work to be done to protect these children, and these workers have joined an army of heroes who are devoting themselves to their salvation. Is there a more noble way to spend one's life? Can there be a higher cause to which one can devote oneself?

The Sexually Inhibited

There are people who are sexually inhibited, who project out their own unacceptable sexual impulses onto others, and see sexuality everywhere. There are individuals who would like to be sexual molesters themselves, are too guilty to accept such impulses as their own, project them out onto others, and then condemn in others behavior that never occurred. What they are really condemning is their own projected fantasies; in this way they assuage their guilt. Such individuals may have minimal degrees of pedophilia (all of us have some) or they have more than the average amount. In either case, they cannot accept such impulses within themselves and must disown them. It is as if they are saying: "It is not I who wishes to involve myself sexually with children. I am too good a person to do such a terrible thing. It is they who are perpetrating these abominations, and I will do everything in my power to rid the world of such perverts." The need to do this may be so great that the condemner does not pay careful attention as to whether the individual did indeed sexually molest the child.

Sadists

Becoming a validator provides sadistic individuals with unlimited opportunities for gratification of their perversion. (Although I hesitate to use the word *perversion* for people who are homosexuals and people with other paraphilias, I have no hesitation using the word *perversion* to refer to the individuals I discuss in this section.) Sadistic individuals need others who can serve as targets for their sadism. In our society, at this time, especially in the present atmosphere of hysteria, child molesters are very much in vogue for such scapegoatism. Society has always needed its scapegoats. Obviously, in societies where adult-child sexuality is the norm, societies where pedophilia is viewed as an acceptable and even desirable form of behavior, such individuals cannot serve this purpose. Life is filled with frustrations and frustration inevitably produces anger. People with formidable degrees of anger must find socially acceptable modalities for its discharge, and sex abusers are now being provided for the gratification of such sadists.

Paranoids

Some validators are overtly paranoid. Paranoia is much more common than is generally appreciated, especially because—in certain situations—it can have social benefit (sometimes real, sometimes fantasized). Paranoids are hypervigilent, are obsessed with any detail that might support their delusional system(s), and view as evil and/or corrupt those who would question their beliefs. And this is what we are dealing with here. What more noble cause can there be than to rid the world of sex perverts, people who perpetrate terrible abominations on innocent children. Paranoids tend to band together with others of similar persuasion and ignore or remove themselves entirely from those who would shake their delusional systems. A paranoid mother may join forces with a paranoid validator and enter into a folie-à-deux relationship. The accused father is then viewed as an enemy, as someone who is evil and corrupt, because he may provide compelling evidence that the accusation is false. Paranoids tend to espouse the satanic ritual theory of child sex abuse. The belief in a widespread conspiracy of satanic cults, through whose influences thousands of children are being sexually molested, must be a delusion. I do not doubt the existence of a small number of isolated individuals who may actually involve themselves in such rituals; what I do doubt is the alleged ubiquity of such groups, as rumor and hysteria would have us believe. Lanning (1992), who has supervised hundreds of FBI investigations into sex-abuse accusations in association with so-called satanic rituals, provides compelling support for this position. As is well known, people who gravitate to the mental health professions (including psychiatry) often do so because of their own psychopathology. Those who believe that we in the mental health professions are necessarily psychologically healthier (whatever that means) than people in the general population are naive. Accordingly, it is reasonable to conclude that there are mental health professionals who are paranoid. Some of these people foster paranoid delusions in their patients, for example, convincing people that they were sexually molested as children and then encouraging their acting out on these delusions. This particular phenomenon is now reaching epidemic proportions. And it is being fueled by the paranoid subset of validators.

Overzealous Feminists

Although I am basically in sympathy with the aims of the feminist movement, feminists (as is true of all groups) have their share of fanatics. Some of the latter have jumped on the sex-abuse bandwagon because it provides a predictable vehicle for venting hostility toward men. These individuals also subscribe strongly (and even fanatically) to the dictum that children never lie and that any allegation of sex abuse must be true. Some of these women were subjected to cruel treatment in childhood by their fathers and other men. Some in this category have generalized from their childhood experiences and assume that all men will be equally abusive to them. Some carry with them a lifelong vendetta and have embarked upon a campaign of vengeance that will involve the destruction of every man who has the misfortune to cross their path and whom they have the opportunity to destroy. These women gravitate toward becoming validators in the same way that iron is attached to a magnet. It is the "perfect" profession for such fanatics. There is a minimum of effort, and with complete social sanction (after all, one is involved in the worthy cause of incarcerating perverts), they can humiliate, destroy, and incarcerate one man after the other in rapid succession.

The Hypocrites

And then there are the hypocrites. These are individuals who have been involved themselves in a wide variety of atypical sexual activities, and some of these people are even pedophiles themselves. Some hypocrites are psychopathic in that they feel no guilt about sitting in judgment over others who have engaged in far less pedophilia than they, or who have engaged in no pedophilia at all. These people are indeed the true "perverts." They are drawn into the field of sex-abuse evaluations because it provides them with a socially acceptable vehicle for the gratification of their pedophilic impulses. I am not claiming that many of these people have actually engaged in pedophilic behavior; I am only claiming that psychologically they are pedophiles because of their obsession with such activities and get vicarious gratification of their pedophilic impulses by their involvement in this area. These people are similar to many of the individuals who gravitate toward professional ethics committees where they sit in judgment of their colleagues.

Only recently (1991), we saw an excellent example of this in the senatorial hearings regarding the appointment of Clarence Thomas to the Supreme Court of the United States. Sitting in judgment of Mr. Thomas was Senator Edward Kennedy, an internationally famous womanizer, a man whose girlfriend drowned at Chappaquiddick in association with an extramarital tryst. And I am convinced, as well, that most of the other individuals on that committee who were sitting in judgment of Mr. Thomas had engaged in various forms of sexual harassment far worse than he and that their sexual peccadilloes may very well have exceeded his. The committee's collective hypocrisy reached its height when they feigned horror when Professor Anita Hill (the woman who accused Justice Thomas of sexual harassment) reluctantly and dramatically revealed that the name of the pro-tagonist of the pornographic videotape she was invited to view was "Long Dong Silver" (a name to which they responded with a "oh-goodness-gracious-me" reaction). Of course, this group of hypocrites know well where their bread is buttered. They know well where the votes are and where the votes are not. To react with anything but horror might compromise their chances for reelection. In one case in which I was involved, one of the prosecuting attorneys was demoted because he and colleagues were found to be spending their time on the job gleefully watching pornographic films that had been confiscated in cases in which they had been involved. So much for the hypocrites.

The Young and/or Naive

Another group of people one sees among the validators are the young and naive. Often, they are just out of training and have accepted as valid whatever has been taught to them. Students, in general, are a gullible lot. They generally accept as valid whatever has been taught to them, especially by a person who has a title like *professor*. To get through the "system," they must memorize significant amounts of material and regurgitate it as accurately as possible. Although certainly independent thinking is encouraged by a small percentage of teachers, the vast majority require submissive receptivity and parroting—their professions to the contrary notwithstanding. It is no surprise, then, that independent thinking is squelched in the course of most educational processes, and it should be no surprise, then, that young people hired at low salaries to work for child protection services just don't know how misinformed they are. Any pity I may have for them is more than counterweighed by my indignation over the terrible consequences of their ignorance.

Monetary Gain

A whole power structure has grown up in which an army of prosecutors, detectives, investigators, and others rely on a continual stream of positive findings and convictions if they are to justify their ever-increasing demands for more funds from legislatures. In the private sector, as well, there is money to be made in the field. I have already mentioned the sea of hungry lawyers who are looking for clients and who are happy to take on any kind of litigation, no matter how preposterous. There is also a sea of hungry mental health professionals (psychiatrists, psychologists, social workers, pastoral counselors, nurse practitioners, family therapists, and a whole group of so-called therapists) who are happy to have anyone's business, no matter how preposterous the reason for seeking consultation and treatment. Accordingly, there is big money to be made in the diagnosis and treatment of sex abuse. It is indeed a "growth industry." The validators, then, are only one part of this network in which they all need one another if they are to take their share of the money pie that has been made available by a hysterical society to support the system. Many of the validators fear (with justification) losing their jobs if they conclude that too many of the investigated clients are innocent or the charges unsubstantiated. There are clinics that receive funds only for the treatment of abused children. If an evaluator concludes that the child has not been abused, then the clinic receives no funding for that child's treatment. If the child's family cannot afford to pay for the therapy (the usual case for patients coming to community clinics), then the clinic must either turn away the child or provide treatment for little if any reimbursement. Under such circumstances, it is not surprising that the vast majority of children examined in such clinics are found to have been "abused."

Other Personality Factors

Underwager and Wakefield (1991) describe some of the personality problems that they consider to predispose an individual to believe many of the preposterous statements made by falsely accusing children, thereby causing them to get swept up in the hysteria of the times. One personality factor they describe is discomfort with *cognitive dissonance.* They state:

> People do not like to see or hear things that conflict with their deeply held wishes or beliefs. Interest in supporting information appears to be greater when there is a lower sense of certainty about the correctness of a belief....Some mental health professionals are committed to the proposition that children are to be believed at all costs. If a person has chosen that belief, but is then confronted with a child saying things that are patently false or highly improbable, a state of dissonance is generated. That means the person will reduce the dissonance. (p. 183)

People who have difficulty tolerating such dissonance are likely to selectively shut out material that conflicts with their original beliefs.

Underwager and Wakefield (1991) describe *scapegoatism* as another factor operative for some evaluators. I have already mentioned this factor with regard to children who falsely profess sex-abuse accusations (Chapter Three), individuals who promulgate false accusations (Chapter Four), and validators who have sadistic tendencies (this chapter). For evaluators, a person who sexually abuses a child can be a convenient scapegoat, someone to serve as a target for the examiner's pent-up hostilities. We are living at a time when there has been a shrinkage of potential scapegoats. The authors state:

> For those conversant enough with contemporary attitudes to know that antisemitism, racism, sexual identity prejudices, and any discrimination is unacceptable, the devil and Satanic devotees are acceptable, indeed a praiseworthy locus for aggression and hatred. It is proper and politically correct to hate the devil. Extremism in the battle of evil is noble. (p. 184)

And the same can be said for punishing those "perverts" who sexually abuse children. Thus we see the overlap between Satanism and sexual molesters. Satanic influences cause them to perpetrate their abominations upon innocent children. The scapegoat allows for hostile expression in two directions simultaneously, namely, Satan and sex perverts.

Intolerance of ambiguity is another personality factor that the authors consider operative. Underwager and Wakefield (1991) state:

> Some people find it difficult to cope with inconsistencies, ambiguities, and unexpected events. Their world needs to be black and white, all good or all bad. (p. 124)

Closely interrelated with this personality pattern is the mechanism of projection, which enables such an individual to project outward onto others thoughts and feelings that would produce intolerable and/or anxiety-provoking ambiguity. The authors also describe other psychopathological processes that may be operative in some of these evaluators.

Of course, there are other kinds of psychopathology that may be present in the kinds of evaluators I describe in this chapter. There are lonely and isolated people who now find meaning in their lives by joining a group dedicated to what is certainly a noble campaign, namely, ridding the world of sexual molesters—people who are so loathsome that they are not even worthy of being considered human beings. Could there be a better cause to which one could devote one's life? Joining with others in the campaign to wipe out sex abuse not only reduces their loneliness but provides them with the ego-enhancement that comes from involvement in such a lofty campaign. And there are people for whom a benevolent relationship is an unknown phenomenon; their only mode of relating is malevolently, and the ongoing battles involved in sex-abuse accusations provide them with such morbid interpersonal gratification. Pent-up rage, which previously could not be easily released, now finds a socially acceptable target.

CONCLUDING COMMENTS

The net result of all of this is that we have here a no-win situation for individuals accused of sex abuse. In the hands of many of these "validators," no one is innocent. Everyone is found to be guilty. Validators operate with impunity. False accusers are protected in most states from lawsuits involving slander and libel. I suspect that these "protective" laws are unconstitutional in that they deprive the accused of the opportunity for direct confrontation with the accuser, a right that is provided by the Sixth Amendment of the U.S. Constitution. In many states the accuser does not even have to mention his (her) name to the reporting authorities and will merely be recorded as "anonymous." Yet, an investigation is embarked upon on the basis of the anonymous call, and people have even been jailed as a result of them.

Our founding fathers knew well the terrible indignities and injustices suffered by innocent victims of the European inquisitorial system of adjudication. Hundreds of thousands (and possibly millions) were convicted of crimes they never committed by accusers and witnesses whose identities were unknown to them. It is clear, at least in the realm of child sex-abuse accusations, that we have not advanced beyond those horrible times as far as we would like to think. I know of no falsely accused person who has instituted a lawsuit against a government agency that has utilized such anonymous witnesses as a source of information contributing to the individual's conviction. My hope is that such lawsuits will be instituted and that at least one such case will ultimately come to the attention of the U.S. Supreme Court. The use of anonymous witnesses must be unconstitutional.

To the best of my knowledge, malpractice suits against these validators have not been common. We would all be better off if there were some well-publicized malpractice suits against such individuals. Such lawsuits might have a sobering effect on the field. Unfortunately, most people who call themselves validators are practicing at the *same* low level of competence (or, more correctly, incompetence) and so do not satisfy an important criterion for malpractice, namely, that the individual's level of practice is far below that which is considered standard for peers at a similar level of training and experience. We are left, then, with a situation in which craziness is considered normality.

Last, I wish to repeat that I recognize that there are many evaluators who are extremely skilled and sensitive and who do not manifest the deficiencies described in this chapter. I recognize, as well, that evaluators, like all other people, exhibit a range of expertise from the most incompetent and defective to the most skilled and insightful. I have focused here on the most common deficiencies exhibited by the most seriously impaired evaluators and am fully appreciative that there are many examiners who do not operate at this low level of professional competence. My hope is that readers who react by becoming offended and thereby reject totally all that I say here will reconsider their position and give serious consideration to the possibility that I may be making some important points that may be useful to them. If such readers can overcome this initial rejection of what I say, they might find here some useful principles and techniques.

☐ SEVEN
LEADING STIMULI, LEADING GESTURES, AND LEADING QUESTIONS

INTRODUCTORY COMMENTS

During the last few years a conflict has been raging over the value and place of anatomically correct dolls (more recently referred to as anatomically detailed dolls) in child sex-abuse evaluations. Studies are coming in from both camps, each claiming that the findings support its position. The *American Psychological Association (APA)* has periodically issued position statements on the use of these dolls, but has yet to come up with a definitive statement. The latest proposal (February 8, 1991) urges "continued research" and hedges a final decision as to whether the dolls per se are ethical to use. The APA recommends that documentation be provided in association with the use of these dolls:

> We recommend that psychologists document by videotape, (whenever possible), audiotape or in writing the procedures they use for each administration. Psychologists should be prepared to provide clinical and empirical rationale (i.e., published studies, clinical experience, etc.) for procedures employed and for interpretation of results derived from using anatomically detailed dolls.

Considering the weaknesses and criticisms that can justifiably be directed at those studies that allege to support the claim that these dolls can be useful for assessing sex abuse, such documentation would be very difficult to provide at this point. In the state of California the dolls are not considered to satisfy the Kelly-Frye test for admissibility, which requires that the procedure has been generally accepted as reliable in the scientific community in which it was developed. This decision was based on the weaknesses of the studies supporting their use (Gardner, 1991a; Underwager and Wakefield, 1990; Wakefield and Underwager, 1988).

The American Academy of Child and Adolescent Psychiatry (AACAP) (1988) has also issued a position statement on the use of these dolls. The AACAP's position is similar to that of the APA's, but is a little stronger with regard to the caveats about the dolls' use. The AACAP makes direct reference to the fact that findings based on the dolls are not admissible as evidence in the state of California.

Even those who are the strongest supporters of the use of the dolls generally agree that "leading questions" should be avoided as much as possible because they can produce responses in the child that may suggest sex abuse when it has not occurred. However, those who warn against the use of leading questions often use them to a significant degree in their protocols. For example, White et al. (1985) warn, "The interviewer should pose questions in a nonleading fashion." Yet, in the same protocol they list 14 questions, each of which most would consider to be highly leading, e.g., "Have you been touched on any part of your body?" "Has anyone put anything on or in any part of your body?" "Has anyone else asked you to take off your clothes?"

Boat and Everson (1988) exhibit the same disparity in their protocol regarding the caveat against using leading questions. The authors state, "Background information should therefore be used only for guiding the conversation (e.g., 'Your Mommy told me you visited Uncle John last week.') and not [except in rare circumstances to be outlined later] for asking the child questions that may be leading or suggestive (e.g., 'Is Uncle John the one who hurt you?').' The authors do not appear to appreciate the fact that the statement: "Your Mommy told me you visited Uncle John last week" is very leading. Perhaps it is a little less leading than "Is Uncle John the one who hurt you?" but it is nevertheless leading in that it directs the child's attention to the visit with Uncle John the previous week, the visit during which some sexual encounter is alleged to have taken place. Furthermore, in spite of this caveat, the protocol itself includes a series of questions, each of which is highly leading [in each of the examples to be given the line (_____) represents the name the child uses for that particular body part], for example, "Has anyone touched your _____ ? "Have you ever seen anybody else's _____ ?" "Has anyone asked you to touch their _____ ?" and "Has anyone taken pictures of you with your clothes off?" Most examiners, I believe, would agree that these questions are highly leading.

Obviously, we have a problem here regarding the exact definition of a leading question. Providing a definition for this term is one of the objects of this chapter. However, I will go beyond this issue and discuss the concepts of what I refer to as "leading stimuli" and "leading gestures." The introduction of these terms is important if one is to appreciate more fully what is actually occurring when examiners use anatomical dolls. As discussed elsewhere (Gardner, 1987, 1991a), in the early 1980s I began seeing the introduction of false sex-abuse allegations in the context of highly contested child custody disputes. This allegation proved a valuable vengeance and exclusionary maneuver. In the last few years I have also been involved in day-care center cases in which sex abuse has been alleged. In association with my involvement in both of these areas, I have had the opportunity to review approximately 300 hours of videotapes of examiners using anatomical dolls in the course of their interviews. These interviews were not simply conducted in the Greater New York City area (where I live and work), but in other parts of the country as well. Accordingly, I have had the opportunity to observe a broad spectrum of interviewers. These tapes have not been viewed leisurely; rather, they have been carefully scrutinized — most often with a sentence-by-sentence analysis — with particular attention to the examiner's gestures, intonations, and other details that might not be given primary consideration by many observers. One of the unanticipated outcomes of such viewing has been the consistency and the similarities of their approaches, which appear to have been influenced significantly by the procedures promulgated by White et al. (1985), White and Halpin (1986), and Boat and Everson (1988). I have not only noted the frequent use of leading questions, even more extensively than used by the aforementioned authors, but the introduction of what I refer to as leading gestures. Although leading questions can easily be seen on the transcripts of these interviews, the leading gestures are rarely described by the transcriber. These gestures play an important role in what is actually taking place during these interviews and, I believe, they play a role in the "programming" process that is occurring with the utilization of these dolls. I will also utilize the term *leading stimuli,* which refers to dolls (especially anatomical), body charts, and other instruments that can serve to contaminate the interview, especially in the direction of drawing the child into talking about sexual issues and contributing thereby to the brainwashing process.

My main purpose is to discuss in detail these three areas of importance in sex-abuse evaluation interviews: (1) leading stimuli (of which anatomical dolls represent one example), (2) leading questions, and (3) leading gestures. Defining these concepts more accurately will, it is hoped, improve communication among examiners, especially with regard to what is and what is not a leading question. It is important that the reader not view these concepts simply as yes/no phenomena, whether present or absent; rather, each is best understood as lying on a continuum from not being present at all to being utilized to a significant degree. For each of the three concepts I will demarcate four points along this continuum: not present (that is, absent), minimally present, moderately present, and maximally present. However, I wish to emphasize that these are merely guideposts for categorization. The general principle that is followed for ascertaining which level is most appropriate is the degree to which the stimulus shrinks the universe of possible responses by the interviewee. The less the shrinkage, the greater the likelihood the stimulus will fall at the "absent" end of the continuum. And the greater the shrinkage or narrowing, the greater the likelihood the stimulus would be considered to be "maximal" in this regard.

Last, I will not make a distinction between leading questions and "suggestive questions." Although some may make a distinction between the two, I will not do so, nor will I use the term. Rather, I will use the term *leading questions* to refer to all types of questions that have the capacity to suggest an answer and utilize terminology that attempts to refine the various degrees of suggestibility within the question. Similarly, I will not make any differentiation between nonleading questions and "open-ended questions." I consider open-ended any question that does not contain within it a contaminating focus for response. My comments here will refer to the various degrees to which a question is open and utilize the terminology herein, which more specifically attempts to define the degree of "open-endedness."

LEADING STIMULI

The stimuli that I will be focusing on here are instruments that are generally used in interviewing by mental health professionals, especially psychologists and psychiatrists. They are instruments that have been designed to elicit verbal responses by the interviewee, especially responses that reveal psychodynamic information and personality manifestations. They all involve an external visual stimulus that serves as a focus for the interviewee's verbal response. They differ from leading questions in that the stimuli in the leading question category are entirely verbal. They differ from leading gestures in that the leading stimuli category includes standard, well-defined materials that are easily recognized as providing visual stimuli. Leading gestures, in contrast, although visual, are an incidental form of visual stimulation that may not be directly attended to by the interviewer or the interviewee but have a profound effect on the process of the interview.

Nonleading Stimuli

The ideal nonleading visual stimulus would be no stimulus at all. The psychoanalyst's blank screen for free associations would be an example. The blank card of *The Thematic Apperception Test (TAT)* (Murray, 1936) would also be a good example. Whereas all the other cards of the TAT depict a particular scene with a specific number of individuals, the blank card is completely blank. The universe of possible stories that the interviewee can provide is basically infinite and the external facilitating stimulus does not provide anything that could reasonably contaminate the associations and thereby "shrink" the universe of possible responses.

Minimally Leading Stimuli

A good example of minimally leading stimuli are the Rorschach cards (Rorschach, 1921). These inkblots were selected because they have only limited similarity with known objects. There are some cards, however, that vaguely resemble known objects such as bats, butterflies, and "two drummers drumming." Surprisingly, these are referred to as the "popular responses" and are not particularly indicative of psychopathology. In fact, not to see these popular responses may suggest the presence of such pathology. Because most of the stimuli are not suggestive, and because the universe of possible responses has not been significantly reduced by these stimuli, I place these cards in the the category of minimally leading stimuli. Another instrument in this category is *The Storytelling Card Game (STCG)* (Gardner, 1988a). In this psychotherapeutic game (which can also be used as a diagnostic instrument for eliciting psychodynamic material), there are 24 scene cards, 4 of which are blank. The nonblank scenes depict scenes only and do not contain any figures, human or animal. Some typical scenes: forest, child's bedroom, city street, farm, etc. The child is asked to select one or more figurines (from an array of 15, ranging in age from infancy to old age), place them on a card, and tell a self-created story. It is almost as if the child is creating his (her) own TAT picture card. The blank card pictures used in the STCG are somewhat more contaminating than the blank card of the TAT because in the former there is an actual visual stimulus (the figurines placed on the blank card), whereas in the latter there is none. Because the children create their own pictures, the STCG pictures are less contaminating than the standard nonblank TAT cards (to be described in the next category).

The instruments used in this category have limited capacity to constrain or contaminate the universe of possible responses. They are well viewed as catalysts for projections created by the interviewee, with little potential by the external facilitating stimulus to modify significantly the interviewee's inner psychological processes.

Moderately Leading Stimuli

In this category the external visual stimuli are quite specific; yet they allow for a universe of possible responses. However, because of the specificity of the external visual eliciting stimuli, the universe of possible responses is smaller than that provided by the stimuli in the previous two categories. Most of the TAT cards fall well into this category. In each of the cards one can identify easily the number of individuals depicted, the sex, and even something about the attitudes or emotions of the individuals depicted (although these tend to be somewhat vague). Some examples: Card No. 1 depicts a boy looking down at his violin, which is lying on the table in front of him. Card No. 2 depicts a school girl (carrying books) behind whom is a farm scene in which an adult female, an adult male, and a horse are clearly indicated. Card No. 5 depicts an adult woman standing at a doorway looking into a room (which could be either a foyer or a living room). Card No. 17BM depicts a naked man climbing up a rope. Obviously, the TAT cards shrink the universe of possible responses much more than the stimuli in the aforementioned two categories. Yet, there is still a universe of possible responses to each of these cards.

Maximally Leading Stimuli

The materials described in this category shrink significantly the universe of possible responses. They provide a highly specific stimulus that is very likely to draw the interviewee's attention directly to it. Generally, they provide stimuli that are likely to bring about strong emotional responses in the interviewee. Many of the cards in the *Children's Apperception Test (CAT)* (Bellak and Bellak, 1949) are in this category. Some examples: Card No. 1 depicts three chickens sitting around a table, in the center of which is a bowl of food. In the background is the adult chicken (most likely the mother). Card No. 7 depicts a tiger leaping menacingly toward a small monkey. His mouth is open. He is approximately ten times the size of the monkey. Card No. 10 depicts a bathroom scene in which there is a toilet. Sitting nearby is a mother dog spanking a baby dog.

The *Children's Apperception Test-Supplement (CAT-S)* (Bellak and Bellak, 1963) also contains cards that warrant placement in this category. Some examples: Card No. 5 depicts a kangaroo walking with crutches. Both his (her) left leg and tail are bandaged. Card No. 10 depicts a female cat, obviously pregnant. Because she is standing up, her abdomen is easily recognized as protuberant. TAT Card 8BM also warrants placement in this category. It depicts a man being operated on by two other men, one of whom is holding a knife (or scalpel). Next to him is a gun. In front of all of this is a young man looking out at the viewer. The presence of the gun, knife, and surgical operation warrant this card's being placed in the maximally leading stimulus category because it provides a much greater shrinkage of the universe of possible responses than is provided by the aforementioned TAT cards, which I considered to warrant placement in the moderately leading stimuli category.

The centerfold of many pin-up magazines warrant placement in this category. Whatever the nature of one's reactions (and I admit to a wide variety), there is no question that such a picture provides very compelling stimuli. Groth (1984) has introduced anatomical drawings that are often used in the assessment of children who are being evaluated for sexual abuse. Their purported purpose is to enable the examiner to learn exactly what terms the child uses for the various body parts. The child is presented with cards on which are depicted naked people. Both anterior and posterior views are presented. I have serious reservations about these cards. They provide maximal leading stimuli and communicate to the child that sexual issues are proper and acceptable topics to focus on. If this were indeed the only example of such stimuli used by the examiner, the cards probably wouldn't be too high a contaminant. However, when used along with anatomical dolls, leading questions, and an atmosphere in which the examiner communicates to the child that sex talk is the "name of the game in this office," they may contribute to the creation and/or promulgation of a false sex-abuse accusation. Their ostensible use for learning the names the child uses can easily be viewed as the examiner's rationalization for sexualization of the interview. The examiner could achieve the same goal by simply asking the mother, outside of the child's presence, what names the child uses for the various body parts. In this way, the examiner would gain the benefits to be derived from having this information without contaminating the interview in the sexual direction.

I consider anatomical dolls to be in this category of maximally leading stimuli. They provide highly compelling and unusual stimuli that cannot but draw the child's attention from other issues that may have been on his (her) mind. Some of these dolls have organs that are disproportionately large; others do not. But in both cases the dolls are unusual and thereby attract extra attention. They are not the kinds of dolls that the vast majority of parents (including evaluators who are parents) are likely to give their children as birthday or holiday presents. If a rambunctious teenager were to surreptitiously pencil in genitals, breasts, and pubic hair onto a set of TAT cards, the examiner would probably consider them "ruined" and be quite upset at the miscreant. Such alteration of the cards obviously makes them even more contaminating and would put them in the category of a pin-up magazine centerfold.

I wish to emphasize that my experiences with viewing the videotapes of examiners who utilize these dolls is that leading questions and leading gestures are greater contaminants than the dolls, their strong contaminating potential notwithstanding, and this is one of the reasons why many of the studies that conclude that the dolls are not contaminating are not reproducing the actual situation in which they are commonly used. Specifically, these studies are usually done under laboratory conditions in which the examiners attempt to reduce significantly the use of leading questions because of the appreciation that they have the effect of biasing a sex-abuse evaluation. A typical study involves a child being allowed to play along with the dolls. If an examiner is present, he (she) says nothing or makes a few catalytic statements. Others generally observe the child through a one-way mirror. Activities or comments that could be construed as sexual are quantified.

The main problem with these studies is that they do not accurately reproduce the conditions out there in the real world where examiners are literally bombarding children with leading questions in association with their use of these dolls. Those that appear to support the conclusion that the dolls are not contaminating usually include a few nonabused children who, indeed, provided responses similar to those one obtains from children who have been genuinely abused. This, of course, argues against their "safety." Of relevance here is the common finding that the majority (usually 80-95 percent) of children do not provide responses suggesting sex abuse. This figure is used to justify the conclusion that the dolls are safe. However, the same studies indicate 5-20 percent false positives, i.e., the dolls facilitating responses that are the same as those seen in children who were genuinely abused. From the point of view of an accused person, these false positives indicate that the dolls are very risky and even dangerous and could contribute to the incarceration of a person who did not sexually abuse the child being evaluated. The situation is similar, I believe, to the one in which a pharmaceutical company would propose placing on the market a drug that they claim is "only 5-20 percent lethal."

The reader who is interested in reading directly the studies that come to the aforementioned conclusions does well to refer to the articles by Gabriel (1985), White et al. (1985), Jampole and Weber (1987), Sivan et al. (1988), Glaser and Collins (1989),

Clarke-Stewart et al. (1989), Thompson et al. (1991), August and Forman (1989), McIver et al. (1989), and Realmuto et al. (1990). Moreover, Yates and Terr (1988a, 1988b) debate the anatomical doll issue and present the common arguments provided by both those who approve of and those who object to the dolls. At this point, I believe that the aforementioned studies do not provide convincing evidence that anatomical dolls are particularly safe. They indicate that the dolls — even when used alone, without leading questions and leading gestures — play a role in bringing about and/or promulgating false sex-abuse accusations.

LEADING QUESTIONS

I use the term *leading questions* to refer to questions that engender in the mind of the listener a specific visual image that is not likely to have been produced had the question not been asked. It usually induces the formation of a visual image that may serve as a reference point for future responses and behavior. When a leading question is asked, the examiner cannot be sure whether the interviewee's response has been suggested by the leading question or whether it would have been provided anyway. Such "seed planting" interferes significantly with the data- collection process, the purpose of which is to ascertain whether something really happened (such as is the case in a sex-abuse evaluation). Leading questions can also contribute to the brainwashing process that can take place in the course of an evaluation. Engendering as they do fantasies of events that might not have occurred, there is the risk that the imagery that leading questions induce will come to be believed by the interviewee. Even adults often have problems remembering the original source of information or a recollection. A visual image can come to have a life of its own, especially if repeatedly suggested and brought into conscious awareness. And children, being more suggestible, are more likely to forget the source of an engendered visual image and are more likely to come to believe that the events portrayed therein actually occurred.

Consider, for example, a three-year-old girl who has never

performed fellatio on her father, was never asked to do so by him, and never even entertained the notion of doing so. An examiner asks this child, "Did your father ever put his penis in your mouth?" The question engenders in the child's mind the visual image of her performing fellatio on her father. It is probable that this particular thought never previously entered her mind. The question, however, creates an image of just such an event. Her initial response may be one of denial and possibly even some revulsion. A few days later, when asked the same question (by the same or another examiner), the fellatio-with-father image is then brought into conscious awareness. However, this time she may not be able to differentiate between a recollection derived from the question asked a few days earlier and images related to an actual event. At that point she may respond with, "I think so— I'm not sure." If the examiner zealously wants the child to respond in the affirmative (a not uncommon situation, in my experience), he (she) may pursue the issue with statements such as, "Think hard," "You can tell me," "It's safe here," and "I'll make sure he won't be able to do it again." If one adds here the child's desire to ingratiate herself to the examiner, who she recognizes wants the answer to be yes, it is more likely that the child will consider the "recall" of the visual image as a manifestation of her having indeed had such an experience. It is for these reasons that leading questions can result in a sex-abuse evaluation that is much more a learning process than an exploratory one. Leading questions, then, play a role in what is often criticized as a "brainwashing" or "programming" process.

Leading questions, like leading stimuli and leading gestures, are on a hierarchy from questions that are not leading at all to those that are maximally leading. There are differentiating criteria that delineate the subcategories, but the reader does well to consider there to be a continuum, with the subcategories serving as guidelines for categorization. First, I focus primarily on the verbal communications of the evaluator (auditory stimuli), and I do not direct myself to visual environmental stimuli (including leading stimuli and leading gestures) that are usually operating simultaneously and also have an effect on the child's productions.

Nonleading Questions

Here, again, the psychoanalytic model can be useful. Although there have been many serious criticisms of Freudian psychoanalysis (and I agree with many of them), I do believe that the blank-screen principle is a valid one. It is the best setting for enabling the therapist to find out what is on the patient's mind, uncontaminated by comments made by the therapist. In the ideal psychoanalytic situation, the session begins without the therapist saying a word. Whether the therapist is behind the couch or face to face is not relevant here. What is relevant is that there is practically no direct verbal communication originating with the therapist. The patient recognizes that he (she) will be expected to start talking about the things that are coming into conscious awareness. Thus, a completely nonleading question, in its purest form, is no question at all. There are opening questions, however, that justify placement in this category. Questions like "So what's on your mind?" and "What would you like to talk about today?" still provide for a universe of possible responses. Potential contaminants provided by these questions are highly unlikely.

Young children, especially under the age of five or six (the age range in which anatomical dolls are most frequently used), do not generally respond well to such questions as "What's on your mind?" and "What would you like to talk about today?" However, after an initial "Hello" and "Please come in" (comments that, in my experience, are genuinely nonleading), the child might be observed by the examiner to see what he (she) will do. The examiner can sit and say absolutely nothing and will sometimes be successful in getting the child to spontaneously verbalize, especially after selecting some object in the room to serve as a focus. However, once this object (often a toy) is picked up, we no longer have a blank screen. (We have, now, a category of leading stimulus.) If, however, the child starts talking spontaneously, then we do indeed have a nonleading- question-type situation. Sometimes the child's talking can be facilitated by the child's parent(s) coming in initially, especially at the beginning of the first interview. The parent's presence, obviously, will make the child more comfortable in a strange situation and increases the likelihood that the child will verbalize. However, in order to ensure that the child's verbal productions will not be contaminated by their comments and/or gestures (no matter how subtle), they must be strictly instructed to say nothing at all. If one is successful in this regard (often the case, in my experience), then one is likely to have a situation in which the child begins to talk spontaneously. Once the child is comfortable, the parent(s) can be asked to leave the room, and then one is more likely to have a setting in which spontaneous verbalizations will come forth. Last, the parents need not be brought into the second interview because of the child's previous familiarization with the examiner and his (her) procedures.

Minimally Leading Questions

These are questions that narrow the universe of possible responses to a very limited degree. They are questions or openings that are rarely used as foci for the interviewee's response. An example would be a situation in which a evaluator provides the child with a wide assortment of materials (dolls, farm animals, zoo animals, drawing paper, crayons, clay, doll house) and simply says to the child, "You can play with anything you would like to play with here." Then, while the child is playing, the evaluator sits silently, awaiting the child's spontaneous comments and verbalized fantasies. There has been some minimal contamination here because the universe has been narrowed somewhat by virtue of the fact that the child is being asked to direct his (her) attention to the play material. However, that universe has not been narrowed significantly because there is still a large universe of possible comments the child might make while so engaged. If the child doesn't say anything, the examiner might say, "What are you thinking about while you're playing with those things?" Again, there is a large universe of possible thoughts the child might have. Here, the examiner might say, "I'd like you to tell me a story about the things you're playing with." Here, too, the universe is not significantly constricted. Children under the age of five, however, are generally not cognitively capable of providing well-organized stories—especially with a beginning, middle, and an end. However, they often will, in response to this question, provide a string of loosely connected associations. (They are likely to comply because of the aforementioned desire to ingratiate themselves to adult authority.)

The same principle is applicable in the introduction to the mutual storytelling technique (Gardner, 1968, 1971, 1992a). The introductory material provided by the therapist in the "Make-Up-a-Story Television Program" is general, nonspecific, and does not include material that has any particular "pull" toward a particular story theme. The examiner's responding story (which is therapeutically designed to include the same characters in a similar setting, but incorporates healthier modes of adaptation than those utilized by the child) does provide highly specific material. However, the response here is a therapeutic message, derived from the child's uncontaminated fantasies, and is not presented as a noncontaminated projection. (The therapeutic utilization of this game is not the purpose of this chapter. Rather, only the use of the mutual storytelling technique's story-eliciting capacity is being focused on here.)

Many (but not all) of the cards in *The Talking, Feeling, and Doing Game* (Gardner, 1973) warrant placement in this category. This board game, which was designed to elicit psychotherapeutically valuable information from children in the context of a mildly competitive board game, involves each player rolling the dice and moving a playing pawn around a curved path from start to finish. When the player's pawn lands on a white square, a Talking Card is taken, on a yellow square, a Feeling Card is taken, and on a pink square, a Doing Card is taken. When a player answers the question or responds to the instructions on the card, a reward chip is obtained. Obviously, the object of the game is not simply to earn chips and acquire a prize, but to use the cards as points of departure for psychotherapeutic interchanges between the therapist and patient. Examples of cards that warrant placement in the minimally leading questions category: "Make up a dream," "Someone passes you a note. What does it say?" "Make believe you're looking into a crystal ball that can show anything that's happening anywhere in the whole world. What do you see?" As can be seen, there is indeed a universe of possible responses to each of these questions. Although not as large as the blank screen universe provided by the facilitators in the category of completely nonleading questions, they are certainly close to this ideal.

Moderately Leading Questions

Questions in this category narrow somewhat the universe from which the questions in the previous category draw; however, the constriction of the universe is not that great that significant idiosyncratic material cannot be obtained. Most of the cards in *The Talking, Feeling, and Doing Game* (Gardner, 1973) warrant placement in this category, for example, "If the walls of your house could talk, what would they say about your family?" "Everybody in the class was laughing at a girl. What had happened?" "A boy has something on his mind that he's afraid to tell his father. What is it that he's scared to talk about?" "Make up a lie." "What's the worse thing that ever happened to you in your whole life?" "All the girls in the class were invited to a birthday party except one. How did she feel? Why wasn't she invited?" and "Suppose two people were talking about you, and they didn't know you were listening. What do you think you would hear them saying?" These questions narrow somewhat the range of responses, but still allow for a universe of possible answers. There is a universe of possible lies that the child could possibly tell. There is a universe of possible reasons why everybody in a class would laugh at a girl. There is a universe of possible things a person could hear others saying about oneself when eavesdropping. Yet, the questions do focus somewhat on a particular area of inquiry, e.g., friendships, lying, antisocial behavior, etc.

When doing an evaluation of children I may ask the following question: "You know, nobody is perfect. Everybody is a mixture of things you like and things you don't like. Your parents are no exception. I'd like you to tell me the things about your mother and father that you like and the things about your mother and your father that you don't like. Which one do you want to start with?" There is a universe of possible responses to this question, even though it narrows down to the assets and liabilities of the child's parents. Accordingly, they warrant placement in the category of moderately leading questions.

A verbal projective instrument designed by Kritzberg (1966) also warrants inclusion in this category. The child is asked the question, "If you had to be turned into an animal, and could choose any animal in the whole world, what animal would you choose?" After the child responds, he (she) is asked the reason for that choice. Following this, the child is asked for his (her) second and third choices and the reasons why. Then the child is asked what three animals he (she) would *not* want to be, and the reasons why. A similar series of questions could be asked about objects into which the child could be transformed and, for older children, the specific persons they would choose and not choose to be changed into if they were free to select from the whole array of humanity, living and dead, famous and not famous, real and fictional. Although there is a finite number of animals, objects, and persons (for older children) from which to choose, the number is still quite large (and the older the child, the larger the number). Although the word *universe* is not applicable here, we still do not have the kind of constriction and seed-planting that one sees in the maximally-leading-question category. Furthermore, once the animal, object, or person has been selected, the reasons for that selection allow for a much larger universe of possible responses. The second part of the question (the "why" part) provides, therefore, the more valuable information because it allows for the tapping of a larger universe of possibilities.

It is in this category that we begin to see some of the contaminating leading questions utilized by many sex-abuse evaluators. For example, the examiner might ask, "Tell me about the school you used to go to." On the surface, this seems like an innocuous enough question and would be the kind that many evaluators might ask in the course of their evaluations. However, in this particular case the examiner knows that the school the child used to attend was closed down because the directors allegedly sexually molested the children there. Taking this into consideration, and taking into consideration the fact that this was the first substantive question asked in the interview, we see how the word *universe* has no applicability here. A response that includes nonsexual events is usually of little concern to such an evaluator. And this is an important point. To the degree that the evaluator is thinking about a particular answer, to that degree the question is likely to be leading. Of course, the inclusion of this criterion makes it more difficult to assess the question on its face value regarding the degree to which it is leading, but it is not usually difficult to speculate about what's going on in the evaluator's mind when every single question is directed toward the alleged sex-abuse event, no matter how unrelated to sex they may initially appear.

I cannot emphasize this point strongly enough. The competent examiner is truly going to be open to *any* response the child provides and use that as a point of departure for further inquiry and elaboration, whether it be for evaluative or therapeutic purposes. This is the opposite of the approach utilized by most of the sex-abuse examiners whose reports I have read and/or whose videotapes I have studied and analyzed. It is clear that they start off from the position that the sex abuse is most likely to have taken place and their job is merely to fill in the details. Noncorroborative data are ignored, denials are rationalized away, and one knows then that ostensibly minimally leading questions such as "Tell me about the school you used to go to" are actually quite contaminating and warrant placement in a higher category of leading questions.

Another example: "Tell me about your Uncle Bill." Again, one must consider this statement at two levels. Ostensibly, it may not be highly leading, although it is intrinsically leading under the best of circumstances because the focus is on one person of the 5.3 billion people on earth. However, there is still a universe of possible statements one could make about Uncle Bill. In this case, however, Uncle Bill is the alleged perpetrator. We know, also, that he has been selected from the wide assortment of the child's friends and relatives who the examiner could have chosen to focus on. We know, then, that the examiner is primarily interested in discussing the alleged sexual encounters between the child and Uncle Bill, even though the examiner may be professing a completely neutral position regarding whether sex abuse took place—the usual position of many evaluators (especially "validators"), professions of neutrality notwithstanding. Accordingly, it has a "seed-planting" effect in that the child gets the message that the examiner is interested in talking about issues related to sex abuse, a subject selected from the universe of issues that could be focused upon in the examiner's office.

Maximally Leading Questions

A maximally leading question is one about which there is no doubt what the examiner is interested in discussing and/or hearing. It is one star pulled out from a million galaxies. Many are totally innocuous, e.g., "How old are you?" "What grade are you in?" and "What's your teacher's name?" These are highly selected questions, point out exactly what the examiner is looking for, and lead the child down a very specific path. Such questions may even have the fringe benefit of relaxing a child during his (her) first interview with a strange therapist. The question "What's the name of your school?" might very well be in the same category. However, if the school is the place where the alleged sex abuse took place, and if the school question is one of the first the examiner asks, then the same question now falls into the moderately leading question category (for reasons described above). If, however, the examiner asks, "Tell me exactly what your teacher, Mr. Jones, did to you after he pulled down your pants," we have a statement that warrants placement in the maximally-leading-question category. It evokes a specific image of Mr. Jones pulling down the child's pants. Mr. Jones may or may not have actually pulled down this child's pants. Once the question is asked, however, the likelihood of our knowing whether or not this actually happened (at least with the child as a source of information) is reduced significantly. (And this problem is compounded by examiners who see only the child and then come to a conclusion regarding whether Mr. Jones perpetrated an act of sexual abuse.)

Many of the questions in the White et al. (1985) and Boat and Everson (1988) protocols warrant placement in this category. For example, the question "Did anyone ever touch you in the wrong place?" engenders the specific fantasy of the child's being touched sexually, whether or not the child ever was. The question "Has anyone ever taken your picture?" seems innocuous enough and, one could argue, certainly does not warrant placement in the maximally-leading-question category. However, we know that the examiner who asks this question is not thinking of pictures taken at the zoo, on picnics, or at amusement centers. Rather, the examiner is thinking about child pornography, and the visual image in the examiner's mind is of an adult with a camera taking pictures of one or more naked children, possibly engaged in a wide variety of sexual activities. This is confirmed by the fact that the question is one of a series, all of which relate to sex abuse. If the child were to respond, "Oh, yes. My daddy took a lot of pictures of me when we visited Disney World," that would not be considered a satisfactory or acceptable answer. In all probability the examiner would then ask about pictures taken in other settings in the hope that a sex-abuse scenario would be described. Or, the examiner might get more specific and ask leading questions about whether the child was naked in the pictures, questions about a particular person (especially the alleged perpetrator) taking pictures, etc. Another example: "Have you ever been without your clothes?" If the child were to say, "Of course, when my mommy gives me a bath, I don't have clothes on," the examiner is not likely to find this an acceptable answer. He (she) is likely to ask more questions about *other* people, especially the alleged perpetrator.

Many yes/no questions fall into this category. For example, "Did anyone ever touch your private places?" serves as an entree into a specific discussion about sex abuse. Whether the child says yes or no does not usually provide useful information. If the child says yes, one doesn't know whether the child is saying so in order to ingratiate himself (herself) to the evaluator or because the child really had such an experience. If the child says no, one doesn't know if the no answer relates to reality or if the child had such an experience and is too ashamed, guilt-ridden, fearful, etc., to answer in the affirmative. But less important than the significant drawbacks of the yes/no question (and lawyers have yet to learn this) is the fact that the question "plants a seed" because it induces a fantasy of a child's being touched in "private places," whether or not he (she) has had such an experience. And this is one of the ways that legal interrogations (with their frequent use of yes/no questions) program children into believing they have had such experiences, when they did not.

LEADING GESTURES

This is a most important area that has not been given proper attention by those involved in sex-abuse evaluations. Written transcripts of videotapes rarely mention the gestures of the evaluator. Only the verbalizations are usually recorded, unless something very unusual and dramatic has taken place. Audiotapes, obviously, tell us practically nothing about gestures and other body movements. Yet, throughout much of the interview, the child is looking at the evaluator and obviously is being affected by what he (she) sees. Children model themselves after adults, especially their parents and other authorities. The emulation process often involves the notion: "If I act like him (her), he (she) will like me better." The imitation factor contributes to children's learning about how to function in the adult world. There is a reflexive need on the part of children to imitate significant adults. It relates to the need to learn the acceptable patterns of behavior that will enable them to be like others and thereby fit in well with and be accepted by the group. I call it the "keeping-up-with-the-Joneses" phenomenon.

Another factor operative here is that of sanction. If the child observes the evaluator to be performing an act that might generally be considered unacceptable (for example, placing a finger in a doll's vagina or stroking a doll's penis), he (she) is more likely to repeat that act, even if aware of its unacceptability. The child often operates on the principle: "If it's okay for him (her) to do it, it's okay for me to do it also."

Again, I divide leading gestures into four categories. Again, we are dealing here with a continuum: from nonleading gestures at the one end to maximally leading gestures at the other, and the categorization is primarily for the purpose of providing guideposts.

Nonleading Gestures

Once again, we start with our old friends, the classical psychoanalysts, many of whom (but certainly not all) are experts at doing nothing. (The reader should appreciate that I myself am a trained analyst and so my criticisms of these people are not based simply on books I have read on the subject.) One of the reasons given for sitting behind the couch is to lessen the likelihood that the patient will be affected by the psychoanalyst's facial expressions and gestures. Although I think much is lost by conducting therapy from this position, especially the human relationship (Gardner, 1988b, 1992b), these people do have a point. Although the psychoanalyst sitting behind the couch provides one of the best examples of nonleading gestures, most children who are being evaluated for sex abuse are not coming to be analyzed and most children who are in analysis do not have analysts who work from behind the couch. Nor am I recommending that sex-abuse evaluators buy couches. The evaluator, however, can indeed avoid leading gestures, gestures that provide communications that will contaminate the blank- screen interview. To ask a nonleading question without any contaminating facial expressions or gestures is easily accomplished. One can say to a child, "What would you like to do here today?" without any kind of directive movement or glances. Also, after asking nonleading introductory questions in the name-rank-and-serial-number category, the examiner just might sit, somewhat expressionless, and watch the child to see where he (she) will gravitate and wait until the child begins to speak.

Minimally Leading Gestures

These gestures, like most of the gestures I discuss here, are usually associated with verbalizations that may or may not be in the same category regarding its contamination of the blank screen. If the examiner wishes to direct the child's attention to the toys, because they are likely to provide catalyzation of the expression of the child's naturally occurring fantasies, he (she) might, with an arc sweep of the hand across the toy shelves, say, "You can play with any of the toys in the room." This gesture is selective in that it strongly suggests that the child confine himself (herself) to the toys and not to other objects in the room. It restricts somewhat the universe of possible activities and state-ments, but it is minimally contaminating. The child still has the option to select any of the toys and if they are intrinsically of low-contamination potential, then the gesture will have served its purpose.

The examiner might take a pad of drawing paper and crayons, put them down in front of the child, and say, "I'd like you to make a drawing. Any drawing at all. Draw anything in the whole wide world that comes to mind. Then, when you finish, I'd like you to tell me about what you've drawn." This can be said while pointing to the crayons and blank sheet of paper. These gestures reinforce the verbal request and increase the likelihood that the child will provide a reasonably pure projection. The same principles hold when one is instructing a child to draw a figure for the *Draw-a-Person Test*, the *Draw-a-Family Test*, or the request that the child play with dolls, clay, fingerpaints, sand, or other traditional play therapy materials. (My assumption here is that the examiner recognizes the contaminating effects of such games as chess, Monopoly, Candy Land, etc. Unfortunately, there are many therapists who do not appreciate this obvious fact.)

Winnicott (1968) utilizes a game that he refers to as "squig-gles." The therapist or the child begins by drawing with pencil on blank paper a nonrecognizable scribble ("squiggle"). The other party then pencils in additional lines and curves. Back and forth they go until the child reaches the point where he (she) recognizes some identifiable figure. Then the figure serves as a point of departure for either storytelling or other therapeutic communications. The gestures here are basically of limited contaminating potential. They contribute to the drawing of a figure of varying similarities to actual objects. However, the child is a contributor and the identification of the figure so drawn is based on what the *child* sees in it, i.e., the child's projections, rather than what the examiner considers the squiggle to look like. Because there is still a large universe of possible associations and stories to the squiggle, the game warrants categorization in the minimally-leading-gesture category.

Moderately Leading Gestures

Evaluators who use anatomical dolls will commonly say to children, "Show me how he did it with the dolls." The ostensible purpose here is to facilitate the child's providing an accurate description in order to compensate for the child's immature level of verbal and cognitive communicative capacity. Another argument given for their utilization is that they help inhibited children talk about sex abuse. Although there may be some minimal justification for these arguments for the dolls being used, the encouragement of the physical enactment tends to entrench the child's belief in the events so portrayed, whether or not they actually occurred. When this direction is given, the evaluator often picks up the dolls and hands them to the child, again strengthening the power of the verbal request.

An example of a moderately leading gesture would be the examiner who says, while picking up a family of puppets, "Let's play with these hand puppets. I'll take the mother and father (places them on his [her] hands) and you take the boy and the girl and put them on your hands. Now what happens?" Under these circumstances the child is likely to start moving his (her) hands and verbalize some kind of activity while engaging the therapist's puppets in a similar activity. If it was the therapist who suggested the game, then the universe of possible associations has been significantly contaminated. But even if the child suggests the game, the game in itself has limitations imposed upon it by the physical structure of the puppets and the hands of the humans who are playing with them. Children commonly will bang the heads of the puppets, one against the other. The examiner who interprets this to mean that the child is angry may be stretching a point significantly. The dolls almost ask to be banged together or to engage one another in various kinds of hostile play. Accordingly, the therapist's leading gestures here bring the child down a somewhat narrow path, the path of hostile play.

Levy (1939, 1940) describes a type of child psychotherapy that he refers to as "release therapy." This method was designed to help children verbalize their thoughts and release their feelings about traumatic situations. In order to facilitate this process he structured the doll play in such a way that the child is likely to talk about a particular situation, especially a traumatic one. For example, if a child was dealing with the trauma of being in a hospital, he might walk a boy doll into a make-believe hospital room, lay the child down in a hospital bed, and ask the child to talk about what's happening to the little boy. The child who is reacting to the birth of a new sibling might be confronted with a structured doll-play situation in which the mother is breast-feeding the baby doll. The little boy doll is walked into the room, looks at the mother and baby, and the patient is asked to describe what the little boy is thinking and feeling. This game clearly involves the therapist in moderately leading gestures. Its risk is that it will pressure children into talking about issues that they may wish to repress or that they may be too anxious to discuss. It also has the drawback of "muckraking" and bringing up past traumas that have already been put to rest in a way that is not pathological.

The principle here is that the more intrusive the therapist is, the greater the likelihood of brainwashing and programming, and the greater the likelihood the therapy will produce psychological trauma. And this is what happens, I believe, with children who have never been abused and who have been "treated" for an abuse that never took place. They are made to believe that they were abused. The effects of such programming have yet to be studied because these children represent what is now a new form of psychopathology (Gardner, 1991a).

Many evaluators are advised to ascertain, early in the first interview, the terms the child uses for the various body parts, especially the sexual ones. As mentioned, the ostensible purpose here is to enable the examiner to communicate better with the child and to understand exactly what organs are being referred to when the child mentions these in the course of the evaluation. This is traditionally accomplished by the examiners pointing to sexual parts on pictures of naked people or special dolls. Commonly, anatomical dolls are used for this purpose, although body charts [such as those of Groth (1984)] are used. Typically, the examiner first points to the various body parts on the clothed doll, e.g., while pointing to the nose the examiner asks, "What's this called?" After a few body parts are identified, the clothes come off. Usually the examiner undresses the doll or will ask the child to assist. Once naked, the examiner routinely proceeds to point to the various body parts (breasts, bellybutton, penis, vulva, buttocks, anus) and asks the child specifically to name the part pointed to.

The message being given here is that it is perfectly acceptable, proper, and even desirable to point to and even touch these organs. This is a very unique situation for the child. If a teacher were to do this, the Board of Education might unanimously vote to discharge him (her). If parents, relatives, or neighbors were to do this, they would be suspect as child abusers. It is important to appreciate that there is not only a verbal question being asked here when the examiner touches the doll's penis and asks, "What's this called?" A physical activity is being performed which basically sanctions such pointing and touching for the child. I have seen videotapes of examiners who, when asking this question, will take the penis between their thumb and forefinger and talk while manipulating it. This, too, communicates to the child that this kind of activity is acceptable to the evaluator and that if the child would like to act similarly with the doll's penis, he (she) is free to do so. This same principle operates even more poignantly when the examiner puts his (her) finger in the doll's vagina or anus and asks the question, "What's this called?" These same examiners will then consider the child's physical activities with the anatomical dolls to be an exact reenactment of their own sexual encounters.

Maximally Leading Gestures

In this, the most contaminating category, the examiner uses the dolls to enact a sexual encounter that has not been enacted by the child and may not even have been described by the child. An example would be of the examiner who takes his (her) finger, inserts it into the doll's vagina, and says, "Did your grandpa put his finger in here?" The child, then, by the processes enumerated above, is likely to engage in this very same behavior with the doll, either in that session or in a subsequent session (either with the same examiner or another evaluator). This is an activity that may never have entered the child's mind previously. Talking about it provides one level of implantation of a visual image of this particular experience. Combining the verbal question with an actual physical enactment provides specific visual details that become incorporated into the mental image of the activity. This serves to enhance the likelihood of a visual image forming, an image that will be referred to in future sessions. And, if the examiner believes that what the child does with the dolls is a true reenactment of actual experiences, then a false sex-abuse accusation is likely to be supported or even created.

In one videotaped evaluation I observed, the examiner was convinced that the alleged perpetrator had taken photographs of the alleged victims of sex abuse in a nursery school. The examiner placed the naked anatomical doll on its back, pulled up the legs, and then asked the child, 'Did he take a picture of you while your legs were up like this?" When the child did not respond affirmatively, he placed the doll in the knee-chest position and asked the question again. This was repeated with other positions, many bizarre, to all of which the child responded positively. In one case I was involved in, the examiner pointed to the vagina of a picture of a naked woman and asked the child, "Did he touch you right here?" The transcript did not in any way indicate that the examiner was pointing to the vaginal area of the picture. Not surprisingly, the child not only answered in the affirmative, but the examiner used this response as evidence that the child had been sexually molested.

On many occasions I have seen transcripts that simply indicate that the examiner is saying, "Show me on the girl doll where he put his penis." Not reported on the transcript is the examiner's pointing to and even placing his (her) finger on the vulva or even inside the doll's vagina. The child, then, takes her finger and puts it in the same orifice. It's almost like playing the game, "First you put your finger in, then I'll put my finger in." Children are the world's greatest imitators. They adhere slavishly to the dictum, "If *you're* going to do it, *I'm* going to do it too." And that's a good enough reason for a three-year-old. And in this insidious way, yet another sex-abuse accusation becomes "validated," with absolutely no evidence in the transcript of what has gone on.

Readers of transcripts are not generally aware of the significant amount of activity that is taking place with the dolls while the evaluator and child are talking. This is especially the case with regard to the dressing and undressing of the dolls. I have seen many tapes in which the child, after a short period of "sex play" with the dolls, wants to dress the dolls. Typically, the examiner will find a wide variety of excuses for discouraging the child from doing so, even to the point of physically preventing the child from putting on the doll's clothing. Obviously, the evaluator wants to prolong the period of exposure of the child to the naked dolls. And even when the child is engaged in activities with absolutely no sexual import (usually only a small fragment of these interviews are devoted to nonsexual material), the naked dolls are prominently present within the child's visual field and, obviously, serve as a reminder that they can once again be played with. Generally, it is only at the end of the session, just before it is time to leave, that the dolls are dressed. But even during the dressing phase, in which both the examiner and the child are engaged, there is visualization and touching of the sexual parts.

CONCLUDING COMMENTS

The primary purpose of this chapter has been to clarify the use of the term *leading question* and to suggest that it be subcategorized for the purposes of understanding better the various levels of leading questions and to improve communication among those who are using this term. This purpose is better served if evaluators are appreciative of the various degrees of leading stimuli (anatomical dolls being one example); again, subcategorization into four classes is warranted. Last, I introduce the term *leading gesture,* to refer to a maneuver that frequently operates simultaneously with leading stimuli and leading questions. My hope is that evaluators will be more sensitive to the importance of this factor in sex-abuse evaluations because it has not been given the attention it deserves. For this factor, also, four categories of classification are warranted.

EIGHT
INTERVIEWING TECHNIQUES

PRELIMINARY CONSIDERATIONS

Serving as a Court-Appointed Impartial Examiner

The evaluator should do everything possible to serve as a court-appointed impartial examiner, rather than an advocate, when conducting child sex-abuse evaluations. Before seeing any of the parties, and (ideally) before getting any substantive information about the case (other than that A is accusing B of having sexually abused one or more children), the examiner wants to accomplish two things: (1) the opportunity to see all three parties (the accuser, the accused, and the alleged child victim and (2) a court order *requiring* all three parties to be involved in the examiner's evaluation. It is typical of a party who is promulgating a false sex-abuse examination to do everything possible to avoid being evaluated by an impartial examiner, especially an examiner who is sensitive to the criteria for differentiating between true and false accusations. My experience has been that such individuals will often spend thousands of dollars in order to fight in the courtroom such involvement. Accordingly, when an examiner learns—even before beginning the first interview—that one of the parties has vigorously resisted the appointment of an impartial examiner, then information has already been obtained, information that already suggests that the resisting party is a false accuser. Obviously, this is not the only criterion that one uses, but it is a criterion nevertheless.

Without a court order the evaluator cannot be certain that all parties will be available. Without such an order, one or more of the parties may decide to withdraw from the evaluation before it is completed. And this is especially likely if one of the parties suspects that the examiner is going in the direction of not supporting his (her) position. As mentioned elsewhere (Gardner, 1982, 1986, 1989), it is crucial that the impartial examiner not communicate, at any point throughout the course of the evaluation, which way "the wind is blowing." To do so may seriously compromise the evaluation. Yet, even if the examiner adheres strictly to this caveat, one of the parties being evaluated may recognize that the evidence being provided is strongly supporting the other party's position. Under such circumstances, it is likely that that individual will want to remove himself (herself) from the evaluation. The court order is likely to discourage such action because it will obviously weigh heavily against that party in subsequent proceedings.

Furthermore, the court order should not only indicate that the evaluator is to serve as the court's examiner, but it should also designate the evaluator by name. Otherwise, the nonsupported attorney can claim in court that the examiner was not truly the court's designate. Under such circumstances the examiner will be viewed by the court as its appointee and the examiner will answer directly to the judge. Because the examiner is not serving as a "hired-gun" advocate of either side, his (her) conclusions and recommendations are much more likely to be viewed as credible by the court.

My usual procedure is to send out a packet of information to all parties interested in enlisting my services in a sex-abuse evaluation. In order to avoid receiving substantive information at this early point—the acquisition of such may be viewed subsequently as a compromise of my impartiality—one of my secretaries generally processes all such calls. The caller (usually a parent or an attorney) is told that I make every attempt to serve as an impartial examiner, but that there are still certain situations in which I may serve as an advocate. Such a role, however, will only be considered *after* the caller has made every reasonable attempt to engage my services as an impartial. This usually involves three steps. The first involves asking the adversary side to join in with the caller in asking the court to appoint me as its impartial examiner. If the adversary side agrees, then the lawyers draw up the proper order in which I am designated the court's impartial examiner and present it to the presiding judge for his (her) signature. Once signed, I am then willing to proceed with the evaluation.

If the adversary side says no, then the second step is for the caller's side to ask the presiding judge to order the participation of the reluctant parent and the child(ren). Under such circumstances, the judge will generally view me as the inviting party's advocate; however, I make it known to the inviting party *and* to the other side that, such designation notwithstanding, I will still continue to conduct the evaluation as if I were a court-appointed impartial examiner and may even come to court and testify on behalf of the initially reluctant party. If the judge agrees to this program, I will proceed with the evaluation in accordance with the aforementioned caveat.

If the judge refuses to order the reluctant side to participate in the evaluation, I will then interview the inviting party, review pertinent documents, and make a decision regarding whether I can support that party's position. If I conclude that I can do so with conviction, then I am willing to serve as his (her) advocate. However, before making that final decision, I insist upon a letter from the inviting party's attorney confirming that the first two steps have been taken, and attached to such a letter must be confirmatory documentation. In this way, when I do come to court, I can testify at the outset that I had made every reasonable attempt to serve as an impartial examiner rather than as an advocate. I cannot emphasize strongly enough how important it is for the examiner to insist upon going through these steps. Without doing so, his (her) credibility is significantly reduced in that the examiner will be viewed merely as a hired-gun advocate of the party whose position is being supported. Once these steps have been taken, the examiner has much more credibility in court, even though formally viewed by the court as the advocate of the supported party.

In the service of helping clients take these steps, the caller is sent a packet. The packet includes a face letter in which the contents of the packet are described (Addendum II), my provisions document that outlines the steps that must be taken to involve my participation and provides other information pertinent to the evaluation (Addendum I), and other materials such as a summary of my curriculum vitae, a statement of my experience in the field of forensic psychiatry, and sample brochures from conferences in which I have presented material on child sex abuse.

It is important for the reader to appreciate that most people who call me are not willing to go through these steps. Most are looking for hired-gun advocates, and either the client or the lawyer is "turned off" by my stringency on these points. In fact, my estimate is that only about 5-10 percent of all those who receive the packet follow through. Although I suspect that for many the cost is prohibitive, there is no question that for many the primary reason for not following through is the desire to engage the services only of a hired-gun advocate. Those, however, who are willing to go through these steps will generally agree that the procedure has served them well. It is also important to appreciate that sex-abuse accusations may be heard in either civil courts (for example, family court) and/or criminal court (which usually involves a jury trial). Sometimes both tracks are operating simultaneously, but often the civil trial is heard first and then the criminal. Following a criminal trial there may be an additional civil trial related to the alleged victim's family suing the alleged perpetrator for damages and compensation. This is commonly the case in the nursery school and day-care center lawsuits. As the reader can appreciate, we are dealing here with a complex legal situation.

My experience has been that criminal courts have not been willing to designate me the court's impartial examiner. There is no good reason under the U.S. Constitution why this could not be done if *both* sides were in agreement that they wanted me to serve in this capacity. The usual reason given for not appointing an impartial examiner in a criminal case is that the accused, under the Fifth Amendment of the U.S. Constitution, does not have to testify against himself (herself). In short, an accused person can go to court and say absolutely nothing and still be within his (her) constitutional rights. However, the Constitution does *not prohibit* the accused from testifying if he (she) so wishes. Speaking with an evaluator is considered to be part of the testifying process in that the accused's cooperation with such an examiner will ultimately involve his (her) revelations being divulged to the court. In short, the examiner is viewed as a vehicle for transmitting to the court the accused's testimony. Accordingly, in criminal cases, the accused has the right to refuse to speak to a psychiatrist, psychologist, or other mental health examiner. However, the Constitution does *not prohibit* the accused from speaking to an evaluator, and if he (she) wishes to do so there is no good reason, as I see it, why he (she) should be prohibited from doing so. If the accused person genuinely believes that he (she) is innocent, the individual should be given the opportunity to speak to any psychiatrist proposed by any side. Many accused parties have told me that they would have *wanted* to speak with the accuser's evaluators but were prohibited by the court.

There are many cases pending now in which people convicted of sex abuse claim that they are innocent and that the courts were prejudiced against them by not allowing them to be interviewed by psychologists, psychiatrists, and other mental health professionals engaged by the accuser. Perhaps these lawsuits will bring about a change in this pattern. However, at this point the examiner should appreciate that the possibility of serving as a court-appointed impartial examiner in criminal cases is practically nil. Accordingly, in criminal cases, I most often have served at the step 3 (advocate) level, but I have only agreed to serve as an advocate after steps 1 and 2 have been taken and have proved futile and, after reviewing materials, decided to support the inviting party's position. I usually accomplish this in two to three hours of interviewing and review of materials. However, in very complex cases it may take more hours, and in one case, a complex nursery school case, it wasn't until after I spent 40 hours reviewing documents and videotapes, as well as interviewing the accused, that I was able to come to the conclusion that I could support with conviction the inviting party's position.

The Request to Evaluate Only the Child

On occasion I have been asked to conduct an evaluation of an allegedly abused child, and I am told that I will not be permitted to evaluate the alleged perpetrator, nor will I be permitted to interview the accuser. Interviewing a child alone, and then stating whether the child has indeed been abused, is certainly possible in some situations. But there are many situations in which it may be very difficult, if not impossible, to accomplish this goal. And this is especially the case when one is dealing with three- and four-year-old children. An examiner is much more likely to be able to make a statement about such abuse if he (she) has the opportunity to evaluate the accused person as well as the accuser. But more important, if one is to ascertain whether it was the accused, or some other party, who abused the child, it is crucial that that party be interviewed. The referring sources usually have some particular alleged perpetrator in mind when they make such a request, and the examiner's statement that the child was indeed abused is tantamount to making an accusation by hearsay that may contribute to the alleged perpetrator's being tried by hearsay. Such a procedure for ascertaining guilt and innocence was commonly used in the days of the Spanish Inquisition. I would like to think that we have gone beyond those times. Seeing a child alone and then making a statement about abuse is a throwback to that tragic era.

Unfortunately, we are living at a time when child protection services typically interview the child alone, with only minimal input from the accuser. In *most* (and I repeat *most*) of the child protection service evaluations that I personally have reviewed, the accused has not been interviewed. This is unconscionable. Furthermore, in most of these cases the involvement with the accuser (usually the mother) has been minimal, and there has generally been a reflexive receptivity to her accusations without any questions about her credibility. In many cases, the child protection service has absolutely refused to interview the father, even though he has pleaded for the opportunity for an interview. Yet this still does not deter many such evaluators from naming the father as the individual who sexually abused the child. Furthermore, the evaluators have often spent limited time with the child, with little appreciation that the evidence supporting the accusation is minuscule, if nonexistent. There are many people who are now in jail on the basis of just such an evaluation. It is my hope that the reader will never involve himself (herself) in such an abomination.

Joint Interviews

As mentioned above, I require a court order in which all parties involved in the abuse are required to be interviewed by me. It is preferable that the order specify that the parties will be interviewed individually and in any combination that I consider warranted. It is important for the reader to appreciate that *I do not automatically place the child and the alleged perpetrator in the room together.* I only insist upon the *freedom* to do so if I consider it warranted. I recognize that such a confrontation may be extremely traumatic for some children and, in such cases, I may not conduct such an interview. It is because of the recognition that such a confrontation may be potentially traumatic that many who are involved in engaging the services of examiners will attempt to protect the child from this trauma and absolutely refuse such permission. I believe that this is misguided benevolence, because to implement it as a blanket rule may deprive the examiner of an important source of information. It deprives the examiner of direct confrontation between the accused and the alleged victim, a confrontation that may be the richest source of data pertinent to the question of whether the abuse actually occurred. The alleged perpetrator is the one who is in the best position to respond specifically to the allegation. For example, a father who is accused of having sexually abused his daughter was presumably at the site(s) where the abuse allegedly took place, and he can thereby conduct a cross-examination far better than the lawyers, judges, and mental health professionals. He is in a better position than all of the other involved parties to "smoke out the truth," and the presence of the examiner can assure that his inquiry will be humane and nonpunitive.

Another advantage of the joint interview is that it enables the examiner to observe directly whether the child is indeed fearful of the alleged perpetrator. In many cases of sex abuse, the child will be quite frightened of the perpetrator because of the pains and humiliations associated with the sex abuse. In cases in which the abuse is genuine, there may be fear of retaliation by the accused. In such cases, I generally will *not* conduct such a joint interview. This is one argument for not doing the joint interviews at the outset, but only after one has collected significant data. One is then in a better position to know "which way the wind is blowing," whether the information seems to be supporting a true or a false accusation. If it appears to be a false accusation, one can conduct such an interview more comfortably and not be concerned about the negative effects of the interview on the child. One will also be able to observe firsthand the child's lack of fear of the alleged perpetrator. My experiences have been that in the false-accusation situation, the child is generally not afraid of repercussions from the accused for having been falsely accused. The falsely accused person generally recognizes that the child is an innocent victim and is being manipulated by the accuser.

Proponents of the adversary system claim that one of its strongest points is that it insures that the accused will be faced by his (her) accuser. This, they claim, is an advantage over the inquisitorial system, in which people were often condemned without any opportunity to know what the charges against them were and who made them. I certainly am in agreement with the principle of the accused facing the accuser. However, the adversary system does not allow for such confrontations in the optimum way. The two face one another in a courtroom in which each is required to provide testimony under extremely restricted and constrained conditions. Proponents of the system do not appreciate fully the drawbacks of such an artificial type of confrontation. Each party comes with prepared presentations, and each party generally has a roster or an agenda of information that he (she) will try to hide from the court. Furthermore, the confrontations between the accuser and the accused are conducted through intermediaries—the attorneys—and are thereby diluted, constrained, and compromised. It is an extremely artificial and unnatural kind of confrontation.

The kinds of confrontations I conduct in my office are much more natural and spontaneous. They allow for a free flow of communication between the two parties and give the accused a much greater opportunity to prove his (her) innocence. Neither is protected by a system designed to provide the judge with selected information. I recognize that there may be situations in which the confrontation between the accused and the accuser might get carried away to the point where someone's life might be endangered. Under such circumstances one could still conduct such confrontations with other parties being present to protect them from one another. I can envision a situation in which they might have to be separated from one another by a glass partition and communicate through microphones. But still, such an arrangement is far superior to the restricted confrontations of the courtroom. Elsewhere (Gardner, 1986, 1989) I have discussed in greater detail these and others drawbacks of the adversary system, especially with regard to the value of its confrontations.

Last, even if the confrontations I conduct were psychologically damaging to the child, I do not believe that they are significantly so because I avoid using anatomical dolls, body charts, coercively leading questions, and other sources of psychological grief to children. Such "trauma," however, must be weighed against the trauma to a falsely accused person of being removed (possibly permanently) from the family home, and even incarcerated. This trauma is often neglected by those who reflexively think only of the potential traumas to the children of the interview process. We are not dealing with a situation in which there is one good solution and one bad solution. We are dealing with a situation in which there are a number of bad solutions, and we have to select the one that is least bad for all parties involved. I believe the interview procedures that I describe here are the least traumatic for all concerned parties, but I am not claiming that it will always be free of such trauma.

The Length of the Evaluation

Examiners do well to ensure that they will have the opportunity to conduct as many interviews as they consider warranted. It is a serious mistake to agree beforehand to conduct the evaluation in compliance with restrictions involving the number of interviews. A court would not restrict a surgeon regarding the number of hours he (she) would be permitted to operate on a patient. Yet courts feel comfortable restricting mental health evaluators in sex-abuse cases. I agree that the child may have been subjected to many interviews and that this is likely to be psychologically traumatic. It is hoped that the evaluator's interviews will not be traumatic, or minimally so. But even if the latter is the case, one has to weigh the negative effects of this trauma on the children against the alternative, namely, the false incarceration or destruction of the falsely accused party. Many investigators confine themselves to one or two interviews in sex-abuse cases. Sometimes this is dictated by the pressures of their positions and the great number of cases that need to be investigated. Such evaluators should appreciate that they are operating under significantly compromised circumstances and that the likelihood of their coming up with valid conclusions may be small.

The acquisition of information about such a delicate issue as sex abuse is best accomplished when there has been a relationship formed between the evaluator and the child—and this is especially the case when the child has *genuinely* been sexually abused. The greater the number of sessions allowed for the inquiry, the greater the likelihood that such a relationship will develop. This is the same principle that holds in treatment: One is much more likely to get accurate data from a patient who has formed a relationship with the therapist, trusts him (her), and has had the living experience over time that divulgences will not result in humiliation or rejection. I generally consider three or four interviews to be a minimum for the development of the kind of relationship that is going to prove useful in ascertaining whether sexual abuse has indeed taken place. This is especially the case for children who have been genuinely abused because of their fears of the consequences of disclosure. Although one may be able to diagnose a parental alienation syndrome in the first interview—and conclude thereby that the allegation has a high likelihood of being fabricated—there is still the possibility that sexual abuse has occurred. Furthermore, even in those cases in which the abuse has indeed been fabricated, one wants to ascertain whether changes take place over a series of interviews in order to confirm one's initial conclusion. So here, too, multiple interviews are necessary.

Although I recognize that the ideal arrangement is one in which the evaluator has the opportunity to form a relationship with the child, it is impractical to insist upon it in all cases. I myself have conducted evaluations in which I have seen children on one or two occasions only. I had no problem doing this when I was convinced that the weight of the evidence supported the conclusion that the sex-abuse accusation was false. I am less likely to do this when the evidence supports the conclusion that the accusation is true. It is the purpose of this chapter to present what I consider to be the ideal circumstances in which to conduct an evaluation. To the degree that the evaluator can reach this ideal, to that degree will the findings and conclusions be valid.

Audiotapes and Videotapes

In many cases it is a good idea to make audiotapes and even videotapes of the interviews. Courts are becoming increasingly appreciative of videotapes because of the recognition that they can be extremely valuable sources of information. Videotapes are especially useful for comparing original statements with subsequent ones—in order to pick up alterations and discrepancies that are valuable for differentiating between true and false sex-abuse allegations. An important further benefit of the videotape is that it can protect the child from the psychological trauma of multiple interviews. If the court will permit the videotape to be shown in the courtroom, it will protect the child from direct interviews with the judge, attorneys, mental health professionals, and others. It may even be used in lieu of the child's giving testimony directly. Courts vary with regard to their receptivity to the use of such taped interviews. I believe, however, that they are becoming increasingly appreciative of their value and are thereby becoming more receptive to their utilization.

The argument that a tape can be tampered with (and therefore risky evidence) is not a good one. Although this may have been the case for audiotapes, it is not the case for videotapes. If one suspects tampering, one can have the tape examined by an expert qualified to detect the presence of such. But even a nonprofessional can often detect an unnatural interruption or break in the smooth flow of a videotaped interview. The fear of such tampering is a throwback to the times when only audiotapes were available. Tampering with them was much less likely to be recognized easily by the average person, and even experts might have difficulty if the tampering was done by an extremely skilled technician.

When I videotape interviews in the course of a sex-abuse evaluation, I generally make three tapes simultaneously, an original and two copies. I keep one in my office and I give one to each of the clients. They, in turn, may reproduce them for their attorneys or other pertinent parties. If I am serving as an impartial examiner, and I am certain that I am going to submit copies of the tape to the court, I will make another copy of the original for the judge. Because each of the parties takes a copy of the tape at the time it is made, each has the assurance that the other is not likely to tamper with the tape. In fact, this is the best protection against tampering. One problem with videotapes is that they are extremely time- consuming to review, edit, and transcribe. This drawback notwithstanding, their advantages far outweigh their disadvantages.

I have found review of videotapes of the interviews of previous examiners to be a valuable source of information in sex-abuse evaluations. Much that I have learned about how "validators" work is via painstakingly careful review of their videotapes as well as detailed analyses of the transcripts made from such tapes. And such information has provided powerful testimony in court. I recall one case in which the "validator" was interviewing a two-year-old girl. The evaluator was stroking the penis of the anatomical doll in a clearly masturbatory fashion. While doing so she was talking to the child about whether the alleged perpetrator had asked her to play with his penis in the manner being demonstrated by the validator. The child, not surprisingly, then began to imitate the therapist and began stroking the doll's penis in an identical way. The validator concluded by this maneuver that this child (who didn't have the faintest idea what the validator was talking about) had been sexually molested by the accused. In the courtroom, I had the opportunity to play that segment of the tape and said to the judge, while pointing to what the evaluator was doing: "Your honor, if you want to know about sexual molestation in this case, you are viewing it with your own eyes. This child is being sexually abused here by this validator. If a teacher or a neighbor did this, that person would be brought up on charges, and probably reported to the child protection services. Yet this mother is voluntarily subjecting her child to this kind of sexual and emotional abuse."

The tapes of previous examiners can provide an enormous amount of other kinds of information. One should look for leading questions. Many evaluators claim that they don't use leading questions, yet it is obvious that they not only use many leading questions, but don't even appreciate that they are doing so. They have little if any appreciation of the basic concepts of leading questions, as described in Chapter Seven. Written transcripts will generally not provide information about leading gestures (again, described in Chapter Seven). The videotape of the aforementioned interview, in which the validator was stroking the doll's penis, was in no way described in the written transcript. Videotapes (and less predictably audiotapes) also provide information about whether the child's affect was appropriate to the ideation. As mentioned previously (especially Chapter Six), the appropriate-affect ploy is utilized by many validators to provide credibility to their statements. Because other parties were not present, they may think they can "get away" with this rationalization. Even the written transcript may not "smoke out" this maneuver. The videotape, however, will provide definite evidence, one way or the other, whether this was indeed the case. One can observe there the child's facial expressions and also hear directly the vocal intonations of the child's voice, the true indicators of affect. One can also see the nods of the child's head in answer to yes-no questions. I have seen transcripts in which the transcriber merely states "uh-huh" or "uh-uh," and the reader doesn't know whether the child has said yes or no. By looking at the facial expressions associated with the aforementioned responses, the evaluator can determine whether the child has indeed given affirmative or negative response to the yes-no question. Of course, such evaluators are not appreciative of the extreme drawbacks of the yes-no question, especially when interviewing young children (see Chapter Seven).

INTERVIEWING THE ACCUSER AND THE ACCUSED

Introduction

It is important for the evaluator to appreciate that the child, especially if young, is the least valuable source of information about whether or not the sex abuse has indeed taken place. Accordingly, evaluators who focus on the child as the primary source of information are depriving themselves of the best sources of data. I have found that the best and most efficient way to proceed in a sex-abuse accusation is to meet with the accuser and the accused first, without the child. This is certainly practical in situations in which the accuser is the mother and the accused is the father, but, obviously, it is less likely to be the case in other situations such as nursery school and day-care centers. However, there is no situation in which this is not the optimum arrangement, and evaluators do well to keep it in mind in every case in which they are involved and consider the possibility of implementing this principle. As has been my pattern throughout the course of this book, I will focus my attention on the intrafamilial situation (whether an intact or separated/divorced family) in which the accuser is the child's mother and the accused is the child's father.

Tracing the Evolution of the
Sex-Abuse Accusation

It is extremely important in the course of this early interview to trace in detail the development of the sex-abuse accusation. I cannot emphasize this point strongly enough. It is one of the best methods for differentiating between the true and false accusation. One does well to ask the accuser to think back and try to pinpoint the *very first time* she thought that the child had been sexually abused. If she provides a response that is clearly about an event that occurred after that first point, the examiner does well to interrupt and ask her to go back, think hard, and describe exactly the circumstances of the *first* inkling that sex abuse had taken place. One wants to know the exact circumstances, especially with regard to the likelihood that the idea derived from actual events that warranted such consideration or related merely to fantasies and speculations. One wants to know about the presence of third parties who might have played a role in engendering the idea. If it was the child who first made the statement, one wants to know exactly what the statement was and the exact circumstances under which the statement was made.

The evaluator should trace step by step the details of the evolution of the sex-abuse accusation. This may be quite time consuming and might take many hours. One may have to review in detail conversations between the accuser and other parties, including the whole parade of individuals who subsequently became involved. This may involve review of past documents, letters, affidavits, motions, certifications, transcripts of depositions and court testimonies, videotapes, etc. It is extremely important that the evaluator do this in chronological order in order to ascertain exactly when and where new elements were introduced into the scenario. This is especially important when the accusation is false, because in that situation the additional elements become introduced by subsequent examiners. One wants to look for the introduction of elements into the scenario that were provided by the accuser and/or supporting parties. When one conducts the evaluation in this way, one is in the best position to make a decision regarding whether it is true or false. Not do so seriously compromises an evaluation designed to make this important differentiation.

In the course of this inquiry the accused should be invited to comment. As mentioned, he is in a very good position to make statements about the credibility of the various steps in the allegation. He can point out inconsistencies and even impossibilities that the examiner may not be aware of. He, better than the evaluator, is in a position to ask specific questions of the accused that can help ascertain whether the accusation is true or false. Obviously, in the courtroom, such confrontations will not be possible, and this, of course, is one of the serious defects in the adversary system, the system that is being utilized in American courts to make this important differentiation. We mental health professionals have the opportunity to use the joint interview, a far better procedure for finding out what really happened when there has been a sex-abuse accusation. I am not saying that it is foolproof; I am only saying that the procedures outlined in this book are far preferable to those utilized in the course of adversarial proceedings.

Of course, the sooner after the accusation the evaluator becomes involved, the smaller will be the pile of documents to review. I myself am often invited to do an evaluation at a relatively late point and therefore am required to go through an enormous amount of material. Having both the accuser and the accused (or the party who is available to me) present makes the process more efficient. Rather than reading the material alone, and then subsequently asking questions from notes taken while reading, I avail myself of the opportunity of having the party right there, reading along with me, so that I can ask my questions immediately. This enhances enormously the likelihood that my questions will be relevant and that the answers will be the most accurate. In addition, I have made the process even more efficient by dictating, at that point, my comments about the document and the input being provided by the parties with me at that time. It lessens the likelihood of errors creeping in and makes my report far more credible. In short, I am already dictating my final report early in the data-collection process, sometimes even in the first interview. It is not necessary to have come to a conclusion before one dictates this material. I am merely dictating the pros and cons on each point. However, as one gets further into the materials, and as more and more documents are reviewed, one gets a feeling of the direction in which the data is pulling one. And this is the reason why it is important to have a court order requiring all participants to continue with the evaluation, even though a party might recognize that the wind is not blowing in his (her) direction.

Individual Interviews with the Accused and the Accuser

Individual Interview(s) with the Accuser   In the individual interview with the accuser one wants to get background information that may be useful in finding out whether the accusation is true or false. It is in this interview that one may get much of the data referred to in Chapter Four, data related to the indicators that suggest a false accusation. One wants to find out here about the nature of the accuser's early family life—the accuser's relationship with parents, siblings, and significant others in one's life. One wants to find out about the sexual development of the accuser, especially regarding whether she was sexually abused, has a history of drug and/or alcohol abuse, and the nature of her own sexual relationships with the accused and former male involvements. One wants her opinion on the sexual activities of the accused, especially with regard to whether any sexual deviations were present.

As mentioned, men who sexually molest children are not generally stable, heterosexual individuals who have a history of good sexual adjustment and relatively narrow heterosexual interests. Rather, they generally have a history of a wide variety of deviant sexual practices; wives, often better than anyone else, will know about these. The wife, then, is the best source of information about sexual deviations, and she may often not appreciate that providing such gives useful information about whether the accusation is true or false. Once she learns, however, that her position will be supported by the description of sexual deviations, she is likely to come up with a few, or exaggerate relatively normal, mildly atypical sexual practices, converting them into serious perversions.

When interviewing the accuser, one should give particular attention to the family patterns of the accuser's early life. For example, a woman who was sexually abused by her father at the age of four might become preoccupied with the same thing happening to her own four-year-old daughter one generation later. Such sensitization might very well serve as a nucleus for a false sex-abuse accusation. A woman whose mother viewed her husband as merely a sperm donor is likely to marry a man whom she will view similarly. In both generations, a wide variety of male exclusionary maneuvers may be seen. Whereas in the earlier generation, a sex-abuse accusation was not in vogue as a method for effecting such exclusion, it is very much in vogue these days. Although people may say that they do not wish to reproduce the painful and psychopathological patterns exhibited by their parents, they most often do so—their professions to the contrary notwithstanding. I cannot emphasize this point strongly enough. In the early years of our lives, our parents serve as our only models and their patterns become our patterns, because we are not exposed to any others. Until later in life, we do not consciously have the opportunity to develop alternative modes of behavior.

Individual Interview(s) with the Accused In the course of the individual interview with the accused, one wants to obtain the kinds of information described in Chapter Two. Here one wants to find out how many of the indicators of pedophilia are satisfied. One wants to go into the background of the accused regarding early family life, especially with regard to the presence of a dysfunctional family. One wants to know about early sexual practices, the onset of sexual urges, a history of sexual abuse, history of drug and/or alcohol abuse, and a detailed history of the sexual life of the accused, especially with regard to the presence of any deviant sexual activities.

Just as the wife is likely to know more about her husband's sexual life than others, a husband is more likely to know about his wife's sexual life than others. Some women who promulgate false sex-abuse accusations are sexually inhibited and they project out their own unacceptable sexual impulses onto others. In extreme cases, this may fuel a paranoid accusation. The wife may have divulged her sexual abuse to her husband and then deny to the examiner that she ever made such a disclosure. Such denial may stem from the belief that the experience lessens the likelihood that her accusation will be taken seriously. As mentioned previously, a woman's having been sexually abused herself is not an important differentiating criterion between a true and a false sex-abuse accusation. One has to get much more information about the accusation to know whether the mother's own childhood sexual abuse increases or decreases the likelihood that the accusation is true.

Subsequent Joint Interview(s) with the Accused and the Accuser Because one may have obtained different information from the mother and father in the course of the individual interviews, one wants to see them again in order to clarify points on which there has been a difference of opinion. Here, as is true throughout the whole course of the evaluation, the examiner does well to work as the "ignorant interrogator." I use the term *ignorant* here to refer not to *stupidity*, but to the *lack of knowledge* (which is the true meaning of the word). The examiner is ever inquiring, ever trying to clarify, ever trying to find out which version seems to be more credible. In the course of such an inquiry an examiner might say: "I am somewhat confused now. You (mother) are telling me one thing and you (father) are telling me another. You seem to be providing diametrically opposed versions of the same event. I would like to try to clarify this." At this point each party is asked to address himself (herself) to the other party's statement, with the examiner going back and forth between the two, ever trying to clarify. I do not make such statements as: "I don't care how long it takes, if we have to take a week, a month, or even a year, I'm going to get to the bottom of this once and for all." No one has the time, the energy, and most often the money to proceed along these lines. And in most cases such a statement is not necessary. After a few rounds, one does well merely to "shelve" the issue and go on to other points. The likelihood is that the important information will be provided on other issues and so a resolution of that particular issue is not crucial. In my final report, I do not make any reference at all to the multiplicity of "shelved" issues that were never pursued. Rather, I focus on those in which the conclusion is compelling as to whose position warrants support. A party's direct statement(s) of admission, obviously, is the best evidence. In addition, the evaluator's own observations are not likely to be discredited in the courtroom.

In this joint interview (especially the first), one might ask both parents about the terminology that the child uses for the various body parts. As mentioned, it is not necessary to use contaminating dolls or charts to get this information. It can easily be obtained from the parents. To obtain it in the traditional way, with the use of the aforementioned dolls and charts, can seriously contaminate the interview, sexualize it, and thereby lessen the likelihood that the evaluator is going to find out whether the child was genuinely abused. One wants to also find out about the family practices of nudity in the home, the dressing and undressing situation, degrees of privacy in the bathroom, and the bathing of the children. A common problem derives from a child's claiming to a validator that her father gave her "bad touches" or "touched her in the wrong place." The child may be referring here to the fact that the father washed her crotch area when he gave her a bath or shower. The evaluator, not considering the possibility that this is part of normal child care, immediately assumes that the child is referring to a sexual encounter. Or the child may have been treated with some kind of cream or salve, prescribed by a pediatrician, and even administered under the directions of the mother. This may be what the child was thinking of when she spoke of being touched in her "private parts." Yet, an overzealous evaluator may interpret this as a "disclosure" that the child has been sexually abused. In this interview one should get a detailed description of the various times the accused has indeed touched the child's genitals, whether it be in the toilet situation, the bathing situation, the medical situation, or some other situation.

It is important also to get background information about marital problems, separation, and divorce. One wants to learn about whether a parental alienation syndrome is present and whether the mother has been programming the child against the father. One wants to know about a past history of overprotectiveness, exclusionary maneuvers, and extreme rage — all of which may fuel a false sex-abuse accusation.

INTERVIEWING THE CHILD

Preliminary Considerations

It is extremely important that the examiner appreciate that it is *not* necessary to be successful regarding obtaining information from the child directly as to whether or not he (she) has been sexually abused. I cannot emphasize this point strongly enough. Most would agree that a one-year-old, especially a preverbal one-year-old (the usual case), is not a reasonable source of verbal information regarding whether or not the alleged sex abuse had taken place. Of course, one may get medical information, but this is not the purpose of my presentation here. Most would agree, as well, that a two-year-old is an extremely poor source of verbal information regarding whether sex abuse has taken place. Most two-year-olds have a limited vocabulary, and even the more verbal ones are generally recognized as being very poor sources of accurate information. They are not cognitively capable of understanding the vast majority of questions being posed to them; accordingly, their responses have little credibility. Furthermore, they are extremely suggestible and are ever trying to ingratiate themselves to adult authority. Accordingly, one can get them to say anything one wants. Yet this does not deter many validators from interviewing them, as if they were credible sources of information. What is really going on here, of course, is that they are very useful individuals for promulgating a false sex-abuse accusation.

Three-year-olds, in my experience, serve as the best subjects for inculcating a false accusation. They are verbal enough to provide somewhat credible descriptions, and yet they are young and suggestible enough to be easily programmed. Four-year-olds fall roughly into the three-year category, although some of them are closer to the five-year-olds, who are not so suggestible and who are harder to manipulate into believing they were sexually abused when they weren't.

Evaluators do well to recognize, then, that young children, below the age of four, are extremely poor sources of information and that one should not feel the need to extract information from them with regard to whether or not the alleged sex abuse has taken place. This comment may come as a surprise to some readers, but I cannot emphasize it strongly enough. I have long said that child psychiatrists are like veterinarians because we have to try to get information from patients who cannot speak with us. In other areas (unrelated to sex abuse) most child psychiatrists, like veterinarians, will comfortably say that they cannot get the required information from the child because of the child's cognitive immaturity and lack of verbal reliability. Yet, many validators are far less modest and humble in this regard. They somehow believe they can obtain validating information from any verbal child, as long as they can extract a few words from him (her).

Accordingly, they generally have no problem with saying that a two-year-old is describing sex abuse, when all they have really been able to extract is a few grunts and head shakes in response to yes-no and leading questions. Or they have been successful in manipulating the child into touching the sexual parts of anatomical dolls and then claim that such behavior is an accurate portrayal of bona fide sex abuse.

It is important for the examiner to determine how many previous interviews there have been. The greater the number of previous interrogations, the greater the likelihood the child will have developed a litany, and this creates problems regarding differentiating between true and false sex-abuse accusations. Also, in the early interviews, the child is likely to use terminology that is natural to the home and uncontaminated by professional jargon. With subsequent interviews the child is more likely to pick up professional terminology to the point where, in later interviews, the child might present him self (herself) as one who has been "sexually molested" or "sexually abused." Obviously, these are not the kinds of terms that normal three- or four-year-olds are likely to use. Children who fabricate sex abuse may use such terms in the first interview because they have been programmed to do so. Also, successive interviews generally entrench feelings of guilt and disloyalty. Many children, especially those who have been abused at ages two and three, may not have initially considered their sexual activities to have been bad, wrong, or sinful. They may have considered themselves fortunate to have had a parent who provides them with such gratification. Generally, once the disclosure is made to a third party, new attitudes toward the activity develop. Of course, when the child has been sexually coerced from the outset, and warned about the terrible consequences of disclosure, then the notion that the activity is wrong and sinful will have been inculcated from the beginning.

Ideally, the child should be brought to the interview by a neutral third person, that is, someone who is neither the accused nor the accuser. In situations in which the sex-abuse accusation is part of a parental alienation syndrome, the child is likely to describe and elaborate upon the sex abuse if the accuser is present in the room, or even in the waiting room. In contrast, if the accused party is present or in the immediate environment, the child is likely to underplay and possibly even deny the sex abuse. In the severer cases of parental alienation syndrome, however, the child may be comfortable making the accusation under circumstances in which the accused is nearby and even brought into the consultation room. In situations of genuine sex abuse, the presence of the perpetrator in the waiting room may be such a source of fear in the child that little information about the abuse will be forthcoming. The presence of the accuser, however, may make it more likely that the child will reveal the information. In all these situations the child appears to operate on the principle that what is said to the examiner in privacy will be immediately revealed to the person waiting outside. Or the child may recognize that the parent who is outside may "grill" him (her) regarding what has been said.

In order to prevent these potential contaminations, the examiner does well to arrange that a neutral third party bring the youngster to the individual interviews. Sometimes the so-called neutral third party may not be so neutral in that the individual may have been selected by a parent and has a particular position with regard to the allegation. Accordingly, the examiner must take into consideration this person's beliefs or biases when conducting the interview. In many cases a neutral third party may not be available to bring the child. Under these circumstances the examiner should alternate interviews so that the child is brought to one or more interviews by the mother and one or more by the father. Under such circumstances it is crucial that the examiner ascertain whether the story varies in accordance with which parent is in the waiting room.

An Important Data-Collection Interview Sequence

When interviewing children to determine whether or not they have been sexually abused, the examiner does well to follow the specific sequence outlined below. I am not as firm with this sequence when interviewing children who have not been sexually abused, but I do believe that the proposed sequence is extremely important when interviewing children under consideration for sex abuse. The sequence follows a progression from the elicitation of material that is *least* likely to be contaminated by stimuli provided by the examiner to material that is *most* likely to be so contaminated. In this way the examiner is most likely to obtain useful data. The more the examiner digresses from this sequence, the greater the likelihood that contaminated data will be evoked.

Direct Verbal Inquiry with the Child

The Blank Screen Principle The best kind of information to obtain from the child in the inquiry regarding sex abuse is that which is derived from directly verbal discussion. I recognize that this may not be possible because of younger children's verbal immaturity and/or inhibitions regarding disclosure of the sexual abuse (in cases where it has been genuine). However, the examiner does well to recognize that this is the optimum way for obtaining information about whether the sex abuse has taken place. The fabricating child, of course, will be happy to provide information about sex abuse and will quickly present his (her) litany. In contrast, the genuinely abused child is less likely to provide a little speech. The child who has been genuinely abused may be extremely reluctant, fearful, and so guilt-ridden that direct verbal communication of the abuse may be extremely difficult, if not impossible, to obtain.

When interviewing the child who is being evaluated for possible sexual abuse, it is extremely important for the evaluator to keep in mind an important principle of the psychoanalytic interview. I am referring here to the concept of the psychoanalytic "blank screen." In order to avoid any potential contamination of the child's comments by anything the examiner may say, it is crucial that he (she) refrain from any comments that might direct the child's verbalizations into a specific area, sexual or otherwise.

In my book on psychotherapeutic techniques with children (Gardner, 1992b) I make the following statement:

> The human brain is like a universe of stars in that the number of possible thoughts that may exist in it is countless. At any point, the therapist cannot know which particular star is blinking most brightly, that is, which one of the universe of thoughts is pressing for expression. Only the patient knows this! And it is only when the patient is given full freedom of expression that the therapist can learn exactly which star-thought to attend to. Therapists who believe they *know* which one of the sea of stars is blinking most brightly, or which star to pluck for examination, are not going to serve their patients well.
>
> The human brain is one of the greatest marvels of the universe. If we are to help our patients, we must respect its complexity, its autonomy, and the laws that govern its functions.

The examiner does well to keep this important principle in mind when conducting interviews, whether they be with adults or children, whether they be with sexually abused people or those who have not been. It is one of the universal principles of interviewing. To the degree that one digresses from this principle, to that degree one contaminates the interview.

Accordingly, in the ideal situation the examiner need say nothing, and the child spontaneously begins verbalizing. Children who are providing false accusations, who recognize that this is the time for their litany, directly go into their little speeches. Such children, even days before the interview, may have been told by the programming parent that the purpose of the meeting with the evaluator is to tell him (her) "the truth." I have even seen videotapes in which validators and therapists are rehearsing the child in a way similar to the rehearsals children would engage in before a school play. Those who have been genuinely abused are less likely to spontaneously verbalize, especially if the evaluator is one of the first to be interviewed. But even in later interviews, those who have been genuinely abused may be quite reticent to talk. One wants to determine what is occupying the child's mind. One wants to find out exactly what thoughts are spinning around in the child's head. One wants to avoid saying anything that might stimulate and/or pull forth a particular line of thinking. The best way to do this is for the examiner to make only the vaguest catalytic comments necessary to elicit spontaneous verbalizations.

Accordingly, I much prefer a "pure" verbal interchange at the outset. Adult patients in analysis know well that the analyst will not be saying anything at the beginning of the session, so they will generally start verbalizing without any comments at all from their therapists. Children may need a little more encouragement. Generally, I will often start the interview by asking the child his (her) name, age, address, and other statistic-type questions. I have not found these questions to be contaminating. They do not serve as points of departure for specific areas of verbalization, nor do they pull the child down a specific mental track. Rather, they progressively reduce the child's tension and anxiety because the child will generally get the "right" answers. It is as if each time the child gets a right answer, tension and anxiety are reduced. I may at this point say nothing more and see if the child spontaneously begins to verbalize. If so, I will follow through with the child's train of thought without introducing anything specific. Rather, I will elicit from the child further elaborations of the material already provided. The child may begin talking about some series of events that are totally unrelated to sex abuse. I do not discourage such verbalizations, as do many examiners because they are so intent on getting the child to move down the sex-abuse track. Rather, I recognize that such verbalizations are revealing of what is on the child's mind and that sex abuse may not be on the child's mind. However, they will tell me something about the child, which may or may not be relevant to sex abuse. Such comments do, however, serve the purpose of making the child comfortable with me and entrenching, thereby, our relationship.

Examiners do well to appreciate the value of this free-expression period, especially because it enhances the likelihood that the child will then provide meaningful information. Examiners who work in situations in which they are pressured by time to skip this phase are compromising significantly their evaluations. I would view all verbalizations as "grist for the mill." The mill, however, is not necessarily the sex-abuse mill, but rather the mill of information that is provided, information that helps me learn about this particular child.

If the child does describe a specific sexual encounter, then the examiner should follow this up with particular questions that provide elaborations and corroboration. Under these circumstances the examiner justifiably wants to obtain details, especially corroborative details in order to ensure that the allegation is valid and not fabricated. For example, if the child states that her father "put his finger in my pee-pee hole," the examiner does well to ask questions about this experience. However, each question should be so posed that it does not introduce any *new* substantive material, but only serves to elicit elaborations. For example, the examiner might say, "I'd like you to tell me more about that" or "Where did that happen?" Each question should have a universe, or at least a multiplicity, of possible answers. If the child says, "It happened in Grandma's house," the examiner might ask, "In which room in Grandma's house did that happen?" The examiner should not ask, "Did that happen in the bedroom or in the bathroom?" Such a question has the effect of "pulling" the child's associations into the rooms in which sex abuse is most likely to occur. The examiner must appreciate that each time one narrows down the universe, one is risking a contamination. (In Chapter Seven I have discussed the various levels of leading questions in greater detail.) One should try to get information about any conversations that may have taken place in the course of the alleged sex abuse and what was said by each of the parties. Children who are genuinely abused often have some recollection of the things said by the abuser: "He told me that this is our secret and that I should never tell anyone," "He told me that he would kill my mommy if I ever said anything to anyone," "He told me that I'm his favorite child." In contrast, children who are falsely accusing will often respond to this question with, "I forgot" or "My mommy remembers; I don't."

It is important also to ask questions about what the participants were wearing. The child who was not abused may say, "I don't remember," because there is no specific visual image of the sexual encounter. Such a child might give different renditions about what was being worn in different interviews. In contrast, the child who was genuinely abused will generally be able to provide this information with a fair degree of accuracy and will do so consistently. Again, the most general questions are the best, e.g., "What was he (she) wearing?" and "What were you wearing?" In the course of such a conversation the child might reveal an inconsistency or an absurdity that is one of the hallmarks of the false accusation. For example, the child might state that she had all her clothes on when her father put his finger in her vagina. One also wants to know about the presence of other parties. A good question would be, "Was anyone else there?" Here, too, the response might provide useful information for differentiating between a true and a false accusation. I have been involved in a number of cases in which the child stated that the mother was there, or that she was hiding in the closet, or that she was listening through the door. In these cases the mother was the accuser and denied such involvement. The inclusion of the accusing mother, then, lessens significantly the credibility of the child's story.

When the examiner does get into more specific details about sexual encounters, it is important to appreciate that questions regarding *when* the alleged activities occurred are of little value because the younger the child, the less the likelihood he (she) will be able to pinpoint the particular time when the event(s) occurred. Such questions will confuse the child and result in misleading and false answers, which then only complicate the problem of differentiating between true and false sex-abuse allegations. Prosecutors and other legal investigators commonly use *when* questions as a carry-over from criminal investigations. They certainly serve well with regard to crimes perpetrated by adults, but obfuscate the interrogatory process when utilized with children who have been sexually abused. It is preferable to use questions that relate to specific visual imagery, such as questions involving *where* the abuse allegedly took place and *what* had gone on—with the request for specific details about the setting, scene, and events. In addition, the examiner does well to appreciate that children are not likely to give accurate data when asked questions about the *number* of times they were sexually abused. This principle, however, is not foolproof. A child may well appreciate one or two events as opposed to a long series, but not know much about the number if the number of experiences was 10, 15, 20, or more.

The examiner does well to ask the child about the various events of the day: from the time the child gets up in the morning until the time the child goes to sleep at night. There are two periods, however, that are particularly important to investigate because they are the times when sex abuse is most likely to take place. These are at *bath time* and *bedtime*. I will discuss each of these separately. As might be expected, the bedtime scene is probably the one in which sex abuse is most likely to occur. A common scenario involves a father's lying down with a little girl, hugging and cuddling her, and relaxing her. This may be associated with telling stories or playing games. Then the time comes to kiss the child goodnight. The father starts with the forehead, then kisses the eyelids, the cheeks, and then the lips. There may be lingering at the lips with tongue kissing. The child may not be aware that this kind of kiss is generally considered improper. The father may then proceed down to kissing the neck, chest, the nipples, the abdomen, and then the genitalia. Kissing the genitalia goodnight may serve as an entree into performing cunnilingus. The child may begin to experience sexual pleasure, but not appreciate that an act considered reprehensible in our society is being perpetrated. The pleasure experienced by the child may serve as an impetus for requests in the future that the father kiss her goodnight again, especially where it "feels good." The child may even be brought to orgasm by this practice. Sometimes another excuse is given for fondling the child's genitalia. The father may "check" the vagina to determine whether the child needs to go to the bathroom. Sometimes a father will use his finger for such checking and on occasion his penis. For reasons already mentioned, such insertion is not likely for younger children, but only those who are older and/or whose tissues have been gradually thickened to allow such entry. Again, the child may not appreciate the fact that this is an improper act and that it is no way to determine whether or not someone needs to urinate.

With regard to such bedtime encounters, it is important for the evaluator to appreciate that most pedophiles do not rape their subjects. Rather, the more common practice is to engage in tender, loving sexual encounters during which the child is praised and complimented. The statements are very much like those made by a lover to his girlfriend. However, in addition to statements about how lovely, wonderful, and adorable she is, also included are comments related to her youth, e.g., "You're my baby," "You're my baby doll," and "You're my lovely little baby."

With regard to bath time, one should ask specific questions about the bathroom routine: Who gives the bath? Who undresses the child? Who is in the bathroom with the child? Does the person who is giving the child a bath have clothing on? Exactly what places are washed? If the bather gets into the tub or shower with the child, then the likelihood of abuse may be enhanced. However, there are certainly parents who do this who are not abusers. One wants to get specific information about special attention given to cleaning the genitalia. It is important for the evaluator to appreciate that young children are not likely to differentiate between genital washing that is not associated with the adult's sexual excitation and such washing that is. And this is one of the reasons why I am critical of those who "educate" children about "good touches and bad touches." The dressing and undressing scene is also a common one for sex abuse. Here, too, one must get specific details, especially with regard to any kind of genital stimulation that may have taken place in the course of dressing and undressing.

If, in the course of such discussions, the child does divulge sex abuse and feels guilty and/or disloyal, these feelings must be explored. A common cause of guilt is the recognition that the child enjoyed the activity. Such children must be reassured that the examiner has known others who have had similar experiences and that pleasurable response is not uncommon. This will help such children feel less loathsome over their enjoyment of an activity that they have now learned is criminal and/or sinful. Attempts must also be made to assuage the child's guilt over disloyalty for having divulged the activity in situations in which the perpetrator has sworn the child to secrecy. Guilt over the consequences of the divulgences of the perpetrator must also be assuaged. In situations in which the child has been threatened by the offender, the examiner does well to reassure the child that the threats are exaggerated and, with rare exception, are not likely to be implemented. But even in those cases in which there is a possibility that attempts will be made to carry out the threat, the child has to be reassured that protection is going to be provided, either by the mother or other authorities who will take measures to remove the father, monitor the father's behavior, and so on. Near the end of the interview, the examiner does well to ask the child again to describe the sexual encounter. This helps determine whether inconsistencies have already manifested themselves. However, it is preferable that the examiner have the opportunity for a few interviews, because he (she) will then be in a better position to ascertain whether changes or inconsistencies are common.

In the course of the child's describing the abuse, one wants to get an idea about the scenario's credibility. In Chapter Three, I have described in detail the criteria for differentiating between a credible and an incredible story. In short, one wants to look for preposterous elements, inconsistencies, changes in the story over time, the introduction of fairy tale and other fantasy elements, and the child's associated emotional responses. The last is sometimes referred to as the "appropriateness of the affect." Specifically, this concept refers to the question of whether the child's emotional responses are appropriate to the verbal and cognitive content of what is being discussed. Typically, the descriptions of children who are fabricating have a singsong-like quality, and they will often recite their scenarios with a certain amount of levity. When they recite well they have feelings of pride, like a child reciting a poem correctly in a classroom. In many of the validators' videotaped interviews I have studied, there is not only the educational element going on (as the examiner is teaching the child what to say) but the child is being praised for getting the "right" answers, producing in the child a certain amount of levity and even joy. Examiners who interview such children subsequently may be able to observe this phenomenon directly.

The Truth Vs. Lie Ritual Many examiners consider it important to establish early in the interview whether or not the child knows the difference between the truth and a lie. Lawyers, especially, may get involved in such inquiries because of statutes that require the establishment of the child's cognitive capacity in this area before determining whether the child's statements should be given credibility. This is simplistic thinking if one is interviewing children below the age of six or seven. And the younger the child is, the less meaningful such differentiation is going to be. Generally, the questions focus on very simple differentiations, differentiations of the kind that the child is likely to easily make. Most three-year-olds can generally differentiate between a boy and a girl. Accordingly, if one shows a three-year-old child a picture of a boy and asks whether it is *a lie* to say that the picture is of a girl, the child will generally say that the examiner is lying. If then one asks whether it is *true* that the picture is of a boy, again the child will correctly state that the examiner is telling the truth. Another example: the examiner may point to a red crayon and say, "This crayon is green. Is that the truth or a lie?" The vast majority of three-year-olds are going to say that the statement is a lie. Then the examiner may point to a blue article of clothing and say, "My blouse is blue. Is that the truth or a lie?" The child will respond correctly that the examiner has told the truth.

It would be simplistic, however, to conclude from these and similar questions that the child can *generally* differentiate between the truth and a lie. For example, the same child may believe in the existence of Santa Claus. If the examiner asks the child whether it is true or a lie that Santa Claus exists, the child is generally going to say that it is true. The same considerations hold for the Easter Bunny, God, monsters, possibly superheroes, and a variety of fictional characters from various children's books. The assumption is also made that the child can make more subtle differenti-ations, like whether the father's touching her vulval area while washing her was done with sexual intent or whether the father's applying a salve to her irritated vulva was done with associated sexual excitation. And the longer the time span between the alleged abuse and the time of the interrogation, the greater the likelihood the child himself (herself) will not be able to make the differentiation between details that are true and those that are false.

In addition, such inquiries lose sight of the obvious fact that being able to differentiate between the truth and a lie does not guarantee that the individual will then not lie. Criminal psycho-paths know well the difference between the truth and a lie and yet their life, in a sense, is a living lie. Also, the question does not take into account delusional material (basically, a lie that is believed) and fabrications that are recognized as such at the outset but then, over time, become believed. Another drawback is that the child may not differentiate between a lie and a "mistake" and may use the terms synonymously. Such questions also may have the effect of encouraging the child to lie. This is accom-plished when the examiner asks the child, "Are you telling me the truth?" The vast majority of children are going to answer yes in that it is a rare child who will admit to lying, especially children under the age of six or seven. Accordingly, I generally recom-mend that examiners not waste time on making this inane differentiation.

I once saw in consultation a four-year-old girl whose parents were litigating for her custody. One afternoon the girl told her mother, among other things, that her father had killed Santa Claus, killed the Easter Bunny, and put his finger in her vagina. This was reported to the proper state investigatory authorities. Obviously, they did not call the North Pole to find out whether Santa Claus had indeed been killed, nor did they send out search parties to find the dead body of the Easter Bunny. They did, however, descend upon the poor father, and they brought him up on charges of sex abuse. In the *in camera* proceedings with the judge and attorneys, they first had to decide whether the child could tell the difference between the truth and a lie. They were complying thereby with state statutes that required them to establish that the child could make this differentiation before accepting as potentially valid the child's statements about alleged sex abuse. They satisfied themselves that the child did know the difference when the child was able to correctly state that calling a picture of a boy a girl was a lie, and so on. In order to establish this, they all had to ignore the fact that the child believed in the existence of Santa Claus and the Easter Bunny, and probably even believed that her father might have killed both of these illustrious figures. In another case (mentioned previously in this book) a child who allegedly knew the difference between the truth and a lie indicated her belief that if she lied her nose would grow like Pinocchio's. Subsequently, in the course of the inquiry, she interrupted the examiner and asked if her nose was growing. All this did not in any way deter the mother and other parties from concluding that the child was telling the truth about the sex abuse.

When I reach the point in the second or third interview when I might want to conduct a verbal interchange that has the possibility of focusing the child on the sexual-abuse issue, I will still use the vaguest questions, questions that have alternative answers having nothing to do with sex abuse. I am strictly careful not to sexualize the interview and thereby contaminate it not only for myself, but for future examiners. Accordingly, I may begin my verbal inquiry with general, open-ended questions such as: "So how are you today?"; "So what's been happening to you lately?"; "What would you like to talk to me about?" If such general introductory questions do not result in the child's talking about the sex abuse, then the examiner might broach the subject in a general way. It is extremely important for the examiner to appreciate that the more specific the question, the more "food for thought" it provides, the greater the likelihood it will contaminate the child's responses. I would consider the following to be good questions to pose to a child at this point, especially a child who the examiner suspects will be receptive to talking about the sex abuse: "I understand from your mother that some unusual things have been going on between you and your father. I'd like you to tell me about them."; "I understand that some special things have happened to you recently. I'd like you to talk about them to me."; "What do you understand to be the reasons why you are here?"; "I understand there are some things that have been happening to you that are particularly hard for you to talk about. I know it may be difficult for you, but it's important that we discuss these things. I think this would be a good time to start talking about them." When using these questions, the examiner is particularly careful not to mention specifically the sex-abuse issue. The more the question makes specific reference to sex abuse, the greater the likelihood it will serve as a contaminant.

"Icebreakers" Many children, especially younger ones, are likely to be tense about the evaluation, especially during the early part of the first interview with a strange examiner. I have often found it useful to have the mother accompany the child at this point, a maneuver that in most cases lessens the child's tension. After the child is more relaxed, the mother can be asked to leave the room. The evaluator does well to make the assumption that the child is tense, and this is especially the case for younger children. The examiner should also be appreciative of the fact that information extracted from a person who is anxious is not likely to be accurate. Evaluators who ignore this important fact are likely to significantly compromise their evaluations. Also, examiners who believe that it is important for them to zero in on sex-abuse issues as early as possible—in order not to "waste time"—are also likely to compromise significantly their evaluations, especially with regard to obtaining accurate data.

The Peabody Picture Vocabulary Test-Revised (PPVT-R) (Dunn and Dunn, 1981) can be a valuable icebreaker for involving children, both those who refuse to speak at all and those who are more receptive. For children in the former category, it will predictably get them to at least say *something* (not necessarily about sex abuse) in the vast majority of cases. And for children in the latter category, those who are more receptive but still tense, it can serve as a facilitator for making the child more comfortable.

The instrument has the fringe benefit of providing the examiner with some information about the child's intelligence; but obviously this is not the primary purpose of the interview. The instrument tests word knowledge, which is roughly correlated with the verbal section of the *Wechsler Intelligence Scale for Children-Revised (WISC-R)* (Wechsler, 1974). The patient is presented with a series of plates, each of which depicts four pictures. The examiner verbally presents a word, and the patient is asked to point to the picture that is most closely associated with the presented word. The words, of course, become progressively more difficult. The instrument is designed to assess word knowledge from age three through adulthood.

Let us take, for example, a seven-year-old boy who is sitting in my office in stony silence. This is his first session and, even though his mother is present, he has informed me that he will absolutely not say a word. To such a child I might say, "You know, if you don't *want* to talk here, you don't *have to* talk here. Have you ever heard of the Constitution of the United States?" The child will generally nod affirmatively, or if not, I may take a few minutes to explain to the child the importance of this document. I will then say:

> The Constitution of the United States guarantees, that mean promises, that every person in the United States will have *freedom of speech*. That means that a person is free to speak and say anything he or she wants. However, that doesn't mean that a person can yell "fire" in a crowded theater or speak in such a way that people's lives will be in danger. Anyway, freedom of speech also means freedom *not* to speak. So, if you *don't want to speak,* I respect your right *not* to speak. (It can be useful at this point to wave one's index finger under the child's nose.) And under the Constitution of the United States you have the right *not* to speak!

In this way, I undermine the passive-aggressive gratifications that the boy had hoped to enjoy by thwarting me in my attempts to get him to speak.

I then proceed:

> Now, because we're both in agreement that you don't have to speak, I'm going to give you this test that does not require you to

speak. This is a test to see *how smart you are.* All you have to do is point to the picture that is closest to the word that I will say to you. Now here's the first picture.

At that point I turn to the first plate of the booklet, the sample that is used for the youngest children to ascertain whether they can understand the basic format of the test. These sample pictures are rarely used for children over the age of four or five because, with rare exception, they can readily comprehend these simple instructions, which are merely to point to a picture that is closest to the word the examiner is verbalizing, e.g., "Point to the doll." Generally, the examiner is instructed to begin with the plate that is commensurate with the child's age level. My reason for starting with the first plate is to ensure that the words I will be giving will not only be readily understandable to the child but significantly *below* the child's age level. The first plate (Example A) portrays a fork, a table, an automobile, and a doll. I will then say to the child, "Please point to the doll." True to form, the child will sit silently, adamantly refusing to point. I will then say, "You don't know which one is the doll? You know, a little baby doll? A little dolly that a girlie plays with?" At this point I will utilize baby talk. Generally, I consider the utilization of baby talk to be contraindicated in child therapy. However, this is a situation in which strict adherence to the rule would not be in the child's best interests. Here I want to *embarrass* the child into pointing. If the child still refuses to respond, I will incredulously say, "Gee, he doesn't even know doll!" And then I will dramatically place a cross mark on the examiner's score sheet.

I then proceed to the second plate (Example B) on which is depicted a person's lips, an adult man, a comb, and a sock. I then say, "Now, I'm *sure* you'll get this one, everyone does. This is *really* an easy one. Please point to the *sock.*" Again, the child may adamantly refuse to point. At this point I will shake my head, again incredulously, and say, "Come on, you *must* know which one is the sock. You know, a sock that you put on your foot?" Again, I purposely use baby talk in order to embarrass the patient into responding. If there is still no response, I will say, "Wow, seven years old and doesn't even know sock. Are you sure you're really seven?" At this point the patient may nod that he really is seven. I will then turn to the mother and somewhat incredulously say, "Is that right? Is he *really* seven years old?" Again, after the parents' confirmation, I may say, "Gee, this is really something. I haven't seen anything like this in a long time. Seven years old and doesn't know sock." Then I will again dramatically place a large cross on the score sheet. (As I am sure the reader appreciates, this is not my traditional way of responding when children get wrong answers on tests that I am administering.)

I now turn to the third plate (Example C), on which is depicted a boy running, a girl climbing up a ladder, a girl on a swing, and a boy drinking from a glass. I then proceed: "I know, for sure, you'll get this one because this is *really* easy. Okay now, please point to the *swing*. Again, after no response from the patient, I will incredulously say, "Of course you know which one is the swing, a swing that children swing on in the playground." Again, I will utilize baby talk.

By this point, the patient is likely to say, "Wait a minute, what's going on here? What's happening?"

To which I will reply, "Well, as I told you before, this is a test to see how *smart* you are. And to be very truthful with you, you're not doing too well!"

In response, the patient is likely to say, "Wait a minute. I know which one is the swing. That's the swing." And the patient will point to the swing.

I will then say, "Oh, very good. I was really surprised when you said you didn't know which one was the swing. You know, you're allowed to change your answers." I will then erase the cross and turn back to the doll and sock pictures, giving the patient another opportunity to provide an answer. I have never yet seen a child who has the guts to sit there while I repeatedly and dramatically give him (her) one cross after another. To date, *all* — even the most stubbornly silent — have succumbed. We then proceed with the test, and I get some idea about the child's word knowledge which, as mentioned, is roughly correlated with the verbal section of the WISC-R.

After the administration of this icebreaker, the child is likely to involve himself (herself) in further activities, even those that involve verbalization. I recommend this instrument highly for its value in this regard. I also recommend it as a quick way of gaining some information about the child's general level of intelligence. Although the purpose of the interview is unrelated to an assessment of the child's intelligence, the information might still be useful as part of a sex-abuse examination. For example, the brighter the child, the greater the likelihood of credibility. Under such circumstances, the examiner might say in his (her) report, "Although Pamela was five years old at the time of the alleged abuse, she is of very high intelligence and is functioning at the seven-year-old level intellectually. Accordingly, her comments have to be taken more seriously than the vast majority of other five-year-olds." Similarly, if the *PPVT-R* reveals that the child is functioning at lower than average intelligence, one might say, "Although Gloria was five at the time of the alleged abuse, she was essentially functioning as a four-year-old. Accordingly, she was much more suggestible than the average five-year-old and much more likely to be programmed by her mother."

Another method for engaging resistant and uncooperative children is the utilization of *magic tricks.* For children over the age of five or so, they are particularly effective icebreakers. It is a rare child who is so recalcitrant, uncooperative, or distractible that he (she) will not respond affirmatively to the therapist's question, "Would you like to see a magic trick?" Although not generally useful as primary, high-efficiency evaluative tools, magic tricks can be extremely useful for facilitating the child's involvement with the examiner. Only five minutes spent in such activities can make a significant difference regarding the success of the session. The anxious child will generally be made less tense and will then be free to engage in higher-order activities. In short, they facilitate attention and involvement. In addition, because they make the therapist more fun to be with and more attractive to the child, they contribute to a deepening of the relationship with the examiner.

The therapist does well to gradually accumulate a small

collection of card tricks, magic boxes and cups, secret mazes, and so on—readily purchased in many toy stores (preferably those specializing in magic tricks). This small investment of time and money is likely to pay significant dividends in the evaluative and psychotherapeutic realms. I am not suggesting that the examiner become a magician for the child; rather, he (she) should use such tricks on occasion, for short periods, for their value in facilitating more highly efficient interchanges.

Following the therapist's presenting a *really* good trick, a child may ask, "How did you do that trick?" My usual reply is, "Well, I usually don't tell people how I do my tricks. Perhaps I'll tell you, perhaps I won't. It depends on how much you're going to cooperate." I have no hesitation in utilizing such a bribe. When I talk about the utilization of such techniques in child psychotherapy, I can guiltlessly say that "the end justifies the means." The child who is sitting silently and is stubbornly refusing to talk may be approached with a deck of cards that are fanned directly under his (her) nose. To such a child I might say, "Go ahead, pick a card, any card at all. You'll see I'll be able to tell you what card it is." I have never yet seen a child who will not rise to this challenge. It is difficult to imagine a child just sitting there, adamantly refusing to draw a card from the deck fanned under his (her) nose for the purpose of finding out whether I can really tell which card has been picked. Again, if the child expresses the wish to know how I did the trick, I will suggest that I may tell him (her) how, depending on the degree of cooperation.

Tricks can be used at the beginning and at various other points in the course of the evaluation in order to lighten the atmosphere, thereby counterbalancing the negative effects of the "grim" subjects being discussed.

Jokes, riddles, and other forms of *humor* can also be used as icebreakers as well as mechanisms for engaging the child and increasing, thereby, the likelihood that the child will reveal anxiety-provoking material. Child therapists should commit to memory a collection of jokes that are traditionally enjoyed by children. Riddles are probably the most common form of such humor. Some examples: *Question:* "Why does a humming bird hum?" *Answer:* "Because it doesn't know the words." *Question:* "What's *Smokey the Bear's* middle name?" *Answer:* "the." *Question:* "What looks like a box, smells like lox, and has wings?" *Answer:* "A flying lox box." Some of these may even have a mildly scatological element. For example: *Question:* "What's invisible and smells like worms?" *Answer:* "A bird's fart." (Jokes such as these are a statement of the levels to which child therapists must stoop if they are to successfully engage their patients.)

Humor serves many purposes. It is a pleasurable distraction from some of the heavier material often focused on in evaluations and treatment. Laughing is ego enhancing, and this in itself is therapeutic. The jokes that the child learns from the therapist may be useful in improving relationships with children outside the office. They make the therapist more attractive to the child and thereby increase the likelihood that the child will want to cooperate in the evaluation. The ability to introduce these elements into the child's evaluation requires the acquisition of talents far above those required of examiners who evaluate adults—who need only devote their lives to the overwhelming task of acquiring competence in helping patients gain insight and providing them with the array of other traditional therapeutic experiences.

The Mutual Storytelling Technique   Utilization of the mutual storytelling technique (Gardner, 1992b) provides the evaluator with a useful instrument for obtaining "blank screen" fantasy material. When playing the "make-up-a-story-television-program," the child is invited to make up a story. One can use the vehicle of a make-believe television program in order to facilitate such a fantasy. Following the elicitation of the story, the child is asked to tell the lesson or the moral of the story. When played therapeutically, the therapist ascertains which of the figures represent various parts of the child's personality and which represent significant individuals in the child's environment. The therapist tries to determine whether there are any pathological themes operative in the ways the figures in the story deal with the life situation being portrayed. Then the therapist creates a responding story, using the same characters in a similar setting, but introducing healthier modes of adaptation than those revealed in the child's story. In the course of a sex-abuse evaluation, the therapist might not wish to tell responding stories because the evaluation is not, strictly speaking, designed to be therapeutic. However, the introduction of a responding story that in no way contaminates a sex-abuse evaluation may be useful in that it can enhance the child's involvement in the evaluative process. I would not, however, introduce stories that involve coping mechanisms for sex abuse unless I was certain that the sex abuse occurred. And this is not likely to be the case at this early point in the evaluative process.

Silcner and Hanson (1989) warn against encouraging children to provide self-created stories in sex-abuse evaluations. They believe that such a practice opens the examiner to the criticism that sex-abuse fabrications might be encouraged by the utilization of this modality. I am in disagreement with these authors on this particular point. There is a general principle in therapy (as well as most situations in life) that it is inappropriate to modify one's behavior in order to avoid anticipated irrational responses on the part of others. If one is to tailor one's behavior to protect oneself from inappropriate reactions by others, then one is going to be completely paralyzed and/or at the mercy of everyone. Eliciting stories is an excellent way of finding out what is going on in a child's mind. The story provides the child with a convenient "mask" and yet allows enough revelation to provide the examiner with important information. The examiner who is genuinely not trying to elicit sex-abuse fantasies is not going to elicit such fantasies by simply encouraging the child to make up a self-created story.

The Three-Wishes Question   I generally ask children what three things they would wish for if any wishes they made could come true. I do not consider this a leading question because there is a universe of possible responses that the child could provide. I do not ask the child to list the three, one right after the other. Rather, I ask for one wish at a time and try to elicit reasons and elaborations regarding why that particular wish was chosen. A common way of introducing this question is, "If any wish in the whole world you could make could come true, what would you wish for?" I may then proceed with, "Why would you wish for that?" I then try to elicit more information about that particular wish with such questions as, "Tell me more about that" and "What else can you tell me about that wish?"

I am particularly interested in differentiating between normal, common responses and those that suggest that the child might have been sexually abused. A common response, for example, is "all the money in the world" or some huge amount of money, like "a billion-trillion dollars." When I ask children who respond in this way *what* they would do with all this money, they generally provide a list of toys and other material possessions. In our materialistic society, it is not uncommon for children to wish for mansions and expensive cars. (I have yet to interview a child who would use the money philanthropically.)

Another common response is, "My first wish would be that I could have as many wishes as I wanted." This response is usually provided as a "joke," but is obviously also a resistance. In response I may tell the child that this answer "doesn't count" and that he (she) must give me a "real wish." A common response provided by children whose parents are separated and divorced is, "I wish that my mom and dad would get together again." Boys commonly wish to be famous sports heroes and children of both sexes will often wish that they could be famous rock stars and other celebrities. I consider the aforementioned to be normal responses, and they do not generally indicate any specific form of psychopathology.

An emotionally deprived boy wished for "a gigantic garage for thousands and thousands of cars." A boy brought up in an extremely bigoted home said, "I wish that I was Adolph Hitler so then I could kill all the Jews." A child whose parents were religious fanatics responded, "I wish that I was a bird so I could fly anywhere." A child who was continually subjected to ongoing parental hostilities wished for "peace all over the world." One girl, who was emotionally deprived by parents who had little time and/or interest in her, gave as her first wish: "Pets, all the different kinds of pets in the world except insects." Her second wish: "Money to buy things for the pets, bird feed, peanuts for the elephants, bananas for the monkeys." I considered the first and second responses to represent the patient's strong identification with lower animals. By gratifying their needs, she was vicariously gratifying her own. By projecting herself into the animals she fed, she could gratify vicariously her own dependency needs. She was also demonstrating at the same time how inferiors and underlings should be treated. Her third response: "A bird, because it can fly anywhere it wants." I considered this response to reflect her desire to remove herself from her home environment because it was not particularly gratifying. Such responses are manifestations of psychopathology, but psychopathology that is not likely to be related to sexual abuse. The examiner is interested in these answers as well, because if the child provides responses related to *other* kinds of problems, this too is information, especially because it argues against the child's having been sexually abused.

Children who have indeed been sexually abused may very well provide responses that indicate, directly or indirectly, that they have been abused, for example, "I wish my mother didn't have to work so then she won't leave me alone with my stepfather," "I wish that my weewee would stop hurting," and "I wish that I had a different family." These responses are the kinds one may obtain from children who have been genuinely abused. It is important for the examiner, when attempting to differentiate between true and false sex-abuse accusations, to ascertain whether the response appears to fit in with the total context of the child's situation.

Children who are promulgating false sex-abuse accusations, especially those who have been in "treatment" for such "sexual abuse," may provide responses along these lines: "I wish that Jimmy (a falsely accused day-care teacher) would be put in jail for a million years and that they feed him on bread and water," "I wish my daddy was dead, I hate him," and "I wish they would burn down that whole school with all those teachers because of all those things they did to all us kids."

The First-Memory Question In my work with adults I have found the first-memory question to be very useful. I generally pose it in this way: "Go back as far as you can and tell me what the first memory of your life is. I'd like you to go further back than the beginning of school if you can." Psychoanalysts, especially, are very interested in this question. Although it may not provide useful information, sometimes it serves as an epitomization of many factors that have played a role in the patient's psychological development over the course of his (her) life. The responses to this question can often provide valuable clues about central psychological themes in the person's lifetime, themes that began in childhood and exist to the present time. Sometimes the actual memory is false and the incident never occurred. However, because the patient believes fully that it did, the response can still be a useful source of information.

A child's first memory is generally a less valuable source of information than an adult's. One might argue that the child's first memory is more likely to be a useful source of such information because the time gap between the actual event and the time the question is posed is much shorter than such a time lag for the adult. When adults are asked this question, they are reaching back into the distant past and are selecting a specific event from a much larger storehouse of recollections, and thus it usually has a much greater psychological significance. One cannot label a child immature or regressed if he (she) remembers being in a crib, being fed a meal, or being taken care of in bed when sick. As is true for the adult, the child may provide a response that is not a true memory, but a fantasy that is believed. But even this fantasy may be an important source of information, selected as it is from the universe of possible fantasies that the child may have provided. Once again, I try to elicit as much derivative information as possible about the response and may ask questions such as, "Can you remember anything more about that?" and "See if you can tell me more about that memory?" As is true of all projective information, one must take care to differentiate the age-appropriate from the idiosyncratic and atypical.

A 12-year-old boy's parents both had minimal involvement with him. His father was a hard-driving businessman, a workaholic, who was often absent from the home because of long business trips. His mother was a frustrated, angry, embittered woman who ranged from tolerance of the patient to utilization of him as a scapegoat. This was the first memory he provided: "I was in kindergarten. The school nun was there. The milk she gave me was frozen and I was scared to tell her that the milk was no good. The other kids told her for me. I was afraid that if I bothered her, she would yell at me." The fantasy needs little analysis. The frozen milk is a clear statement of the patient's view of his mother as unmaternal. In addition, he fears complaining about her lack of affection because he might then be traumatized in retaliation and thereby add to the difficulties he was already suffering in association with his emotional deprivation.

A 14-year-old girl was referred because of severe outbursts of rage. She described this event occurring when she was five:

> My mother went down a one-way street in a car. She went the wrong way. A policeman stopped her. I didn't like police at that time. I thought they were mean. I was scared of them. I cried a lot and said, "Don't hurt my mother." I was screaming and crying and yelling. It got him so frustrated that he said, "The heck with it," and he got rid of us. And he didn't give us a ticket.

The patient's mother was a woman who felt overwhelmed by the usual frustrations and disappointments of life and was often confused about where she was heading and what her future would be. One manifestation of this problem was her poor sense of direction, which prevented her from adequately driving distances more than a few miles from her home. The patient's recalling of her mother going down a one-way street is a statement of her view of her mother as a woman who doesn't know which way she is going in life. The patient's recollection of avoiding the consequences of her own behavior by having a violent outburst of rage epitomizes her life pattern. The patient's temper outbursts did indeed enable her to avoid the consequences of her unacceptable behavior. Early in life she had learned that if she were to rant and rave long enough, she would get her way. In this case the policeman, the symbol of the punitive authority, is dissuaded by her tantrums from administering appropriate punishment.

The two examples above were provided by children who were not sexually abused. They are selected as examples of the wide variety of responses one may obtain from children, responses related to the particular problems that may be causing them difficulty. Children who have been sexually abused, especially those whose abuse dates back to the earliest period of their lives, may provide a response related to the abuse. For example: "Every night, as far back as I can remember, my father would get into bed with me and cuddle and hug me. I can't remember a time when that didn't happen. He used to put his hands between my legs and that felt good." Another sexually abused girl responded:

> I remember once, the first time he did it. He said he was going to kiss me goodnight. I was about three years old. He kissed me on the top of my head, and then he kissed me on the lips. But then he stuck his tongue in my mouth. I didn't know that that was wrong. Then he went and he kissed my boobies and then my belly button, and then my peepee hole. I thought that was strange. It felt good, but I was also scared.

In contrast, children who are promulgating false accusations are not likely to be able to create a credible response to this question. As is true of all material provided by children in the course of interviews, the examiner has to think about four possible categories (at least): (1) normal responses, (2) psychopathological responses unrelated to sex abuse, (3) responses related to false accusations of sex abuse, and (4) responses related to true accusations of sex abuse.

Dreams   As mentioned on many occasions throughout this book, validators consider a child's "nightmares" to be one of the hallmarks of sex abuse. My experience has been that it is rare for such examiners to pay particular attention to the *content* of such dreams. Their existence per se is enough to warrant the conclusion that sex abuse took place. Nightmares are normal and there is hardly a child who does not have some, especially in early-to-mid childhood. A typical nightmare involves some kind of a malevolent figure (a dot, a cloud, a "monster") or some other ominous figure coming ever closer to the child. Then, just as the malevolent figure is about to reach the child, he (she) wakes up quite frightened. Nightmares are commonly seen after frightening experiences, such as viewing a "scary" movie on television or in the cinema. Such nightmares often reproduce the frightening figures observed during the viewing. The purpose here is to provide a kind of a desensitization to the mild trauma to which the child voluntarily subjected himself (herself) because of the other gratifications (e.g., hostile release) that these experiences provide.

If a child is traumatized in a more dramatic way, such as being involved in an automobile accident, operated on in a hospital, or subjected to beatings by other children, it is likely that such events will be revealed and dealt with in nightmares during the ensuing days and weeks (depending upon the extent of the trauma). Similarly, if the child has been sexually abused—*and* if the child views the abuse as a painful, upsetting experience—then this trauma, as well, may very well be dealt with and/or responded to by nightmares. However—and this is a very important point—I do not believe that such nightmares are likely to *begin* occurring months and years after the trauma has discontinued. I do not believe that the trauma is somehow encapsulated in some unconscious compartment of the brain and then—months and even years later—becomes released in the hands of some validator with the use of anatomical dolls. Furthermore, the nightmare must have some particular relationship to the sex abuse if one is to conclude that it is indeed a derivative of it. This is no place for fanciful psychoanalytic speculations. This is no place for assumptions that a particular malevolent figure automatically represents the alleged abuser. One might be able to indulge oneself in such speculations in the therapeutic situation where a correct or incorrect speculation is not likely to have a significant effect on the life of the child and others with whom he (she) is involved. However, if one is dealing with a sex-abuse accusation, and if the interpretation (equals speculation) is going to be used to determine whether an alleged abuser did or did not indeed sexually abuse a child, then one must strictly avoid the utilization of such speculations.

Children who have been genuinely abused, *and* who consider the abuse to have been psychologically painful, may have nightmares in which the abuser is pursuing them and they are escaping, dreams in which they are protecting themselves from the abuser. They may have dreams in which they are utilizing coping mechanisms by which they remove themselves from the abuser. They may have desensitization dreams in which they relive the sexual experience (similar to the kinds that adult women have after being raped). In contrast, children who are promulgating false accusations are not likely to provide dreams in this category – unless they have been taught them by the kinds of "therapists" who treat nonabused children and consider them abused.

In short, the examiner does well to ask the child about dreams and to try to pinpoint exactly when the dreams began and the time frames in which they occurred. The examiner should not specifically ask about nightmares, but ask about all kinds of dreams. Recommended questions: "Tell me about your dreams" and "Everybody dreams. What kinds of dreams have you had?" It is important to try to ascertain the relationship between the time frame of the alleged abuse and the time frame of the nightmares. It is extremely important to get a detailed description of the content of the dreams. (This is often not done by "validators," who consider a nightmare per se to be evidence for sex abuse.) Here, the examiner does well to try to elicit as much information as possible, e.g., "What else can you tell me about that dream?" "Is there anything else that happened in that dream?" and "Think hard. Can you tell me anything more that happened in that dream?" I have only touched here on what I consider to be the most superficial aspects of the dream phenomenon. I have not in any way delved into the issue of dream analysis, which is a very complex and controversial area. Elsewhere (Gardner, 1992b), I have discussed this issue in great detail.

Verbal Projective Questions   Useful information can often be obtained from the kinds of verbal projective questions described by Kritzberg (1966). I introduce the technique with the question: "If you had to be turned into an animal, and you could choose any animal in the whole world, what animal would you choose to be changed to?" After the child has provided an animal, I will then ask, "Why do you want to be that animal, of all the animals in the world?" Here again, I try to elicit as much elaboration as possible before asking the second question: "If you couldn't be (name of first choice animal), what animal would you then want to be?" or "Suppose they ran out of (first choice animal). What animal would you then want to be?" Again, I elicit the reasons and then invite elaborations. Last, I ask, "Suppose they had run out of that animal as well, but they promised to make you your third choice animal. What animal would you then choose?" Again, I ask for reasons and elaborations.

Next, I will say, "Now, just to be sure they don't turn you into an animal you wouldn't want to be, what animal do you want to tell them to be sure not to change you into?" Again, I ask for reasons and elaborations and then repeat the question for the second and third choices of animals the child would *not* want to be.

I have found this to be a useful instrument for obtaining psychodynamic information from children. As is true for other verbalized material, the child's responses may be normal, representative of psychopathological processes having nothing to do with sex abuse, related to bona fide sex abuse, or manifestations of a false sex-abuse accusation.

A seven-year-old boy came to treatment because of social difficulties associated with his neurologically based learning disability. I considered his parents, especially his mother, to have dedicated themselves in an unusually healthy way to his education and treatment. These are the responses he gave to the animal questions:

(+)1 A horse. It's fun to go on a horse. Cowboys go on horses.
(+)2 A cow because I like to pet a cow and get milk.
(+)3 A skunk. It smells. It's fun to make smells to people.
(+)4 A pig. They can go oink-oink.
(−)1 A lamb. I can't say the sound of a lamb.
(−)2 A llama. It has a bad smell.
(−)3 I don't know no other animals.

The (+)1 response is normal. The (+)2 response relates to the patient's affection for his mother and his dependence on her. It speaks well for their relationship, which, clinically, was an excellent one in that she was warm and tender and was unusually patient with him. The (+)3 answer reveals the so-called "sweet-lemon" way of dealing with a defect. In this process, which is the opposite of "sour grapes," the person lessens the psychic pain he (she) would experience regarding a deficiency by turning it into an asset. The patient basically considers himself to smell like a skunk, and this attitude is related to his awareness of his deficits. This self-loathing contributed to an actual symptom in which he considered himself to smell. By using the odor in the service of expressing hostility—and rationalizing then its usefulness—he reveals his low self-esteem and again claims to enjoy those qualities within himself that he inwardly despises.

The (−)1 response suggests something about feelings of performance impairment, but little else can be said about his answer. In the (−)2 answer the bad smell theme appears again, but this time he more overtly wishes to reject those qualities within himself that have become epitomized in the "bad smell symptom."

Again, there is a certain amount of speculation regarding the interpretation of the child's responses to this question. A child who has been sexually abused may provide responses indicating that he (she) feels dirty (pig), defective (skunk), or a kind of low-life (worm or snake). However, more important than the *examiner's* association to these animals is the patient's. A child who has been genuinely abused might say, "I feel like a dirty pig because of the terrible things I did with my father" or "I feel like a skunk because my private parts seem to smell since I did those things with the bus driver." The child who has not been abused or the child who is promulgating a false sex-abuse accusation is not likely to be creative enough to provide responses to this question that indicate sex abuse.

There are other elaborations of this question that may prove useful to the examiner: "Animals are living things. Now I'd like you to tell me what thing you would choose to be changed into if you were to be changed into something that isn't alive, an object." Once again, the examiner asks for the reasons why (and elaborations) and then elicits the second and third choices. Then, one should go on to asking the child what things he (she) would *not* want to be, just to be sure that no errors are made. Sometimes, when trying to find an answer to this question, the child might look around the room in order to get ideas before providing an answer. Obviously, the examiner does well to discourage this practice.

For children over the age of eight or nine, I have found this question useful:

> If you could be changed into any person in the whole history of the world, living or dead, past or present, real or not, who would you choose to be? You can choose anybody at all, even people from books, movies, or television. You can choose people who are famous and people who aren't famous. You can choose from people you know and from people you don't know. You can choose from anyone at all from the whole history of the world.

Children under the age of eight or so are not likely to provide useful responses to this question. Their repertoire of individuals from whom to choose is narrow, and so the selections are most often not particularly useful. For example, boys will commonly select superheroes. This is a typical, age-appropriate response, but it does not provide useful psychodynamic information. It is the idiosyncratic response that is useful for the examiner, although the normal response provides information in its own right.

Another elaboration: "If your mother had to be changed into an animal, what animal would suit her personality. I am *not* asking you what animal she would *like* to be if she could choose, but what animal is like her, like the kind of person she is." Because children (especially younger ones) may misinterpret the question and provide responses related to what animal they think their mothers would like to be transformed into, I emphasize the point that I want animals that would suit the mother's personality.

An eight-year-old boy entered treatment because of excessive sibling rivalry with an older brother who was doing far better than he academically. In addition, he would often use somatic complaints in order to avoid going to school. His relationship with his mother was essentially a good one, and his responses to the questions related to animals that would suit his mother's personality did not reveal significant difficulties in his relationship with her.

> (+)1 A soft kitten. She's playful, helpful, happy, fun to be with.
> (+)2 A butterfly. They go places. They're fast. They never touch the ground. My mother's always doing something.
> (+)3 A deer. She likes to investigate and find new things.
> (−)1 A bear. She's not grouchy.
> (−)2 A beaver. She doesn't like to destroy things. A beaver will cut down a tree.
> (−)3 An ant. My mother wouldn't like to be small. She wants important things. She works for the PTA and in the community.

These are examples of normal responses. There is nothing here that is significantly pathological. In the (+)2 response, the mother's going fast from place to place is not a reflection of actual rejection on her part or such active interest in other things that the patient is neglected. Knowing the clinical situation helps in making the decision as to whether the response is normal or

INTERVIEWING TECHNIQUES   425

pathological. In the (-)2 answer we see some evidence of ambivalence in that the child is sensitive to certain hostile elements in the mother, but the degree here is not pathological. One expects ambivalence and a certain amount of repression of unacceptable ideas about a parent. These are considered pathological when they deal with morbid themes or are excessive.

If a child's mother has sexually abused him (her), then the responses to this question *might* provide information about the child's reactions to the abuse. A child promulgating a false sex-abuse accusation is not likely to provide the kinds of responses that would support the sex-abuse accusation. A similar question, of course, should be posed about the father, especially if he is considered to have abused the child. One can also use the object questions but reword them in such a way that the child understands that the objects being asked for are objects that would *suit* each parent's personality rather than the object that the child suspects that parent would want to be transformed into. For older children with a larger repertoire of people, one can ask the child what *person* would suit each parent's personality if that parent had to be so transformed. Last, one could apply the same questions to the child regarding alleged perpetrators.

The Talking, Feeling, and Doing Game (Gardner, 1973)   Most of the questions in *The Talking, Feeling, and Doing Game* are verbal projective questions and have a universe of possible answers. The child who has been traumatized by a sexual encounter with an adult is likely to have thought frequently about the abuse, and such thoughts are likely to be revealed in answering the questions on the cards. However, it is important that the examiner significantly modify the game before utilizing it in a sex-abuse evaluation. Specifically, rather than using it as a therapeutic game—a game in which *both* the therapist and the child answer the questions—it should be used as a diagnostic instrument. When played in the traditional fashion, both the patient *and* the therapist respond to the cards and the therapist attempts to provide responses that are tailor-made to the child's difficulties. Providing such responses in the course of a sex-abuse evaluation might very well contaminate the blank screen. Accordingly, one must modify the game in such a way that the therapist is *not* required to answer the questions.

I have selected certain cards (itemized below) that are more likely to elicit responses about sex abuse, but which are still so vague that they still allow for a universe of possible responses. I myself do not answer the questions, nor do I pick cards. In order to maintain the "game" atmosphere, the child is allowed to take a reward chip from the treasure chest for each response and, when we are finished, is given a prize for acquiring the chips. Generally, I do not state the number of chips that must be obtained to get a prize. However, for children who need motivational enhancement, I may say that the child will get one prize for every 10 chips. The game quality can be enhanced even further by allowing the child to select at random one card from each pile. These are placed face down, so the child cannot screen in advance in order to choose a particular card. It is important that the examiner display only the three piles of cards and not the board, playing pawns, spinner, etc. To do so only invites the child to make inquiries about the traditional game, and the examiner does not want to be in the position of being asked to play it. Under such circumstances, the examiner will be placed in a conflictual situation. If the child's request is granted, then the evaluation is compromised. The evaluation is compromised by the responses that the examiner is required to provide in the course of playing the game. If the request is refused, the child may feel frustrated and resentful, and this too may compromise the interview.

Listed below are the **Talking Cards** that I have found most useful for the purpose of eliciting information from a child being evaluated for sex abuse:

> If you could make yourself invisible, what would you do?
> If a fly followed you around for a day and could then talk about you, what would it say?
> No one is perfect. Everybody has both good and bad parts. Name two bad things about someone you love.
> If the walls of your house could talk, what would they say about your family?
> A girl was listening through the closed door of her parents'

bedroom. Her parents were talking and didn't know she was there. What did she hear them saying?

What do you think about a girl who curses at her father?

What is the worst thing a parent can do to a child?

If you could invent or discover anything, what would you choose? Why?

If you became mayor of your city, what would you do to change things?

Of all the places in the world, where would you like to live the most? Why?

You're walking past a house and you hear some noises inside. What is going on?

What's the best number of children to have in a family? Why? If you could be born again and could be either a boy or a girl, which would you choose to be? Why?

Say something good about your mother.

What do you think your life will be like twenty years from now?

Make up a dream.

What is the worst thing you can say about your family?

A boy heard his mother and father fighting. What were they fighting about? What was he thinking while he was listening to them?

You're looking into someone's window. What do you see?

If someone wrote a book about you, what do you think the title might be?

If you could live your life all over again, what things would you do differently?

Tell a secret to someone. What's the secret?

What is the worst problem a person can have? Why?

What's the worst thing you can do to someone?

Say something bad about your mother.

Suppose two people you knew were talking about you and they didn't know you were listening. What do you think you would hear them saying?

If you had to be changed into someone else, who would you choose to be? Why?

What things come into your mind when you can't fall asleep?

What is the best thing you can say about your family?

What's the most disgusting thing a person can do? Why?

Tell about the worst mistake you ever made in your whole life.

If people could come back to life after they died, what would you like to be like? Why?

You've just written a book. What are you going to call it? What are you going to say in the book?

Say something bad about your father.

These are the **Feeling Cards** that I have found most useful in sex-abuse examinations:

A girl heard her mother and father fighting. What were they fighting about? How did she feel while she was listening at the door?

What makes you feel disgusted? Why?

A boy is ashamed to tell his mother about something. What is it that he's ashamed to talk about?

What do you think is the ugliest thing in the whole world? Why?

What's the worst thing that ever happened to you in your whole life?

A girl was crying. What was she crying about?

A boy has something on his mind that he's afraid to tell his father. What is it that he's scared to talk about?

How do you feel when you learn something bad about someone whom you love? Give an example of a time when that happened.

A boy was afraid to bring children home to his house. What did he fear they would see?

What is the most painful thing that can happen to a person? Why?

Tell about something that's sad.

What "bugs" or bothers you the most? Why?

A girl is ashamed to tell her father about something. What is it that she's ashamed to talk about?

Name some things that a person must do in order to be loved by another person.

A boy was scared to make a telephone call. What was he afraid of?

What's the worst thing a girl can say to her father?

What often gets you upset?

What part of your body do you like the least? Why?

What is the most important thing that can make a family happy?

Tell about something scary that once happened to you.

Two people are whispering about you. What are they saying? How do you feel about what they are saying?

Say something about your father that gets you angry.
Tell about something you did that you are ashamed about.
What is the thing about yourself that you dislike the most? Why?
A boy has something on his mind he is afraid to tell his mother. What is it that he's scared to talk about?
Name three things that could cause a person to feel sad.
Was there ever a person whom you wished to be dead? If so, who was that person? Why did you wish the person to be dead?
When was the last time you cried? What did you cry about?
What frightens you the most?
Tell something about your mother that gets you angry.
A girl was very angry at her father and wished he would get hit by a car. Later that day he was hit by a car. How did she feel? What did she think?
Make up a dream that has feelings in it.

Last, these are the **Doing Cards** that I have found to be most useful when conducting sex-abuse evaluations:

Make believe you're sleeping. What are you dreaming about?
What is one of the stupidest things a person can do? Show someone doing that thing.
Make believe you're doing something disgusting.
Make believe you're having a temper tantrum. Why are you so angry?
Make believe you're having a bad dream. What's the dream about?
Make believe you're reading a magazine showing pictures of nude women. What do you think about such magazines?
What is the most foolish or silly thing a person can do? Make believe you're doing that thing.
Act out what you would do if you found that you had magic powers. Do you believe there really is such a thing as magic?
Tell about something that you feel angry about. Act out what you would do if that thing were happening right now.
Make believe that something is happening that's very frightening. What is happening?
Make believe you're doing a sneaky thing.
Show what you would do if you were turned into your father.
Make believe you're dreaming. What is the dream about?
Make believe you're looking into a mirror. Describe what you see. How do you feel about what you see?

Make believe you're reading a magazine showing pictures of nude men. What do you think about such magazines?

Make believe you're saying something nasty to someone. To whom are you talking? What are you saying?

Make believe you're crying. What are you crying about?

Make believe you're doing a bad thing.

Show what you would do if you were turned into your mother.

Make believe you're having an argument with someone. With whom are you arguing? What are you arguing about?

The child's responses can be used as a point of departure for further inquiry. For example, for the card, "Say something about your father that you like," the child might give a single response. One can ask for *other* things about the father that the child likes. After that, the examiner might ask the child to say things about his (her) father that she *doesn't* like. Again, more than one response should be elicited.

Another example: "If you could be born again and could be either a boy or a girl, which would you choose to be? Why?" After the child provides the first reason, the examiner might ask if there are any *other* reasons and go on to two or three more. A sexually abused girl might say that if she were a boy the abuser might not have molested her.

Another example: "If you could make yourself invisible, what would you do?" A child who has been sexually abused might very quickly provide an answer in which he (she) would use the invisible status to avoid the indignities of the sexual molestations.

To the card, "Say something bad about your mother," a child who is being sexually abused by her father might respond, "She didn't believe me when I told her what he was doing."

Concluding Comments About the Verbal Inquiry with the Child
It is my hope that the reader has come to appreciate the enormous amount of information that can be obtained from children by merely talking with them. Examiners must appreciate that play materials are facilitating instruments and should be used

primarily *after* one has gotten as much mileage as possible out of verbal interchanges. The less skilled and competent the examiner, the greater the likelihood he (she) will rely on play materials as facilitating instruments. Last, I wish to emphasize again that the examiner's point of departure for the verbal inquiry should be the material that the child presents. This is the "handle" that the examiner should grab. This tells the evaluator what is on the child's mind at that point, and the examiner does well to "flow" with it and see in which direction(s) the child will go. It may be that, after a few interviews, the child will have spoken about a wide variety of issues, none of which having anything at all to do with sex abuse. Under these circumstances, many examiners would feel frustrated because they have not yet gotten the child to talk about the sex abuse and believe, therefore, that they are not fulfilling their obligation to extract this important information. Such examiners should appreciate that they have learned something very important, namely, that sex abuse is not something that is "bugging" that child. And this lessens the likelihood that the child has been abused. Accordingly, valuable information has been obtained here. In contrast, in the same setting, a child who has been genuinely abused is highly likely to provide information along those lines, especially because such a nonintrusive and noncoercive approach is likely to result in the child's developing a truly trusting and warm relationship with the evaluator. And it is in the context of such a trusting relationship that the child is likely to divulge bona fide abuse.

The Freely Drawn Picture A freely drawn picture is a good object on which to project fantasies, because at the outset there are no stimuli at all to potentially contaminate the fantasy. The stimuli that serve as foci for the projections are drawn by the child—are self-created—and are projected out onto the blank paper. When a self-created story is elicited in association with the picture, even more information may be obtained. Such a picture provides, therefore, a truer and less contaminated reflection of the child's inner psychic life than a doll does. Accordingly, examiners do well to start with this superior form of facilitation by giving the child drawing paper and asking him (her) to draw a picture of anything and to talk about it. A typical instruction: "Here's a blank piece of paper and some crayons. I want you to draw here anything at all, anything in the whole world. I want to see how good you are at drawing. Then, I'd like you to tell me about what you have drawn." The freely drawn picture does have intrinsic limitations because the child might want to limit his (her) story to the figures or objects depicted in it. The examiner does well to encourage the child to go beyond the picture's borders, so to speak, and to elaborate on the story in any way whatsoever. In this way the examiner can circumvent this limitation. Most children have little difficulty providing such expansions and elaborations. The child who has been genuinely abused is more likely to tell a story about sex abuse—primarily as a method of desensitization to the trauma.

One wants to not only look at the picture but pay attention to the content of the story that is derived from it. Both can be a source of information regarding whether or not sex abuse has taken place. In fact, I believe the story is a more valuable source of information about the child's mental life than the picture, whether or not the child has been sexually abused. Children who have been sexually abused and who have been traumatized by their sexual encounters are likely to introduce themes into their pictures and stories that relate to the abuse. These may be done directly or symbolically. These may be done with or without the child's conscious awareness of what is taking place. Abused children are likely to introduce themes of trauma and persecution that may or may not involve actual sexual encounters. There may be flights from malevolent figures, "bad men," and "monsters." However, the examiner must be careful not to assume that all such fantasies of flight from malevolent figures relate to sex abuse. There may be other sources of trauma in the child's life that are being depicted, and one must always consider the projective element, that is, the child's projecting his (her) own hostility onto the menacing figure.

A sexually abused child might sexualize the pictures and

involve various activities of loving, marriage, rubbing, and even more overtly sexual themes. This reflects the child's early introduction into adult levels of sexual excitation. Yates et al. (1985), after studying the drawings of children whom they considered to be sexually abused, found poorly developed impulse control and that many of the children's pictures emphasize repression, especially of sexual features in the figures. They conclude that sexually abused children tend to either exaggerate sexual features or defend themselves against the need to express them in their drawings. Naitove (1982) provides numerous examples of sexually abused children's drawings in which the sexual scenario is vividly portrayed, often with specific reference to the genitals of the abuser and the sexual act.

Schetky (1988) is in agreement with Sgroi (1982) that asking the child to draw a picture of the abuse can help the child describe its specifics. I personally would be very wary of using drawings in this way. I prefer to use the free drawing, without any particular suggestions regarding what the child should draw. If, however, the child has indeed described the abuse, and does so in a credible way, then I would be receptive to the suggestion that the child draw in order to enhance the child's ability to describe his (her) thoughts and feelings. If the examiner is not convinced that the child was indeed abused, then drawing the picture can entrench the notion that the abuse took place. It is as if the examiner is saying, "I agree with you that you were abused. Now just draw it for me so that we can both get a clearer idea about what happened."

Schetky (1988) describes a 10-year-old boy who was abused by his teenaged male babysitter. He drew a picture of himself lying on the floor with his sitter standing over him with an exposed, erect penis, threatening to "shoot him." One girl, who was hesitant to talk about her abuser, drew a picture of him in jail clothes. She describes another child who spoke about her abuser and then drew a picture of him falling off a cliff. Although I am focusing in this chapter on the use of freely drawn pictures for diagnostic purposes, namely, ascertaining whether the child was sexually abused, such pictures obviously can be useful points of departure for therapeutic interchanges with the child who was indeed abused.

The Draw-a-Person Test   For patients five to six years and above, I sometimes use the *Draw-a-Person Test*. First, I begin by asking the child to draw a person, and I do not specify sex or age. I then ask the child to tell me a story about the person drawn. Following this, I ask the child to draw a person of the opposite sex. Last, I ask the child to draw a picture of a family and then tell a story about the family. As described elsewhere (Gardner, 1992b), I consider the stories that children create about their pictures to be a more valuable source of information about underlying psychodynamics than data obtained from the picture itself. The interpretations in both areas are speculative, but I believe that those made from the story are generally more valuable than those derived from the picture. An atypical rendition of a picture *may* be indicative of a particular personality characteristic, but it may not. Generalizations made about these atypical depictions are just that, generalizations, and there may be exceptions. For example, the child who draws a very small picture in one of the bottom corners of the page may indeed feel fearful and insecure; however, he may not. In contrast, a self-created story is truly a product of the child's own mind, is idiosyncratic to his (her) psychic structure, and is much more likely to reveal things that are related to that child's psychological makeup.

With regard to the picture itself, some sexually abused children may demonstrate anxiety when drawing sexual parts, with the result that there may be shading in or covering of these areas. Some children will draw sexual parts. This may be a manifestation of their experiences as well as premature sexual excitation. Children who fabricate sex abuse are far less likely to draw explicit sexual parts in their pictures. Because children do not generally draw sexual parts when asked to draw a figure, the appearance of explicit sexual parts should alert the examiner to some problem in this realm (DiLeo, 1973; Koppitz, 1968). Hibbard et al. (1987) compare the drawings of children known to be sexually abused with those who were considered to be nonabused and found that the abused children were 6.8 times more likely to draw genitalia than those who were not abused. The child who has been genuinely abused may draw the sexual organs in an attempt to facilitate desensitization and working through of the sexual trauma. If the child's story includes sexual material, then one has a point of departure for a discussion regarding whether the story is "pure fantasy" or whether the story relates to sexual abuse that the child himself (herself) would have been subjected to. Accordingly, pictures may be valuable for serving as a point of departure for a discussion of sexual issues. What is important here is that the examiner in no way suggest the drawing of the body organs, and its spontaneously being done is a manifestation of the child's reduced anxiety over and special concern with this subject.

The Use of Dolls   There is a general principle in child therapy that the ideal doll is no doll at all. By this I refer to the fact that the ideal fantasy for learning about a child's inner psychological life is the one that is projected out into space, with no potential contamination by an external facilitating stimulus such as a doll. A doll has a form, a shape, a size, and identifying details that can serve as a stimulus for a particular fantasy, draw the child's fantasy onto it, and channel it into specific directions. Many (if not most) examiners use dolls to facilitate the child's talking about the abuse. Children naturally project their fantasies onto these dolls and often do not recognize that they are revealing themselves in their doll play. Most child therapists find these fantasies extremely useful as rich sources of information about the child's conscious and unconscious psychological processes. The younger the child, the less the likelihood that the child will appreciate that the fantasies so revealed are referring to his (her) own experiences. There is a kind of self-delusion operating here that appears to be part of the child's natural cognitive world. In the course of a child's sex-abuse evaluation, the examiner must be extremely cautious regarding the interpretation of these fantasies.

They are projections, and they may very well introduce distortions, wish fulfillments, etc. Just because a little girl presents a fantasy of her father's involving himself with her sexually does not necessarily mean that the father did so. It may simply be a verbalization of a wish. And, at a time when young children are being exposed significantly to such material, the wish can be engendered from stimuli other than an actual experience with an alleged perpetrator. The more detailed, personal, and idiosyncratic the projected sexual fantasy is, the greater the likelihood that it relates to a particular incident of true sex abuse. The examiner does well to present the child with a tray or box of a *large assortment* of dolls and allow the child to select one or more. To present a specific limited number, especially figures that relate to a sex-abuse experience (for example, an adult man and a little girl), is to "load the dice" and makes the information elicited thereby less credible.

I usually then present the child with a box of dolls in which are to be found human figures (a variety of family members) as well as animals (farm, zoo, and jungle animals). The figures range in height from about 1-1/2 inches to 4 inches. The human figures are dressed. I do not have dolls with specific sexual features, especially of the kind seen in anatomically correct dolls. My experience has been that it does not matter whether the children choose animals or human figures, so powerful is the need to project a particular fantasy. Generally, this power is greater than the power of external facilitating stimuli (such as dolls) to distort or pull a fantasy in a particular direction. This is an important point and is crucial to the practice of child psychotherapy, namely, that the power of the external facilitating stimulus to distort or pull a projection down a particular track is generally weaker than the power of the unconscious to project a particular fantasy. However, when the external facilitating stimulus includes very compelling elements, then the balance may be tipped in the opposite direction, and the external stimulus may contaminate, distort, and pull the fantasy in a particular direction and/or down a particular road. Anatomically correct dolls have the power to do this, and therefore they have absolutely no place in an evaluation for sex abuse.

Children who have been sexually abused may use doll play as an opportunity to talk about their experiences, primarily as part of the desensitization process. Such desensitization normally takes place via the child's repeatedly thinking about the trauma, talking about it, and reiterating the experience in fantasy play (with or without dolls). It is as if each time the child relives the experience in fantasy, it becomes a little more bearable. Finally, after varying periods of time the trauma loses its power to affect the child adversely. Investigatory procedures interfere with this process. The child may be continually reminded of the trauma long beyond the time when natural desensitization processes might have buried the whole incident, or at least reduced its capacity for creating tension and anxiety. Doll play can facilitate this process. The child is engaging in a natural form of systematic desensitization. Accordingly, I refer to this as desensitization play. This phenomenon is sometimes referred to as *traumatic reliving* and *spontaneous reenactment.* Children who have not been abused are not aware of this phenomenon and so are not likely to engage in such doll play. Such doll play may also introduce coping mechanisms, such as putting the perpetrator in jail or having him killed in an automobile accident. Goodwin (1987) describes the punitive and retaliatory elements in such play, which is typical of children who have been genuinely abused. Such children use the doll play as a vehicle for gratifying these desires without consciously appreciating that they are doing so. In this way they release their hostility without experiencing the guilt they might suffer over conscious recognition of what they are doing. Evaluators, then, should listen carefully to the child's self-created stories and attempt to ascertain whether they are of the kind seen in children who have been genuinely abused. The content of such stories can serve as an important criterion for differentiating between true and false accusations of sex abuse.

The Storytelling Card Game   This game, although designed primarily as a therapeutic instrument, can also be used diagnostically, i.e., as a method for eliciting self-created fantasies and other forms of psychodynamic material. I will focus here *only* on its utilization as a diagnostic instrument. The diagnostic equipment consists of 24 picture cards, 20 of which depict common scenes (forest, farm, classroom, school library, school stage, suburban street, etc.) and 15 figurines ranging in age from infancy to old age. None of the pictures includes figures, either human or animal. The child is asked to select a picture and place on it one or more figurines. The child is then asked to tell a self-created story about the scene so created. As a source of information about mental processes, the instrument is superior to the *Children's Apperception Test (CAT)* (Bellak and Bellak, 1949) and the *Thematic Apperception Test (TAT)* (Murray, 1936). My reason for saying this is that in the CAT and TAT, the patient is presented with a picture that has a specific number of figures depicted, figures that can be counted, and figures whose approximate ages can be surmised. Although there is a universe of possible responses to each of the CAT and TAT pictures, there is still a certain amount of channeling and contamination by the specificity of the figures depicted in the picture. In contrast, when children provide free fantasies to *The Storytelling Card Game* cards, there is a greater universe of possibilities, because they are creating their own pictures and deciding themselves exactly how many and which figures they will place therein.

I do not use the CAT and TAT cards when assessing children for sex abuse because they might draw the child's fantasies away from sex abuse, in that none of the pictures specifically make reference to this kind of activity. However, I could not conceive of utilizing sexually explicit cards, i.e., cards that depict specific sexual scenes, because of their obvious draw in the sexual direction. Also, they might even provide visual nuclei for a false sex-abuse accusation. A draw in either direction "loads the dice" and increases the likelihood that the examiner will obtain material in accordance with which kind of picture is being presented. As is true for the other projective instruments described above, the child who has been genuinely abused is likely to provide information related to the sexual abuse, whereas the child who has not been abused is not likely to do so.

Final Comments on the Interview Sequence

The interview sequence, then, should be direct talk first, with the examiner's trying to elicit as much as possible via this vehicle. *After* the examiner has gotten as much "mileage" as possible from direct verbalization, then the next step would be blank-screen verbal projective instruments, such as the mutual storytelling technique, the three-wishes question, the first-memory question, dreams, verbal projective questions, and selected questions from *The Talking, Feeling, and Doing Game*. Then, one utilizes techniques that will provide projective material, such as the freely drawn picture, the *Draw-a-Person Test*, free doll play, and *The Storytelling Card Game* (used diagnostically).

There is no place in the sex-abuse diagnostic evaluation for body charts of naked people, such as those introduced by Groth (1984). Nor is there a place for anatomically correct dolls, which, as described in great detail in Chapter Seven and elsewhere in this book, are an extreme contamination. There is a wide variety of other interview aids utilized by "validators," e.g., picture books, story books, coloring books, audiotapes, and videotapes. Some of these are designed to be used therapeutically in order to introduce coping mechanisms such as "saying no" and enlisting the aid of adult authorities. Some are designed for the purposes of prevention, that is, helping children be alerted to the early signs of sex abuse in order to protect themselves from such molestation. However, many examiners use them in the diagnostic process in the hope that the verbalizations they elicit will provide information about the child's alleged molestation. As mentioned earlier, I am critical of these materials for many reasons. Pertinent here is their effect on the sex-abuse evaluation. They sexualize the interview and make it difficult to determine whether the child's productions are related to the materials introduced by the examiner or the results of actual experiences. When used therapeutically, there is the danger that children who have not been abused will come to believe that they were so because the books and other materials start off with the assumption that the child who reads (hears/listens to) them has indeed been abused. And when used preventively, I believe they produce an enhanced state of vigilance and distrust of the world, which cannot but be detrimental to children. I believe that for every child who has actually been protected from potential abuse by such instruments, there are hundreds who have been made more vigilant and tense. Therefore, I believe that their disadvantages far outweigh their advantages.

CONCLUDING COMMENTS

It is important for examiners to appreciate that the longer the passage of time between the alleged sex abuse and the time of the evaluation, the more blurred will be the events in the mind of the child. Also, the younger the child, the greater the likelihood that confusion will distort the events even further. And this is especially the case if the child has been subjected to a series of sexualized interviews by a "validator" who is convinced that the abuse did indeed take place. There is even the likelihood in many cases that the child will reach the point where he (she) does not actually know any more whether the abuse actually occurred. All of us have had the experience at times of not being sure whether an event really happened or whether we imagined it happened. In fact, we will sometimes create a scenario about something occurring and then years later actually believe that it did indeed take place, when in fact it had not. Adults who speak with their parents about their childhoods will invariably learn about distortions. Adults will be certain that an event occurred in one way, and their parents will insist that it occurred in another way. I am not claiming that the older individuals' recollections are necessarily more likely to be valid than the younger, but it is more likely that they are. We all distort and transform reality to some degree in compliance with our wishes. And this phenomenon is more likely to take place in children of three or four years of age. The ability to differentiate fact from fantasy in a three- or four-year-old is very limited.

I once again wish to emphasize the point that the examiner

should accept the fact that the interview techniques described here will *not* guarantee that the child will provide information about sexual abuse. I believe that the genuinely abused child, especially the child who has been traumatized by the abuse, is highly likely to provide information about it over the course of three or four interviews conducted in the manner described in this chapter. If, however, after these interviews there is nothing forthcoming to indicate sex abuse, then the examiner should be able to make a statement along these lines: "On the basis of my interviews with this child, nothing has come out to confirm that the child has been sexually abused. There are two possibilities here: (1) the child has not been abused and (2) the child has been abused, but my interview has not been successful in eliciting confirmation." The examiner then must rely more heavily on other sources of information, especially information derived from detailed interviews with the accuser and the accused. The examiner must feel comfortable with the conclusion that no probative information was obtained from the child. Examiners who believe that it behooves them to obtain such information are likely to compromise the interview significantly and are likely to utilize the kinds of coercive techniques that result only in contaminating the interview. As a result, they do not obtain valid information. Sgroi (1982) suggests that trickery and deceit are acceptable in order to gain evidence from the child. She justifies this position on the basis of the fact that sex abuse is such a heinous crime. I am in full disagreement with her on this point. Trickery and deceit are rarely justified, and when they are utilized in the sex-abuse evaluation, I consider them immoral and unethical—especially because they lessen the likelihood of finding out whether the child was abused. Sgroi's position, however, not only reflects the sense of frustration that evaluators will have if they believe that it behooves them to extract information about sex abuse from young children, but it is yet another reflection of the bias of her methods, a bias revealed by the title of her chapter: "Validation of Child Sexual Abuse" (Sgroi, 1982). I once received a call from a judge who asked me to evaluate a four-year-old girl who was allegedly abused at the age of two. Since that time there had been two years of ongoing litigation and interrogations. Many of the people who were involved in these evaluations used anatomically correct dolls and leading questions. I knew two of them well enough to know that they had seriously contaminated their evaluations by these techniques. The judge wanted me to see the child in "therapy" to find out once and for all what "the truth" was with regard to the question of whether the child had indeed been sexually molested. He told me that the parents consistently gave different stories with regard to the alleged abuse, the father insisting that he had never abused the child and the mother insisting that the child had told her that she had engaged in various sexual activities with him. I informed the judge that he was asking me to do something that was probably impossible. I told him that he had much more respect and faith in therapy than I did, especially a therapy designed to obtain information about sex abuse under the circumstances that existed in this case. I told him that the contaminations of the series of evaluations (especially those utilizing body charts, leading questions, and anatomical dolls) probably made it impossible for the child to know any more what actually had happened. He was not receptive to my refusal, believing that therapy somehow would be able to accomplish this task. He was unconvinced, and the conversation ended with his stating that he was sure he could find a therapist who was skilled enough to elicit "the truth." I believe he is going to have a long and futile search.

Interestingly, I spoke to the same judge about two years later, and he told me that another therapist had seen the child in "treatment" and was able to elicit information from her that confirmed sexual abuse dating back to the age of one. He believed that this was a result of her skills and talent. When I told him that experts in the field of memory generally agree that human beings cannot possibly relate accurate information dating back to the age of one, he was incredulous. I do not know whether this particular child was abused. But I do know that the belief that the child remembers events occurring at the age of one is most likely a delusion, a delusion shared by the judge, the therapist, and the child's mother.

# NINE

HALLMARKS OF NURSERY SCHOOL AND DAY-CARE CENTER SEX-ABUSE HYSTERIA

INTRODUCTION

During the 1980s we witnessed a frightening phenomenon, namely, the spread of sex-abuse hysteria in nursery schools and day-care centers. Elsewhere (Gardner, 1991a) I have described what I consider to be the factors operative in bringing about this wave of hysteria. Interestingly, although the outbreaks have appeared in various parts of the country, the development and manifestations appear to be uncannily similar.

In the mid-1980s I was invited to conduct evaluations of the children in two of the earliest and most well known nursery school sex-abuse cases. I declined these invitations because I was told that I would not be allowed to interview the children and that I would have to come to my conclusions on the basis of my interviews with the defendants and my review of selected materials (not even all) that might become available to me. At that time, I was quite stringent with regard to the requirement that I be allowed to see all three parties—the accuser, the alleged perpetrator, and the alleged child victim—before embarking on an evaluation. This is the policy that had proven valuable and even necessary in child custody evaluations, and I held strongly that there was no good reason not to implement the same principles in the nursery school sex-abuse cases. Furthermore, I had already been seeing sex-abuse accusations in the context of child custody disputes, and here again I had been successful in requiring the participation of all three parties before embarking upon my evaluation. It seemed to me reasonable, therefore, to decline an invitation in which I was asked to make comments about whether certain children were sexually abused, without being given the opportunity to directly examine the children. I subsequently relaxed my position when it became apparent that there were cases in which my strict adherence to this requirement would deprive sorely needed aid to falsely accused individuals. I learned that this requirement was much more easily accomplished in civil courts than in criminal courts, where it is extremely rare for a judge to order a reluctant party to submit to a psychiatric evaluation.

My present policy is to make it known at the outset that I am making no promises beforehand that I will support the position of the inviting party. Most often this involves requests for court orders requiring that all such individuals participate. If such efforts fail (and they most often do in criminal cases, but less often in civil cases), I can at least state in my final report and at the beginning of my courtroom testimony that I have made every reasonable attempt to do the optimum type of evaluation, namely, one in which all three of these parties are seen. After receiving verification that these attempts have been made and have proved futile, I meet with the inviting party. However, even then, I make no promises beforehand to the participating party that I will support his (her) position. Rather, after interviewing and reviewing documents (including review of videotapes and audiotapes, especially of the children), I come to a point where I make a decision, one way or the other, as to whether I can support with conviction the inviting party's position. If I support the inviting party's position, I then serve as that party's advocate. If I decide that that party's position does not warrant my support, for example, if I believe that the defendant did indeed sexually abuse the child(ren), then I will notify that party of this position, and we will generally part ways.

As mentioned, involving all three parties is more easily accomplished in civil than in criminal cases. Generally, criminal courts work much more stringently, especially with regard to bringing in impartial evaluators who are ordered by the court to see parties on both sides of the controversy. One factor operative in this stringency is the protection of an accused person's constitutional right not to testify against himself (herself) in a court of law. This right is protected under the Fifth Amendment of the U.S. Constitution. An accused person being interviewed by a psychiatrist whose services have been invited by the accuser is considered to be giving up this protection guaranteed to him (her) by the Constitution. Often (and even lawyers do this), this principle will be extended to *preventing* the accused from being interviewed by such parties. Such prevention requires a misinterpretation of this right. The Constitution does not *prevent* an accused party from speaking on the stand (in fact, most accused parties do), although some may invoke the Fifth Amendment and refuse. Nor does the Constitution prevent an accused party from speaking with court-appointed impartial evaluators and even evaluators who have been enlisted by the accusers. Many accused individuals have complained bitterly that they were never extended the opportunity to speak with any party involved in the accusation, e.g., the original accuser, psychologists, psychiatrists, the "validators" assessing the child, the detectives, the prosecutor, and lawyers. This practice has resulted in many false imprisonments. I have seen many cases in which I was convinced that prosecutors and others involved with the accuser would not have so zealously pursued the case, and would not have been so convinced of the guilt of the accused party, if they had taken the opportunity to speak in depth with the accused.

Not surprisingly, most of the parents involved in these cases are also suing for damages. Generally, two legal tracks are involved: the criminal and the civil. The criminal case generally involves state prosecutors who are seeking to incarcerate the accused. Usually, this involves a jury trial and very strict adherence to courtroom procedures. The civil case generally comes about because the parents are suing the nursery school for negligence for having allowed such "perverts" to have subjected their children to a wide variety of sexual abominations. Sometimes the nursery school administrators are not the owners of the school and sometimes they are. In both cases, there is usually an insurance company that is liable. Suits around one million dollars are not uncommon. Often the prosecutors recognize the potential for notoriety that they may enjoy when prosecuting such cases.

I will be discussing here nursery school situations in which there is every reason to believe that absolutely no sex abuse took place and that we are dealing with hysteria. I will not be discussing situations in which there is good reason to believe that there was sex abuse.

THE PARENTS

Origins and Background of the Accusations

As mentioned previously, it is crucial for the evaluator to trace meticulously the evolution of the sex-abuse accusation, from the very first time anyone in the setting mentioned sex abuse. Typically, the hysteria begins with one parent who seizes upon a single event, often innocuous, and becomes excessively concerned about its import. A typical scenario involves exaggerating the significance of the event, especially in the direction of its being a subtle and mild manifestation of physical and/or sexual abuse. I have often had the feeling that much grief—for the accused party(ies) and their families—could have been avoided if I had had the opportunity to meet with the initiating party at the outset and possibly could have "nipped things in the bud" at that point. However, from everything I know of these cases, I do not believe that I would have been successful. In all the nursery school cases that I know of, the individuals who got things started were generally quite disturbed, although the manifestations of their disturbances may not have been apparent to the judge and juries. Accordingly, my attempts to stop things at that point probably would have been unsuccessful. In the well-known McMartin case it was a psychotic woman who incorporated the staff of the Manhattan Beach Day-Care Center into her delusional system.

Sometimes the initiators are consciously aware of the fact that the accusation is false. It is a deliberate attempt to hurt and even destroy the owners of the nursery school. I recall one case in which the owners of the school claimed that babysitters in their area had consciously conspired to create a sex-abuse scare in the hope of driving the school out of business. The school, which was relatively new in the area, was taking away their business, and they could think of no better way to rid themselves of this competition. I have seen a few children who, when asked by examiners how they know the sex abuse occurred, answered, "My mother told me it happened." This response, of course, "lets the cat out of the bag" in that it is a statement by the child of the coaching he (she) has been subjected to prior to the interview. There are other cases in which there is no conscious fabrication; rather, the initiators actually believe that the abuse took place, even though there is no good reason to believe that it did. Many of these people are truly delusional. Accordingly, we do well to view false accusations as lying on a continuum, from those who consciously fabricate the allegation to those who make such accusations as part of a delusional system. And, of course, we have all points in between these two extremes, points at which there is probably a combination of conscious fabrication and delusion. Last, we often see a progression, over time, during which what was originally a conscious fabrication ultimately becomes a delusion. And hysteria fuels and intensifies the process and tends to move the point along toward the delusional end of the continuum.

I often compare sex-abuse hysteria in nursery schools to the Great Fire of Chicago in 1871. Legend has it that it began in the barn of a Mrs. O'Leary whose cow kicked over her lantern, thus igniting the hay, then the barn, and ultimately a significant portion of Chicago. Examiners do well to find out exactly who

"Mrs. O'Leary" was and exactly what the steps were by which she started the conflagration. Examiners do well to try to ascertain then what the particular factors were—in that particular nursery school—that led to the spread of the hysteria. It is important to appreciate that mass hysteria can begin with one person. One person's hysteria can then spread to two, and then to others, in geometric progression. The inquiry is analogous to finding out exactly where in Chicago the fire began, exactly what the method was by which the fire started, and then the details regarding where and how it spread.

Obviously, this inquiry should not stop at the point where the examiner has unearthed the initial contributing causes of the conflagration. Rather, the examiner does well to trace the evolution of the accusation in order to ascertain how the fire grew, especially with regard to which examiners fueled the flames in the course of its progression. A detailed description of the evolution of the false accusation can be especially useful in the courtroom. Commonly, juries will take this position: "Okay, we don't believe all of these things happened because some of them are just too ludicrous and preposterous. However, *something must have happened* if we have all this commotion and excitement." It is extremely difficult to prove that something *did not* happen. In fact, it may be a futile endeavor. Accordingly, those who testify do well to provide the jury with information about what *did* happen to produce all the turmoil, and a detailed description of the evolution of the accusation serves this purpose well.

Personality Qualities of the Initiators

Although it is extremely difficult to make generalizations about the personality types of parents who initiate day-care center hysteria, I have come to preliminary conclusions. I am comfortable making these generalizations because of my previous experiences of sex-abuse allegations in custody cases, and because of the uncanny similarities between the two types of sex-abuse accusations. If one is to be dealing with hysteria, there must be some hysterical personalities involved, especially at the point when the hysteria begins. The hysterical personality disorder is referred to as the histrionic personality disorder in *DSM-III-R*. The *American Psychiatric Glossary* (Stone, 1988) states that the histrionic personality is characterized by "excitability, emotional instability, overreactivity, and attention-seeking and often seductive self-dramatization, whether or not the person is aware of its purpose. People with this disorder are immature, self-centered, vain, and unusually dependent." The important word here, for the purposes of the nursery school sex-abuse hysteria situation, is *overreactivity*. These people (typically mothers [hysteria is much more common in females than males]) overreact to events that pose the slightest danger to their children. They see dangers where others do not. They are ever vigilant and overcautious. They are the first ones to make complaints if anything seems amiss, awry, or atypical with their children. They overdramatize their children's difficulties and bring them to the attention of authorities. They generally exhibit a lability of emotion and general psychological instability. They are viewed by the authorities at the center or school as troublemakers—and indeed they may cause much trouble.

It is important for evaluators to appreciate that many hysterics are skilled actresses. They do very well on the witness stand and may be especially convincing to judges and juries. Such individuals can turn their "acts" on and off at will and, when not providing a public performance (such as in one of the side rooms of the courthouse), they will be calm, well organized, and completely free from any signs of emotional disturbance. Like professional actresses, they require an audience, and when they do not have one there is no act.

In some cases the degree of the exaggeration of danger reaches the point of paranoia. In fact, there is a continuum from normal reactions to danger to hysteria to paranoia. There is a continuum, from those who, when they see danger, shrug their shoulders, to those who act judiciously, to those who act in an exaggerated fashion (hysteria), to those who see danger when there is none (paranoia). I am certain that many of the parents who initiate sex-abuse hysteria are on the hysterical/paranoid end of this continuum, and this is also the personality pattern of many who subsequently jump on the bandwagon.

Overlapping the attention-seeking qualities of the hysteric is impulsivity. These parents are typically impulsive and take quick action without much forethought and planning. Accordingly, they are quick to bring to the attention of outside authorities (child protection services and other community agencies to which people report child abuse) their complaints and concerns. Either they contact these organizations directly or bring their suspicions of abuse to the attention of authorities, who, they often recognize (even before the first consultation), are required by law to make such reports—especially doctors, psychologists, and lawyers. In situations where others would have tried to work things out, keep things quiet, and not bring the suspected event to the attention of outside authorities, these people seem to relish the opportunity to do so. Both the initially complaining party and the consulted authority are quick to use the rationalization that the law *requires* them to report such suspicions, no matter how slight. In any borderline situation, and in any situation in which there might be a question as to whether or not abuse occurred, these people are convinced that the worst possible scenario is indeed the one that took place. The legal requirements notwithstanding, the events that brought about the suspicion are generally not ones that the vast majority of people would consider in the category that warrants such reporting.

An example of the kind of exaggerated response one sees in such cases is the group of parents who will invite the *Federal Bureau of Investigation* to conduct an investigation because there is the suspicion that the alleged perpetrators were taking photographs of the children for the purpose of selling them to publishers of child pornographic magazines. The only pictures taken were the traditional photographs taken periodically in many nursery schools. The suspicion arose from an evaluator's asking the children if any photographs were taken. The evaluator, obviously, was thinking about photographs taken by bona fide perpetrators for pornographic purposes. The child, recalling the aforementioned group photographs, responds affirmatively. Because mailing such photographs across state lines is a federal offense, the crime is justifiably a matter for the FBI. During the investigation, any cameras found on the scene are confiscated and may be considered evidence that such pictures were indeed taken. Needless to say, I have never been in a case (nor do I know of one) in which actual pornographic photographs were found. What were found were pictures of birthday parties and other special events, often pictures in which the parents were participants, pictures in which the alleged perpetrators are posing with the children. And these pictures, which are inevitably found in the school and the child's home, are considered "evidence" (not necessarily by the FBI, but usually by the prosecutors and the hysterical parents).

A discussion of hysteria is not complete without a discussion of the sexual element. The word *hysteria* is derived from the Greek word meaning *uterus.* (A hysterectomy is an operation in which the uterus is removed.) The Greeks considered the hysterical woman to be suffering from a malady that was a result of the loosening of her uterus from its normal position in the pelvis and its wandering around in her body. (As is true today, hysteria was more commonly seen in women than in men.) The link here to sexuality is implied, but somewhat loosely. It was Sigmund Freud who linked hysteria closely with sexual urges. He considered hysteria to result from a damming up of sexual urges in women who were too inhibited or guilt-ridden to openly express them, especially with regard to the gratification of their sexual drives. Although psychoanalysts today would consider this a somewhat oversimplified theory, there is no question that many hysterical women do have sexual inhibition problems. There is no question, also, that there are women in other psychiatric categories who have sexual inhibition problems. And there is no question that there are many hysterical women who do not have sexual inhibition problems.

Some sexually inhibited people deal with their pent-up sexual urges by the mechanism of projection, in which they psychologically project out onto others their own unacceptable sexual impulses, thereby seeing sexuality when others do not. I believe that this factor is operative in many of the women who exaggerate the sexual implications of nonsexual behavior and contribute thereby to the likelihood that a sex-abuse allegation will be made. The normal touching, fondling, and kissing that one sees in nursery schools becomes – for them – manifestations of sexual foreplay and prove that further sexual activities have taken place. Their condemnation of these acts is a derivative of their condemnation of their own sexual impulses – now projected outward. It is as if they are saying, "It is not I who have these loathsome and filthy sexual thoughts and feelings; it is those people out there: those nursery school teachers and others who have helped them perform (and passively watched) their abominable orgies." The *American Psychiatric Association Glossary* makes reference to the sexual element in hysteria when it describes these individuals as exhibiting "seductive self-dramatization." And *DSM-III-R* presents as one of the criteria someone who "is inappropriately sexually seductive in appearance or behavior" and "is overconcerned with physical attractiveness."

Although for me as a psychiatrist, the link between the repressed sexual impulses of the accuser and the observation of sexuality externally – when there is no evidence for it – is obvious, it is very difficult for many people to accept this phenomenon. To me, it is clear that if something does not actually exist in the world and an individual sees it to be there, then the idea must be originating in the mind of the beholder. Where else could it have come from? People who read about day-care center sex abuse will often say: "Although I don't believe everything these children are saying, something must have happened to have caused all this brouhaha" (or words to that effect). Although the "something" that has happened is quite complex, there is no question that *one* of the factors operative is the projection of pent-up sexual urges onto the perpetrator and the children being viewed as abused.

Pathologizing the Normal

One sometimes wonders whether these parents have an intellectual deficiency, because they seem to be so ignorant of normal childhood behavior. Most, I believe, really do know that normal children fluctuate in terms of behavioral development, have good days and bad days, and do not mature at a steady upward incline on the developmental curve. I suspect also that, at some level, they appreciate that atypical and undesirable behavior is part of normal childhood development. However, when they jump on the sex-abuse bandwagon, they seem to lose all perspective regarding the expected behaviors of children. Then, any kind of behavior that might justifiably be considered a sign of emotional disturbance, no matter how inconsequential, becomes seized upon as a manifestation of sex abuse. I refer to this phenomenon as *pathologizing the normal.* Probably the best examples of this phenomenon are the plethora of guidebooks that have been published in recent years, guidebooks that list the most common manifestations of sex abuse for people who want to know what these may be. Some of the more common: nightmares, bedwetting, behavioral fluctuations, and periods of irritability. All of these are normal phenomena seen in all children; yet those who are committed to the notion that the children were sexually abused will quote these guidebooks and the "authorities" who wrote them in order to justify the accusation.

Blaming the Alleged Perpetrator for The Child's Psychopathology

If the allegedly abused child does show symptoms indicative of psychological problems, those are also blamed on the accused rather than on anything the parents might have done. This of course "gets them off the hook" and contributes to the scapegoatism of the alleged perpetrator(s). After the hysteria has been rolling, just about every psychological problem exhibited by any of the children is attributed to the accused individuals. The accuser's hysteria, paranoia, and other forms of psychopathology that may have spawned the accusation in the first place are ignored as possible sources of the child's psychopathology. The parents then become completely exonerated of guilt for any psychological problems their children may have exhibited. Furthermore, these children are often "in therapy," therapy that is in itself so psychologically traumatic (Gardner, 1991a) that they inevitably exhibit symptoms attributed to the sex abuse. Even though the symptoms began long after the child's exposure to the alleged perpetrator, they are considered to be delayed reactions to the abuse.

Retrospective Reinterpretation

I utilize the term *retrospective reinterpretation* to refer to a common phenomenon exhibited by parents involved in sex-abuse hysteria. In the course of the child's investigation and treatment, parents will claim that they realize *now* that certain events, previously considered part of normal childhood development or possibly manifestations of slightly atypical behavior, are now better understood as manifestations of the sex abuse that had been taking place. Typically, parents will point to events that were considered normal at the time, e.g., fluctuations in toilet training, alterations in mood, and periods of irritability and noncompliance. Sometimes these retrospective reinterpretations reach absurd proportions, e.g., "She stopped liking vegetables. I wondered about that at the time, but didn't realize what was going on. Now I know that she was being sexually abused," "She stopped wanting her picture taken with the rest of the family. We know now that she was being sexually molested at that time and he (the alleged perpetrator) was probably trying to take pictures of her and the other children whom he was abusing," and "She started to refuse to go to church. And that was just about the time that we now know that she was being abused." Sometimes therapists will join in with the parents and agree that these behavioral manifestations, too, in retrospect, were indeed manifestations of the sex abuse.

Zealous Collectors of Evidence

Once the lawsuits are progressing, and the hysteria is spreading, these parents can be relied upon to be zealous collectors of evidence. Any supportive data, no matter how inconsequential or how remote it may appear to others, becomes important "proof" for these parents. They take careful notes of anything the child might say that could be used to verify the abuse, and they often keep diaries. Typically, these notes and diaries are brought to the child's therapist, who gives them serious attention and uses them as points of departure for material to bring up with the child in sessions. (This contributes to the cross-fertilization process, to be discussed below.) The lawyers, also, may be flooded with all this "evidence." Typically these parents will grill their children in order to extract as much material as they can, although these same parents will often say that they do not do this.

One mother of a seven-year-old "victim" invited her daughter's friend for a sleep-over date. The guest had attended the same nursery school but had not previously been considered one of the victims. While the two girls were bathing together in the bathtub, the visitor was observed to be rubbing her vulva. The mother concluded that this act proved that this visiting child too had been sexually molested. She reported this event to the police, who considered it important enough to open a file. The police had already been involved in the case and were happy to get more "evidence." This vignette is a good example of the warping of the human mind that takes place in sex-abuse hysteria. I am certain that under other circumstances the police would have considered such a mother to be a strange individual indeed, and the event might have served as a focus for police-station jokes for many weeks thereafter.

Cross-Fertilization

In the nursery school setting, there is much talk among parents, children, and therapists about the various indignities that their children have been subjected to. They frequently ask one another questions regarding whether a particular child experienced a particular kind of abuse. Commonly, one parent goes home and asks the child whether he (she) experienced the same type of molestation that another child described to his (her) parents. With all this gossip and "buzzing," it is no surprise that the children ultimately come up with similar scenarios. I refer to this as the *cross-fertilization* that takes place in these situations. I also refer to this phenomenon as the *seed-planting* process. Some use the term *contamination*. I prefer the terms *cross-fertilization* and *seed-planting* because of the implication that the process "makes things grow" and increases the contaminants.

There is an endless flow of such contaminations. Parents talk among themselves and ask their children whether they too were subjected to a particular abomination. The therapists talk among themselves about the particular revelations their patients are providing. They then go back and ask their patients if they have had a similar experience, and may even mention the name of the child who reported it. This, of course, provides "food for thought" for the patients so interrogated and, considering children's suggestibility and their desire to ingratiate themselves to adult authority, will inevitably describe similar experiences. The children are often playmates outside of the school setting. In the playground and on sleep-over dates, they talk with one another about the exciting things that are being discussed in their families, especially descriptions of their sexual adventures. The aforementioned diaries and note-taking also provide for cross-fertilization. Prosecutors, lawyers, psychotherapists, and others who interrogate the child often ask specific leading questions that plant seeds. Questionnaires may be sent to parents, instructing them to ask their children about a wide variety of sexual acts that are enumerated therein. In one church-affiliated nursery school scandal there were prayer groups, the purpose of which was for the parents to pray for the soul of the alleged perpetrator. Group meetings at homes are also common. The parents then go home after these meetings and ask their children specific questions about whether they had a particular experience similar to one experienced by a classmate.

Meetings conducted by the school, in order to alert parents to what has happened, also serve this purpose. When psychologists and other "experts" are brought in to provide support and understanding about what has happened, further seeds are planted. Parents may be provided with a list of questions to ask their children in order to find out whether they too had been sexually abused. And these questions also engender images of specific sexual acts, sexual acts to which the children were never subjected. And, when "satanic ritual experts" enter the scene, their "investigations" serve to implant in everyone's mind scenarios that are ever more dramatic and preposterous. These people gravitate to nursery school sex-abuse scandals like iron to a magnet.

Detailed inquiry will often reveal that the mothers know one another to varying degrees. All the mothers already share in common the fact that their children were attending the same nursery school. Accordingly, they have many opportunities to meet one another. Sometimes they are friends and relatives of one another. Although initially they may not have been friends, they now become so because they have become bonded together in a common cause. One lawyer may have many clients from the same nursery school, and he (she) will ask questions from one case when evaluating another. And this is the same for therapists, who, in my experience, have been an important source of cross-fertilization, their vows of client confidentiality notwithstanding. Prosecutors, therapists, and others who get swept up in the hysteria will then use the similarity of the children's stories as "proof" that the sex abuse really took place. I consider it proof that the cross-fertilization process has occurred.

Monetary Gain (The Greed Element)

Generally, as mentioned, in a nursery school "scandal" there are two lawsuits operating simultaneously, one criminal and one civil. The prosecutor's office can be relied upon to provide an army of investigators, detectives, and others to "get to the bottom of this whole thing." As mentioned elsewhere (Gardner, 1991a), such a "scandal" can provide unknown prosecutors with the promise of notoriety and promotion that they might not have previously even hoped for. On a parallel track is the civil lawsuit. Typically, the parents will sue the school for enormous amounts of money (generally the maximum allowed for by the school's insurance coverage [sometimes one to two million dollars]) in order to compensate them for the damages (both physical and psychological) that they and their children have suffered. Typically, these children are in "therapy," which is also to be compensated for. And, of course, the therapists are happy to see these children in "intensive treatment" with the prospect of such a large bundle of money being dumped into the parents' laps. So greedy are these parents that they must blind themselves to the psychological trauma to which they are subjecting their children, in association with the long series of inquiries, examinations (psychological and physical), interrogations, unnecessary therapy, courtroom appearances (even on the witness stand), and the psychological tolls of notoriety. Such therapy itself, if extensive, can actually make these children psychotic. I will discuss this in detail in Chapter Ten.

Complete Absence of Adult Witnesses

Typically, in these cases, there are absolutely no adult witnesses who have actually observed even one event involving sexual molestation. We have a nursery school where dozens (and in many cases hundreds) of children are registered. Although there may be fixed time slots for parents' and children's coming and going, there are invariably children who are brought late and picked up early. Throughout the course of the day, staff members frequently move about from one room to another. Also, others come to the school throughout the course of the day, e.g., mail deliveries, food deliveries, and others who may have business with the school. With all this traffic over months and even years, not *one single* adult is brought forward who will testify that he (she) has actually observed the sexual abuse. Even orgies were never observed. Orgies—in which groups of children were stripped, fed feces and urine, where adults danced around in costumes, where babies were mutilated—were never observed even once by a single adult. So skillful are the perpetrators that they have been successful in eluding these would-be intruders by

NURSERY SCHOOL AND DAY-CARE CENTER SEX-ABUSE HYSTERIA   459

quickly dressing all the children and getting them to appear as if they were continuing in their normal routines. Yet, as soon as one of these adults is out of range, the whole orgy is reinstituted. Some of these activities are described to have taken place outdoors in broad daylight, and sometimes at night under moonlight. Often, the adults so involved were wearing costumes (especially black cloaks or clown costumes), yet none of this was ever observed by a single adult. In all the nursery school cases that I am aware of, no one has yet produced a parent or visitor to the school who has testified that he (she) actually observed the orgies that are described to have taken place.

The lawyers in the McMartin case claim that the main reason they were so successful in court was the fact that they paraded through the courtroom a few hundred parents, each of whom claimed that they had never seen *anything* suggesting, even remotely, that children were being traumatized.. The lawyers in subsequent cases that were successfully defended also utilized the same procedure and believe that this played a role in the defendants being found not guilty of sexually abusing the children in the nursery schools.

Oblivion to Legal Process Trauma

Parents who falsely claim sex abuse are typically oblivious to the psychologically traumatic effects on their children of their being dragged through the offices of lawyers, pediatricians, investigators, detectives, prosecutors, psychologists, psychiatrists, child protection services workers, "validators," therapists, and other examiners and investigators. Although each of these evaluators professes that he (she) is sensitive to the psychological needs of the child and does not cause any kind of psychological trauma as a result of "sensitive" interviewing techniques, the facts are that such interviews are psychologically traumatic. Most important, they have the effect of producing in the child the belief that sexual abuse did indeed take place, and this belief may persist throughout life. These interviews cause the child confusion because, at least at the outset, the child does not know to which events the examiner is referring when asking questions about sexual molestation. Over time, the child learns what the "right" answers are and then becomes less confused about the questions. The examiner's questions indicate that a terrible thing has happened to the child—even though initially the child may not have been aware of it—and this produces unnecessary fears and anxieties. The child is often taught hatred of a person who was either neutral or even a loved one.

Parents of these children do not appear to appreciate what they are subjecting their child to. If they do, the pathology that generates their involvement in the hysteria blinds them to the obvious effects of these interrogations on their children. Sometimes this blindness relates to paranoia. The belief is that as long as the perpetrator(s) are not in jail, no child is safe. It is therefore a public service to do everything possible to incarcerate the alleged molester(s). As I will discuss in Chapter Ten, we are breeding a generation of psychotics, a psychosis that has a new cause, not previously present. Predictions are always risky, but I have no hesitation making this one: I am convinced that therapists in the future will be dealing with this category of psychotic individual, adolescent and adult.

I consider myself a sensitive examiner and certainly do not subject my patients to the kinds of abominable interview techniques described above (and below). But even I do not deny that there is at least some psychological trauma associated with my interviews. I justify them with the argument that one must weigh the minor psychological trauma to the child of my interview against the severe psychological trauma of an innocent party being incarcerated for an alleged crime that was never committed.

THE CHILDREN

Not surprisingly, there are significant similarities between those children who are programmed to profess sex abuse in the nursery school setting and those who profess such abuse in the context of a child custody dispute. However, there are additional factors that are often operative in the nursery school and day-care center situation, factors related to the mass-hysteria element. In Chapter Three, I focused on child custody disputes. In this chapter I focus on the nursery school and child-care center, with some reference to child custody disputes.

The Optimum Age for Indoctrination

I generally have an aversion to simple explanations. Most often, many factors operate to produce a particular event, psychological or otherwise. However, there are, at times, relatively simple explanations for a phenomenon. And there is one simple explanation for the fact that sex-abuse hysteria is more likely to take place at the nursery school and day-care center level than at higher educational levels. In fact, the higher the level, the less the likelihood of hysteria. It is not that the parents of older children are immune to hysteria; it is that children at the nursery school level are the best candidates to get swept up in such a brouhaha. One- and two-year-olds are too young to verbalize meaningfully, and even those who can are too young to provide predictable responses. Three- and four-year-olds are old enough to verbalize, yet suggestible enough to deny their own perceptions. The older the child, the less the suggestibility. The reader will note that I did not provide a cutoff point beyond which individuals are not suggestible. There is no such cutoff point. We are all suggestible. However, the older we get, the less the likelihood we can become programmed, deep-seated human gullibility notwithstanding. Accordingly, three- and four-year-olds are the best candidates for such indoctrination. I have seen many situations in which the older siblings of these children, the five- and six-year-olds, steadfastly deny any such occurrences, even though they too may have been attending the same school or center.

Early Manifestations

Typically, those investigators who first see the children, especially soon after the time of the alleged abuse, will find that the children deny sex abuse, especially if they have not been significantly programmed already by their parents. However (and this is an important point), children involved in sex-abuse hysteria will not provide the kind of denial seen in children who have been genuinely abused. Genuinely abused children typically are hesitant, ashamed, and fearful of disclosure. Because they have been warned of terrible consequences if they reveal the "secret," they may deny abuse. In contrast, children who have not been abused are more matter-of-fact about their denial. They seem somewhat confused about the reasons for their being questioned. The differentiation between the calm, slightly confused denial of the child who was not abused and that of the embarrassed and inhibited denial of the child who was abused may be difficult, and this is especially the case for younger children, ages three to four. It is more easily made for children over six or seven.

There are many evaluators who consider the child's denial as "proof" that the child has indeed been abused. The child is considered to be denying because of threats that the perpetrator has made to the well-being and even life of the youngster and nearest of kin. Or, the denial is explained as a derivative of the child's guilt, embarrassment, and other emotional reactions to the abuse, reactions that inhibit disclosure. This, of course, places the accused in a no-win situation. If the child describes such abuse, then he (she) will be found guilty. If the child denies such abuse, he (she) will also be found guilty. Sometimes these examiners will justify their utilization of denial as verification for abuse by quoting the work of Summit (1983). They seem to be oblivious to the fact that Summit described denial as one of the phases of adjustment to be found in children about whom there was every good reason to believe that they had indeed been abused. He did not present his series of symptoms as a diagnostic sequence; rather, he presented it as a series of psychological reactions exhibited by genuinely abused children. (I will discuss this issue subsequently.)

Once in the hands of a zealous evaluator (especially one who uses anatomical dolls, leading questions, and leading gestures [Chapter Seven]), the child will gradually come to believe that sex abuse did indeed occur. The principle is this: Young children are suggestible and they also wish to ingratiate themselves to adult authority. When they sense that the adult investigator wants them to talk about sex abuse, they will comply. The leading questions plant seeds and create visual images of events that never took place. Then, when subsequently asked about whether such events took place, this particular visual image will be brought to conscious awareness. The child, however, will then be confused regarding whether this mental image relates to an event that really occurred or whether it relates to the image engendered by the questions asked by the same or previous examiner. The younger the child, the less the likelihood of his (her) being able to make this differentiation.

At that point, the child may answer the question as to whether the particular event occurred with a comment like "I think it happened" or "It might have happened." The examiner may then push on with a repetition of the question in order to get the child to be more certain. The child, again being suggestible and wishing to ingratiate himself (herself) to the examiner, may finally be brought to the point of saying yes. It doesn't take more than a few such sessions to get the child to actually believe that the sex abuse indeed occurred. Examiners who review videotapes of children subjected to this kind of inquiry can readily verify this process. It is one of the hallmarks of the false sex-abuse accusation. The mothers of such children may make statements along these lines: "At first she denied it happened and I know she was then afraid to tell. Then, she said that she 'thinks' it happened. Later on she was able to tell the whole story, thanks to her therapy." Therapists do well to be aware of this progression and be alerted to its subtle manifestations by the use of such words as "I think..." and "It might have...."

Other alleged early manifestations of a false sex-abuse accusation in the nursery school setting include a wide variety of normal behaviors seen in just about every child. Also included are the wide variety of psychopathological disorders that children may exhibit. These become considered manifestations of sex abuse. In the section on therapists, when I discuss the indicators of child sex abuse, I will elaborate on these allegedly early manifestations.

The Hiatus

Another important manifestation of the false sex-abuse allegation is what I refer to as *the hiatus*. Typically, this involves a significant period—months and even years—between the time of the alleged abuse and the time of its disclosure. This gap usually refers to the period that begins when the alleged perpetrator abused the child and ends with the time when the abuse was disclosed. During this period the child may not have had any opportunity for involvement with the alleged perpetrator. Typically, the child was asymptomatic during this time or exhibited only mildly abnormal, atypical behavior. Then, when the abuse is disclosed, a wide variety of symptoms manifest themselves, especially if the child is in "therapy." Although the child may then be considered to be manifesting symptoms of a post-traumatic stress disorder (PTSD) (the usual label given to sexually abused children), an important manifestation of this disorder is not present, namely, the appearance of symptoms at the time or soon after the exposure to the stress. Vietnam veterans (to whom this label is most often given) did not *start* getting upset about their experiences months or years after their return home. Rather, their symptoms began at the time of, or within hours or days after, their exposure to the psychological traumas of combat. Their psychopathological manifestations began around the time of combat and generally persist. A symptom-free hiatus is one of the hallmarks of the false sex-abuse accusation.

The *DSM-III-R* includes a subcategory of the post-traumatic stress disorder: "delayed onset." Specifically, this subcategory is warranted "if the onset of symptoms was at least six months after the trauma." Prosecutors and validators may point to the delayed onset subtype of PTSD as support for their belief that the symptom-free period is one in which all reactions to the child's sexual trauma were repressed and suppressed, especially because of the threats of the alleged perpetrator. This is a specious argument because the delayed onset of the PTSD symptoms is *not* preceded by a period in which the individual is completely asymptomatic (such as is most often the case for children involved in these nursery school scandals). Rather, individuals who ultimately exhibit PTSD symptoms exhibit problems to varying degrees during the hiatus, but not to the point where the PTSD diagnosis is warranted.

Vietnam veterans who suffer with PTSD do not happily fly home from Vietnam and then, six-plus months later, suddenly become psychological basket cases. Rather, prior to the onset of the symptoms they generally suffer with a wide variety of other symptoms, such as depression, tension, and work inhibition. The PTSD diagnosis ultimately becomes applicable as a result of the intensification of the earlier symptoms and is best viewed as an elaboration of them. Furthermore, delayed onset is relatively rare. The vast majority who suffer with the PTSD start exhibiting symptoms at the time of the trauma or soon thereafter. (The reader must differentiate what I say here from "flashbacks," in which the individual relives certain battlefield experiences. These are additional manifestations, and they do not arise in a person who has exhibited absolutely no symptoms previously.) In contrast, children in nursery school hysteria typically exhibit a hiatus. In fact, the vast majority exhibits this symptom-free period, and those who appear not to are generally not exhibiting PTSD symptoms but other symptoms, completely unrelated. Examiners do well, therefore, to be very dubious about therapists and lawyers who point to the delayed-onset section of the PTSD material in *DSM-III-R* in an attempt to refute the argument that a symptom-free hiatus speaks against bona fide sex abuse.

One argument given for the hiatus is that the children were threatened by the alleged abuser that if they were to divulge "the secret" there would be terrible consequences, such as murder of their parents, body mutilation of themselves, and other dire consequences. The children, then, because of such threats, were allegedly silent about the indignities they were suffering at the nursery school. People who make these claims must be lying, self-deceiving, or completely ignorant about normal children. The best way to get a three-year-old to keep a secret is to dramatically whisper in the child's ear, "I'm going to tell you a secret now and I want you to promise you'll never tell it to anyone else in the whole wide world for the rest of your whole life!" Of course, the child will promise lifelong secrecy—so great is the engendered excitement and curiosity. Predictably, within minutes, that child will divulge the secret, at least to one other person. The three-year-old will be bursting with the desire to divulge the news to the next possible person, the promise notwithstanding.

Furthermore, if the children were indeed subjected to such abominations and were indeed to have been threatened with dire consequences for disclosure, it is impossible to imagine *all* of them successfully suppressing their fears and other emotions related to the threat. If, indeed, a child were subjected to the kinds of abuses typically described in sex-abuse hysteria, he (she) is likely to come home filled with tension and anxiety. Invariably, a parent is going to notice the child's distress, especially because of facial reactions and bona fide behavioral changes. Inevitably, the parent is going to ask the child what's wrong. Perhaps some children might be able to restrain themselves for short periods; but the vast majority are going to burst out, very quickly, their distress and through their tears they are going to talk about the abuses. A child's inability to keep a secret relates to the poor judgment I consider most pedophiles to have because they rely upon children to keep their secrets. Perhaps older children, especially in the prepubertal period, are able to keep such secrets; but not younger ones, ages three to four, those most frequently involved in nursery school sex-abuse scenarios. This phenomenon, also, makes the hiatal period described by these examiners to be highly improbable.

Elaboration and/or Distortion of Normal Childhood Fantasies

One will often see in the children's scenarios elements of normal childhood fairy tales, fables, and stories. These serve as nuclei for the sex-abuse elaborations. In one case in which I was involved, the children's fantasies included everybody at a four-year-old boy's birthday party dressed up in big-bad-wolf costumes, chasing the children around with whips while yelling,

"Piggy, piggy, piggy." Obviously, this fantasy derives from the well-known story about the big bad wolf and the three little pigs. In fact, adults' dressing up in animal costumes, especially for the purposes of hiding one's identity, is a common element introduced into these scenarios. Clown costumes are especially popular. The theory here is that pedophiles frequently don clown costumes because clowns are so attractive to children and serve as part of the seductive process. Although I cannot claim that I have thoroughly researched the pedophilia literature, I have never come across any reports of this as a *common* practice by pedophiles. In contrast, they usually try to hide their activities because of their appreciation of the social stigma and other consequences (such as years of incarceration). Costumes would predictably have the effect of the child's disclosing these events because of the excitement they inevitably would engender. Examiners, then, do well to be alert to the presence of these fragments that are lifted from traditional children's stories and incorporated into the sex-abuse scenarios. Although young children who have been genuinely abused may exhibit such incorporation, especially because of their cognitive immaturity and suggestibility, it is relatively rare. In contrast, it is a common phenomenon among children who are fabricating sex abuse. The greater the number of such incorporations, the greater the likelihood the accusation is false.

The frightening dreams that children have, often after watching "scary" television programs, may become incorporated into the sex-abuse scenario—especially when the evaluators consider such fantasies as "proof" of the child's molestation. In one case in which I was involved, the child had watched a videotape of Pinocchio and thereafter had a few dreams in which Stromboli the puppet master was included. Particularly frightening to the child was the part in which Stromboli locked Pinocchio in a wagon and took him away to become a slave. Rather than provide the most reasonable explanation, namely, that this was related to the child's having observed this frightening element in the story, it was considered a manifestation of a sex abuse, with Stromboli being considered symbolic of the sex abuser. The examiners in this case were uniformly oblivious to this well-known phenom-enon and seemed to have no appreciation that such dreams serve as a form of systematic desensitization to this common form of psychological stress.

Another child became concerned about drowning. The eval-uator concluded that this preoccupation related to the alleged perpetrator's threats that he would drown the child if she ever told her parents. The child's teacher reported that there had been a boy in the child's class who had almost drowned and he had told the class about his frightening experience. Following this, a few of the children in the class became fearful that they too might drown. Rather than accept this more reasonable explanation, the evaluator still maintained her position that the fear of being drowned had nothing whatsoever to do with the child's class-room experience, but related to the perpetrator's threats. And this is typical of these evaluators and therapists. Whenever they are given an explanation that does not support the sex abuse, it is rejected. These "validators" and therapists also seem to be oblivious to the ancient wisdom that "the most likely thing is most likely." (I will elaborate further on this point in the section below, devoted to therapists.)

Changes and Inconsistencies in the
Sex-abuse Scenarios

A person who has had an actual experience, and is asked to describe what happened, will usually do so on the basis of the visual image that comes into mind when the question is asked. This image is mentally referred to in the course of providing a detailed description of the event. The child who has not been molested has no such internal visual display (especially at the outset). Accordingly, each time an inquiry is made, a new display is brought to mind because the child does not have a bona fide experience to serve as a basis for the response. Accordingly, these visual renditions will vary. (No one's memory is perfect, and a three-year-old's even less so.) Therefore, the child's story varies from rendition to rendition. And this is one of the hallmarks of the false sex-abuse allegation, namely, the inconsistencies from rendition to rendition.

One problem here is that no person's memory is perfect (regardless of the individual's age), and even a person with a very good memory may occasionally exhibit inconsistencies. The problem also is that the younger the child, the greater the likelihood one will see such inconsistencies, even when examining the child who has been genuinely abused. It behooves the examiner, then, to differentiate between the inconsistencies that one might see in a child who has actually been abused with the inconsistencies seen in the child who has not been abused. The best guideline here is the *degree* of the inconsistencies, especially their frequency and their variations. The greater the number of inconsistencies, the greater the likelihood that the allegation is false. And the greater the variations, the more different they are from one another, the greater the likelihood of fabrication. And this principle is applicable for most of the differentiating criteria presented in this book. There is a continuum, from the complete absence or rare occurrence of a criterion (which is to be found in children who are genuinely abused) to its frequent occurrence (which is more characteristic of those who are providing false accusations). In addition, one must combine the inconsistency criterion with others presented here, especially the *content* of the scenarios and the presence of preposterous elements.

The Preposterousness of the Allegations

One of the hallmarks of the false sex-abuse allegation is preposterousness. It is not difficult to understand how preposterous scenarios arise. We have a child who has never been abused being interrogated by parents, therapists, and other examiners who are convinced the child was abused. Being suggestible, and trying to ingratiate himself (herself) to these authorities, the child tries to create stories that will be acceptable to the examiners and "get them off his (her) back." Because of the young child's cognitive immaturity, and because there were no actual events to draw upon to provide answers, the child will create scenarios using as nuclei the material provided in the examiner's leading questions. Because there was no actual experience in the first place, the corroborative and derivative material has to be manufactured. Because of lack of experience and cognitive immaturity, the child's created elaborations are likely to be improbable and often fantastic. Accordingly, the child may throw out elaborations in the hope that these will be acceptable to the examiner, without the appreciation that they are preposterous. Adults generally are more convincing liars than little children. Unfortunately, validators and other evaluators exhibit a "willing suspension of disbelief" when assessing children who allege sex abuse, a disbelief that they probably would not suspend under other circumstances. An important hallmark, then, of the false sex-abuse allegation is the *combination* of the child's preposterous scenarios and the evaluator's willingness to believe them (or rationalize them when their ridiculousness becomes completely impossible to believe).

Some examples: One child's mother accused the nursery school teacher of having sexually molested her child. When the child was asked by a validator, who was present when the sex abuse occurred, the child said, "My mother was watching." Even the examiner did not believe that the mother was an observer to these events. Yet, this absurdity did not lessen one iota her belief that the child had been sexually abused. Typically, as time goes on, the scenarios become ever more elaborate and ever more ridiculous. Their absurdity reaches the point of extremely high statistical improbability and even impossibility: "He made us eat our doo-doo and then when we vomited the doo-doo, he made us eat what we vomited up." Another: "He put a sword up my poo-poo hole." (The fact that this would cause instantaneous death and the fact that the medical examination of the child's anus was completely normal did not seem to lessen the parents' and the evaluator's belief that this actually occurred.) One more: "He cut up a little baby and made us eat all the parts and then we vomited." (No one ever found even a speck of blood at the site of this alleged cannibalistic orgy.)

Often there is a progression from the less ludicrous to the

more ridiculous. This coincides with the progression of the "therapy," in which the therapist is ever encouraging the child to reveal more and more under the theory that there was an initial reluctance to do so and the therapy is helping the child tell "the whole truth." When one combines ridiculous scenarios with the progression of ever more bizarre fantasies and changing scenarios, each tends to support the other and provide an important hallmark of the false sex-abuse accusation.

The inclusion of role-reversal fantasies, especially ludicrous ones, is also one of the hallmarks of the false sex-abuse accusation. Children normally involve themselves in role-reversal fantasies. These play many purposes, one of which is that they are a method for entrenching in the child the personality patterns of an adult role model. For example, a girl whose mother is primarily a homemaker and child rearer is likely to reenact the daily activities of her mother in the course of her doll play, especially when playing "House." A girl whose mother works primarily outside the home is more likely to include elements involved in her mother's occupation. Boys are more likely to involve themselves in adventure and superhero fantasies. Many of these involve rescuing innocent victims from the hands of powerful malevolent figures, and other fantasies are very much in the "crime doesn't pay" category. These fantasies serve to entrench macho qualities that are strongly fostered in our society. Such fantasies serve other purposes (such as conscience development and desensitization to trauma), but it is beyond my purposes to elaborate upon these here.

Of concern here is the incorporation of these normal childhood fantasies into the sexual-abuse scenario. One five-year-old boy proudly claimed that, in the course of a sex-abuse orgy with a group of nursery school children, he jumped on the perpetrator and beat him so severely that he fled the scene. Another claimed that he reported the perpetrator to the police and they took him off to jail. (Needless to say, there were no police reports providing confirmation of this child's important social contribution, yet this did not dissuade the prosecutor's office from believing that the abuse did indeed take place.) One four-year-old boy told me that his molester had offered him "wine, beer, and cigarettes," while his mother sat by and encouraged the boy to partake. He, however, sanctimoniously refused such indulgences, claiming, "They're bad for me." Here the child is using this fantasy to entrench normal age-appropriate dictates against such involvement. One child claimed that he and his two sisters were confronted by the perpetrator at gun point, but he took the gun and threw it out the window, thereby saving the children from an ugly fate.

One type of absurdity seen in false allegations relates to young children's need for symmetry. When creating a sex-abuse scenario at the behest of the examiner, the child may feel the need to provide a certain amount of symmetry, especially when providing corroborative details, for example, "He put his penis in my poo-poo hole three times and he put his penis in Janie's wee-wee hole three times" and "When he did it in the morning he did it in the two-year room and when he did it in the afternoon he did it in the three-year room." Obviously, these senseless elements in the scenarios lessen their credibility and are one of the hallmarks of the false sex-abuse accusation.

The Incorporation of Satanic Rituals

A common late development is the incorporation of satanic rituals. Sometimes this ingredient results from questionnaires and guidelines for detection provided by "satanic ritual investigators" who may swarm to the scene. It is almost as if they sprout out of the ground. There are, however, books, to be found in practically every bookstore, that can provide parents with this material. One must make a sharp differentiation between actually observed and proven satanic cults (which, I believe, probably exist in very small numbers and are extremely rare) and the *rumors about* their existence (which are ubiquitous). I remember in college being told about people who had "photographic memories," who could read a page of a book only once and then recite its contents verbatim. I was always interested in meeting such people. I was quite envious of their abilities and wished that I too could have such uncanny recall. When I would ask *who* specifically these individuals were, the usual answer provided was that the person that I was speaking to knew someone who, in turn, knew that individual. I was never, however, given the opportunity to meet directly the individual who possessed these powers and who could demonstrate them directly to me. Accordingly, I plodded along and slaved away to remember whatever fraction of the taught material I could. It certainly would have made my labors in college and medical school easier if I too could acquire this ability. I mention this college experience here because it is similar to the satanic influence phenomenon. Like people with "photographic memories," everybody seems to know someone who knows someone who knows such a person, but no one has had direct personal experience with such an individual.

Although I have come across many parents who are convinced with 100-percent certainty that their children were subjected to such satanic ritual sex abuse, I have never personally seen any concrete evidence of their existence over the ten-year period in which I have been involved in these cases. I have been in cases in which children have described visits to cemeteries, and I have even read about cemeteries that were dug up. I have been in cases in which reports of ritualistic murders of babies have been described, but I have never been in a case in which the actual blood stains, flesh fragments, bone fragments, etc., have been found. The child victims often report involvement in ceremonies in which groups of people are wearing robes and costumes while chanting strange songs and litanies. They describe animal and human sacrifice, mutilation, murder, and cannibalism. Torture, vampirism, and the drinking of urine and the eating of feces are also described.

Matzner (1991) states, "There has never been a single piece of objective evidence documenting such systematic cult activity in connection with any crime or reported abuse. Lanning (1992), who has investigated "several hundred" such cases as head of the FBI division involved in such investigations, states:

In none of the multidimensional child sex ring cases of which I am aware have bodies of the murder victims been found—in spite of major excavations where the abuse victims claim the bodies were located. The alleged explanations for this include: the offenders moved the bodies after the children left, the bodies were burned in portable high-temperature ovens, the bodies were put in double-decker graves under legitimately buried bodies, a mortician member of the cult disposed of the bodies in a crematorium, the offenders ate the bodies, the offenders used corpses and aborted fetuses, or the power of Satan caused the bodies to disappear.

Not only are no bodies found, but also, more importantly, there is no physical evidence that a murder took place. Many of those not in law enforcement do not understand that, while it is possible to get rid of a body, it is even more difficult to get rid of the physical evidence that a murder took place, especially a human sacrifice involving sex, blood, and mutilation. Such activity would leave behind trace evidence that could be found using modern crime scene processing techniques in spite of extraordinary efforts to clean it up.

In addition, in none of the cases of which I am aware has any evidence of a well-organized satanic cult been found. (pp. 18-19)

Lanning (1992) also states:

Until hard evidence is obtained and corroborated, the public should not be frightened into believing that babies are being bred and eaten, that 50,000 missing children are being murdered in human sacrifices, or that satanists are taking over America's day care centers or institutions. No one can prove with absolute certainty that such activity has **NOT** occurred. The burden of proof, however, as it would be in a criminal prosecution, is on those who claim that it has occurred. The explanation that the satanists are too organized and law enforcement is too incompetent only goes so far in explaining the lack of evidence. For at least eight years American law enforcement has been aggressively investigating the deals with large-scale baby breeding, human sacrifice, and organized satanic conspiracies. (p. 40)

In one case in which I was involved, a skull was found and was sent to a pathologist, in Washington, D.C., who reported that it was the skull of an opossum. This was not surprising because the skull was found in a place where boy scouts meet. Typically, the sexual orgies that allegedly take place in association with satanic rituals include people dancing naked, people wearing a wide variety of masks and costumes, the sacrifice of babies and animals, cannibalistic orgies in which people eat the remains of the slaughtered infants, drinking blood, eating feces, and drinking urine. Typically, as well, not one drop of blood is left at the site, not one piece of skin, not one shred of concrete evidence that such an orgy has actually taken place. In fact, what is typical of these cases is that there are absolutely no *adult* witnesses to any of these events, only children whose descriptions of them vary from rendition to rendition and from child to child. I am still looking forward to the day when I will actually interview directly an adult who will describe in detail actual observations of such rituals.

Kenneth V. Lanning, of the U.S. Federal Bureau of Investigation, has supervised the investigation of hundreds of cases of so-called satanic ritual sexual abuse and has never come up with one scintilla of concrete evidence for the ritualistic murder of babies, cannibalism, or sex abuse that allegedly took place in a group setting in association with such ceremonies. He does agree that there are individuals who espouse the satanic ritual, and that they may indeed (on rare occasion) involve themselves in minor crimes such as trespassing, vandalism, cruelty to animals, and petty thievery (Lanning, 1992). However, the FBI has no evidence—from investigations conducted in the 10-year period from 1981 to 1991—of child abuse, kidnapping, murder, and human sacrifice attributed to such rituals. Yet, the hysteria about satanic ritual sex abuse has reached such proportions that "hundreds of people are alleging that thousands of offenders are abusing and even murdering tens of thousands of people as part of organized Satanic cults, and there is little or no corroborative evidence" (Lanning, 1992). Examiners do well, therefore, to make a sharp differentiation between the *rumor and belief* in satanic rituals and *actual concrete bona fide evidence* and proof of such. Of importance here is that the introduction of the satanic ritual is an important hallmark of the false sex-abuse accusation.

I believe it was while I was in college that I first came to appreciate the following principle: "If it is humanly possible to be done, there is a high likelihood that there are individuals who have indeed done that thing, and there will be many who will be happy to do it." And this principle holds for just about any possible deed, act, or activity that a human being could possibly be involved in or perform. Accordingly, none of the aforementioned satanic rituals—as absurd, bizarre, and preposterous as they may appear—is impossible and, I am certain, there are human beings who have actually involved themselves in one or more of these bizarre forms of behavior. In fact, I am sure that there are individuals who have probably engaged in *all* of them at some time or other. I believe, however, that the number of people who have actually engaged in such activities is very small, and that the percentage of cases of child sex abuse in which satanic rituals are involved is minuscule. I would not be surprised if someday there is actually brought to the public's attention one or two cases in which children were indeed sexually abused in the context of such rituals and indeed were subjected to one or more of the abominations described above. However, this does not in any way negate my belief that such experiences are an extreme rarity and are not to be found in the vast majority of cases with which we are dealing today.

Furthermore, human beings are very gullible and crave to "go along with the crowd." With all the publicity being given these rituals in recent years, it is likely that some ideas will be planted in the minds of some individuals who, in fact, will actually reproduce the kinds of ceremonies depicted above. Accordingly, we can expect an actual increase in the number of such rituals, but this does not mean that past cases involved them, and it does not mean that a very high percentage of future cases will necessarily involve such ceremonies. All it means is that there are many naive individuals in this world who are willing to believe anything, no matter how preposterous, and others who are disturbed enough to involve themselves in some of the sickest kinds of behavior known to humanity. The phenomenon is similar to the epidemics of teen suicide that often follow the suicide of one youngster, as well as other self-destructive fads that people engage in.

Not surprisingly, there have sprung up "experts" in satanic investigations who, again not surprisingly, will suddenly appear at the scene of one of these nursery schools and offer their services (for money, of course). When there is money to be given away by gullible individuals, there will always be some who will be happy to make a quick buck and then get out of town. Lanning (1992) states:

> There are those who are deliberately distorting and hyping this issue for personal notoriety and profit. Satanic and occult crime and ritual abuse of children has become a growth industry. Speaking fees, books, video and audio tapes, prevention material, television and radio appearances all bring egoistic and financial rewards. (p. 29)

Some of these people, I suspect, are just plain psychopaths and know that they are exploiting their prey. Others, I suspect, actually believe in the existence of what they are looking for and will use as confirmation that such cults do indeed exist (and, as mentioned, I believe they do exist but that they are extremely rare) as proof that ritual abuses are far more widespread than is believed by many. Victor (1991) ascribes the social, psychological, and cultural factors that he considers operative in the satanic cult hysteria that we are witnessing at this time. Underwager and Wakefield (1991) have described what they consider to be the personality impairments that enable otherwise intelligent and presumably knowledgeable professionals to get swept up in this belief. Richardson et al. (1991) and Hicks (1991) have written what I consider to be excellent reviews of the issue of sex abuse and satanic cults, and they agree that there is absolutely no evidence for the belief that there is a widespread conspiracy among satanic cults to involve children in the atrocities described here. I strongly recommend these books to the reader.

The Increase of Symptoms over Time

Typically, the behavioral manifestations of the sex abuse— which, as mentioned, cover all forms of normal behavior as well as every symptom described in *DSM-III-R*—become intensified and multiply. When these children are in therapy (often the case, especially because of the large monetary award), the therapist attributes the symptoms to the anxieties and tensions caused by the ever-increasing number of disclosures. Actually, the symptoms are a result of the coercive therapy as well as subjecting the child to the parade of other evaluators associated with the lawsuit and criminal investigation. The symptoms are also related to the child's exposure to the prevailing atmosphere of hysteria. Because these cases last for years, the exposure to such detrimental influences are profound and the symptoms engendered by these factors are likely to be lifelong.

Secondary Gain

Mention has been made that one of the primary reasons children provide an ever-expanding elaboration of scenarios is that they thereby gain the approval of significant authorities, all of whom are telling them that the more elaborations they provide, the more affection they will receive. But there are fringe benefits as well, the psychological traumas of being subjected to such inquiries notwithstanding. One relates to attention. Never before in their lives have these children received so much attention. A parade of examiners is interested in every word and takes down careful notes. Audiotapes and videotapes are made, tapes that are listened to by an expanding army of investigators. It is almost like being a child movie star. Associated with this attention is a feeling of power. Children typically are very impotent in their relationships with others in the world. Suddenly they have power. They recognize that the utterance of certain words will result in their parents, therapists, and others leaping out of their seats, grabbing pencil and paper, and jotting down every word of what they say. All this enhances self-esteem (although in a sick way).

In some cases, the hysteria can be a source of adventure. Being brought to a cemetery by the police to point out graves is quite exciting. Being brought to police stations to identify criminals is not something that every child has the opportunity to do.

Participating with the police in searches throughout the school, into every nook and cranny, to be asked to identify any and all relics of the various abuse scenarios is quite exciting. One family involved itself in frequent Sunday excursions in order to hunt down symbols of satanic cults (not hard to find these days) as proof of the sex abuse.

Final Comments

Characteristically, as time progresses, more and more children become involved. This occurs almost in geometric proportion. Word gets around that children in the school have been molested, that lawsuits are in progress, and that "megabucks" can be made. Some parents join in because of the aforementioned psychopathological processes. Others join in because of greed. And others get swept up for both reasons. These factors result in a progressive expansion of the number of children who allege that they have been sexually abused. Accordingly, more and more families jump on the bandwagon, and this too is one of the hallmarks of nursery school sex-abuse hysteria. Yet, there are still others who are healthy enough to recognize what is going on and do not subject themselves or their children to the aforementioned indignities. Unfortunately, my experience has been that the latter group tends to be more passive and laid back. Were they to more vociferously complain about what they see to be going on, they might serve well the cause of innocent defendants.

Happily for these children, there seems to be a cutoff point beyond which children are less likely to become useful victims (and I do not hesitate to use the word) for their parents, therapists, prosecutors, lawyers, etc. Although there is a continuum (like most things in life), my experience has been that children over the age of six or seven are far less likely to get swept up in the hysteria. Three-year-olds seem to be the best subjects for such utilization. I have seen five-year-olds (who are probably very bright) who denied continually that anything had gone on in spite of intensive "therapy" designed to uncover what the therapist knew happened. One would think that when the three-year-olds who allege abuse become six, they might then "see the light" and recognize what has happened to them. Unfortunately, my experience has been that the brainwashing process has been successful, and they come to actually believe that they had been subjected to the abuses they were programmed to describe. And this belief, I suspect, will be lifelong. Two-year-olds are not very good subjects. They are too cognitively immature, are not reliably programmed, and so cannot predictably repeat what they are taught by their evaluators and therapists. In short, then, three-to-four-year-olds are the best subjects for such victimization, and this is one of the reasons why the hysteria appears to be confined primarily to nursery schools and day-care centers.

THE EVALUATORS AND THERAPISTS

Introductory Comments

When I use the terms *evaluators* and *therapists* here, I am referring to those who operate on the principle that "children never lie" and that if a child says that he (she) has been sexually molested, it must be true. These are the people who sanctimoniously wave the banner: "Believe the Children." They look down with scorn and derision on people like myself who do not "believe the children." Some of these people refer to themselves as "validators," a loaded title if there ever was one. These are the people who use anatomical dolls and claim that they are not contaminating. These are the people who use leading questions and deny that their questions have in any way affected the children's responses. Many claim that they do not use leading questions, but do not have the faintest idea about what a leading question really is. These are the people who use leading gestures and do not appreciate how contaminating such gestures are. They are the ones who go through the rituals of ascertaining whether the child can differentiate between the truth and a lie. They have their body charts, which allegedly are used to find out what names are used in that child's household for the genitals, breasts, etc. They are the ones who believe the preposterous and rationalize as credible the incredible. They selectively ignore the impossible, pathologize the normal, and consider just about every symptom in *DSM-III-R* to be a probable indicator of sex abuse. They believe in the existence of the "sex-abuse syndrome" and use Summit's (1983) "sexual abuse accommodation syndrome" as an instrument for diagnosing sex abuse. And these are the same people who exhibit some of the other misguided evaluation practices described in detail in Chapters Six and Seven. Because of the similarities between the procedures utilized by validators in divorce cases and those utilized by evaluators and validators in nursery school cases (often these are the exact same people), it was relatively easy for me to do evaluations in the nursery school realm after my experiences with sex-abuse accusations in child custody disputes. In Chapter Six and elsewhere throughout this book, I have described in detail many of their techniques. Here, I will focus on certain evaluative and therapeutic elements that are peculiar to the sex-abuse hysteria in the nursery school and day-care center situations, phenomena that are less likely to be present in other situations in which sex abuse is alleged, such as incest situations and child custody disputes.

Cross-Fertilization

Mention has been made of parental cross-fertilization, the spreading of rumors throughout the community, telephone calls, parents comparing notes, parents bringing their children's diaries and notes to therapists, therapists speaking with one another, etc. Therapists, as well, commonly cross-fertilize in these cases. It is not uncommon for them to tell a patient that other children have told them about specific sexual acts, and the therapists even mention the names of these children. Such therapists recognize (consciously or unconsciously) the importance of what I refer to as the keeping-up-with-the-Joneses phenomenon. The basic message given to the child goes along these lines: "Mary told me that Mrs. J. touched her wee-wee, and Billy told me that Mrs. J. touched his wee-wee, and Gloria told me that Mrs. J. touched her wee-wee," etc. The basic message being sent to the child is: "Are you going to be the only one in the whole class whom she didn't do this to?" This serves to foster a divulgence by threatening the child (implicitly or explicitly) that not to do so will create the reputation of being atypical and deprive him (her) of the good feeling associated with being "one of the crowd." In one nursery school case in which I was involved, the abuse was alleged to have taken place in a teepee outside of the home of an alleged perpetrator. The fact that there was no teepee outside the home of this person did not lessen the therapist's belief that the abuse did indeed occur there. Child A was asked by this therapist to draw the teepee and then provide details about the abuse. This was dutifully done and included a detailed description of the various sexual orgies that took place within this teepee. Subsequently, the therapist took Child A's picture, presented it to Child B, and asked her to describe the details of the abuse that she was subjected to in the very same teepee.

Another common method of cross-fertilization is to begin a comment with: "Your mother tells me that you said..." and this material is obtained from a mother who has obsessively been keeping notes on every utterance of the child that might relate to sex abuse, no matter how much one would have to stretch the imagination to do so. The children themselves are often friends, especially because they attend the same nursery school. They too may still play together and, of course, trade their stories and experiences. In one case in which I was involved, a big-bad-wolf dream was making the rounds among the children who had allegedly been molested. Mothers were asking other mothers if their children had had the big-bad-wolf dream, and therapists were asking their patients. The prosecutors and therapists considered all the children's relating the same dream to be proof of sex abuse. The more likely explanation—that this is a story known to most children, and that therapists, parents, and children were cross-fertilizing it in one another—was not even considered.

Another practice that contributes to cross-fertilization is what I refer to as the "spread-the-word-that-X-has-made-a-disclosure" phenomenon. The child, let us call her Sara, may have been seen by evaluator A, whose findings were "inconclusive." Sara's mother may have had "suspicions," but nothing was revealed by the child except, possibly, denial. And the same thing might have occurred with evaluator B. Subsequently, in the allegedly more skilled hands of evaluator C, the child "disclosed" sex abuse. Word quickly gets around regarding the divulgence. The news is rapidly transmitted to evaluators A and B: "Did you hear the news? Sara made a disclosure?" Everybody gets very excited and, of course, is interested in *all* the details. The divulgence becomes a happy event in the community of validators, and A and B, especially, feel quite clever in having suspected the abuse and not turned the child away and risked, thereby, being subjected to further sexual indignities. The idea that the "disclosure" was the end result of a series of interviews in which the child was being taught what to disclose does not enter the minds of these individuals. Furthermore, as mentioned previously, the word *disclosure* is used in one sense only, namely, that the sex abuse took place. No consideration is given to the possibility that the disclosure is merely a verbalization and might be either true or false. The word *disclosure,* then, has become a shibboleth for divulgence of bona fide sex abuse.

Even the material provided in sex-abuse prevention programs provides cross-fertilization. The children exposed to such programs are fed certain terms that commonly become incorporated into their sex-abuse scenarios. Some of the most common are: "good touches," "bad touches," and "private places." Krivacska (1989) has provided an excellent description of the ways in which these programs may contribute to false sex-abuse accusations.

Monetary Gain (The Greed Element)

Typically, the therapists of these children will not be able to make any predictions regarding how long the therapy will take because (1) "the child has just started to divulge and one cannot possibly know how many other disclosures will be forthcoming and how long it will take before everything has been told" and (2)"the amount of abuse has been so extensive and the amount of trauma so pervasive that years of therapy, at best, will be necessary." When I first entered psychiatry, psychotherapy was done primarily by psychiatrists and psychologists, and occasionally social workers. Since that time there has not only been a burgeoning of people in each of these three fields, but many other types of therapists have entered the scene, e.g., family therapists, marital counselors, nurse practitioners, pastoral counselors, and a wide variety of other types of "psychotherapists." Accordingly, there is much competition for patients and there are many hungry psychotherapists around. Children who require such extensive treatment are not to be found everywhere, especially children whose treatment can be financed by an insurance company that, as everyone knows, must be rich.

SOME ADVICE TO EVALUATORS FOR PROVIDING TESTIMONY IN SEX-ABUSE HYSTERIA CASES

Elsewhere (Gardner, 1982, 1986, 1989) I have written extensively on the techniques examiners may find useful when providing court testimony in child custody disputes. Furthermore, there is much in this book that should prove useful to those who provide court testimony in sex-abuse cases. I focus here on some special points that may prove useful for those providing testimony in nursery school and day-care center cases in which the hysteria factor is operative.

I wish to emphasize, at the outset, a point that has been made repeatedly in my other publications, that the examiner does well to make every attempt to interview all parties involved directly in the accusation, namely, the accuser, the accused, and the alleged child victim. This is difficult enough to accomplish in civil cases, but it is even more difficult to accomplish in criminal cases. Even when the accused volunteers to be interviewed by legal and mental health professionals from both sides, he (she) may not be permitted to do so. With regard to the children, courts traditionally allow prosecutors and others who support the accuser to have the children interviewed, but typically will not provide the same opportunity for the defense. I am convinced that this is unconstitutional, but, unfortunately, it is a widespread practice. My advice to evaluators is that they be sure to make every attempt to satisfy this important criterion of the optimum evaluation.

The examiner should not agree to proceed with the evaluation until all reasonable attempts have been made to involve all three parties. Written confirmation of each thwarted attempt should be obtained. This is most effectively and convincingly accomplished (for the purposes of subsequent courtroom testimony) if one has a letter from the inviting attorney describing specifically the efforts that were made to involve the reluctant parties with confirmation of the rejections (preferably written rejections). If interviews of the children are not permitted, then at least attempts should be made to view videotapes of such interviews (an increasingly common occurrence in recent years). Then, and only then, should the examiner begin the interviews of the available parties and review of pertinent documents. Even at that point the evaluator should not make any promises to support the position of the inviting party. Only after reviewing documents and interviewing all those who are available for interview should the examiner make any statements regarding whether he (she) can support with conviction the position of the inviting party. And this too should be spelled out in the final report and at the beginning of one's testimony. It is also useful to state the exact point that this decision was made, especially with regard to the number of hours that were expended before coming to this conclusion. In one nursery school case in which I was involved, I did not reach this point until 40 hours of work were completed, work that included interviewing and analyzing videotapes of interviews conducted by the "validators" and a four-hour interview with the alleged perpetrator.

Evaluators who are convinced that no sex abuse has taken place in nursery school or day-care center cases face an uphill fight when testifying before a jury (the usual situation because we are dealing here with criminal charges). One of the biggest problems relates to the general view that "Something must have happened. All these children and parents are so agitated. Perhaps not everything these children claim occurred, but *something* must have happened if all these parents and children are so upset." The problem is further compounded by the fact that it is extremely difficult (if not impossible) to prove that "nothing happened." People who read about these "scandals" in the newspapers are likely to have the same position as the jurors: "Okay, so maybe some of the more preposterous things didn't happen, but *something* must have happened to have caused all this commotion." The person testifying, then, does well not to confine himself (herself) to trying to prove that "nothing happened" — an almost impossible task if there ever was one. Rather, the examiner does well to take this position: "It's not simply my job to convince the jury that there was *no* sex abuse, but also to try to explain what *did* indeed happen."

As mentioned, I like to compare sex-abuse hysteria to the Great Fire of Chicago in 1871. Legend has it that Mrs. O'Leary's cow kicked over a lantern. Nearby hay caught fire, then the barn, then the rest of the farm, and then ultimately a major part of the city of Chicago. Even the largest fires may start with one match, and it is the job of the evaluator to try to trace down exactly who lit the first match and why. The evaluator then does well to trace the spread of the hysteria from this first person to others. Because this usually occurs in geometric progression, one may have difficulty getting many of the details, but at least the basic principles should be presented.

Both in the written report and at the beginning of one's testimony, the examiner should begin with a statement of the desirability of the optimum program and delineate the attempts that were made to achieve this goal. When providing court testimony, the examiner does well to begin with a review of such efforts. Not to do so places the examiner in the same category as validators who are perfectly comfortable interviewing the child only, then concluding that the child was abused, and then identifying the accused perpetrator — without even having invited that party to participate. At least the examiner should be able to say that he (she) made every reasonable attempt to extend such invitations and conduct such interviews.

In the course of one's testimony, one does well to repeatedly mention the ancient wisdom: "The most likely things are most likely." This is especially applicable when dealing with the ludicrous scenarios. One does well to begin with a statement in which one considers the *possibility* that the scenario described really did happen. This provides confirmation that the evaluator is balanced and impartial, utilizes principles of "scientific objectivity," and demonstrates willingness to consider all possibilities. One does well then to enumerate the reasons why one believes the alternative, namely, that this particular event did not happen, and then give the reasons why. For example, on a number of occasions I have testified along these lines:

> I cannot deny the *possibility* that all six of these children did indeed involve themselves in an orgy of feces eating and smearing with Mr. X. However, each of their parents stated that their children never once came home with even a speck of feces on his or her face or clothing. Furthermore, hundreds of people passed through the nursery school during the period when these events allegedly occurred and not one adult—and I repeat, not *one* single adult—ever saw anything even suggestive of such an orgy. Furthermore, by this age, children have learned that feces are disgusting and respond with words like "yuck" at even the prospect of such an activity. This further lessens the likelihood that they would come home completely free of any reactions. Accordingly, with regard to this particular aspect of the allegation, I think it is far more likely that it did not happen than that it did.

Then, one does well to repeat the principle that "the most likely things are most likely."

One then tries to get across the more complex principle that the greater the number of times the unlikely explanation has been given priority by the validators, the greater the likelihood that one is dealing with a false sex-abuse accusation. Unfortunately, it is very difficult to get across to a jury the obvious mathematical principle that if event A has a one in four chance of having occurred, and if event B has a one in four chance of having occurred, then the chances of *both* of these events taking place is 1/16 (1/4 x 1/4). If an event is only remotely possible, for example, has only a 1 in 16 chance of occurring, and another event has a similar likelihood (1/16) then the chance of *both* occurring (1/16 x 1/16) is 1/256. Last, if an event has a 1/1000 probability—we are now moving closer to the events described in a sex-abuse hysteria situation—and a whole string of events each have a 1/1000 probability, then the chances of all of them occurring can only be represented by a fraction whose denominator is in the trillions, and so the chances of all the events taking place is almost zero. Unfortunately, an evaluator is not likely to have the opportunity to present these basic principles of probability theory to a judge and/or jury. Furthermore, even if such an opportunity were provided, it is not likely that the presentation would be convincing and/or understood by the average juror (and, unfortunately, by the average judge [in my experience]). Testifiers do well to talk about the principle of the symptom-free hiatus, so frequently referred to in nursery school sex-abuse scandals. They should emphasize that children are not famous for their ability to keep a secret, especially under pressure, and the best way to get a child to tell something is to whisper into his (her) ear that the divulgence is a "big secret" that should never be divulged to anyone in the whole world. Furthermore, the child who has been threatened is not likely to be able to withhold the information long because of the severe state of tension and fear engendered by the kinds of threats generally described in the nursery school sex-abuse scenario. If the prosecutor and his (her) supporters point to the delayed onset subcategory of post-traumatic stress disorder (PTSD) as confirmation of the hiatus, the examiner does well to point out that this is not truly an asymptomatic period (such as was the case with these children) but a period in which there *were* symptoms, but did not warrant PTSD categorization in the early phases.

Typically, those who support the allegation present a series of rationalizations that attempt to make the incredible appear credible. The examiner does well to point out that each time one does this, one is adding to the likelihood that the accusation is false. This point has been elaborated upon in the section on therapists. And this point may be repeated in the course of the testimony as each one of the mind-stretching rationalizations is presented. Under these circumstances I may testify along these lines: "The greater the number of times one provides an unlikely explanation to justify not using the more likely explanation, the greater the likelihood we are dealing with a false sex-abuse accusation."

When testifying, one does well to avoid professional jargon and speak in everyday English. One does well to look directly at the jury, make eye contact with a series of jurors, and try to establish a relationship with them, even though there will be no direct interchanges. And the same holds true for the judge. Decisions by juries and judges are far less related to "the facts" and the allegedly objective assessment of them. This is a common myth, often perpetrated by the system that ignores it continually. Rather, the most important determinant of the decision is the feelings, often subjective (and even prejudicial), of the people involved in making them. And the feelings the judge and/or jury have about the testifier—feelings that derive from the relationship they have with him (her)—are the most important determinants as to whether he (she) will have credibility. If the members of the jury dislike the testifier, they are not likely to be swayed to his (her) position, no matter how brilliant and convincing his (her) exposition. In contrast, if they are enamored of the testifier, they will accept as valid any drool that dribbles out of his (her) mouth. And judges, as well, are not immune to this process. This may present a conflict for a person testifying. If one is there to "butter up" the jury, then one may have to compromise what one is saying. Doing so may serve the ends of the accused, but it compromises the dignity (and possibly ethics) of the testifier. Being true to oneself, and expressing with conviction one's views, may satisfy one's personal requirements for honesty and dignity, but it may result in the accused ending up in jail.

My own approach to this dilemma is most often to argue directly and honestly and "pull no punches." However, in certain situations I will occasionally omit and modify somewhat my comments because of my awareness that the straightforward approach might not be in the best interest of the defense, and might indeed result in severe punishments and even incarceration. The modifications I am referring to here do not involve any deceit; rather, they involve judicious toning down and, on occasion, omissions, which if presented directly might work against the person for whom one is testifying. In such cases I have spent many hours consulting with defense attorneys in order to clarify what things can be said with safety and what comments need be modified. For example, it is no surprise that many of the nursery schools in which outbreaks of sex-abuse hysteria have occurred are closely affiliated with churches, especially churches whose congregants are strict fundamentalists, many of whom are rigidly religious, and some of whom are even fanatic. These are the people whose backlash to the sexual revolution of the sixties and seventies has played a role in the sex-abuse hysteria that we are witnessing today (Gardner, 1991a). It may be that the judge and/or members of the jury share the religious beliefs that are fueling the hysteria. Under these circumstances the examiner does well to "steer clear" of religion entirely, both in one's written reports and in one's testimony. The examiner does well just to keep this information in his own "little head" and use all other information to support one's arguments. This is a tricky business, and not something mental health professionals are generally trained to do. Those who are going to testify in sex-abuse cases do well to learn the risks and pitfalls of direct, honest testimony if they are to best serve the interests of the patient in whose support they are testifying.

☐ TEN
TREATMENT OF NONABUSED CHILDREN PROGRAMMED TO BELIEVE THEY WERE SEXUALLY ABUSED

THE POTENTIALLY TRAUMATIC EFFECTS OF SEX-ABUSE EVALUATIONS FOR BOTH ABUSED AND NONABUSED CHILDREN

The Evaluative Procedure

A sex-abuse evaluation conducted by an overzealous and/or incompetent examiner can be an extremely traumatic experience for a child. I am not referring simply to the acute trauma of the evaluation(s), and I am not even referring to the subacute trauma of a series of investigations (commonly the case), but also of the long-term sequelae of such examinations. The latter relate to the child's being made to believe that he (she) was sexually abused if that was *not* the case. The evaluations may be conducted by investigators who have little training, use coercive interview techniques, are convinced that "children never lie," and believe that all alleged perpetrators are guilty. Detectives and/or prosecutors, who previously worked only with criminals, and others with little or no training in proper interview techniques are brought into the act. Quick courses are given in which little if anything is said about the possibility that the sex-abuse allegation may be fabricated. Practically every child is found to be abused. Policemen appear on the scene; the alleged perpetrator may be jailed (often without due process); and the child cannot but feel that a heinous crime has been committed. Often the investigators are referred to as *validators*. As mentioned, the name itself is a disgrace in that it implies that the investigator is merely there to "validate" the abuse—with the implication that it definitely occurred and merely requires confirmation. In many settings, the validators know where their bread is buttered and recognize that if they conclude that most of the accusations are false, they may be out of a job.

In most states the reporting of sex abuse is mandatory, even for therapists who are deeply involved with the patient and may have everything under control. The therapist may be far more experienced and knowledgeable about sex abuse than the individuals who are being asked to investigate. The therapist may be an extremely experienced evaluator with exquisite sensitivity for differentiating between true and false sex-abuse accusations; yet the law requires him (her) to refer the child for evaluation by someone who may have just completed training in a short crash course and whose knowledge and experience are practically at the zero level. And if such a therapist does not comply with the law, he (she) may be subjected to criminal action and even a jail sentence (Denton, 1987). Obviously, following such reporting, any meaningful therapy is completely destroyed, even though the end-result of the investigation may be that the child and/or alleged perpetrator are required to go into treatment.

I, myself, am in this position in the state of New Jersey. Specifically, if an unreported case comes my way and I suspect that sex abuse *might* have taken place, it is not legal for me to make that decision. Rather, the law requires me to report the suspected abuse to the *New Jersey Division of Youth and Family Services* in order that the examiners there may determine whether the child has been sexually abused. Although I *might* be allowed some input, the final decision is theirs. It is they who decide on the competence of their examiners, and it is they who make the decision regarding whether the child was sexually abused. I recall one case in which one of their examiners mockingly flaunted to me his agency's ability to determine whether a child had been sexually abused by merely seeing the child alone in a period of less than an hour. What is most sad here is that he genuinely believed he could do this for the parade of children who filed through his office.

Under these circumstances children cannot but suffer with significant psychological trauma. They may feel guilt over their participation, whether real or fabricated. After all, their statements have resulted in the appearance of police, detectives, prosecutors, and other powerful authorities. These are people usually associated with criminals, and the child cannot but feel that he (she) and the accused have been involved in criminal behavior. If the child has indeed been sexually molested, and enjoyed the sexual activity, then additional guilt may be incurred. The child is likely to feel shame over involvement in the sexual activities (whether actual or alleged) and anticipate public condemnation. The child may feel that his (her) genitals have been damaged, especially if there have been extensive medical examinations. There is a sense of helplessness as the child is swept up in the investigations and shunted from examiner to examiner. There are associated feelings of impending disaster in the home, demoralization, and depression (Renshaw, 1987).

Sometimes (if not often), the psychological damage caused by the investigation is greater than that which results from the abuse, especially if the abuse was transient. The interrogations interfere with the natural desensitization process necessary for working through the trauma. Such desensitization normally takes place via the child's repeatedly thinking about the trauma, talking about it, and reiterating the experience in fantasy play (with or without dolls). It is as if each time the child relives the experience in fantasy, it becomes a little more bearable. Finally, after varying periods of time, the trauma loses its power to affect the child adversely. The interrogatory process interferes with this process. The child may be continually reminded of the trauma long beyond the time when natural desensitization processes might have buried the whole incident, or at least reduced its capacity for creating tension and anxiety.

Courtroom Interrogation

In court the child suffers additional traumas. Most often the child is interviewed by the judge in his (her) chambers. However, on occasion the child is required to testify on the stand in open court. Although the court recognizes that such testimony may be psychologically traumatic, the alleged victim is entitled to face his (her) accuser in an open courtroom, and such testimony is considered one of the rights of the accused under the United States Constitution. The alleged perpetrator's attorney is likely to interrogate the child repeatedly, as is the accuser's lawyer. The legal professionals are basically trained in direct and cross-examination techniques. Whereas these may be applicable to the adversary courtroom setting, they are most often psychologically traumatic to children, because they inevitably attempt to zero in and focus on the most sensitive material. Therapists know well that the confrontational approach is often the most anxiety provoking and may be the least efficient method for getting at "the truth." Furthermore, some legal professionals hammer away, badger, and attempt to wear down the witness to the point where an individual will say anything just to get off the stand. And many such individuals do not consider children exempt from such inquiries.

Or, the court may allow the child to be interviewed in the judge's chambers. However, even here the child is generally quite fearful, because the judge is viewed as an awesome figure of authority. The child's recognition that what he (she) says may ultimately result in the alleged perpetrator being sent to jail adds formidably to the child's tension and anxiety. Feelings of fear, guilt, disloyalty, and low self-worth are inevitable under such circumstances. The child may even believe that he (she) may be sent to jail, especially when the allegation is true. The judge may promise the child that everything said will be held in strict confidence; but this ultimately proves to be a deceit in that the information provided is ultimately communicated to the attorneys and parents who, most often, directly or indirectly, will transmit the divulgence down to the child. The sense of betrayal that results adds to the child's feelings of distrust and betrayal.

Removal of the Child and/or Alleged Abuser

When the court concludes that the abuse did indeed take place (whether this is a valid conclusion or not), it is often the case that either the abuser or the child must be taken from the home. This is traumatic enough when the allegation is fabricated; but when it is true, it is not necessarily the only course to take. In spite of the abuse (which may have occurred on only one occasion), the abuser may still be removed from the home or, in certain situations, the child. This is especially the case when the mother is considered unfit and likely to foster or expose the child to further abuses. The disruption of the parent-child bond here may be formidable and the psychological trauma significant, and this is especially the case when the molestation has been mild or there has been no abuse at all.

ADDITIONAL TRAUMATIC EFFECTS OF A SEX-ABUSE INVESTIGATION WHEN THE ALLEGATION IS FALSE

All of the aforementioned psychological traumas are likely to result in children subjected to sex-abuse investigations – whether the accusation is true or false. However, when the allegation is false, additional psychological damage is likely to result.

The Systematic Erosion and Destruction of the Parent-Child Bond

The child may feel guilty over the destruction of the parent's life that was the result of the false allegation. Such parents may become pariahs, and their social and professional lives correspondingly ruined. Some of these children are placed in treatment. The child, then, is being placed in therapy for an experience (or experiences) that never occurred. It is not uncommon for the therapist to work on the assumption that no child ever fabricates sex abuse. Such "treatment," then, cannot but be detrimental. The child may come to actually believe that the abuse took place and suffer with subsequent feelings of guilt and low self-worth. Often the therapist actively fosters expression of hostility and vengeance against the innocent parent, which may result in permanent alienation. In practically every session the child is encouraged to act out hostility toward the father, often with the help of dolls that the child is encouraged to punch, kick, and hit. Nothing good is said about the father. Comfort with normal ambivalence is discouraged. There is progressive pro-gramming of the child to believe that the father is the incarnation of all the evil that has ever existed in the history of the world. The destruction of this relationship is tragic for both the child and the father. Even if the father had sexually abused the child, such "treatment" would be inappropriate. The child is taught to be sadistic, to act out hostility without guilt, and this of course contributes to the development of antisocial behavior, and, of course, it creates an iatrogenic disruption of the parent-child bond (Benedek and Schetky, 1987).

"Empowering Techniques"

The child is taught "empowering" techniques, techniques allegedly designed to help the child deal with the father and others who might try to abuse him (her). At the most simple level children are taught to "say no" in situations when abusers approach them. They are taught to run away, to hide, and to appeal for help from a wide variety of authorities. They are also taught that many people may not believe them when they claim that they are in danger of being abused, so they may have to go to a series of authorities before they will receive help. Such "treatment" not only creates belief in the child that perpetrators are lurking everywhere, but that children should be in a constant state of vigilance in order to protect themselves from sex abusers. This cannot but create unnecessary tensions and anxieties, and in extreme cases, paranoid thinking.

The Inculcation of Sexual Psychopathology

Such "treatment" also inculcates in children the view that sex is filthy and dangerous. The word *love* hardly appears in such therapy. Certainly there is no love from the father, and if there is any love from the mother, it is the kind that protects the child from danger. The idea that love can be combined with sex is not introduced. Obviously, such indoctrination can have serious effects on the child's future sex life. And the aforementioned programming against the father is likely to be generalized to all men, with the result that there is further interference in the child's capacity to develop a healthy sexual orientation.

Such treatment is generally interminable. The therapist is ever trying to elicit more and more details about the sexual abuses. And these children, in order to ingratiate themselves to their therapists, continue to pour forth with a never-ending stream of abuses that soon reach the level of atrocities. Ultimately, there is no sexual abomination that is not described, and this is especially the case in the nursery school and day-care center situations, where the mass hysteria element prevails. I am convinced that many of these children are being programmed to become psychotic as a result of this kind of "treatment." And the psychosis so engendered includes bizarre delusions in the sexual realm.

The Creation of "Victims"

Children in such "treatment" are taught that they are victims of sexual abuse. They become deeply indoctrinated with the notion that they have been victimized, and this cannot but affect their future psychological development. Victims of sex abuse tend to see themselves as victims in other situations. The prophecy may very well be realized, with the result that lifelong patterns of self-destructiveness may become embedded. Such an attitude engenders the notion that they are not responsible for unacceptable, painful, and even terrible things that may happen to them. Rather, they tend to view themselves as the innocent victims of persecutors, and this pattern can contribute to the development of sadomasochistic behavior as well as paranoid thinking.

INDIVIDUAL WORK WITH THE CHILD

Removal of the Child from Treatment With an Overzealous Therapist

Before one can treat the child, it is crucial that the youngster be removed from "treatment" with the kind of zealous therapists described earlier in this chapter as well as throughout this book. If the mother has not been convinced that there is no sex abuse, and has become deeply bonded with the aforementioned kind of therapist, it may require a court order to bring about a cessation of the treatment. Furthermore, it may require a court order to restrain the mother from bringing the child to another therapist who will proceed along the lines originated by the first. Unfortunately, there is a sea of zealous therapists who are quite committed to the kinds of therapeutic programs described throughout this book. The likelihood of a reasonable therapeutic program (such as the kind I describe in Chapter Eleven) working while the child is in treatment with one of the aforementioned zealous types described is practically zero. I personally would not agree to embark upon a therapeutic program while the child is simultaneously receiving the type of aforementioned "treatment." Once this has been accomplished, the therapist is in a position to proceed.

The Crucial Role of Family Therapy

It is hoped that the work with the child and both parents can be accomplished under a voluntary arrangement in which both parents agree that one therapist should work with the family. Obviously, this is the most efficacious approach to the treatment of a child who has been subjected to and embroiled in a false sex-abuse accusation. If, however, this cannot be voluntarily accomplished, and it is not likely in the situation where the mother is delusional, then a court order may be the only way to effect such treatment. Generally, such a court order is not likely to have much effect without some threat of sanction if the mother does not comply. These usually fall into the categories of monetary penalties, loss of primary custody, and a jail sentence. The awareness that these may be implemented (and the judge must be serious) can often help such mothers "cooperate" in the therapeutic program. Elsewhere (Gardner, 1992a) I have described in detail such court-ordered therapeutic programs for families of children suffering with a parental alienation syndrome.

Children Who Do Not Require Treatment

It is important for the therapist to appreciate that treatment may *not* be necessary. A thorough evaluation must be conducted, not only of the child, but of the mother and father. It is important to trace in detail the evolution of the sex-abuse accusation, from its very beginning, and to understand point by point the various contributions to the scenarios that subsequently developed. Without this information the therapist is ill equipped to provide therapy for the wide variety of distortions that have been so engendered in the child's mind. In addition, one wants to look for signs of a post-traumatic stress disorder (PTSD). I am not referring here to the PTSD that resulted from the alleged sex abuse (a PTSD that the validators would like to believe exists), but a PTSD that results from the interrogatory processes. Furthermore, one wants to assess for the presence of other psychological problems, problems that might have resulted from other factors unrelated to the legal process trauma. I will not, however, direct my attention to the treatment of these disorders, because they go beyond the purposes of this book. Rather, I will focus specifically on psychological problems that derive from the child's being subjected to a series of interrogations focusing on sex abuse when no such abuse took place.

If one is dealing with a PTSD, it is important to appreciate, as mentioned above, that often no treatment at all is necessary. One must respect the natural desensitization processes. The child's preoccupation with the traumatic experiences tends to provide a kind of systematic desensitization to the trauma. It is as if each time the child thinks about the trauma, he (she) becomes more accustomed to it and it becomes less painful. The therapist does not want to muckrake and dredge up this old material that the child is attempting to bury and lay to rest. When I was in medical school we were often taught, "Don't do something. Stand there." This is an ancient wisdom. We may not be able to make our patients better in many situations, but we certainly shouldn't make them worse. Hippocrates, long ago, said it in other words: "Above all, do not harm." Hippocrates was referring here to the importance of physicians recognizing that their highest obligation is to be sure that they do not leave their patients worse than they were before the medical treatment.

Accordingly, there are many situations in which I have told the family that they should do nothing at all and just go back to the natural course of living. Sometimes judges react with incredulity to my recommendation here. Judges (as well as many other people in this world) seem to have a deep-seated conviction for the value of psychotherapeutic treatment. Generally, they have far more commitment to the therapeutic process than I and consider it to be a far more efficacious modality than I do. Often, this is merely a way of "washing their hands" of the whole case and moving on to the next case. It is like shifting responsibility over to the therapist, who is somehow going to pick up the pieces and make everything all right again. Accordingly, the idea that things will be "all right again" if one does nothing does not fit in well with this approach. Most mental health professionals, unfortunately, share judges' views of the value of the therapeutic process. There is a sea of hungry therapists out there and, I am sure, monetary gain plays a role in this commitment to the therapeutic process. My experience has been that the younger therapists have much more conviction for the value of therapy than more seasoned people. Perhaps their optimism is good, but in certain situations it can backfire and do more harm than good, and such is the case for children who are suffering with the effects of a series of sex-abuse interrogations.

Accordingly, I may see the child initially once or twice and will often merely recommend a "vacation" of a few months in order to see how the child is doing without treatment. I have no specified time such as one, two, or three months, in that such predictions are ill advised in our field; rather, I merely tell the parents to see how the child is doing without treatment and to look for signs and symptoms of significant psychological difficulty. Of course, they are advised to check in with me if they have any questions. Obviously, if the child starts to exhibit symptoms that warrant treatment, the child will receive it.

The Importance of the Blank-Screen Approach

Whether the child is being evaluated for treatment or whether the child is in treatment, the therapist does well to be a strong adherent of the "blank-screen" approach. These are children who have been subjected to sexualized interviews and whose view of therapy is that it is a place where one talks about sex. Other things that may have come into the child's mind have been shunted aside in order to achieve the goal of discussing sexual matters. Accordingly, it is crucial that the therapist not repeat the same error and provide specific points of departure for discussion, sexual or otherwise. The best way to find out what's "bugging" the child is to give the child free rein to express whatever is in his (her) mind. Obviously, there is no place in any therapist's room (whether in this situation or any other) for anatomical dolls, body charts, sex-abuse prevention books, leading questions, leading gestures, and leading stimuli. Rather, the traditional playroom equipment will generally suffice, and an atmosphere in which the child is allowed free expression is the one in which the evaluator is going to be in the best position to find out what's going on in the child's mind, especially with regard to whether treatment is indicated.

Dealing with Cognitive Distortions

Preliminary Work with the Mother It is to be hoped that the mother will have been convinced that the sex abuse did not take place. Obviously, if the therapist can accomplish this, then it is going to be much easier to treat the child. If, however, she remains fixed in her belief that the sex abuse occurred and does not believe competent evaluators and a court decision that the sex abuse did not, then the therapy of the child is likely to be compromised. In either case, the therapist does well to communicate to the child exactly what the mother's position is. Accordingly, if the mother has changed her mind, the therapist does well to make comments along these lines:

> Your mother had the wrong idea. She thought that your father had done those bad things to you. You, I, and your father all know that those bad things didn't happen. Your mother used to think they happened. Now she knows that they didn't. She realizes that she made a big mistake. No one is perfect; everyone makes mistakes; and your mother is no exception.

If, however, the mother still believes the sex abuse took place, the therapist must take a different tack:

> Although your mother's thinking is okay in many different ways, I believe that her thinking is wrong when she talks about you and your father. She thinks that your father did something to you. *You* know that never happened. *Your father* knows that never happened. And *I* believe it never happened. The *judge* doesn't believe it happened. Yet she doesn't believe all of us. She believes Ms. X (the "validator") who also, in my opinion, doesn't think right. I hope someday your mother will change her mind and see things the way they really are.

There are some examiners, I am sure, who would take issue with my approach here, because I am directly criticizing the mother in a very important area. I believe that all competent therapists criticize parents in the course of psychotherapy, whether it be for a false sex-abuse accusation or otherwise. The child does best to grow up in a situation in which he (she) has the most accurate view of the parents, their assets and their liabilities; and this process should take place whether or not the child is in therapy. It is hoped that therapy facilitates this process and provides the child with more accurate information about the parents than might have been obtained without it. The aforementioned comments, then, are not only made in the service of this general therapeutic principle but, more specifically, in the service of helping the child correct the distortions associated with the false sex-abuse accusation. I am careful, however, to circumscribe the mother's isolated delusion(s) and not expand it into a chronic state of paranoid schizophrenia. I try to help the child appreciate that this is an isolated deficit on the mother's part, and I am careful to point out her positive qualities as well. In the service of this goal, I say something along these lines: "For some reason your mother believes Ms. X much more than she believes me, Dr. Y, Dr. Z, and the judge." All these people know more about these things than Ms. X. But you and I *know* that these things *never really* happened.

The Correction of Cognitive Distortions   For children who do need treatment, an important area to focus on relates to the cognitive distortions that have been introduced in the course of coercive evaluations and presumed "therapy." Children who have been subjected to the aforementioned types of interrogations are likely to have difficulty differentiating between fact and fantasy. They have been led to believe that certain things happened that in fact never occurred. The younger the child, the greater the likelihood these misconceptions will become embedded in the child's psychic structure. Accordingly, it behooves the therapist to find out exactly what these distortions are, and these must be addressed and corrected. This is a crucial part of the treatment of these children because, as mentioned, there is a high risk for the development of psychosis and so everything possible must be done to correct these misconceptions in order to lessen the likelihood that they will become permanently entrenched in the child's mind. We see here, then, an excellent example of a situation in which a cognitive therapeutic approach is warranted. One does well to elicit from such children exactly what they themselves recall regarding the events surrounding the sex-abuse accusation. In a neutral atmosphere, especially an atmosphere in which they are not being asked to "validate" the sex abuse, they are more likely to say what they know is true, namely, that nothing happened.

Many of these children have been brought to the point of believing that they were sexually abused. In such cases it behooves the examiner to communicate to the child that a "big mistake" has been made and that all those people who thought that the father did those things to the child were "wrong." One does well to be specific here and identify the parties who participated in the promulgation of the false sex-abuse accusation. One can say, "Your mother had a wrong idea. She thought that your father touched your wee-wee, but she was wrong." Other comments that can prove useful in the course of such discussions are: "Your father was right all the time when he said nothing happened. He was the one who was telling the truth when he said that he never kissed your pee-pee." "The judge is a very smart man. He spent a lot of time listening to all the people and he decided that nothing happened. He decided that your mother made a mistake. In fact, the whole thing has just been one big mistake." "The police were wrong when they thought that your father did those things to you. They just didn't know what they were talking about. They weren't there, so they don't really know. You were there, and you really know that nothing happened." With regard to the "validators" I make statements along these lines:

> Ms. X has something wrong with her thinking. She doesn't think straight. She thinks just about every child she sees had something bad happen to the child. That's not so. You know and I know that she wanted you to say that these bad things *really* happened. She used to get upset with you when you said that *nothing* happened. She would only be pleased with you when you said that bad things happened. Remember how upset she used to be when you said that nothing happened? She used to get out all those funny-looking dolls with all the private parts showing and wanted you to show with the dolls what your daddy did to you. If you said that your daddy didn't do anything to you — which is what really was true — she would get upset with you. And your mother would have been upset too, because she, too, thought that

something happened. She also used to teach you that your father was a bad person. She used to tell you to hit that big Bozo doll with your fist and to kick it. I think that was a bad idea. Your father's not a bad guy. He didn't do those things to you. She shouldn't have taught you to be angry at him. I know the judge was angry at her for teaching you these things.

I suspect that some readers will believe that I am "coming down too heavily" on some of the people involved in promulgating the false sex-abuse accusation. They probably believe that I should "soften" somewhat my criticisms of these examiners. One could even argue that I should have more pity than scorn for them. Obviously, my scorn far outweighs any pity I have for these "therapists," primarily because of the terrible damage that they have done and are continuing to do to thousands of children. I am not ashamed of this scorn, however, and I believe that it can play a therapeutic role if judiciously released. It adds conviction to my statements about these examiners' misconceptions, distortions, and even stupidity. It can fuel the enthusiasm with which I approach the treatment of these children. The enhanced credibility of my statements then increases the likelihood that they will have clout with the child and contribute thereby to a correction of the distortions that have been engendered by them.

The examiner does well to bring in the authority of the judge because of the awe that young children generally have of him (her). Quoting them can enhance the efficacy of the therapist's messages. However, more important is the relationship that the therapist has with the patient. If this is a good one, then the child will be receptive to this therapeutic "debriefing" program.

The Shibboleth "The Truth"   The child may have used the code-term *the truth* to refer to the sex-abuse scenario. The therapist does well to help the child appreciate that the real *truth* was not the sex-abuse scenario, but the reality of the father-child relationship, especially the reality in which there was no sexual molestation. The child has to be helped not only by words, but by living experience, to appreciate that in this new therapy the search for "the truth" in no way relates to reciting the litany of the sex-abuse scenario. The truth in this new therapy is the *real* truth, not only with regard to the correction of distortions about the alleged sex abuse, but with regard to all other realities in the child's life. Here the child should genuinely validate (and I use the word in the healthiest sense) what he (she) has actually seen. The child should be helped to trust his (her) own observations—at an age-appropriate level of expectation—and then make statements that are commensurate with the observations. In this way the child will be helped to learn what is the real truth in a wide variety of areas having little if anything to do with sexual matters.

Concluding Comments Although one can never be one hundred percent certain that no sex abuse occurred, it is not meaningful for a young child to be told that competent evaluators and the court are "99 percent certain" or that there is "not enough evidence." Rather, the therapist does well to "round things off" and merely state that *"nothing happened"* and "he did *not* do it." Other distortions, as well, may have to be corrected. The child may believe that his (her) genitals have been damaged and this should be discussed, with possible reference to medical examinations by the pediatrician. Correction of other distortions, unrelated to the sex abuse, may be useful. The general approach here is to help the child—at an age-appropriate cognitive level—differentiate fact from fantasy, to differentiate what is "real" from what is "make believe." For some children, especially those above the age of five, *The Talking, Feeling, and Doing Game* (Gardner, 1973) may be useful. The vast majority of the cards are reality-oriented and provide the child with catalytic questions and statements that can serve as points of departure for psychotherapeutic interchanges. Some sample questions are: "What is the worst thing that ever happened to you in your whole life?" "Name three things that can make a person sad." "Name three things that can make a person happy." "A girl had something on her mind that she was ashamed to tell her mother. What was it?" "Name three things that can make a person angry?"

Obviously, the older the child, the more likely some of the

aforementioned messages will "sink in." When we are dealing with three- and four-year-olds, it is not likely that most of them are going to have much of an effect. It is only when we reach the five- and six-year-olds that some of these messages may prove therapeutically efficacious. More important than these messages, however, are the child's actual living experiences, which will serve to prove to the child that the father is not the dangerous individual he was made out to be. The reader is probably familiar with the old Chinese proverb: "A picture is worth a thousand words." I would add to this: "An experience is worth a million pictures." Accordingly, unsupervised visitations, having natural experiences with the father over time, is probably the best therapeutic approach to the alleviation of the psychological damage done to children subjected to the aforementioned kinds of interrogations.

Dealing with Emotional Problems

Some of the child's emotional problems obviously derive from the cognitive misrepresentations that have been engendered by the zealous interrogators and "validators." It behooves the examiner to learn about the cognitive distortions that form the basis of these abnormal feelings. One does well to delineate these and to use each distortion as a point of departure for conversations in which an attempt is made to correct the misrepresentations. As mentioned, this is a good situation for the utilization of cognitive therapeutic techniques. (It would be an error for the reader to conclude here that I view myself as a "cognitive therapist." I do incorporate the principles of such therapists into my therapeutic program but, as I hope the reader appreciates, it is much broader, because I believe that a pure cognitive therapeutic approach is somewhat oversimplified.)

Pathological Feelings About Sex The child's feelings about sex are likely to have become significantly pathological. Some children who have been subjected to the aforementioned types of evaluations and "treatment" have not experienced any particular sexual feelings. (This is the more common situation.) Accordingly, their accusations have no genuine sexual element with regard to sexual *feelings*. They have been basically reciting scripts, without any appreciation of the sexual-emotional significance of their verbalizations. Others have experienced varying degrees of sexual expression (i.e., varying levels of sexual excitation, masturbation) and know something about sexual pleasure. For these children, however, the sexual feelings were not the result of sexual molestation. Rather, they were children who naturally and normally exhibited sexual feelings at an early age (a not uncommon situation, prevalent myths to the contrary notwithstanding) or have been prematurely sexualized from experiences having nothing to do with sex abuse, e.g., exposure to other children's sexuality and discovery of masturbation as an antianxiety practice or antidepressant. Children in both of these categories are likely to have been taught by "validators" and "therapists" that sex is dirty and dangerous and that people who engage in such activities are somehow seriously defective and perverted.

It is rare for the association between sex and love to be introduced in the course of these children's "therapy." Accordingly, these children have to be helped to view sex in a healthy way and come to see it as a normal desire that grows stronger as one gets older, especially during the teen period. For many children this is purely an intellectual exercise because they don't have the faintest idea what the therapist is talking about. For other children, however, it may have some meaning, and it is for these children that such comments will be most meaningful. Such children have to become comfortable with their masturbatory practices and to learn that, in our society, such activities are generally engaged in privately. They may have interest in normal age-appropriate sexual exploratory play and they must be helped to appreciate that, although such interests are normal, children who engage in such activities may "get into trouble." If, however, in spite of the therapist's mild admonition regarding such behavior, the child is found to be engaged in such activities (an almost universal phenomenon), the parents should be advised to avoid even the mildest kind of disciplinary measures. The child should be told – in a matter-of-fact way – that such behavior is okay and acceptable and that it is not considered proper in public; however, it is certainly acceptable to do it privately. The greater the difficulty the therapist has convincing the parents of these children to utilize this approach, the greater the likelihood the child will suffer with pathological thoughts and feelings about sexuality.

Some of these children's sexual interests involve playing sexual games with other children. (Again, I am referring here to children who have not been sexually abused, but who are exhibiting early sexual interest for the reasons described above.) Such children also have to be told, in as matter-of-fact a way as possible, that in our society such behavior is not considered acceptable and that those who engage in these activities might "get into trouble." Such children can be told, however, that when they get older they will have more opportunities for such activities. However, this too rarely works well, in that most human beings in this world do not easily accept a waiting period of 10 to 15 years before having an opportunity to enjoy a particular form of gratification, especially one that is very intense. However, the futility of the advice notwithstanding, it is still better to be offered some hope in the future than no hope at all.

Hatred of the Father With regard to the feelings of hatred toward the father that have been engendered in the "treatment," the child has to be helped to appreciate that the father is a loving, affectionate person who is deeply committed to the child (the usual case). However, the treatment of the child in this situation is not for the therapist to provide a total "whitewash" as an antidote to the "backwash" to which the child has been subjected. Rather, the therapist does well to help the child appreciate that the father, like all human beings, is a mixture of qualities that are likable to the child and those that are not. All human relationships are ambivalent, and parent-child relationships are no exception to this principle. The child should be helped to become comfortable with feelings of resentment, when justified, and to deal with them appropriately. Unfortunately, the "validators" consider the appropriate way to deal with anger is to hit and kick a doll and to pour forth profanities at it. They do not appreciate that the appropriate way to express anger is to express directly, in civilized words, exactly what one's resentments are toward the *person* (not the symbol) who is causing the frustration.

Pathological Guilt   The child may feel guilty over the grief that the accusation has caused the accused. In such situations the therapist does well to help the child appreciate that he (she) was brainwashed by the mother, validators, and interrogators, and was really helpless to do otherwise, considering the forces to which the child was subjected. The child may feel shame over having been accused of engaging in "bad touches" and "bad acts." The child has to be helped to appreciate that no such activities were engaged in and, therefore, neither guilt nor shame is appropriate. The people who should feel guilt and shame are those who contributed to the promulgation of the false sex-abuse accusation, and these people should be identified to the child.

Psychopathic Behavior   If the child's "treatment" has engendered psychopathic attitudes regarding the expression of hostility toward the father, then the therapy must involve attempts to *increase* the child's guilt. This statement may come as a surprise to some therapists who believe that it is improper for therapists to increase guilt under any circumstance. I do not agree with this position. Some people with hypertrophied consciences need relaxation of the internal guilt-evoking mechanisms. There are others, however, who do not have enough guilt, and the therapeutic approach to them is some expansion of their consciences and intensification of their potential to feel guilt. (There are far more psychopathic types in this world than there are people with hypertrophied internalized guilt-evoking mechanisms.)

Feelings of "Empowerment"   The therapist must deal with the so-called empowering maneuvers taught by the "validator" therapist. First, the child may have come to believe that sex-abuse perpetrators are ubiquitous and they must ever be vigilant if they are to protect themselves from further abominations. One has to help the child appreciate that sex abuse, although it does occur, does not take place as frequently as the child has been led to believe. The younger the child, the greater the likelihood the therapist will have difficulty getting across this notion. In fact, for children from ages three to four (the most common age level for successful indoctrination), it may be impossible to get across the notion of *relative degrees of frequency.* (Unfortunately, there are many adults who have problems with this concept as well.) The "empowering" maneuvers of saying no, running for help to an authority, etc., have to be addressed one at a time and put in proper perspective. Rather than provide the child with a sense of true empowerment, the empowering maneuvers are likely to have had the opposite effect because the child is really not in a position to implement them. The effect they have is to increase fears and confuse the child regarding what acts to take. This cannot but contribute to feelings of inadequacy (the opposite of empowerment). The child may have come to believe that all male relatives are potential perpetrators, and these distortions must be corrected. Each relative should be discussed and the child helped to appreciate that such an individual is not going to molest her (him).

DEALING WITH THE FALSELY ACCUSING MOTHER

A mother who promulgates a false sex-abuse accusation generally falls along a continuum, with conscious fabrication at the one end and delusion at the other. Not only does her belief in the sex abuse fall at some point along this continuum, but it may have shifted back and forth throughout the course of the child's interrogations. Sometimes a fabrication progresses to become a delusion, especially when supported by a coterie of "validators," each of whom shares the delusion that the sex abuse did indeed take place. Obviously, the earlier the mother has exposure to competent people who can prevail upon her to reconsider her position, the greater the likelihood of preventing the deterioration of her thinking down the delusional track. Because of the variations among these women, I cannot provide any standard approach to their involvement in the child's treatment. I will, however, comment on dealing with mothers at the two ends of the continuum, namely, the fabricated end and the delusional end.

If the mother is in the delusional category and the delusion is fixed, there may be absolutely nothing the therapist can do to change her mind. If she is in "treatment" with a therapist who shares her delusion, the likelihood of her changing her opinion is reduced to the zero level. Unfortunately, there are many such *folie-à-deux* therapeutic arrangements, much to the detriment of the children of such mothers. One could argue that a court order that the mother discontinue such treatment would be advisable. Forgetting for the moment the legality of such an order, it is not likely to work. Because there is a sea of such zealous therapists, a court order constraining the mother from involvement with her particular therapist would only result in her involving herself with another of the same ilk. More practical is the court giving serious consideration to a transfer of primary custody to the father. I am not stating that this should automatically be done. What I am suggesting is that the court review the whole picture. If the false sex-abuse accusation is part of a larger package of denigrations, and if the mother is in the severe category of parental alienation syndrome, then transfer of primary custody may be the only way of protecting the child from the mother's campaign of denigration of the father—with the resultant attenuation (even to the point of obliteration) of the child's bond with the father. It is almost impossible to treat a child effectively as long as the child remains in the home of such a mother. No matter how skilled the therapist, no matter how many times a week the child is seen, if the child is subjected to the mother's programming throughout the rest of the week, therapy is going to prove futile.

At the other end of the continuum is the mother who initially fabricated the accusation and knew with certainty that it was false. Also at this end of the continuum are mothers who may have had some concern, who thought there might have been sex abuse, and then were dragged along toward the delusional end by zealous "validators." If one is successful in helping her regain her sanity, to the point where she recognizes that there was no such abuse, then she can be worked with effectively. Such a mother can then be encouraged to tell her child that her accusation was a "big mistake," and she should try to explain to the child how she naively went along with the fanatic and/or naive validators. In such cases she can use the same approaches to the child described above for the therapist, i.e., the various communications in which clarification is provided the child regarding what actually did happen in his (her) situation. Obviously, the mother's input provides clout to the therapist's clarifications, and when one adds the fathers as well, such a program of "debriefing" is likely to be successful.

With regard to the mothers in the middle, that is, between the fabricated and delusional ends of the continuum, the closer the mother is to the fabrication end, the greater the likelihood the therapist will be able to work with her and, conversely, the closer she is to the delusional end, the more hopeless therapy will be.

DEALING WITH THE FALSELY ACCUSED FATHER

As mentioned, the most important part of the therapeutic approach regarding the child's relationship with the father is for the child to have living experiences with the father that are friendly and loving. In the context of such a relationship, there will be no sex abuse and the child is not likely to then continue to fear such activities. The father too should communicate to the child information regarding what the mother's exact status is, i.e., at what point along the aforementioned continuum her position is regarding whether the sex abuse took place. If the mother has recanted, then he should use terms like *mistake* in his communications. If she is at the other end of the continuum, however, he does well to make comments along these lines: "Although your mother has many fine qualities, she has the wrong idea about my having done these bad things to you. She believes Ms. X (the validator) and some of her friends, who also have the wrong idea. I hope your mother changes her mind. You and I know that these things didn't happen" and, if appropriate, "It was because of these wrong ideas that the judge has decided that you should live with me. That's the only way to protect you from her putting all these wrong ideas in your head."

FAMILY WORK

In addition to individual work with the child and parents, joint conferences can also be useful. If there is still some possibility of improving the relationship between the parents (their marital status notwithstanding), everything should be done to do this. Even though divorced, and even though the grief has been intensified significantly by the false sex-abuse accusation, attempts should still be made to bring about some degree of rapprochement between the parents. Obviously the attempt here is not to bring about a reconciliation of the marriage; rather an attempt should be to bring about an improvement in their relationship for the sake of the child. This is in accordance with the general principle that children of divorce do better if their parents can communicate and cooperate with one another, their animosity notwithstanding. Joint sessions with the father and the child can also help to improve their relationship, especially with regard to the improvement in communication and the correction of distortions. Such meetings also provide the kinds of *living experiences* that can contribute to the reduction of distortions derived from the sex-abuse accusation. Joint interviews with the mother can also be useful. Here the mother can explain her position, especially if she is in the "mistake" category. If in the delusional category, the joint interviews can help the therapist clarify the mother's position and confront the child and mother with the mother's distortions. (I recognize that this approach is not going to be particularly useful for younger children, such as those at the three-to-four-year level. I recognize also that the child may thereby be witness to a conflict of opinions and that this may be a detrimental exposure.) My hope is that the negative effects of such exposure will be more than counterbalanced by the therapist having the opportunity to address himself (herself) to the mother's distortions in the presence of the child. This can help the child put them in proper perspective. Again, such discussions are not going to be very meaningful for three- and four-year-old children, but may be for older children.

FOLLOW-UP STUDIES

To the best of my knowledge, there are very few follow-up studies on the effects of this kind of legal process trauma on children. I suspect that one of the reasons for this is that the majority of people who are doing these evaluations are not appreciative of the kinds of trauma to which they are subjecting these children. Obviously, this category of "professionals" is not going to be conducting studies on the untoward effects of their manipulations. Those who are appreciative (and our ranks are growing) will, I am certain, be conducting such studies in the future. Another reason for the paucity of such studies is the fact that the phenomenon is a relatively recent one, having increased in frequency only in the last 10 years. As mentioned, I am convinced that a new breed of psychosis is being developed and that many of the children being subjected to the kinds of "therapy" described in this book will be permanently damaged, even to the point of being permanently psychotic. One cannot tamper in this way with the minds of three-year-olds and expect them to be unaffected. One cannot induce significant distortions of reality – over a long period – and expect the child to get away unscathed (if he [she] is lucky enough to get away).

Underwager and Wakefield (1991) provide follow-up data on some of the well-known nursery school and day-care center cases in which orgies of sexual abuse have been alleged. They quote Robson (1991), who states with regard to the Scott County, Minnesota, case:

> More than seven years later, the legacy of Scott County has been one of children crying for their parents in the middle of the

night; of divorce and dysfunction among nearly all the families involved; of perhaps permanent emotional damage to the accused and the accusers alike. (p. 50)

Robson further describes subsequent school problems, behavioral difficulties, sexual confusion, and drug and alcohol problems in adolescence. Underwager and Wakefield (1991) describe other cases in which children suffered significant emotional damage after being taken away from their homes, subjected to numerous interrogations in which the interviewers refused to believe their denials, and other psychological sequelae.

I recently had the opportunity to interview some children one year after their "treatment" was discontinued. The termination of therapy had nothing to do with their being "cured." Rather, it related to the fact that the lawsuits had come to an end, the psychologists' testimonies were no longer necessary, and the parents then decided that they could no longer afford treatment. These children had been in "treatment" approximately two-and-a-half years and ranged in age from seven to eight. Interestingly (and gratifyingly), they did not exhibit serious psychological difficulties as a result of their "therapy." From what I could gather, they were presenting their little scenarios to parents and therapists, but otherwise they were not significantly preoccupied with thoughts about their alleged abuses. They had learned that when you go to the therapist's office, you recite the sex-abuse scenario and then go home and go about your business. Because there was no basic sex-abuse experience, there was no real trauma, and there was none of the kinds of preoccupations one sees in a PTSD (their diagnoses by their therapists notwithstanding). Accordingly, the scenarios were not deeply embedded in their psychic structures. When I subsequently saw them, I had the feeling that their litanies were like well-rehearsed parts in a school play, learned well enough to recite under the proper circumstances, and then forgotten because they were no longer serving any purpose. These children were lucky enough to have been removed from treatment early. There are others, however, who are not so fortunate, whose parents and therapists go on for years convincing them that they were subjected to terrible abominations, entrenching thereby their pathological processes.

PREVENTION OF THE TRAUMATIC EFFECTS OF SEX-ABUSE EVALUATIONS

At this time the sex-abuse evaluation situation is a national scandal, no less horrible (and much more widespread) than the Salem witch trials (Gardner, 1991a). People are literally arrested and incarcerated on the basis of hearsay. And often the hearsay is the words of a two- or three-year-old child.

Dealing with the Money/Power Structure

The field of sex-abuse evaluations is indeed a "can of worms." There is not only a vast number of incompetents who wave the flag that "children never lie," but there is also a financial power structure that has been set up around sex-abuse evaluations. There is much money to be made in sex-abuse investigations, and people are moving into the field with increasing frequency. The more they see sex abuse, the more they can justify asking legislatures (and other resources) for money, and the more powerful their structure becomes. In the service of the perpetuation of this system, evaluators have to deny the ubiquity of false allegations of sex abuse, especially in the context of custody disputes. They also must deny the mass-hysteria element that clearly plays a role in nursery school epidemics of alleged sex abuse. There is no question that in some of these cases there has been genuine sex abuse; but there also is no question that in many of these cases children have been led to believe that they were actually abused in association with the mass hysteria of prosecutors and parents. And this is subsequently strengthened by the aforementioned "validators" and investigators. Legislators have to be alerted to the enormous amount of financial support they are funneling into this power structure. Such funding has to be more judiciously allocated, with the weeding out of the incompetents, freeloaders, fanatics, and other participants to this nationwide form of public exploitation.

There is no question that a money/power edifice has been built on sex-abuse evaluations, an edifice that is going to resist significantly attempts to bring in people capable of providing a more balanced type of evaluation. The obvious solution here is to cleanse child protection services of the incompetents, fanatics, and zealots who are currently operating within them and to replace them with better-trained, better-educated, and more highly skilled evaluators who are indeed impartial and know how to conduct a proper sex-abuse evaluation. This too would serve as an excellent type of preventive psychiatry that would lessen the likelihood of the development of the kinds of psychological traumas focused on in this chapter.

Revision and/or Rescinding of Mandatory Child Abuse Reporting Laws

Much grief has been caused by mandatory reporting of sex-abuse allegations. These laws should be changed in such ways that qualified therapists are given the option to report, or not to report, depending on what they consider to be in the best interests of their patients. Mental health professionals are faced with a terrible dilemma regarding such reporting. If they do report the abuse, they will generally destroy the therapeutic relationship they have with the child and/or at least one of the parents. In addition, such reporting can easily be considered an illegal, immoral, and unconscionable divulgence of confidential material. Not to report the abuse may result in criminal action against the therapist. The courts and the law appear to be oblivious to the implications of such divulgence to therapy. They give the therapist little option, little room to decide whether the allegation is indeed valid. Laws requiring such automatic re-porting are often based on the principle that if the child makes the allegation, the people who are in the best position to evaluate whether it is true are workers employed by child protection services. Typically, these are young, inexperienced individuals, often trained by individuals who are naive and incompetent. The statutes also appear to be based on the premise that children rarely if ever lie about sex abuse.

One possible solution to the problem would be each community's having a roster of people who are well known to be competent sex-abuse evaluators, people who do not fall into the category of zealots, people who take a balanced view of the situation, people who do not have to necessarily report any and all accusations of sex abuse. These would also have to be people who would *not* be required to process a never-ending parade of individuals for whom they could only provide limited time for the evaluation. These would also have to be people who would be required to see all parties, the accuser, the accused, and the alleged victim. (I recognize that this would be more difficult to accomplish in criminal cases than civil cases; however, even in criminal cases the requirement could be satisfied if the accused voluntarily wished to participate.) I am not claiming that this is a perfect solution to the problem; I am only claiming that it would be a vast improvement over the situation that we now have. I am not claiming that the people on such a roster would be infallible; I am only claiming that they would be far more likely to do a better job than the vast majority of people who are currently operating in the child-protection-service system.

Punitive Treatment of False Accusers

At this point, those who make false accusations of sex abuse have immunity from prosecution. This is an unconscionable situation. Those who make sex-abuse allegations should be required to stand up to their accusations and suffer some penalty if the accusation proves to be maliciously motivated or frivolously made. Such laws would certainly make many brainwashing parents think twice before initiating and/or promulgating a sex-abuse allegation in the context of a child custody dispute. Generally, such accusers are immune from retaliatory lawsuits, unless the accused can prove that the accusation was made with malice. Because it is practically impossible to prove malice (an internal psychological state), these people, in effect, make their accusations with absolutely no fear of retaliatory lawsuits or other consequences. Accordingly, at this time there are no actual consequences for such maliciousness and perjury. If the allegation is proven false, the only thing the fabricating parent loses is one important bit of ammunition in the custody fight. Even though there are no other consequences for the parents who fabricate the abuse, the parents who have been falsely charged may never be able to live down the humiliation and public disgrace.

Expanded Use of Videotaped Interviews

Courts are becoming increasingly receptive to the use of videotapes. However, they do not permit the kinds of face-to-face confrontations envisioned by the founding fathers when they wrote the United States Constitution. Videotapes certainly protect the child from the psychological trauma of testifying in an open courtroom in that the videotape can be used in lieu of direct testimony. Furthermore, even if not utilized in court, the videotapes can be useful to examiners in making decisions without unnecessarily interviewing the child many times over. Courts are also becoming increasingly receptive to interviews through one-way mirrors and closed-circuit television. Here, too, the direct face-to-face confrontation is circumvented in order to protect the child from the psychological trauma of testifying in an open courtroom. I am a strong proponent of the use of these interviewing instruments. However, we are still left with the problem of the accused having the opportunity to directly confront the accuser. Observing the child being interviewed on videotape by a third party is not the same as being present in the room when the child is being interviewed and having input into the interviewing process. The former is not true confrontation (as envisioned by the founding fathers); the latter is.

I believe that one solution to this problem would be the accuser's having the opportunity to sit in the room while the child is being interviewed and videotaped. Under these circumstances, the accused would have the opportunity to question the child directly, and this videotape could be shown in the courtroom. One could argue that this system would inevitably compromise an evaluation. The argument would be that the abused child would be subjected to the terrible trauma of being asked to speak of the abuse in the presence of the accused. I do not deny that this may be the case. Accordingly, I would not *automatically* conduct such interviews in situations in which there was a high degree of likelihood that the abuse took place. Rather, I believe that such interviews should be confined to situations in which there is a high likelihood that the abuse did not take place. Under such circumstances the accused would have the opportunity to "smoke out" the weaknesses in the child's accusations and demonstrate exactly where the fabrications lie. I have done this on many occasions in the course of my own evaluations. Under some circumstances, one might conduct two or more video interviews with the child without the accused and interviews in which he is present. This program does not preclude interviews in which the child and the accused are never placed together; it only proposes that such interviews be considered and conducted when appropriate. It is unfortunate that this practice is not being given the receptivity it deserves.

☐ ELEVEN
TREATMENT OF CHILDREN WHO HAVE ACTUALLY BEEN SEXUALLY ABUSED

INTRODUCTION

One should not even begin thinking about the treatment of a child who has allegedly been sexually abused until one is certain that the child has indeed been sexually abused. The use of such terms as "possibly," "symptoms consistent with sex abuse," and "probably" implies a level of certainty that is inadequate for the purposes of treating a child for sex abuse. To treat under such circumstances is to risk involving oneself in the kind of sham therapy described in detail in Chapter Ten. The crucial question, then, is *how* certain a therapist must be before embarking on a treatment program for such children. The answer: a very high degree of certainty. I am not stating that the only patients who should be treated are those whom the therapist himself (herself) has observed in an act of sexual abuse. Rather, I am only saying that the therapist should be convinced that the child has been abused before embarking on the treatment. Such conviction is best obtained if the therapist has conducted the evaluation and has personally come to the conclusion that the abuse has indeed taken place. Such an evaluation, as mentioned so many times previously, should include the allegedly abused child, the accuser (most often the mother), and the alleged perpetrator (whenever possible). Therapists who have not conducted the initial evaluation themselves do well to consider the credentials and credibility of previous evaluators who have come to the conclusion that the child was sexually abused. If the previous evaluator has conducted the type of examination utilized by the kinds of "validators" described in Chapter Six, then it is crucial that the therapist do a follow-up evaluation. Such an evaluation should not only include a careful review of previous reports and examinations, but an update examination conducted oneself in accordance with the guidelines described in Chapter Eight.

It is important, when conducting such preliminary examinations (whether they be the child's first evaluation or a pretreatment follow-up), that the therapist consider other sources of the presenting symptoms, sources unrelated to sexual abuse. The child's symptoms may be the result of legal-process trauma associated with the series of interviews to which the child has been previously subjected. Or the symptoms may be the result of the so-called treatment that the child has previously received, treatment of the type described in Chapter Ten. If the child has been embroiled in a child custody dispute, then one must consider the possibility that the symptoms derive from that exposure and embroilment rather than the alleged sex abuse. Elsewhere (Gardner, 1976, 1986) I have described in detail the symptoms commonly exhibited by such children.

Most judges are very quick to order treatment for children who have allegedly been sexually abused, no matter how minuscule the evidence and no matter how improbable the likelihood that the child was indeed abused. They do this in part because of some deep conviction for the efficacy of psychotherapy, a conviction that I do not share. Furthermore, judges often do this to "cover" themselves and thereby protect themselves from criticism that they did not do everything possible to protect the child. Such referrals reflect profound ignorance about the psychotherapeutic process. The idea that someone can treat the child for a disorder that may not be present is absurd. Unfortunately, my experience has been that the vast majority of therapists are willing to take on such referrals, especially in clinic settings where an arrangement has been made for the clinic to provide therapeutic services for all court referrals. But even in the private-practice setting there are many therapists who reflexively accept such referrals. This is a misguided and even dangerous practice and can result in the kinds of problems described in Chapter Ten. There are many therapists who naively believe that they have no choice but to accept a court referral. They do not seem to appreciate that we are not living in a totalitarian state, and that we cannot be court ordered to treat anyone whom we do not wish to engage in therapy. The judge can do absolutely nothing at all to a therapist who refuses to accept a child into treatment. Therapists who fear that such refusal will cut off a supply of future referrals are prostituting themselves. However, they are not simply acting reprehensibly; they are bringing about psychiatric disturbances in those nonabused children whom they are treating because the judges decided that the sex abuse took place.

In this chapter I focus primarily on the treatment of children whose sex abuse has taken place in the intrafamilial setting. In most such cases the accuser is the mother, and the accused is the father or stepfather. I will not make a sharp differentiation between those sex abusers who are married to the mothers and those who are not. The marital status of the parents is often of little relevance to the child. What is relevant is whether the abuser is likely to continue abusing the child and what can be done (if anything) to salvage a relationship that has been compromised by the sexual abuse. Accordingly, I will be dealing with situations in which the therapist has access to the abuser. Of course, there are many children who have been sexually abused by strangers and even unknown individuals. Obviously, under those circumstances, it is extremely unlikely that the therapist will have any involvement with the abuser. However, many of the therapeutic techniques described in this chapter are still applicable. Accordingly, these techniques (with minimal modifications) should prove useful in the treatment of children who were not abused in the home, but were abused elsewhere, e.g., in school settings and by strangers. Because the accuser is most often the mother, I will, for simplicity of presentation, refer to the accuser as the mother and the accused as the father. However, I recognize that there are certainly families (admittedly a small percentage) in which the abuser is the mother and the accuser is the father.

SOME COMMENTS ABOUT THERAPISTS WHO TREAT SEXUALLY ABUSED CHILDREN

I recognize that there are many highly skilled and sensitive therapists who are treating sexually abused children. I recognize, as well, that there are many therapists who take a sober attitude regarding the treatment of these children and have the same concerns as I regarding their treatment, especially with regard to my caveats about the treatment of children who are not genuinely abused. I recognize that there are many well-qualified and well-credentialed individuals who are not in the categories I am describing below. These are not the people about whom the public need be warned. It is about the unqualified "therapists" and the fanatics that the public should be aware.

We are living at a time when there are tens of thousands of people (and perhaps more) who are treating children who have allegedly been sexually abused. It is impossible to know exactly how many individuals are engaged in such therapy because many of them have no formal credentials for providing this treatment. Accordingly, they are not listed as members of any of the traditional organizations of therapists. In addition, even within those disciplines that are recognized and accredited to provide such treatment, it is very difficult to determine how many of these individuals are actually treating such children. It is reasonable to say, however, that there are many people who are providing such "therapy" who have no formal training recognized by any formal discipline. Accordingly, many of these people are charlatans, and/or psychopaths, and/or incompetents. And even in the traditional professions in which the training of therapists is in some way monitored, there is still a significant percentage of people in the charlaton/psychopath/incompetent category. Treatment of sexually abused children is very much a growth industry in these times of sex-abuse hysteria (Gardner, 1991a). Under these circumstances there *appears* to be a burgeoning need for such therapists, which predictably will result in the appearance of individuals who will be happy to provide such services. It is almost as if they sprout out of the ground, stream out from hidden places, or just somehow spring into existence—ready and willing to treat the ever-growing mass of sexually abused children that we are led to believe are in dire need of such services.

Like all fields, child sex abuse has its share of individuals who enter for psychopathological purposes, and my own field of psychiatry is no exception to this phenomenon. When I was in medical school, in the early 1950s, the general consensus was that the craziest people went into psychiatry. Unfortunately, this was often a valid observation. I remember in college making the observation that some of the paranoid types gravitated toward law. And this, too, was a valid observation. Now to the field of child sex abuse. There are women who were sexually abused themselves who gravitate toward this field. For some of these women the choice may be a healthy one, and their child patients may enjoy enormous benefit from the personal experiences of these women. They have "been there" themselves, and they know what it's all about. They may be able to bring to these children a degree of sympathy, empathy, and sensitivity not possessed by others who have not been subjected to such experiences. There are other sexually abused women, however, who have not resolved the problems that derived from their experiences, especially problems related to ongoing resentment toward men. They are attracted to the field because it allows them to gratify vicariously their ongoing pent-up hostilities toward men. They ever wave the banner that "children never lie" and, when serving as evaluators (or "validators"), no man is innocent. When serving as "therapists," the therapy is focused on a continual campaign of denigration of the child's father—both symbolically and actually.

The feminist movement, as well, includes a wide variety of women on a continuum from the healthiest and most reasonable to the most fanatic. Some of those in the fanatic group also gravitate toward the child-sex-abuse field because it provides them with the wonderful opportunity to vent rage on all men. What better way to wreak vengeance on men than to be party to a process that can incarcerate them almost instantaneously after extracting a few choice words from a child, with the assistance of anatomically correct dolls and leading questions. What better way to wreak vengeance on men than to systematically program a child – over weeks, months, and even years – to believe that the father is a despicable individual and deserves the most vile and sadistic treatment.

Therapists who assume that a sexual encounter between an adult and a child will necessarily cause the child to suffer with severe psychiatric disturbances are going to be compromised in the treatment of these children. The therapist must appreciate that there are many children who have had such encounters who do *not* suffer untoward reactions. We adults, in our society, would consider them to have been abused. However, as mentioned previously (especially Chapter One), there have been and still are many societies in which such encounters are not viewed as heinous crimes or terrible sins and the children who involve themselves with adults in this way do not suffer psychiatric disturbances. Therapists who do not accept this possibility are going to produce in their patients psychiatric disturbances that would not have otherwise arisen.

Many sexually abused children exhibit high levels of sexual excitation. They have been brought prematurely into adult levels of sexual arousal that may continue even after the cessation of the sexual stimulation. (My experience has been that sometimes such excitation dies down and sometimes it does not.) Because of such children's cognitive immaturity, impulsivity, and lack of good judgment, they may make sexual overtures to the therapist in a variety of ways. The child may attempt to rub his (her) genitals against the therapist or try to touch or fondle the therapist in a sexual manner. Therapists who become unduly upset or even sexually excited by such overtures may be compromised in their treatment of these children. I will discuss below the therapeutic recommendation of masturbation in reducing the excitation of sexually abused children. The therapist who has the conviction for such a recommendation may thereby protect himself (herself) from uncomfortable reactions attendant to such overtures.

To the best of my knowledge, all 50 states now have laws requiring the reporting of child sex abuse. It is not my purpose here to discuss the pros and cons of such laws. I will focus here on the effects of such reporting on the therapeutic process. Such reporting, however justified, will inevitably compromise the child's therapy. Competent child therapists recognize the importance of the therapist doing everything possible to have a good relationship with both of the child's parents, regardless of their marital status, and regardless of the kinds of behavior (sometimes alienating) they may manifest. If the child is caught in the middle of a tug of war between the therapist and a parent, the parent is likely to win and the therapist is likely to lose. But the tug of war in itself compromises the treatment. A parent who harbors formidable hostility toward the therapist is likely to compromise significantly the child's treatment. And "blowing the whistle" on an abusing parent to outside authorities (such as a child protection service and/or the police), authorities who might very well place that parent in jail, is likely to engender enormous rage in that parent. Accordingly, individuals who have been the initial reporters of the abuse to outside authorities should not be the ones who embark upon the treatment. I cannot emphasize this point strongly enough. If, after the reporting has been made by someone else, the evaluator becomes the therapist, then there need be no problems regarding the alienating of a parent by such reporting. But things are not that simple. If the accuser, the accused, and the child all agree that the abuse took place, then the evaluator can indeed serve as therapist. If, however, the accused denies that the abuse took place, and the evaluator is convinced that it did, then the therapy will be compromised by the accused's position. The accused will view the therapist as someone who is trying to extract the truth from him, and this cannot but compromise his relationship with the therapist and, by extension, the therapist's relationship with the child.

THE CLINICAL PICTURE OF THE SEXUALLY ABUSED CHILD

Introduction

First, I wish to emphasize that there is no *typical* clinical picture of the sexually abused child. There are many children who have sexual encounters with adults who do not suffer at all any untoward reactions. Children who have not been traumatized are not going to reveal symptoms and so may not warrant any treatment at all.

But even those children who have experienced sexual encounters with adults, and who have reacted negatively to the experience, do not present any typical clinical picture. Rather, they present with a wide variety of symptoms that do not lend themselves well to being placed under any particular rubric. Accordingly, therapists do well to appreciate this variety and try to avoid pigeonholing the child or trying to determine whether the child fits into some particular diagnostic category. The therapist does well to view the symptomatic reactions to lie along a continuum from no symptoms at all to chronic psychosis, and all points in between.

The So-Called Child Sex-Abuse Syndrome

On a number of occasions, especially in legal documents associated with court cases in which sex abuse is alleged, one comes across the term *the child sex-abuse syndrome.* The implication here is that there is indeed a particular syndrome that is diagnostic of children who are sexually abused. Typically, the syndrome includes nightmares, bedwetting, mood changes, fears, withdrawal, depression, and a long list of other behavioral manifestations (both normal and abnormal) to the point where practically every disorder found in *DSM-III-R* would be included. As mentioned, there is no such syndrome and the quest for such is futile. From the legal point of view, an attempt is being made to verify the abuse by the invocation of this mythical syndrome. It is basically the attempt to enhance the examiner's credibility by using the "scientific" nomenclature of medicine. Although there is no such syndrome to be found in any authoritative medical or psychiatric text, examiners who use this term hope to gain greater credibility in the courtroom. From the evaluator's point of view it may be used to verify that the child was indeed abused. And from the therapist's point of view, its existence may be considered a justification for embarking on treatment. I often like to use the analogy here to the "battered woman syndrome." There is no such entity as a battered woman syndrome. There is a wide variety of reactions that women have to such maltreatment, so wide a variety that the reactions do not lend themselves to such categorization. It is no surprise, then, that *DSM-III-R* has no category even closely related to the so-called sex abuse syndrome or battered woman syndrome.

The Sexual Abuse Accommodation Syndrome

Elsewhere (especially Chapter Six) I have discussed Summit's (1983) "sexual abuse accommodation syndrome," especially with regard to its use by "validators" as a diagnostic instrument. As mentioned, it was designed to describe phenomenologically the sequence of reactions some children have after they have been sexually abused. In addition to its misapplication as a diagnostic instrument, it even has drawbacks as a description of children's reactions to bona fide sexual abuse. At the time when Summit published his article, it was indeed the case that mothers and child protection services were likely to be disbelieving, and such disbelief played a role in producing the symptomatic sequence Summit describes. Such incredulity is no longer common. In fact, just the opposite is true, namely, people are too willing to accept as valid the most preposterous and frivolous sex-abuse allegations. Without the disbelief contribution, the symptomatic series described by Summit is less likely to occur. Furthermore, the series of reactions that Summit describes is applicable to children who are abused in the intrafamilial situation, especially by fathers and stepfathers. So "trapped," they are more likely to exhibit the kinds of symptomatic accommodations that result from their

entrapment. Accordingly, the reaction pattern is less likely to be
seen in nursery schools, day-care centers, and situations in which
the abuse is perpetrated by a stranger. Moreover, Summit's
patients were generally school-aged children. Many sex-abuse
accusations today are made by younger children, especially in
nursery schools and day-care centers. It may very well be that,
even in Summit's time, the reactions of these younger children
might have been different. Accordingly, we see yet another
reason why Summit's symptoms are not applicable to a sex-abuse
evaluation. In short, evaluators of sexually abused children, even
children who were abused in the intrafamilial situation, are not as
likely to find the same symptoms Summit saw a decade ago.

Some of the Symptoms *Sometimes* Seen in Sexually Abused Children

The reader will note that I have emphasized the words *some*
and *sometimes* in the above heading in order to emphasize the
point that the symptoms described below are not universally
seen, nor are they *typical* of children who are sexually abused.
They are common, however, in children who have been traumatized by repeated sexual abuse. This is especially the case if the
child has been programmed to believe that a heinous crime has
been perpetrated. Under these circumstances, the child may
exhibit symptoms related to the natural desensitization process
that takes place following a trauma.

Natural Desensitization This desensitization process involves repetition of the trauma, both verbally and emotionally.
The individual is preoccupied with thoughts and feelings about
the trauma, so much so that it may become an obsession. Every
opportunity is taken to talk about the experience(s). And even in
one's dreams they may be replayed. The purpose here is primarily desensitization. It is as if each time the person relives the
experience it becomes a little more bearable. One can say that this
phenomenon is an excellent example of nature's treatment process: behavior modification.

Post-Traumatic Stress Disorder (PTSD) (*DSM-III-R* **309.89)**
As mentioned, there is no category in *DSM-III-R* that specifically delineates the symptomatic reactions a child will have to sexual abuse. The category that is most often used for such children is the PTSD. These are a series of reactions that individuals may manifest following exposure to an unusual trauma, and sex abuse is one such trauma. I present here the main criteria that are pertinent to the sexually abused child. I will comment on each criterion, especially with regard to its application and misapplication.

(1) Recurrent recollections of the trauma, both verbally and in play. The play recollections may be represented symbolically because of the child's guilt and/or embarrassment over direct revelation. The recollections may not be verbalized if the child has been threatened with dire consequences if a disclosure is made.

(2) Recurrent dreams of the sexual events. All children dream and all children have nightmares. It is important to differentiate between the predictable and inevitable nightmares that all children have and nightmares that are particularly related to sex abuse. A common error made by overzealous evaluators is to assume that all nightmares are manifestations of sex abuse. This may lead to a faulty conclusion of sex abuse and even incarceration of innocent individuals. For a dream or nightmare to be considered a manifestation of the PTSD, it must have very specific symbols that are definitely recognizable as related to sexual encounters. This is no place for analytic speculations and projections by the evaluator.

(3) Reliving of the experience. This manifestation is related to #1. There is not only recollections and emotional reactions, but actual hallucinatory experiences in which the individual actually believes that the events are taking place. My experience has been that this is a very rare phenomenon in sexual abuse, although one may see it commonly after combat traumas and severe traumas such as earthquakes, hurricanes, and fires.

(4) Intense psychological distress associated with exposure to events that symbolize or resemble the trauma. The child may generalize from the accused and become fearful of all men. Or the child may become unduly anxious when entering bedrooms, the bedroom having been the site of the sexual abuse.

(5) Withdrawal to avoid thoughts, feelings, or activities that remind the child of the trauma. Sexually abused children may

withdraw in general in order to protect themselves from exposures that remind them of their sexual encounters. Accordingly, a sexually abused girl may not only be fearful of all men, but may withdraw and isolate herself in order to protect herself from any encounters with them.

(6) Manifestations of a high tension level. The tensions and anxieties attendant to the abuse may result in other symptoms that are derivatives of high tension level. These include irritability, difficulty concentrating, and sleeplessness. The sleeplessness may also relate to a fear of going into the bedroom lest the sexual encounter be repeated.

(7) Hypervigilance and exaggerated startle response. Continually concerned with a repetition of the abuse, the child may become hypervigilant and may react with an exaggerated startle response to minor discomforting stimuli.

The PTSD has become the "rubber-stamp" diagnosis for children who have been alleged to have been sexually abused. One reason for this is that it is the only diagnosis in *DSM-III-R* that can be used for "validation." Stating that the child exhibits symptoms of the PTSD lends a note of scientific credibility to the conclusion that the child under consideration was indeed sexually molested. The diagnosis, then, is similar in this regard to Summit's sexual abuse accommodation syndrome. Accordingly, the PTSD has become a favorite diagnosis for zealous evaluators, who will utilize every possible maneuver to justify their preconceived conclusion that the child was sexually abused. In many such cases I myself saw few if any symptoms of the PTSD. What was clear was that the examiner exaggerated occasional and fleeting thoughts and feelings to a level warranting this diagnosis. In some cases I was convinced that the evaluator was fabricating and even deluding himself (herself), so great was the need to fit the child's symptoms into the procrustean bed of the PTSD.

Symptoms Unrelated to the Post-Traumatic Stress Disorder

In Chapter Three, in my discussion of the indicators of child sexual abuse, I have presented a series of other symptoms that one may see in children who have been sexually abused. It is unfortunate that many evaluators ignore these because of their rigid and reflexive gravitation toward the PTSD. Their need to provide the PTSD diagnosis, which they believe adds credibility to the conclusion that the child was sexually abused, lessens the likelihood that they will utilize the criteria that are more likely to differentiate between true and false sex abuse. In Chapter Three I have delineated these in great detail. My descriptions of the differentiating criteria include symptoms that may be seen in sexually abused children, symptoms that are not to be found under the PTSD rubric. In addition, in this chapter I will describe the treatment of some of the more common symptoms of sexually abused children, e.g., guilt, loss of trust, anger, depression, and school difficulties.

PRELIMINARY CONSIDERATIONS REGARDING THE TREATMENT OF SEXUALLY ABUSED CHILDREN

The Child May Not Need Treatment

It is *extremely* important for therapists to appreciate that the child who has been genuinely abused may *not* need psychotherapeutic intervention. This statement may come as a surprise to many, but I believe that this option has not been given the attention it deserves. First, for some children there has been no actual trauma; there are no symptoms; and so treatment is not necessary. For others, there may have been trauma, but this doesn't mean that psychotherapeutic intervention is necessary. I have mentioned already that the PTSD is nature's natural form of systematic desensitization. In fact, the PTSD is the only disorder listed in *DSM-III-R* in which the symptoms are part of the curative process. Each time the child relives the trauma, he (she) becomes a little better accommodated to it. All of us have had the experience of being traumatized, and all of us have had the experience of dealing with it by a mild form of PTSD. A good example would be involvement in an automobile accident. Immediately following the experience, one becomes preoccupied with the event, talks incessantly about it to friends and relatives, and may even dream about the experience during the following days and even weeks. However, for most people, over time, the preoccupations diminish—often to a point where they may be entirely forgotten. A similar process occurs when we mourn after the death of a loved one. We must have the greatest respect for nature's desensitization process and not artificially prolong it by the kind of "muckraking" that may take place in the psychotherapeutic situation. We want to facilitate the desensitization process, not artificially prolong it.

On the one hand, we certainly want early evaluation and intervention—if warranted. On the other hand, we don't want to make the person worse. What should we do then? How do we know whether intervention is necessary? I find quite useful in this regard an inquiry into *other* areas of the child's functioning—areas not directly related to sexual abuse—in order to ascertain whether the child is exhibiting symptoms unrelated to the sexual abuse. Accordingly, I inquire into school functioning, relationships with peers, and home functioning. I try to determine whether other *DSM-III-R* diagnoses might be applicable. I try to determine whether any of the symptomatic manifestations to be found in the list of indicators presented in Chapter Three are present. If none of these additional symptoms is present, then I am less likely to provide treatment. In short, if there are no symptoms that I consider to be derived from the sex abuse, and there are no other symptoms unrelated to sex abuse, then I will not treat. I make the assumption that the sex abuse was not traumatic or, if it was, the child has dealt with the trauma by a natural desensitization process. In short, if there are no symptoms, I will not treat because I have no symptoms to serve as targets for my treatment. This refusal to treat does not preclude, however, providing advice, recommendations, and periodic follow-ups.

Psychotherapeutic Work With the *Whole* Family

I believe that the optimum therapeutic approach is the one in which *one* therapist works with the whole family: the mother, the father, and the sexually abused child. This statement, I suspect, will surprise and even startle some readers. The notion of the same therapist working with a child and the "despicable pervert" who perpetrated this heinous crime on this innocent child victim is unthinkable to some therapists. As I will emphasize below, therapists do well to be very cautious about bringing about a situation in which they promulgate alienation of a child from a parent, even the parent who has sexually abused the child. Of the more than five billion people on earth, the child has only two biological parents and that is all that nature (or God) is going to assign that child. If a parent wishes healthy involvement with a child, sex abuse history notwithstanding, that parent should at least be given the opportunity—when safe—to effect such a relationship. The best way to accomplish this goal is for the same therapist to be involved with all three parties, both individually and in joint interview.

Courts commonly assign each of the parties his (her) own separate therapist. Ostensibly, this "covers the ground" and everyone is being taken care of. The judge has discharged his (her) duty in what is seemingly an effective and thorough manner. Little consideration is given to the inevitable divisiveness of such a therapeutic approach. I am not referring here simply to the divisive effect of this approach on intact families (sex abuse notwithstanding); I hold the same position for separating and divorced families. Even though separated or divorced, both parents are still parents and both should be involved in the child's life, and treatment is one segment of the child's life.

Meaningful Protection from Further Sexual Abuse

No matter how skilled the therapist, and no matter how knowledgeable, treatment is going to be seriously compromised if the child is not first protected from further abuse. No matter how productive the sessions, if the child returns to an environment in which there is an ongoing danger of repetition of the abuse, the therapist's attempts are likely to prove futile. Accordingly, the therapist must make an attempt to assess the degree of danger and assist in the implementation of whatever measures may be necessary to provide the child with protection. In some cases this is not possible while the offender and the child are living in the same home. My experience has been that courts and child protection services tend to be overzealous and overcautious with regard to removing people from homes when there has been an allegation of sex abuse. Commonly, either the father or the child is precipitously removed from the home, often with only minimal evidence that sexual abuse has taken place. Often little consideration is given to the devastating effects of these maneuvers on family stability. These individuals (who wield great power) often work on the principle: "If there is any risk of sexual abuse, no matter how small, no matter how remote, we must zealously protect the child from the perpetrator, and the breakup of the family unit is a small price to pay when one compares the detrimental effects of such disruption with the devastating effects of further abuse." And this position is often taken even when the evidence is minuscule. It is taken in order to "be on the safe side."

Competent evaluators make some attempt to assess the degree of danger, especially with regard to the likelihood of recurrence. Many pedophiles are indeed compulsive, and separation from the child is a reasonable measure to take. Other perpetrators, however, are not that compelled to act out on their impulses, especially after their behavior has been brought to the attention of child protection services and legal and judicial authorities. Sometimes the therapy will be possible under circumstances in which all three are still living together. In other situations, it may be necessary for the perpetrator to leave the home, with the child visiting with him under reasonable surveillance. I believe it is preferable that such visits take place in a home situation rather than in the more sterile environment of a community facility, the visits taking place under the surveillance of community personnel such as social workers and probation workers.

In situations in which the offender is so compulsive, punitive, and abusive that permanent removal is warranted, the child does well to form a relationship with a father surrogate. Under such circumstances the therapist might try to encourage deeper involvement with male relatives such as uncles and grandfathers.

Group Therapeutic Experiences

Group therapy can also be useful as an adjunct to the individual and family therapeutic programs. This is especially useful for children ages 10 and above. (My experiences have not been good with group therapy with younger children. They are much too rambunctious and there is much too much horseplay.) Many sexually abused children consider themselves to be unique with regard to their experience. This contributes to feelings of self-loathing. Having the experience that there are other children who have been similarly abused generally helps them to feel less loathsome. Although I generally prefer heterogeneous groups over homogeneous groups (Gardner, 1988b), this is probably one situation in which homogeneous groups are indicated. Group therapy can also help sexually abused children work through other problems.

There is an organization, *Parents United International*, that helps families who have suffered child sex abuse. Help is provided for both the victims and the parents. The ultimate goal is to rebuild a better-functioning family. However, help is provided for families in which this goal may not be possible because of the strength of the abuser's need to sexually abuse the children. The individuals who do the counseling are often people who themselves come from families in which sex abuse has been a problem. Older members help newer members work through some of their common problems. The children come in contact with other children who have been abused and this helps them feel less loathsome about their experiences. Furthermore, the children also have the opportunity to form relationships with father surrogates, ideal in situations where it is necessary to remove a parent permanently from a home.

The Effects of Litigation On the
Child's Treatment

At the outset, the therapist should do everything possible to discourage continuation of litigation. The likelihood that the therapy will be successful—while litigation still continues—is very small. When the litigation involves a child custody dispute, it will inevitably contribute to the development, prolongation, and/or intensification of the child's psychopathology. Therapists who believe that their efforts can successfully counterbalance the negative effects of such litigation are being unrealistic and even grandiose. The litigation also has the effect of "muckraking," bringing up the old material, and thereby working against the evolution of the natural desensitization process. Litigation may add additional traumas in association with the child's being interviewed by psychologists, psychiatrists, lawyers, and judges. In many cases it involves the child's giving direct testimony in the courtroom (and this is especially true of older children), and this too can be psychologically traumatic. If the accused is on trial for the sex abuse, and a decision is going to be made regarding the penalty, this will also have profound effects upon the treatment. The tensions and anxieties associated with such trials are enormous, and these inevitably filter down to the child. The guilt that such a trial engenders in the accusing child is generally enormous, and the fear of retaliation and/or retribution by the abuser may be formidable. Although therapists are often quite impotent regarding their ability to affect the speed (or more accurately, slowness) with which these proceedings progress (or more accurately, creep), they should still make every attempt (through the parents, lawyers, and courts) to emphasize the importance of rapid decisions and resolutions.

TECHNICAL ASPECTS OF THE TREATMENT OF
SEXUALLY ABUSED CHILDREN

Introduction

In this section, I focus on psychotherapeutic approaches to some of the more common symptoms exhibited by sexually abused children. I will not elaborate in detail on the specific technical maneuvers I utilize; rather, I will present general principles and approaches that should prove useful in the alleviation of selected common symptoms. I will, however, at the end of this chapter, provide some illustrative clinical examples that will enable the reader to learn exactly how I implement my methods. The reader who is interested in further details about my specific techniques may wish to refer to my full-length text on this subject (Gardner, 1992b).

The Home Videocassette Recorder

Elsewhere (Gardner, 1992b) I describe the utilization of the home videocassette recorder in child psychotherapy. The instrument can be an extremely valuable therapeutic adjunct. It can be particularly useful in the treatment of the sexually abused child because of its capacity to provide reiteration of psychotherapeutic messages. The sexually abused child needs desensitization and, as mentioned, one of the ways such children provide themselves with such desensitization is by repeatedly thinking about their trauma. Because of this benefit, some children who have been sexually abused will repeatedly request to view the videotape. Of course, other benefits are being derived simultaneously, e.g., an opportunity to hear once again my therapeutic messages that recommend specific coping mechanisms and protective maneuvers. Furthermore, the reexposure has the effect of reentrenching the relationship with the therapist and this, of course, is crucial if the child is to have a meaningful psychotherapeutic experience.

Desensitization Play

I have already mentioned desensitization as an important factor in the self-curative process following trauma. Children are likely to incorporate the desensitization process into their play. The symbols and other metaphors thereby created allow the desensitization process to proceed in a manner that lessens guilt and anxiety, because the child does not recognize consciously that the play is actually portraying his (her) own experiences. This process should be respected and the therapist does well *not* to try to bring into conscious awareness the material so produced. Therapists with a strong commitment to the psychoanalytic concept—people who believe in a strict application of Freud's dictum: "Where there is unconscious, there shall conscious be"— are likely to try to help the child gain conscious insight into the underlying meaning of these symbols. Although a psychoanalyst myself, I believe that there are situations in which such an approach can produce unnecessary guilt and anxiety and compromise, thereby, the psychotherapeutic process. And this is one of the situations in which such an approach is likely to bring about this untoward and unnecessary result.

However, it is not the purpose of therapy simply to catalyze and facilitate the expression of such desensitization material. Rather, the therapist should be listening carefully to its content and be trying to use the material so produced as a point of departure for responding therapeutic interchanges. These may be provided at the symbolic level (for younger children this is preferable) or by direct discussion (for those children who are less needful of the symbolic disguise). Commonly, sexually abused children will introduce themes in which they are fleeing the perpetrator. The perpetrator may not be consciously recognized as such or symbolized as some fearsome creature who, by the nature of his acts, is a clear representation of the abuser. Following such scenarios, the therapist does well to introduce alternative coping mechanisms such as vigilance, call for help, avoiding situations in which the abuse might recur, and reassurance that the abuser will not be in a situation that will allow him to repeat the abuse. The therapist does well to substitute appropriate and reasonable adaptive mechanisms for inappropriate ones (such as being protected by a superhero). The child (especially boys) may introduce unreasonable macho-type fighting mechanisms as an attempt to cope (such as throwing the perpetrator out the window), and these too must be substituted (preferably symbolically) with more reasonable modes of adaptation.

PSYCHOTHERAPEUTIC APPROACHES TO SOME OF THE COMMON SYMPTOMS OF SEXUALLY ABUSED CHILDREN

Hypersexualization

Some children who have been sexually abused are prematurely brought up to adult levels of sexual excitation. Even when the abuse discontinues, they may continue to have strong sexual urges, urges far stronger than other children their age. Obviously, I am talking here about the children whose sexual activities involved physical gratifications, especially to the point of orgasm. I am not talking here about those children whose sexual encounters have been primarily, if not exclusively, painful. Parents can be advised that the level of high sexual excitation may very well reduce by itself as time passes; however, they should also be informed that for some children this may not be the case. I generally advise parents of hypersexualized children to try to distract them into involvement in other areas such as games, sports, and schoolwork. However, as adults well know, these sublimatory activities have their limits and may not be completely successful in channeling off the sexual urges.

Many of the children in this category are obsessed with desires to engage in sex play with peers. I generally advise parents to respond to these requests along these lines: "I know what you want to do, and what you want to do is not bad. It's not wrong. It's not a sin. It's not a crime. It's not something they'll put you in jail for. However, it's not allowed. You'll get into a lot of trouble if you do that. Janey's (Billy's) mother and father will get very upset if you do that. When you're older, and you have a girlfriend (boyfriend) and you love one another very much, and if the two of you want to do things like that together, that's your private business and most people think it's okay. Now why don't we just play a game, take a walk, etc...."

One problem with the aforementioned approach is that the child may respond with questions such as "*Why* can't I play those games with Janey (Billy)?" and "Why do their parents get angry about those games?" The best answer I have for these questions (and I am not claiming that it is a perfect one) is that in our Western society such practices are considered improper and even sinful. Some societies are neutral to these practices among children, and there are even societies that encourage such activity among children. Many books and doctoral theses have been written to explain the reasons for these cultural differences. And all the answers, I am certain, are not yet in. Such discussions may enable adults to spend some very interesting hours, but they are beyond the comprehension of the children I am talking about here. Accordingly, the best answer is "It's not allowed." However, parents who feel the need might add, "When you're older you'll be able to understand better why it's not allowed." The parent who feels the need to give the child the *real* reasons is not likely to be successful in imparting this information because it is generally far beyond the level of comprehension of younger children.

When these more conservative measures do not work, I will then discuss with the parent the question of encouraging the child to masturbate. Some parents are quite receptive to this consideration and others "flip out." Few are neutral on the subject. For those who are unreceptive, I try to emphasize the value of this practice as an important contribution to civilized society. Because of masturbation, no one needs to tolerate ongoing sexual frustration and no one needs to get involved in the enormous amount of trouble that individuals can bring upon themselves with unsatisfied sexual cravings. For the parent who is receptive to considering this valuable psychotherapeutic outlet, I recommend comments along these lines: "I'm just not going to let you go around touching people's private parts. That's not permitted. If you still feel that you want to do those things, I suggest you go into the bedroom or bathroom, or some other private place, and rub or touch yourself. You can touch your *own* private parts. If you do that for a while you may get rid of those strong feelings. That's a perfectly fine thing to do, but it's private. It's not the kind of thing people do in public." Again, for the precocious child who might ask, "*Why* is it not proper to do these things in public places," I have the same answers provided above for why Billy and Janey can't fondle each other's genitals. Unless the children who ask these questions are going to move to one of those places that anthropologists have written libraries about, the child is going to have to resign himself (herself) to the constraints and inhibitions of Western civilization.

One could argue that encouraging masturbation is tantamount to encouraging an activity that may predictably contribute to the perpetuation of the high level of sexual excitation. One could argue that the prepubertal child does better to go back to a low level of sexual excitation and can wait until puberty to deal with the masturbatory outlet at that time. I am in full agreement that this would probably be the preferable course and that the recommendation may very well contribute to a maintenance of the high level. However, the reader should note that I introduce this option only *after* others (the more conservative ones) prove futile. The negative effects on the child of walking around in a constant state of "horniness"—especially excitation that is not permitted release and gratification—are worse, i believe, than the negative effects of the maintenance of the higher level of sexual excitation, excitation that may result from masturbation. Like most problems and dilemmas in life, things cannot simply be reduced to one good solution and one bad solution. Rather, like most things in life, there are many good solutions and many bad solutions. Here we have to choose which is the less detrimental of two bad solutions.

Regression

Children who have been sexually abused often exhibit regressive symptoms. These include thumbsucking, bedwetting, soiling, baby talk, desire to suck a bottle, enjoyment of the fetal position, excessive demand for cuddling, etc. Sometimes these regressive symptoms reflect a failure to progress along the developmental track. Sometimes they reflect a regression from higher levels of functioning. In either case, they represent an attempt to remain fixated at lower levels of psychological functioning as a form of protection from traumas associated with more advanced levels. Obviously, it is unlikely that the child is going to progress along the developmental track as long as there is a danger of the repetition of the abuse—thus the importance of this danger being removed or a low-risk danger reassuringly clarified at the outset of the treatment.

Children who are progressing along the developmental track in the course of their treatment may periodically still exhibit the desire to regress to the earlier levels. Parents should be encouraged to allow such regressive indulgence for short periods but, at the same time, firmly advise the child that such indulgence will be short-lived. To indulge it on an ongoing basis is to contribute to its perpetuation. And the therapist, as well, may choose to provide such indulgences—on occasion, and for short periods—in the course of the treatment. Children who are significantly deprived (emotionally and physically) prior to the trauma may have a greater need for such regressive gratifications. Those children who have been subjected to coercion and domination in a family in which all members have been dominated by an overbearing father may also have an inordinate need for regressive satisfactions. An example of such extra indulgence—for those children who therapeutically warrant this—would be allowing the child to sit on the therapist's lap while rocking him (her), allowing occasional use of a pacifier or thumbsucking, and providing more than the usual and age-appropriate level of cuddling.

Guilt

The word *guilt* is used in many ways, so much so that it may cause confusion. When a judge declares that the accused person is guilty of having committed a crime, he (she) is talking about an entirely different phenomenon than the guilt a psychiatrist refers to when he (she) states that the patient feels guilty. In the former situation, the word *guilt* is being used to refer to the court's conclusion that the individual has indeed perpetrated an illegal act. In the latter case the word refers to an inner feeling of lower self-worth associated with certain thoughts, feelings, and actions.

But even the psychiatrist's use of the word is not that clear-cut and there are many different forms of guilt, each of which requires its own definition. (Below, I will provide specific examples of these different types of psychological guilt.) It probably would have been better if our language developed in such a direction that different words were used for these disparate phenomena. This is the general definition of guilt that I use when referring to psychological processes: *Guilt is the feeling of low self-worth that an individual experiences after entertaining thoughts, experiencing feelings, or committing acts that the person has been taught are wrong or bad by significant figures in early childhood.* In addition (and this is not an intrinsic part of the definition), there is a high likelihood of some anticipation of punishment or rejection if others learn about the unacceptable thoughts, feelings, or behavior.

At this point I discuss the different forms of psychological guilt, with particular focus on their role in symptom formation and treatment of sexually abused children.

Guilt About the Effects of the Divulgence on the Offender
Many children have been warned and even threatened that divulgence of the sexual activities will have dire consequences for the child and/or the perpetrator and other family members, and when the child divulges the abuse, these predictions are likely to prove valid. Whereas originally the consequences were purely theoretical, and possibly not even appreciated by the child, now they become a reality. And the reality may be that the home is descended upon by police, detectives, prosecutors, and a parade of people from child protection services. This may be followed by a courtroom trial and even incarceration of the perpetrator. These events cannot but produce enormous guilt in the child. The abuser may then make comments to the child along these lines: "You see, you didn't keep our 'secret.' You told everyone what's happened, and now look at the terrible things they're doing to me." And this may only serve to increase even further the child's guilt. The perpetrator is essentially saying that the child is a terrible person for having disclosed what was going on. And such a message directs itself to the core of the child's guilt mechanism.

Therapists do well to impress upon such children that they have been the innocent victims of the perpetrator's behavior, that the fault lies within the offender, and that it was the abuser who committed the crime—not the child. This approach is most likely to be successful when the child has not been the initiator (the usual case). There are, however, children who do initiate the sexual encounter with an adult. Sometimes this is part of normal childhood curiosity and the lack of appreciation that certain parts of other people's bodies are private and not to be touched or investigated. Sometimes a child has been brought to higher levels of sexual excitation by a third party (child or adult) and then carries over the sexual excitation to the party who then becomes the offender. In either case, the therapist does well to try to impress upon the child that even here it was basically not his (her) fault. Rather, attempts should be made to get across the message that when adults are so approached, it behooves *them* to refuse to involve themselves in such activities. One also does well to communicate to the child that the court will not consider the child's initiation to be a reason for the adult's exoneration.

Guilt About Participation in the Sexual Act   At first, the child may not have realized that the sexual behavior is considered bad or wrong in our society. When children come to appreciate how reprehensible adult-child sexual acts are considered in our society, they may blame themselves for having engaged in the sinful and/or criminal act(s). And this will especially be the case if the child has enjoyed the activities. There is a whole continuum that must be considered here: from those children who were coerced and who gained no pleasure (and might even be considered to have been raped) to those who enjoyed immensely (with orgastic response) the sexual activities. The former children are less likely to feel this type of guilt; the latter are much more likely to experience such guilt. Children who enjoyed the sexual activities must be helped to appreciate that it was the abuser who committed the antisocial act(s).

The child may feel guilt over the *pleasure* enjoyed in the experience. If the child comes from a very religious family, a family in which pleasurable activities are somehow considered sinful, then this form of guilt is likely to be present. The examiner must try to get across the message that sex can be an enormously pleasurable activity and there is nothing intrinsically wrong with a person who enjoys it. However, there are the *wrong times* and the *wrong places* to enjoy sex with another person, and there are the *wrong people* with whom one can gain the pleasures of these gratifications. In our society, we generally consider it wrong for children to have sexual activities with adults, but we do not consider it wrong for children to have sexual pleasures by stimulating themselves. Obviously, we are once again dealing here with the question of values. As mentioned, rather than get into the philosophical, psychological, and anthropological factors operative here, I think one does well to basically subscribe to Western society's Judeo-Christian ethic regarding these matters.

Older children may be helped to appreciate that sexual encounters between an adult and a child are not universally considered to be reprehensible acts. The child might be told about other societies in which such behavior was and is considered normal. The child might be helped to appreciate the wisdom of Shakespeare's Hamlet, who said, "Nothing's either good or bad, but thinking makes it so." In such discussions the child has to be helped to appreciate that we have in our society an exaggeratedly punitive and moralistic attitude about adult-child sexual encounters. It would be an error for the reader to conclude here that I am condoning sexual encounters between an adult and a child. I believe that it is still a form of exploitation, but not one that should be dealt with as punitively as it is in our society. For example, in most states the punishment for a first-offense murder is less than a first-offense sexual abuse.

Guilt as a Component of the Self-Denigration Aspect of Depression   One psychodynamic factor operative in some forms of depression is repressed rage. The depressed feelings are derivatives of the bottled-up anger that the individual feels too inhibited to express. Sometimes the individual can express such rage, but not direct it toward those who are the sources of the anger. Rather, the person may fear that such expression will result in terrible consequences to himself (herself). Accordingly, the anger may be redirected toward the depressed individual himself (herself). This "retroflexed" rage may manifest itself in self-derogatory comments, e.g., "What a stupid idiot I am" and "What a loathsome, vile worm I am." For sexually abused children the anger may result from the feelings of being exploited and betrayed. Or it may result from the punishments inflicted upon the child for the divulgence.

This form of guilt is treated by helping the child become more comfortable with the expression of anger. One must help the child appreciate that such anger is inevitable and that the guilty feelings are inappropriate. However, one does not want to encourage wanton and unbridled expression of anger. One wants to channel it constructively and encourage its expression in humane and civilized ways.

Guilt About Having Been Selected or Preferred Over Siblings In some families, one child is selected for sexual encounters. In others one or more of the siblings may be involved as well. There are situations in which each of the children is led to believe that he (she) is someone special and is the only one to have been selected for such encounters and gratifications. This communicates to the child that he (she) is superior to the others and deserves special attention. At the same time, it communicates the message that attention is being withdrawn from siblings. The sense of exclusivity may produce fear of jealous reprisals by the nonfavored siblings. The anticipated rejections and sense of alienation may produce feelings of self-loathing. The guilt here, derived from this feeling of self-worth, is associated with the belief that one has engaged in reprehensible activities, activities that will bring about the scorn of significant others (in this case the child's siblings). Such a child is essentially saying to himself (herself), "What a terrible person I am for having engaged in these behaviors for which they are all criticizing me." The therapist does well to impress upon such children the notion that it was not their fault for having been so selected. The child may have been selected because he (she) is the oldest, or the only girl, the only boy, or some other selection criterion having nothing to do with the intrinsic worth of the youngster.

Guilt as a Mechanism for Controlling the Uncontrollable
Some children develop the delusion that the sexual encounters were their fault. And this may be seen in situations in which there was absolutely no initiation by the child (the usual case). By considering the abuse to be under the child's own control, the child can then presumably start it and stop it at his (her) will. This belief thereby puts power into the child's hands. It transforms impotency into potency. The notion "It's my fault" implies control. The mechanism is similar to that used by children whose parents are divorcing. Such a child might say, "Daddy, I know you're leaving because I was bad. I promise I'll never be bad again. I'll be good. I'll never hit my sister. I'll turn off the television when you tell me to. Then you won't have to leave." We use the term *guilt* here because of the child's use of the words, "It's my fault." However, it is a poorly selected phrase because we are basically talking here about a delusion of control over the uncontrollable. Elsewhere (Gardner, 1969, 1970) I have discussed this type of guilt in greater detail.

The therapeutic approach here is to help such children differentiate between things children can control and things they cannot. One can discuss in detail various examples of experiences in the two categories. For example, the child can be helped to name things that he (she) *can* control, such as when to watch television, when to do homework, whether or not one hits a sibling, etc. The child can be helped to then name things that he (she) cannot control, such things as thunder, lightning, where one's parents choose to live, whether or not one's parents get a divorce, etc. Being compelled or seduced into sexual activities is generally an activity over which children, especially younger ones, may have little if any control. The child should be helped to place sexual abuse in the category of activities over which one may have little if any control. This delusion may also be reduced by helping the child develop realistic coping mechanisms, which can reduce the need for fantasy control. Providing the child with reasonable "weapons" (e.g., calling out, threatening to report the abuser, and running away) lessens the need to provide delusional forms of protection, one example of which is the form of guilt being discussed here.

Concluding Comments on Guilt   Obviously, values play an important role in guilt. As mentioned, we learn from significant individuals in our society the things about which we should feel guilty and those things about which we need not feel guilty. The therapeutic approaches to the alleviation of such guilt involves an imposition of the therapist's values on the patient. But this is no different from any other kind of psychotherapeutic encounter, which, the therapist's disavowals notwithstanding, inevitably involves some attempt on the therapist's part to impose his (her) values on the patient. As I have described in detail elsewhere (Gardner, 1992b), the imposition of the therapist's values on the patient is an inevitable part of the psychotherapeutic process. Accordingly, one does well to explore guilt and value issues in depth with the child's parents and to enlist their aid and support in communicating these messages. As I am sure the reader can appreciate, this may not be easy. The father, as the offender, may be unreceptive to some of these messages. And the mother, too, may be unreceptive to some of the guilt-assuaging recommendations because of her anger toward her husband and her desire for retribution (commonly the case).

Self-Esteem Problems

Some children who have been sexually molested suffer with what is sometimes referred to as the "damaged goods syndrome." Such children feel that their genitals have been damaged, sometimes irreparably. In some cases there is reality to this belief, because there has indeed been physical damage to the genitals. However, even when there has been some physical damage, in most cases it is not permanent. Other children have not sustained any genital damage at all, but feel this way nevertheless. Such feelings, in part, relate to society's attitude toward adult-child sexual encounters. We have selected the genitals as a special part of the body and have given enormous charge to experiences centering on that particular area. These are the "private parts." These are the parts that the child learns strictly to cover very early in life. These are the areas that if touched, played with, or otherwise manipulated by certain people may result in many years of incarceration for the initiating participant. It is easy to see how such input can contribute to the child's developing a damaged-goods syndrome, and this cannot but contribute to feelings of low self-worth. The child's body image (which is an intrinsic part of self-worth) is compromised by the feeling that one of the most important parts of the body has been harmed.

Such children need reassurances that the genitals have not been permanently damaged (most often the case). If there has been some damage—e.g., from abrasions and inflammation— these are generally transient, and these children should be reassured that with proper medical care their genitals will return to the normal state. It is more difficult to help the child who has sustained permanent damage and/or scars. The child has to be helped to appreciate that only *one* part of the body has been changed, and generally this is not in a way that should interfere at all with functioning in life. These and other distortions about the implications of the damage have to be corrected in the course of the psychotherapeutic process.

Many sexually abused children feel betrayed, impotent, and helpless. And such feelings cannot but contribute to a lowered sense of self-worth. The protection from such exploitation must come from two sources: external and internal. The child must be given reassurances that external authorities (such as the therapist, the other parent, and people involved in the child protection and legal systems) will be vigilant enough to provide protection. However, such reassurances are not likely to assuage fears completely, in that 24-hour vigils are not possible and in many cases the perpetrator may still have access, even though illegally so. Such reassurances, then, must be real, practical, and reason- ably predictable. False and empty reassurances are not likely to work and will compromise the child's trust in the reassuring person. If this person is a therapist, meaningful treatment may no longer be possible, even though the two may still meet with one another. When these reassurances are real and practical, the child will feel more protected; there will be fewer feelings of impotence and helplessness; and this can compensate somewhat for the child's lowered feelings of self-worth.

In addition, the child must be helped to learn reasonable methods of self-protection. Impressing upon such children their right to say no, to scream out, to run for help, and to otherwise assert themselves can be useful. However, examiners do well to appreciate that such "empowerment" is of limited value considering the age and size differences between the adult perpetrator and child victim. Much attention is given to this aspect of such children's therapy these days; I believe that it is overrated with regard to its therapeutic efficacy. If the lessons in self-assertion are expanded to nonsexual realms as well, there is a greater likelihood that the sex-abuse protective "empowerment" lessons will be successful.

As mentioned in the section on guilt, a central element in guilt is a feeling of low self-worth. If guilt is present, then it will inevitably reduce the child's feelings of self-worth. Accordingly, it behooves examiners to ascertain exactly which type or types of guilt they are dealing with in order to address themselves properly to the lowered-self-esteem aspect of the child's guilt problem. And the examiner does well to follow the therapeutic guidelines recommended in that section.

Self-esteem is a fundamental problem for most people in treatment, and there are many factors that may contribute to a lowered sense of self-worth. Elsewhere (Gardner, 1992c) I have discussed self-esteem problems in great detail. Examiners do well to ascertain which of the many factors that can reduce self-esteem are operative in the particular child they are treating. It is only by delineating these factors that one is in a position to start alleviating them. Last, enhancement of self-esteem may be viewed as a general antidote to a wide variety of psychogenic symptoms, those associated as well as those unassociated with sex abuse.

Loss of Trust

Exploitation by the abuser causes distrust. There may not have been distrust originally, prior to the time the child learned about the significance of the sexual encounters, but there is likely to be distrust once the child reaches the point of such apprecia-tion. The child may then complain about the abuse to her (his) mother. If she, in response, refuses to believe what the child is saying or, more overtly, calls the child a liar, then there is likely to be even further distrust. If the mother then continues to permit the abuse by her denial mechanisms or failure to interfere, then a further sense of distrust is engendered. If, when confronted, the abuser then denies the abuse and calls the child a liar, further distrust is generated. And such distrust may be generalized to other individuals, especially those of the same sex as the abuser.

The development of a trusting relationship with the therapist may play a role in reducing the child's general feeling of distrust. Accordingly, male therapists are preferable if the abuser was a male, even though the child may initially be fearful of a male therapist. Any therapist—male or female—who believes that helping the child cope with sex abuse involves engendering a state of ongoing animosity toward the abuser is not going to help the child reduce distrust. Rather, it only entrenches the notions that the father is a dangerous person and that untrustworthiness is one of his many defects. Many examiners consider it an important part of the therapy of sexually abused children to encourage the expression of hostility toward the perpetrator. In most cases this is a therapeutic error. The aspect of this misguided approach that I wish to focus on here relates to the child's sense of distrust. Such an approach will inevitably increase the child's feelings of distrust, rather than reduce them. The therapist must also work with the mother and reduce any elements in her reactions to the abuse that may have engendered distrust. The father, too, must not only be open and honest about the abuse, but other issues as well. Both parents have to develop a different reputation regarding honesty and trustworthiness, and this cannot occur quickly; rather, it can only occur over a long time, a period in which the child gradually develops increasing trust. Reputations are not changed overnight; rather, they only change after multiple corrective experiences over time.

Anger Problems

The child may not be angry about the abuse prior to learning about its social implications. Afterward, however, when the child comes to appreciate the exploitation, there may be anger. If the mother and/or father denies the abuse, then there may be anger associated with the frustration engendered in the child by such denials. And such anger is even further intensified if the child is called a liar. Or, the child may be blamed for initiating the abuse and this, too, cannot but cause resentment when the child knows that he (she) was not the initiator (the situation in most cases). There are, of course, other possible sources of anger for abused children. The abuse may be only one part of a larger program of emotional and physical abuse, and such abuses inevitably cause significant anger.

The anger may be acted out directly or, more commonly, it is suppressed or repressed. Under such circumstances it may contribute to the formation of a wide variety of symptoms, e.g., psychosomatic complaints, depression, compulsions, phobias, and other forms of psychopathology. Therapists who work on the principle that the best way to treat such suppressed and repressed anger is to facilitate its release are taking an oversimplified approach to the treatment of such problems and are not likely to be successful. It is the belief of such therapists that the main purpose of treatment is to facilitate the cathartic release of pent-up hostility. They will often provide such children with punching bags, boxing gloves, large stand-up inflatable dolls that bounce back when struck, and other toys that facilitate anger release. The more the child screams, yells, rants, and curses, the greater they believe to be the therapeutic benefit. I sometimes refer to this as "diarrhea therapy." Of course, getting in touch with one's angry feelings is a good *first step*, and releasing the pent-up anger is also useful. However, what one must do is to use the anger constructively in such a way that there is a reduction or removal of the stimuli that are causing the anger to generate in the first place. And this is best done in the early phases of anger generation—when the anger has not reached uncontrollable proportions and when the anger can be focused directly on the noxious stimuli. It is then that therapeutic benefit is most likely to take place. There is little therapeutic benefit to be gained when an individual has been charged up to levels of rage and fury.

I often use the analogy here of a tea kettle on a stove. The flames represent the noxious stimuli that are generating anger, and the boiling water symbolizes the hostility being engendered by the noxious stimuli. Let us consider a person with an anger-inhibition problem who is using repressed anger to fuel the formation of a wide variety of symptoms. Such a person could be symbolized by a cork or plug being placed in the spout of the tea kettle, thereby inhibiting the release of the anger. Therapists who consider it their role merely to help the patient remove the cork are being simplistic, as the analogy clearly shows. The removal of the cork has not in any way served to extinguish the flames, the cause of the boiling rage. Rather (to carry the analogy further), therapists should not only help the patient remove the cork, but connect a rubber tube to the spout, a tube that is then directed toward the flames that are causing the water to boil. The boiling water will then be used to extinguish the flames, flames that are generating the boiling in the first place. This is true treatment, and this is the course that is most likely to prove effective.

There are some children who, rather than inhibiting expression of their anger, act it out. Such children need a strengthening and an intensification of their guilt mechanisms. One of the reasons why they act out their anger is that they do not have enough internal inhibitory mechanisms to suppress and repress it. Guilt and shame are two such mechanisms. There are some therapists who believe that it is antitherapeutic to increase a patient's guilt and/or shame. I am in disagreement. Some people need less guilt, and some people need more. In fact, I think there are more people who do not have enough guilt than there are people who have too much. Each patient has to be evaluated with regard to whether more or less is needed, and the therapeutic approach should be planned accordingly. Some children *need* to feel more ashamed of themselves, and it is the role of the therapist to engender such shame. Some people need a "guilt trip," and to deprive them of such is to contribute to the perpetuation of their psychopathology. Therapists who engage in the aforementioned type of "diarrhea therapy" are likely to perpetuate and even intensify such acting out, much to the detriment of the children and their families (even the abuser).

Last, there are some children who need guilt intensification in some areas and guilt alleviation in others. (Things are generally much more complex than they may initially appear.) Again, it behooves the therapist to tailor the therapy in such a way that guilt is encouraged or discouraged, depending upon the particular behavior.

Depression

I recognize that in recent years most psychiatrists view depression to be primarily a biological phenomenon and do not give much credibility to theories that involve psychodynamic components. Although I do not deny that depression may have a biological substrate, I believe that for most patients who are depressed, the psychological and environmental factors are paramount. I am not talking here about bipolar depression, which probably has a high genetic loading; rather, I am referring here to the wide variety of other types of depression with which psychiatrists must frequently deal. Children who are sexually abused may be depressed, and they often have much to be depressed about. They are captive, they are subjugated, and they are often maltreated in a wide variety of other ways. These are enough environmental indignities to depress anyone. To the degree that the therapist can change the environmental situation, to that degree will he (she) contribute to the alleviation of such children's depression.

Children who have been frequently abused, over time, are

likely to become depressed. If the sexual activities have been associated with terrible threats regarding disclosure, then there is an even greater likelihood that the child will become depressed — living as he (she) does in a world of constant fear of retribution. The main manifestations of depression usually include: depressive affect, listlessness, loss of appetite, loss of general enjoyment in life (especially in play), impaired school motivation and curiosity, and insomnia. There may also be a sense of hopelessness, especially in situations where the child feels helpless to do anything about the ongoing exploitation and about adults who might very well protect the child but refuse to do so, either by denial or overt refusal to interfere.

One factor that may contribute to a sexually abused child's depression is pent-up resentment that is not allowed expression. The "retroflexed rage" so engendered sometimes contributes to depression. Such self-flagellatory comments as "I hate myself" and "I'm stupid" are the hallmarks of self-deprecation and provide confirmation that the retroflexed rage element is operative in that particular child's depression.

Sometimes a depression becomes so severe that a child exhibits suicidal tendencies. This is much more likely to be the case when the abuse has occurred in the home situation and the child feels trapped. One must then assess the degree of suicidal risk, and in some cases hospitalization may be necessary. Elsewhere (Gardner, 1988b) I have discussed in detail the criteria I use to determine the depth of suicidal risk.

Obviously, the longer the child remains in the captive state, the longer the child is not protected from the exploitation, the less the likelihood of alleviating the child's depression. Accordingly, antidepressant medication is going to be of little value for such children. As long as they remain in the depression-engendering situation, they will be depressed. Antidepressants might certainly provide a little "lift" under such circumstances, and they might even play a role in reducing suicidal risk. However, at best, such medications should be viewed as adjunctive in these cases, and the primary thrust of the treatment should be to take whatever steps necessary to provide the child with a safe situation. Sometimes this can be accomplished with the child still living with the perpetrator, but this is not likely to be the case in those situations in which the abuse has reached the point where the child has become depressed. Of course, the therapist must make inquiries regarding the particular things about which the child is depressed and try to effect environmental changes that may reduce the depression. If the retroflexed-rage element is present, then one must help the child feel less guilty about the expression of anger.

Another factor that may contribute to a sexually abused child's depression is the loss of the father—if he has been removed from the home. Even when the father is an abuser, the child might still want to live in the home. The child may be locked in in a somewhat masochistic way with the abusing father, and this is a very common pattern. It sometimes comes as a surprise to people who administer shelters and residential treatment centers when children run away in order to return to homes in which they will predictably be subjected to further abuses. There are children whose abuse has not been significantly traumatic and who consider the advantages of a relationship with the father (the sexual encounters notwithstanding) to outweigh its disadvantages. Community authorities, however, reflexively break up families without giving enough attention to the arguments supporting maintenance of the family structure, the abuse notwithstanding. Accordingly, whether it is the child who is removed from the home, or the abusing father who is removed from the home, the child may feel depressed about the loss of the relationship—even though there has been abuse. Even when the family unit was unstable, it may be preferable to no family unit at all or to the surrogate family unit in which the child now finds himself (herself). Once again, to the degree that the therapist can help bring about a stable family (either the original family unit or the substitute one), to that degree will this element in the child's depression be reduced.

Fears, Tension, Anxiety, and Derivative Symptoms

Children who have been sexually abused, especially if the abuse has taken place over time, are likely to develop a multiplicity of fears, tensions, anxieties, and problems derived from such symptoms. Psychosomatic complaints would be one such derivative group of disorders. Whereas in some people fears and tensions do not have physical concomitants, in others they do. Accordingly, one might see gastrointestinal complaints (such as diarrhea and vomiting), breathing difficulties, palpitations, musculoskeletal problems, headaches, etc. Another derivative complaint would be insomnia. The child has difficulty falling asleep, not only because of the tensions associated with the abuse but, in many cases, because the child fears that the abuser will come into the bedroom and perpetrate further molestations. Ongoing tensions may contribute to the chronic state of hypervigilance and increased arousal that is one of the important manifestations of the PTSD. This results in the "frozen watchfulness" described by Goodwin (1987). The fears may be especially prominent in those settings in which the abuses took place, e.g., bedrooms, bathrooms, showers, washrooms, etc. And the fear may extend to others of the same sex as the perpetrator.

The fears may also be related to the anticipated consequences of divulgence, especially if the child has been threatened with murder, beatings, suicide, abandonment, etc. There may be fears related to the breakup of the family, sometimes actually the case. Of course, I am describing here the extreme examples, but knowledge of them puts the therapist in a better position to detect the less extreme manifestations.

Obviously, the first step toward reducing such fears is to do everything possible to protect the child from further molestation. Without providing this security the therapist is not likely to be helpful. Providing the child with statements about safety and protection are certainly useful, but such reassurances are not likely to work quickly—especially for children who have been subjected to chronic sexual abuse. It is only over time, during which such children have experiences that confirm that they will not be subjected further to the abuses, that these fears are likely to lessen. Having ongoing intimate experiences with a therapist who, although alone with the child on many occasions, does not exploit the child sexually can also contribute to a reduction of such symptoms.

The child's fears may be intensified by environmental attitudes regarding the significance of the sexual acts and their consequences. As mentioned repeatedly, we live in a society that reacts in an exaggerated fashion to child sex abuse, and this is especially obvious when we consider the punishments meted out to sex abusers compared to the punishments given to people who perpetrate other crimes, even murder. Living in such a world, the child is likely to be exposed to these exaggerated reactions. Accordingly, the therapist does well to identify and explore the child's specific fears and anticipations and do everything possible to correct distortions and provide other therapeutic experiences that can potentially lessen such fears. For example, a girl may fear that no boy will ever want to date her and no man will ever want to marry her. The child has to be helped to appreciate that child sex abuse is a common occurrence and that this is not generally a reason why a man does not marry a woman.

One of the unfortunate consequences of child sex abuse is the youngster's growing up fearing and loathing sex in general. It is one of the sources of sexual inhibition in many adolescent and adult women. Accordingly, it behooves the therapist to communicate to the child that the sexual act, in the context of a loving and tender relationship, can be one of the most beautiful and gratifying human experiences. Obviously, the older the youngster, the more meaningful such comments will be. One of the criticisms I have of the so-called "therapy" that is frequently provided such children is the repeated communication of the notion that sex is invariably disgusting and painful. Although this might not be directly stated in such treatment, the exclusion of any positive comments about sex easily leads the child to conclude that it is a despicable act per se, regardless of the circumstances.

Confusion

Children who have been sexually abused often become very confused, especially after the divulgence. At first, they may have thought that the sexual act was an enjoyable experience, and this is especially the case if they were continually praised and complimented in the course of the sexual encounters. Now they learn that they have been involved in a despicable act that is considered by society to be a heinous crime. This cannot but cause confusion. After the divulgence, the abuser may vehemently deny that the sexual activities took place; but the child knows with certainty that they did. However, children are suggestible, and many perpetrators have strong psychopathic tendencies. Over time, with continual denials by the perpetrator, the child may become quite confused regarding whether or not the sexual activities did indeed occur. Sometimes the perpetrator will claim that the child was the initiator when this was not the case. This too can contribute to confusion.

Confusion is further produced by reassurances provided by parents and therapists that the abuser is the one who is at fault, and the child is not. Here we have a situation in which two people are involved in the *same* activity; yet only one is considered to be at fault, and the other an innocent victim. One may go to jail, and the other does not. This seems to be a unique example of a situation where one of the collaborators in a crime is considered guilty and the other innocent. This cannot but be confusing to the child, especially if both enjoyed the experience. Accordingly, therapists should appreciate that such reassurances are a mixed blessing. On the one hand, they help the child feel less guilty; on the other hand, they may produce confusion.

As mentioned, therapists should help sexually abused children appreciate that sex is not necessarily an exploitative act and a despicable crime. Rather, under certain circumstances, it can be one of the most gratifying of all human experiences. If the child's sexual experiences were painful, it may be particularly difficult to get this message across. Attempts to do so may cause confusion as one tries to impart to the child the notion that sex can be tender, loving, and pleasurable—aspects that are not within the realm of the child's experiences. It may be difficult, if not impossible, for the child to appreciate these alternative kinds of sexual activities, and attempts to do so may cause confusion. However, if the child's experiences were pleasurable, then the comments will also cause confusion. Here, the child has engaged in a pleasurable act with the abuser, an act that was physically and psychologically pleasurable. Now the child learns that this act with a father or relative is bad, wrong, and even a crime. Yet the same act with a boyfriend, lover, or husband in a loving relationship is not in any way reprehensible, but even desirable.

Most children these days have been subjected to child sex-abuse prevention programs in which they are taught about "good touches and bad touches." Such programs inevitably produce confusion. It is okay for fathers to wash their little girls in the crotch area in association with bathing. And it is okay for fathers to wipe little girls in the crotch area in association with toilet functions. Yet, he can do this in a "good way" and he can do this in a "bad way." To ask a three- or four-year-old to make this distinction is an impossible expectation. One is asking such a child to ascertain that point on the continuum where the normal, inevitable friction associated with such activities ends and the sexual molestation degree of rubbing begins. For the vast majority of children in this age bracket, this is an impossible goal to achieve. Yet this is exactly what the instructors in such courses are asking of these children. They are being asked to make very subtle differentiations in other areas as well. When Uncle Bob or Grandpa sits three-year-old Janie on his lap, she now has to be careful that he is not touching her in a "bad" way. She has to think about whether the kiss is "good kiss" or a "bad kiss," whether his touch is a "good touch" or a "bad touch." If she decides that what he is doing is "bad," she is taught to blow the whistle on him to everyone in sight. Uncles, grandfathers, divorced fathers, teachers, and other males who may have contact with little girls are now "running scared." It has become a dangerous world for little girls and postpubertal males. No one knows exactly how to act and this too produces confusion.

The child may have been given misinformation in the course of the abuse. For example, the abuser may have told the child that he has to "check" whether or not she has to go to the bathroom. Such checking may involve his putting his finger into her rectum or, in some cases, into the vaginal area (when the child has been properly prepared for this over time). The child may even have come to believe that putting the penis in these orifices is the way to find out whether one has to go to the bathroom. The child may have come to believe that sucking on one another's tongues is normal kissing. The child may have been taught that all little girls engage in sexual behavior with their fathers. After the abuse has been disclosed, the child is given very different messages by investigators, lawyers, and therapists. Obviously, it is the role of the therapist to correct these distortions. However, there will be inevitable confusion created in the child in the course of such cognitive rectification.

With regard to the therapeutic approaches to such confusion, it is in this area that the educational aspects of therapy are obviously the most important. All therapy, to a certain extent, involves education—especially the correction of distortions. However, the therapist must recognize the degree of cognitive immaturity of the child and the inability of the child to appreciate some of the distinctions referred to above. It may be that only with time, growth, and increasing cognitive maturity that some of these distortions will ultimately be corrected and the ensuing confusion reduced. This is one of the reasons why I do not believe in short-term psychotherapy. I am not claiming that such children need be seen two to three times a week; I am only claiming that their therapy may have to be extended over a long period. They have to develop enough cognitive maturity to understand the therapist's communications, which are designed to correct the distortions that are at the foundation of the confusion.

School Problems

As mentioned in Chapter Three, school problems are a poor criterion for differentiating between true and false sex-abuse accusations. Impaired academic and social performance in school may result from a wide variety of psychological and family problems, problems having absolutely nothing to do with sex abuse. Overzealous evaluators often lose sight of this obvious point and consider any school problem to be one of the "indicators" of sex abuse. It is true, however, that the sexually abused child, especially the child who has been abused over a long period, *may* exhibit difficulties in school, both in the academic and behavioral realms. Tensions and depressed feelings may compromise academic curiosity and motivation. Children cannot be expected to concentrate in school if they are living in a constant state of terror associated with their being subjected to ongoing sexual abuse. They cannot be expected to concentrate in school if they have been terrorized by a perpetrator who threatens terrible consequences if the abuse is divulged. Children cannot be expected to concentrate in school if they dread returning to a home where they will be subjected to painful sexual experiences.

There are some children who are sexually abused who exhibit an unusual symptom regarding school. Specifically, they do everything possible to arrive at school early and try to find any excuse that will justify their staying late. They thereby distinguish themselves from the vast majority of other children who have just the opposite attitude. In such cases, the school is being used as a refuge from the home. The more such children stay out of the home, the less subjected they are to sexual abuse. In some cases these children actually run away from home and then, of course, do not come to school at all. In contrast, there are some sexually abused children who will find excuses for not going to school because of the embarrassment they suffer over their poor academic performance, i.e., academic impairment related to the aforementioned tensions, anxieties, depressed affect, and other symptoms that interfere with concentration and cooperation in school. Accordingly, we have two kinds of attitudes toward school engendered by sex abuse. Some of these children want to come early and stay late (to remove themselves from their homes) and others want to come late and leave early (to protect themselves from embarrassment caused by their academic impairments). Both situations, then, should be warning signs.

Obviously, we are once again dealing here with a situation in which therapy is going to be of little value unless the child is safe and protected from the perpetrator. It is only then that the therapist is in a position to explore other areas in which he (she) may be of help. Special tutoring may be necessary for the child to make up for the lost academic experiences. Academic motivation and curiosity may also have been compromised. To the degree that the therapist can serve as a model for these healthier attitudes toward education, to that degree may some of these attitudes "spill off" onto the child. Academic motivation and curiosity may be engendered in the child by the child's desire to emulate an academically motivated therapist and enjoy thereby the gratifications he (she) gains from such pursuits. In the course of the treatment, the therapist should do everything possible to stimulate intellectual curiosity in the child. Unfortunately, such lack of academic motivation and curiosity is seen in many, if not most, families and even in some schools. Accordingly, such children's impairments in academic motivation and curiosity go way beyond those that result from sexual abuse. Furthermore, fathers who abuse their children and/or mothers who facilitate such abuse are not likely to be the kinds of people who have a high commitment to the educational process. Accordingly, the therapist has to recognize that there may be contributory factors to the child's academic difficulties that are way beyond his (her) control. Under these circumstances only limited therapeutic goals are reasonable.

Pathological Compliance

All children, by necessity, are compliant. And the younger the child, the greater the compliance. It cannot but be otherwise. However, in the course of development children gradually achieve varying degrees of independence from their parents. And this process begins quite early. Healthy one- to two-year-olds typically insist upon feeding themselves and will intermittently grab the spoon from the feeding person. Toddlers typically run away from caretakers. However, they periodically turn around just to be sure that the caretaker is still in close range. Three-year-olds typically pass through a "no" stage in which they are negativistic to most requests by adult authorities. In this way they convince themselves of their independence. And the process continues in subsequent years. Adolescent rebellion is yet another example of this phenomenon.

Children who have been sexually abused may live in a home in which the mother and all the children are very much under the domination of the father. The family may feel that their very survival depends upon submission to the father. The sexually abused child may live in a home in which he (she) may be controlled in both body and mind. It is only through compliance that the child may be protected from the implementation of the father's threatened consequences for noncompliance. Many of these children develop a cheerful facade and inhibit themselves from expressing dissatisfaction in any situation. Identification with a compliant mother (commonly the case) may contribute to the child's pattern of compliance. And this pattern of compliance is likely to extend outside the home in areas where there is no pressure on the child to be submissive. Accordingly, in school the child may be inhibited in self-assertion. In relationships with peers, as well, the child may be passive and submissive. Obviously, these qualities interfere with academic performance and social functioning. Submissive children do not ask questions and so learn less than they might have otherwise. Submissive children do not "stand up for their rights" in social situations and so are easily taken advantage of. They are not as respected as those who are more assertive, and so they are not particularly desirable playmates for most children.

Once again, the likelihood of helping such children become more self-assertive is reduced significantly as long as the child remains under the domination of a controlling and coercive father. Even though the situation may have so changed that the likelihood of sexual abuse has been reduced significantly, the personality patterns of domination/submission are still likely to manifest themselves. If the situation is one in which the domineering father is still in the home (because of the extremely low likelihood of repeated sex abuse), it is probably more difficult to help such children with their passivity than if they were living separately. In either case, such children have to be helped to assert themselves in a wide variety of situations. The therapist who focuses primarily on messages related to sex-abuse overtures ("say no") is taking a very narrow view of this compliance problem. It is preferable to recognize that self-assertiveness spills over from one situation to another, and help in a wide variety of nonsexual areas is likely to spill over into the sexual-protection realm.

When approaching this problem, the therapist does well to focus on a specific situation in which the child exhibited inhibition in self-assertion. One should then ask such children what exactly was going through their minds at the time they inhibited themselves. Often the thoughts are appropriate ones, but they have not been verbalized; nor has there been any action taken on them. For those children who have exhibited the capacity to have responded cognitively to an appropriate degree, one does well to inquire about *why* they have not verbalized their thoughts and taken action. If the child's thoughts involve the use of profanities or other ideas that would be insulting and alienating, one has to help the child express these ideas in words that are more polite than those that entered his (her) mind. One has to find out from the child what negative feedback was expected, what terrible things she (he) anticipated would happen if such thoughts were to be expressed. Then one has to help the child verbalize these thoughts, take reasonable action on them, and have living experiences *over time* that the anticipated repercussions will not be forthcoming. For the child who is so inhibited that healthy, self-assertive thoughts do not even come to mind, the therapist has to embark on an educational program. Here the therapist has to suggest specific examples of self-assertion for the child's consideration, discuss the advantages and disadvantages, and hope that the child over time will incorporate these into his (her) psychological repertoire. Obviously, under these circumstances, help in this area is going to be slower and more prolonged. In all cases the therapist should serve as a model for self-assertion, especially against parents and others who may be trying to take advantage of him. Fee payment is a common area in which the therapist has the opportunity to demonstrate self-assertion and thereby serve as a good model for the child in this realm.

Pseudomaturity

Using a daughter as a sexual partner may expand into other areas in which she is treated like an adult, especially as a wife. Accordingly, such girls may be pressured into assuming many adult-type household tasks such as housekeeping and helping care for the other children. Sometimes the child's mother has actively fostered this role as an extension of her facilitating the child's serving as a substitute sexual partner for her husband. She may be a woman who considers sexual activities odious and uses her daughter to substitute for her and submit to sexual acts. And this may extend into the broader domestic realm in which she encourages the girl to take on other roles traditionally assumed by a wife. Both mother and father may cooperate (both overtly and covertly) in grooming the daughter into assuming additional wifely roles. Although the child may comply with these parental encouragements and demands, she certainly is not up to these tasks; beneath the facade of maturity one is likely to find a frightened child (Sgroi, 1982).

Once again, direct work with the child is not likely to be successful. One has to deal with both adults, as well, and focus specifically on the parental contributions to this symptom. The therapist does well to deal with the child at an age-appropriate level, neither higher nor lower. Obviously, praising the child for her pseudomaturity is antitherapeutic. The therapist does well to try to get beneath the facade and address himself (herself) to the child's underlying fears and anxieties. This approach is the first step toward helping the child gain insight into the pathological processes operative in bringing about this symptom and is the best route to bringing about an alleviation of this problem. For example, the child may be ashamed of the fact that she is not up to the tasks being expected of her. Such a child has to be helped to appreciate that this is a normal, healthy reaction and she should not feel so ashamed. She may feel guilty over the desire to refuse, and may fear parental disapprobation and even punishment if she does so. She has to be helped to assert herself in such refusal and, of course, one must deal with the parental contribution in order to ensure that these efforts will prove successful. She may feel resentful over the exploitation, especially if this involves excessive housework and excessive obligations in the care of younger children. Resentments must be expressed, and the therapist must work with the parents to reduce such utilization of the youngster to an age-appropriate level of involvement in housekeeping and child-care activities.

Problems in the Relationship with the Father

As mentioned, it is important for the examiner to appreciate that the father is the only father the child will ever have in this life. Even though the sex abuse represents a significant compromise in parenting capacity, it may still be the case that the father's bonding with the child is stronger than that of any other man on earth. There may be stepfathers, father surrogates, and other relatives who may indeed have strong bonds with the child. This does not negate the possibility (and even high probability) that the father's bonding with the child is stronger than that of any other male—past, present, and future. The examiner does well to give consideration to what I refer to as the *kidney-transplant-principle*. Specifically, examiners should ask themselves this question: "If this child required a kidney transplant, who would be lining up at the hospital door to volunteer to donate one?" If the father, in spite of the deficiency of having sexually abused the child, would still be on that line, then the examiner does well to do everything possible to salvage the relationship. Obviously, the relationship is not going to be salvaged if there is still a danger of sex abuse. If this can be accomplished, i.e., the child placed in situations in which there is safety and protection, then everything should then be done to bring about an improvement in their relationship. It is unfortunate that many zealous evaluators and therapists are not appreciative of this very important fact.

In the course of such attempts toward rapprochement, it is obvious that both individual and joint interviews (both with the father and the mother, in all combinations) are warranted. It is important for the therapist to get across to the child the message that all human relationships are ambivalent and that we have "mixed feelings" about all people, even parents. There is no such thing as a parent who is perfect. There is no such thing as a person who has only qualities that we like. Everybody we know has personality characteristics that we dislike as well. The sexual exploitation has to be put on the negative list, but positives as well must be appreciated. The child must have living experiences, over time, that the abuse will not recur and that the counterbalancing positive qualities of the father are indeed present and operative. The rapprochement is not likely to be possible if the abuser denies the abuse in the face of incontrovertible evidence to the contrary. Under such circumstances I might say to the abuser:

> I have done a thorough evaluation of the sex-abuse allegation. I have interviewed in depth you, your wife, and your child. I have reviewed the pertinent evidence and I am convinced—to a very high degree of certainty—that you sexually abused your daughter. I did not see it with my own eyes, and so I cannot be 100 percent certain. But there are all the hallmarks of bona fide abuse in this situation. If you can see your way clear to admitting this, we have a point of departure for a therapy that would be designed to bring about reconciliation with your daughter and an improvement in your relationship with her. If, however, you insist upon denying this, then I see no point to my trying to effect rapprochement. I cannot conduct meaningful therapy in a situation in which a patient is lying to me, over time, about an issue that is central to the therapeutic process. And this principle is applicable to all patients, regardless of the issue about which I believe they are lying.

One of the problems here is that such an admission might subject the father to criminal action. Under such circumstances, he might protect himself from incarceration but he will compromise significantly the opportunity for meaningful rapprochement. Therapy is not for everyone. Judges, lawyers, and (unfortunately) many mental health professionals do not appreciate this obvious fact. People are ordered into therapy for problems that are basically impossible to resolve via psychotherapeutic methods, and this is one of them.

Ordering accused perpetrators into therapy is a widespread phenomenon. There are thousands of judges who do this and there are thousands of mental health professionals who have no problem accepting such individuals into treatment. Such judges have fulfilled what they consider to be their obligation, namely, to order a sick person into treatment. And the mental health professionals believe they are doing a noble thing by helping to "cure" a person with a psychiatric disorder. These people do not seem to appreciate a well-established therapeutic fact, namely, that one cannot treat a person who is lying to the therapist about a fundamental problem, and one cannot treat anyone who does not indeed have the sickness for which he (she) is ostensibly being treated. Accordingly, whether or not the abuse occurred, such deniers are not candidates for treatment.

Problems in the Relationship with the Mother

If the mother has denied the abuse, and there is incontrovertible evidence that it took place, then the mother must be brought to the point of admitting that it occurred. In many situations, this may not be difficult. However, one must still deal with the child's resentment over the mother's having denied the abuse in the past. The child must be helped to express such resentment, but not via such techniques as banging hammers, hitting clay, or punching dolls. Rather, this kind of cathartic displacement has little value. The child must express directly to the mother the thoughts and feelings she (he) has over the mother's refusal to hear her (him) on this matter. One of the aims of such expression is to help the mother appreciate the kinds of psychological damage that can be done from such denial. This message is more likely to "sink in" if *both* the child and the therapist confront the mother. If successful in this regard, then there is less likelihood that she will deny the abuse again if there is ever a recurrence of the molestation.

One wants, also, for the mother to reach the point where she will spontaneously apologize to the child for what she has done. It is important for the therapist to appreciate that there is an enormous difference between an apology that derives from genuine inner remorse and one that is perfunctorily verbalized in order to squelch the complainant's expression of resentment. The former can be very useful therapeutically, the latter of little therapeutic value. Accordingly, the therapist who initiates the suggestion that the mother apologize is making a serious therapeutic error. To do so is to compromise significantly the likelihood that the mother's apology will be effective. People who say "I demand an apology" are naive. They are making an error. The apology that they may then be successful in obtaining (or extracting) is of little value. The recipient of the apology does not know then whether it is genuine or not. One does not know whether the apology would have been forthcoming if it had not been requested or demanded. Accordingly, this is clearly a situation in which the therapist does well to keep quiet and not open up his (her) mouth. If the mother herself initiates the apology, and the therapist suspects that the mother is merely going through the motions of an apology, then he (she) should point this out and get across the message that such artificial apologies just do not work. The therapist's task, then, is to help the mother reach the point where she is *genuinely* remorseful. At that point apologies (again originating within her) are more likely to be effective.

In association with the mother's denial, the child's distrust of the mother is generated. Trust is not likely to be regained in a short time. Rather, the child must have living experiences, over time, that the mother can be trusted to protect the child once again. If the mother persistently denies her role as a facilitator of the abuse, *and* the therapist has good reason to believe that she knew about it but was blinding herself psychologically, then the therapist does well to work with her in the hope that she will gain insight into what she has done. If the therapist is successful in this regard, then therapeutic work directed toward the mother's remorse and apology is possible and the child's trust may ultimately be regained. However, if the mother continues to deny her participation (when, in fact, it took place), then the likelihood of these compromises in the mother-child relationship being resolved is very small. Obviously, we have an analogy here to the father who denies being the abuser. In both cases therapy is so significantly compromised that, for all practical purposes, it will be ineffective for the resolution of these particular problems that derive from the sexual abuse.

Retraction (Recantation)

Children who have been abused may retract the accusation once they begin to appreciate the effects of the divulgence. The abuser's threats had heretofore been theoretical, and the younger the child, the less capable the ability to appreciate the consequences of the divulgence. It is extremely unlikely that most children will be able to appreciate fully the consequence of their divulgence of sexual abuse. Suddenly, as if from out of nowhere, there is a degree of commotion that may be greater than anything the child has ever experienced. Suddenly, policemen, detectives, and lawyers appear on the scene and the child is dragged through a series of interrogations by a parade of "validators," psychologists, social workers, child protection workers, etc. There are interviews with judges, courtroom testimony, and possibly a jury trial. The father may have been taken away by the police, handcuffed, and put in jail—almost immediately. Under such circumstances it is not surprising that the child may recant in the hope of turning back the clock and undoing all that has been done. The anger at the abuser notwithstanding, the child may not have wished such devastating consequences. The child may fear that the anticipated repercussions will be realized once the abuser has the opportunity to implement them. Or, the child may feel significant guilt over the consequences of the divulgence, never having realized how formidable they would be. The retraction, then, usually results from a combination of fear and guilt.

Children who fabricate a sex-abuse accusation may also recant. For them there may also be the guilt element, as they come to appreciate how terrible are the consequences of the accusation. Here there is guilt related to the knowledge that the accusation is false, *in addition* to the guilt over the consequences. Accordingly, the fabricating child will have two contributing elements to the guilt, rather than one. For both types of children, however, there must be a cognitive/maturational level reached where they can experience guilt. Accordingly, one sees little if any guilt in children under the age of three or four. I am not suggesting here that we have a sharp cutoff point. Guilt, like other complex human psychological processes, is a developmental process in which there is increasing capacity as the child grows older. The fabricating child may also have fear of retaliation. The fear here is not related to previous threats over divulgence (there were no threats made), but the fear that the accused will retaliate for the false accusation. Generally, the child who has falsely accused will be less fearful because there have been fewer (if any) threats regarding divulgence. Such fabricating children, however, may have been subjected to threats *after* their false accusation. My experience has been, however, that such threats are rare.

It is for these reasons that recanting is not a particularly good criterion for differentiating between the true and false accusation. Children in both categories will retract the accusation. Mention has already been made (especially in Chapter Six) of examiners who invoke Summit's "sexual abuse accommodation syndrome" as an instrument for confirming sex abuse. Recanting, which may be seen in many sexually abused children, is then used to justify the conclusion that the child indeed was abused. Such examiners seem not to appreciate that children who falsely accuse will also recant.

TREATMENT OF THE MOTHER

Dealing with the Mother's Hysteria

If the mother has reacted to the abuse in a hysterical fashion, or used it as an excuse for a campaign of denigration of the father, then the therapist does well to try to "sober her up." The more brouhaha she makes over the abuse, the greater the likelihood the child will react in an untoward manner. Her hysterics will increase the child's guilt, self-loathing, fears, and other untoward reactions to the abuse. She will contribute to the child's feeling that a heinous crime has been committed and will thereby lessen the likelihood of any kind of rapprochement with the father. One has to do everything possible to help her put the "crime" in proper perspective. She has to be helped to appreciate that in most societies in the history of the world, such behavior was ubiquitous, and this is still the case. One must quote to her Shakespeare's Hamlet: "There's nothing either good or bad, but thinking makes it so." The therapist need not sanction the behavior, but should try to reduce the exaggerated reaction to pedophilia that most individuals in our society have at this point.

Discouraging Litigation

If the mother is involved in litigation, she must be helped to appreciate that the longer she involves herself in lawsuits, lawyers, prosecutors, "validators," etc., the longer the child's problems will persist. She has to be helped to appreciate that such litigation will interfere with the natural desensitization process and will subject the child to a wide variety of interrogations that will inevitably be psychologically damaging. If such litigation is fueled by vengeful rage, she has to be helped to appreciate that the way she is dealing with her anger is inevitably going to be detrimental to her child.

Group Therapy

Both individual and group therapy may be useful for such mothers. Although I consider the disadvantages of homogeneous groups to outweigh the advantages, there are certain situations in which a homogeneous group may be useful. By *homogeneous*, I refer to a group in which the individuals are suffering with the same problem (such as alcoholism, obesity, etc.). In a *heterogeneous* group, each individual's primary symptoms are different, but, by dealing with the fundamental problems of life, the numbers work from a broader base and, I believe, are more likely to get to the underlying problems that are at the foundation of their difficulties (Gardner, 1992b). Furthermore, in the heterogeneous group the participants are less likely to keep specific thoughts about their presenting symptoms spinning around in their brains and thereby entrenching the psychopathological processes. This is an aspect of the psychotherapeutic process that is not given the attention it deserves. Although there are certain benefits to be derived from talking about one's symptoms, both at the manifest and latent levels, the process per se has the effect of entrenching more deeply thoughts and feelings about the symptoms and thereby perpetuating them. I am not claiming that homogeneous groups have no value; I am only claiming that they have certain limitations that are often not appreciated. With regard to mothers of sexually abused children, I believe that homogeneous groups can sometimes be useful in helping them appreciate that they are not alone and helping them reduce the aforementioned hysteria and vengeful rage that can be detrimental to all concerned. In addition to these therapeutic experiences, the mother will often require joint interviews with the father and child. Referral to *Parents United International* can also be useful. There the mother can meet with other mothers who have had similar experiences. These groups help newcomers deal with the trauma of their experiences.

Improving the Mother-Child Relationship

It is important for the therapist to explore the area of the mother's sanctioning (consciously or unconsciously) the sexual relationship between the father and the child. Although this is common, it is not always the case and the therapist does well to determine whether or not such sanctioning (the more common situation) did indeed occur. If there was such sanctioning, the therapist does well to find out what the reasons were. A common reason relates to the mother's own abhorrence of sex and the use of the child as her sexual surrogate, thereby forming a replacement for herself with the father. Sometimes such abhorrence stems from the mother's having been sexually abused herself as a child. (I will comment below in greater detail on the therapeutic approaches to such a mother's sexual inhibition problem). Relevant here is the mother's becoming increasingly aware of the mechanisms of her sanctioning—especially in situations in which she is unaware, or only dimly aware, of them. Without such awareness the steps that need to be taken to improve the mother-child relationship will be more difficult to accomplish. Furthermore, without such awareness the likelihood of the mother protecting the child in the future is also reduced. Without such awareness she is less likely to appreciate the child's sense of betrayal and thereby take steps toward reducing such feelings in the child. Without such awareness she is less likely to feel guilt, guilt that will also enhance the likelihood of rapprochement with the child. Accordingly, she will be less likely to spontaneously express her regrets and apologies over what she has done. As mentioned, apologies made without conviction are not only of no value, but they may make the situation worse.

In joint sessions in which both mother and child are present together, the therapist can focus on the mother's denial and betrayal and have each party verbalize their feelings about this situation. Obviously, the younger the child, the less likely the child is going to provide meaningful input into the joint sessions. In the course of such meetings, the mother must increase her capacity to be sensitive to the child and listen with receptivity to what the child is saying. I cannot emphasize this point strongly enough. There are tens of thousands, and possibly hundreds of thousands, of adult women who complain that when they were sexually abused as children, their mothers were unreceptive to their complaints, denied them, and threatened punishment if they were to speak further on the subject. The resultant feelings of betrayal can be lifelong. Accordingly, the therapist should do everything to reverse this insidious process at the earliest possible time. It is indeed a good example of preventive psychiatry in that, if successful, one can prevent the prolongation of a symptom that might be lifelong.

The mother and child must be encouraged to spend more time alone together in which the two of them enjoy mutual experiences. It may be that one of the reasons why the daughter turned toward the father is the impairment in the child's relationship with the mother. One should investigate into the existence of difficulties in the mother-child relationship, unrelated to the sexual abuse. Resolution of these problems cannot but prove useful. Furthermore, improvement of the mother-child relationship may reduce the likelihood of the child's turning to the father for sexual affection.

As mentioned elsewhere (Gardner, 1975, 1992b), therapists do well to work closely with parents and utilize them as "assistant therapists" in the psychotherapeutic process. Accordingly, in my work with most child patients, I have the mother join me throughout the course of the session. And the younger the child, the greater the likelihood the mother will be so involved. I generally refer to this procedure as *individual child psychotherapy with parental observation and intermittent participation*. Although this may be a cumbersome label for a procedure, it states exactly the nature of the parental involvement. I do not routinely and reflexively include the mother; I only prefer to have her involvement. I still recognize that there are certain situations in which her involvement may be contraindicated, e.g., in situations in which there is a symbiotic tie between the mother and child, a tie that must be attenuated if the child's symptoms are to be alleviated. For the child who has been sexually abused, such involvement may provide the mother with information useful to her in reinforcing the therapist's comments between sessions. This is especially important with regard to coping maneuvers and desensitization experiences.

If the child's abuse has involved an early introduction into adult levels of sexuality, the mother must be helped to deal with this problem. In some cases, the child returns to lower levels of sexuality after the abuse has stopped. In other cases, it may continue. For many such children, masturbation is the only reasonable outlet and should be encouraged. If the mother has some inhibitions regarding this practice, every attempt should be made to reduce them so that the child can be allowed this outlet. Of course, other methods of dealing with the sexuality can also be utilized, such as distractions, sports, and sublimatory activities. However, it should be emphasized that these substitute vehicles for release are not likely to be entirely successful, and the more direct sexual outlet must be given respect. I generally advise such mothers to make comments to the child along these lines: "If you want to rub yourself there, that's fine with me. However, that's not the kind of thing that people do in front of others. That's a private thing and it should be done in private places. Therefore, if you want to go into the bedroom or the bathroom and close the door and do that there, that's fine." For the child who is obsessed with touching or looking at other people's breasts and genitals, I advise comments along these lines: "I can understand your wanting to touch people in those private places. But that's not allowed. People get very upset with you when you try to do that. If you want to touch yourself in private places, when you're alone, that's perfectly fine with me. And when you grow up, and when you have a boyfriend (girlfriend), and the two of you love each other very much and want to do that together, that's okay with me too."

If the mother has been a contributor to the child's pseudo-maturity problem, her role in bringing about this difficulty must be explored and she has to gain insight into the ways in which she has contributed. If she rationalizes such utilization of the child, by claiming that it is good for her to assume adult responsibilities and/or that she needs help in the care of the younger children, one must help her differentiate between the normal, healthy needs of the child for such mature tasks and their pathological degree. It can sometimes be difficult to find that point where the healthy becomes the pathological, but the therapist does well to attempt to do so. One certainly wants the child to feel the sense of ego-enhancement that comes from assuming responsibilities, as long as they are age-appropriate aspirations and as long as the child is not being overburdened. When the exploitation elements are operative, we are then dealing with a pathological situation.

The mother also has to be helped to gain insight into the fact that encouragement of pseudomaturity may be part of a larger program of having the child become a substitute wife for the husband, a role in which the sexual aspect is only one part. In joint sessions, the child has to be helped to express to her mother

her innermost thoughts and feelings regarding the assumption of this role. Perhaps the mother herself has problems in assuming adult female roles. If the therapist is successful in helping such a mother become more comfortable in the role of wife, she will have less of a need to pressure her child into assuming this role. It is important for the reader to appreciate that my use of the word *wife* should in no way be construed to imply that I am encouraging an inegalitarian situation. The husband/wife relationship can be an equal one. To encourage a relationship in which the wife's role is subservient is to perpetuate yet another kind of psychopathology.

Dealing with Passivity and Inadequacy

In some families the sexual molestation is only one part of a broader program of the father's domination over all family members. Everyone is under his subjugation in both the sexual and nonsexual realms. One manifestation of the family's passivity to the father is the mother's inability to effectively protect the children from his using them sexually. Such a mother may then serve as a model for the child's own submissiveness. Those who provide children with sex-education programs in which they teach children to "say no" do not generally give consideration to the fact that the child's passivity is not simply related to immature age and its attendant feelings of impotence and helplessness. A factor that is often operative is the child's identification with a mother who is similarly passive and inhibited in the ability to express herself. Accordingly, without work with the mother, the likelihood of success for such programs is reduced significantly.

The mother's mother (that is, the child's maternal grandmother) may have served as a model for such passivity and one cannot know how many generations of such modeling there have been. Accordingly, the therapist must have limited goals with regard to helping the mother with this personality problem. This aspect of the mother's therapeutic program may also be compromised by the fact that such assertion may be difficult, if not impossible, for the father to handle and, as a result, he may leave the marital home. His own model may have been a domineering, coercive father, and one may not know how many generations down the line this pattern has been promulgated. Domination of men over women is a deep-seated pattern in the history of the human race, and it is somewhat grandiose on the part of the therapist to believe that he (she) can alleviate such a problem with such a weak instrument as psychotherapy. However, the therapist should still try. The mother has to be helped to get in touch with her inner thoughts and feelings engendered by the father's domination. She has to be helped to assert herself and to deal with the consequences of such assertion. Joint sessions with the father may be useful. Unfortunately, many such fathers do not "believe in" psychotherapy and so are not available for treatment. Men who feel so insecure that they have to compensate by dominating women and children are not likely to have the ego-strength to tolerate the confrontations necessary for psychotherapy to be meaningful and effective. Group therapy can also be helpful, especially groups that can provide the mother with support and advice regarding self-assertion.

Sometimes the mother's complicity in the sexual abuse of the children is not related to the father as abuser but related to other male sexual partners. These individuals may *require* the child's involvement in their sexual activities with the mother as a proviso for their continued involvement with her. They may not only threaten abandonment of her, but physical violence as well. We are dealing here, then, with group sex experiences. The mother may have initially been reluctant to involve her children in such activities, but she does so lest she lose the affection and involvement of her companion. The children may then come to enjoy the experiences because they have been prematurely brought into adult levels of sexual excitation. The therapist may reflexively try to help the mother remove herself from such a man, especially for the sake of the children. Such therapists do well to be realistic with regard to the mother's potential for a different companion (especially one who will not make the same demands) and not engender high hopes or unrealistic aspirations regarding the acquisition of a more mature, healthy, and desirable companion who might ultimately marry the mother and create a traditional nuclear family. And the same warning holds true for mothers who assert themselves against domineering husbands. Many of these mothers are deeply masochistic, and sadomasochistic relationships with men have been the family pattern as far back as one knows. The likelihood is that if such a mother were to extract herself from the sadistic man with whom she is involved, she will gravitate toward another sadist. It is almost as if she doesn't know how to relate to someone who treats her well. If such a woman does find herself with a man who is affectionate, tender, and caring, she feels like a "fish out of water." It is a strange environment for her and she does not know how to react in it. It is a world that may be entirely unknown to her. Obviously, under such circumstances, the therapist does well to have limited goals. Such masochistic mothers have to be helped to assert themselves, both in the sexual and the nonsexual realms. It is hoped that assertion in one area will "spill over" into the other.

Many of these mothers are social isolates and the social isolation has come about, in part, because the husband has tried to sequester the family from involvement in the greater world outside the home. This situation, too, contributes to feelings of inadequacy and helplessness. Such mothers have to be helped to overcome the tensions and anxieties that inhibit their movement into the mainstream of the world. She may have dependency problems, especially dependency on the husband, that have to be worked out. If such a woman becomes less dependent on her husband, she may risk alienating him. Furthermore, if she loses him, there is always the risk that she will gravitate toward another man upon whom she is dependent. This too may not easily be changed, considering that there may have been many generations in which this was the pattern for the relationship between the husband and wife.

Dealing with Sexual Problems

It is likely that the mother has sexual problems, and these must be delineated and identified. In many cases she herself was sexually molested as a child. If she has thereby become sexually inhibited and views sex as disgusting, the therapist must help her reduce such fears and guilt and reach the point of enjoying sex herself. She may never have achieved an orgasm—in spite of the fact that she was sexually molested, in spite of the fact that she had many lovers, and in spite of the fact that she is now married. The therapist, then, does well to try to help her achieve such gratification. Verbal statements about the pleasures of orgastic response are not likely to prove very useful. One has to encourage experiences, under proper situations of relaxation, which will enable her to achieve the goal of orgastic response. If she has never masturbated, one should explore her reasons why and try to convince her that there is no *good* reason why one should *never* masturbate, at any time in one's life. Vibrators can be extremely useful in this regard, and one must try to overcome any inhibition she may have with regard to their use. There are thousands (and maybe millions) of women whose first orgastic responses were enjoyed with a vibrator, and this enabled them to then go on to enjoy orgasms in other ways. (Obviously, accurate statistics on this subject would be extremely difficult to obtain.) Her own diminished guilt over masturbation will make it easier for her to encourage the practice in her daughter, if this is warranted. And her increased sexuality may lessen the need for her husband to return to their daughter for sexual gratification.

Mothers who have been sexually abused as children may have residual anger toward her molesting father or other sexual molester, and this may be interfering with her relationship with her husband. This should be explored in depth, and she should be helped to reduce such residual anger. Sometimes a "he's-more-to-be-pitied-than-scorned" attitude toward her father can be useful. Perhaps she can be helped to appreciate that in the history of the world his behavior has probably been more common than the restrained behavior of those who do not sexually abuse their children. I am not claiming here that the therapist should sanction parent-child sexuality, rather to put it in proper perspective and help the mother appreciate that it has not been universally considered the heinous crime that it is viewed to be in Western society today. The mother has to be helped to appreciate that her experiences with her father and her child's experiences with her husband do not justify the generalization that *all* men are sexual abusers. Such a conclusion will interfere with her relationships with men in general, especially if she views them all to be dangerous perverts.

The mother has to be helped to appreciate that an ongoing campaign of vengeance against her husband is going to lessen the likelihood that their child will achieve some sort of rapprochement with him. Again, joint interviews with the husband may be useful in reducing such anger. Furthermore, attempts should be made to reduce anything the father is doing that may be contributing to the mother's anger toward him, provocative behavior that is fueling the mother's rage. This anger may be a factor contributing to her lack of sexual responsivity. If one is tense and angry with a man, one is less likely to achieve sexual gratification. Accordingly, this is a less direct, but nevertheless important, method for helping alleviate the mother's sexual problems.

TREATMENT OF THE FATHER

Introduction

First, and I cannot emphasize this point strongly enough, it is not possible to meaningfully treat a sexual offender unless he admits that he committed the offense. It is naive on the part of courts to refer to treatment a person who denies having sexually abused the child. It is naive on the judge's part to say, "If you don't go into treatment, I'll put you in jail." This makes a mockery of treatment. The therapist who goes along with this naive utilization of the therapeutic process is not serving well the court or the patient. I am reminded here of many telephone conversations I have had in recent years. They basically go along these lines:

> *Caller:* Dr. Gardner, my name is John Doe. I'd like to go into treatment with you.
> *Gardner:* Can you tell me something about your problems?

Caller: The judge said I have to go into treatment or else he'll put me in jail.

Gardner: What are the problems for which he has ordered treatment?

Caller: For sexual abuse of a child.

Gardner: Did you sexually abuse a child?

Caller: No, absolutely not.

Gardner: Do you have any *other* problems, other than this alleged sexual abuse?

Caller: No.

Gardner: Is there *anything* that bothers you that you think you would like to talk to a psychiatrist about?

Caller: No.

Gardner: Would you be calling me now if the judge hadn't ordered you to do so? *Caller:* No.

Gardner: Let me tell you this. There are two possibilities. You *have* sexually abused this child and you're lying to me, or you *have not* sexually abused the child and you are telling me the truth. If you *have* sexually abused the child and you are lying to me, then there is absolutely no basis for treatment because you would be lying to your psychiatrist about a central issue. Even minor lies to a psychiatrist may compromise the treatment, but a major lie—one that relates to the primary focus of the treatment—makes the treatment a sham, a mockery. Accordingly, if you have *indeed* molested this child, and are denying it to me, then I will not see you because I will not embark on a treatment program that, from the outset, is a sham.

If, however, you are telling me the truth and you *have not* indeed molested this child, then we still have no basis for treatment. What are we going to talk about? Are we going to sit here and look at one another and talk about how you didn't do that? That would be a waste of time and money. You can't have meaningful therapy for something that you didn't do.

Accordingly, it was naive on the judge's part to refer you for treatment and I will not agree to make the first appointment unless there is something you can tell me to convince me otherwise.

Caller: Are you saying then that you won't make an appointment with me?

Gardner: Yes, that is what I am saying. Unless you can give me some good reason why I should treat you under these circumstances.

Caller: Well, I guess I can't have an appointment with you. I'll have to find someone else. Can you recommend someone to me?

Gardner: No, I could not recommend any person who would be willing to treat you under such circumstances. However, I'm sure you will find someone else. And that's unfortunate. But I personally never have, and cannot see myself going along with this kind of a mockery of the therapeutic process.

Caller (in an angry and frustrated tone): Thank you very much, Doctor, for your time.

Gardner: You're welcome!

There seems to be some kind of an unwritten collusion between judges and therapists on this point. There are thousands of judges who are routinely ordering into therapy people who deny sexual molestation. They have much more respect for treatment than I. They believe they are doing their job and putting these people into "good hands." What they are really doing is perpetuating a myth about the efficacy of psychotherapy in general, especially for people who deny the problem for which they are in treatment. And they are encouraging a sea of hungry therapists (psychotherapy today is certainly a buyer's market) to "treat" people in this category.

There are situations, however, in which a father will admit that he did indeed abuse the child, but will refuse therapy. Under such circumstances, a court order that the father be treated may sometimes (I repeat sometimes) prove useful. If, within a few sessions, the therapist is successful in engaging the father, then the court order may give the father a rationalization for involving himself. The father may have operated on the principle that anyone in therapy must be crazy, and he may need the court order as a rationalization for involving himself in treatment. Such a man is similar, then, to the adolescent who claims he is only in treatment because his parents are forcing him to so involve himself. If the father is in a group therapy experience with others who have sexually abused children, then he may become more comfortable with himself, come to appreciate that he is not so unique or atypical, and then become more comfortable with the therapeutic process. In other cases, however, it is quite obvious that the therapy is going to be useless because of the continued lack of motivation for treatment. Under such circumstances, the therapist does well to discontinue the treatment and advise the court that it cannot be successful.

Group Therapy

As mentioned, I am generally much more in favor of heterogeneous group therapy than homogeneous group therapy. A heterogeneous group, by definition, consists of individuals with a wide variety of problems. A homogeneous group is one in which the individuals all have the same (or closely related) disorder(s), e.g., obesity, alcohol, drug abuse, etc. The problem with the homogeneous group is that it focuses primarily on symptomatic manifestations and thereby keeps thoughts and feelings about the presenting problem spinning around in the brain. It does not properly or frequently address itself to the underlying psychiatric difficulties (which the patient shares in common with all other human beings) that are contributing to the development of the symptom which is the focus of the group. The heterogeneous group does not have this problem. However, there are certain benefits to be derived from the homogeneous group that cannot be enjoyed by the heterogeneous group. Specifically, a pedophile may feel terribly isolated and rejected in a heterogeneous group, and there may be some justification for his feeling of alienation. He is less likely to suffer such rejection in a homogeneous group. Also, he may feel less loathsome about himself when he has direct experiences with others with the same problem. Considering the drawbacks of both situations, I believe that the ideal group for a pedophile is to be in a group in which there are both nonpedophiles and pedophiles. In this way the benefits of both can be enjoyed and the drawbacks of both types of group reduced.

The previously mentioned organization, *Parents United International*, can help fathers who initially may be reluctant to admit the abuse. In such an organization, via having multiple experiences with other sexual molesters, they may become more comfortable admitting their problem. They feel less atypical, less "perverted," and so more comfortable with their propensity. The organization also works in a positive direction toward bringing about reconciliation between sexual molesters, their wives, and their children.

Improving the Father-Child Relationship

First, one has to attempt to ascertain the degree of risk of further molestation. Obviously, there is a continuum here from little if any risk to extremely high risk, with all points in between being represented. Of course, the therapist cannot objectify this to a particular point on this continuum, but should be able to gain some information about the degree of risk. Obviously, the degree of safeguards and protections will be determined by the degree of risk. Furthermore, the degree of risk will also determine whether the child and father can remain living in the same home. As mentioned, meaningful therapy of the child is not likely to take place if there is a high risk of recurrence. Similarly, treatment of the father is not likely to be successful if he is in a highly tempting situation in which the possibility of molestation recurring is great. One does not treat alcoholics by giving them jobs as bartenders. There is an old German proverb that has applicability here: *"Die Gelegenheit macht den Dieb"* ("The opportunity makes the thief"). Accordingly, one should not set up opportunities for such molesters.

It is also important to appreciate that people who have exhibited an ongoing pattern of pedophilia are not likely to be "cured." In contrast, those for whom the pedophilic act has been an isolated experience, especially if it occurred only once or twice under certain stresses, have a much better prognosis. When the father and child do have contact, one must decide whether monitored contacts would be the only ones that are warranted at that particular point. One has to decide whether the monitoring can take place in home situations or whether it is necessary to put the two together in neutral places under the supervision of others, such as community agencies. One has to be especially concerned about the two being together alone in such situations as bathrooms, bedrooms, and dressing. Without the implementation of such precautions, therapy of the child is not likely to prove successful, nor is the therapy of the father likely to be effective. Even if the father does not act out the pedophilic impulses, if he is being placed in tempting situations the pedophilic impulses will become intensified and the therapy is not likely to succeed.

Joint interviews with the father and child are important if one is to successfully bring about rapprochement. What I said previously about the mother's apologizing to the child holds for the father as well. Therapists should strictly avoid recommending that the father apologize. Rather, they should hope that he will reach the point of doing so on his own. Once the therapist recommends it, one does not know whether the apology is genuine, or whether it is merely an attempt to "look good" in the therapist's eyes and to comply in robot-like fashion with the therapist's recommendation. The child must have living experiences, over time, that the molestations are not going to recur. Promises and resolutions that they will not recur are of limited value only. The father's reputation for being an abuser must change, and this can only take place over time.

The child should be helped to express anger, sense of betrayal, fears, and other feelings that were probably engendered by the molestation. The father's reactions to these must be expressed, and the child's statements used as a point of departure for psychotherapeutic interchanges. The two must come to know one another as human beings with a wide variety of thoughts and feelings, including ambivalence toward each other. Both must be helped to be brought to the point where each can have the attitude regarding the other that "he (she) is more to be pitied than scorned." Some people have expressed surprise regarding my use of the term *pity* as a therapeutic goal. They consider *pity* to be intrinsically denigrating and antitherapeutic. I am not in agreement. One must differentiate between pity that is *benevolently* motivated and pity that is *malevolently* motivated. To say that we have pity for a person who is deformed, handicapped, or subjected to terrible human experiences (such as earthquakes, fires, concentration camps, etc.) can be benevolent. It does not necessarily mean that we are denigrating such individuals or looking down upon them. There are, however, people who will pity others as a manifestation of self-aggrandizement and the need to consider themselves superior to those who are less fortunate. Such noblesse-oblige pity is demeaning. What we want to engender in both the father and the child is a healthy sense of pity for each other's plight. The child should be able to pity the father for the curse (in our society) of having pedophilic tendencies. In other times and other places, he would be considered normal. And the father should be able to pity the child for having been a victim of his molestation, especially a victim in a society that considers his behavior a heinous crime and/or a mortal sin.

As is true for all meaningful therapy, it is preferable that much of the time *not* be spent simply focusing on the primary problem, in this case, sexual molestation. To do so may be antitherapeutic. Certainly, one must focus on the presenting problem if one is to bring about its alleviation. However, too much focus on it has negative effects. First, for children who are sexually abused, it may involve a certain amount of "muckraking," which interferes with the natural desensitization process. Also, such continual focus may have the effect of keeping the material "spinning around in the brain," when it might otherwise reduce itself. Proper attention is not given to this important negative effect of therapy. We want to help people forget about their problems. This is not going to be accomplished simply by saying, "Forget it." This is more likely to be accomplished by talking about other things that may also be therapeutically beneficial. And this should be carried out of the therapeutic situation as well, in that both father and child do well to share a wide variety of experiences that healthy fathers and children enjoy — experiences that contribute to strong bonding and healthy maturation for both.

Enhancing Self-Esteem

Most pedophiles in our society suffer with feelings of low self-esteem. They are generally viewed as pariahs and subjected to terrible scorn. It is hard to imagine pedophiles feeling good about themselves while living in such a world. In Chapter Two I described the narcissism of many pedophiles, but I indicated, as well, that such narcissism is compensatory for feelings of low self-worth. Certainly, such feelings stem from factors that antedated and contributed to the development of the pedophilia. But such low self-esteem is intensified, as well, by society's reaction to such behavior.

The father has to be helped to appreciate that there is a certain amount of pedophilia in all of us, and that all of us, as children, are "polymorphous perverse." If he doesn't know this already, he has to be helped to appreciate that pedophilia has been considered the norm by the vast majority of individuals in the history of the world. He has to be helped to appreciate that, even today, it is a widespread and accepted practice among literally billions of people. He has to come to appreciate that in our Western society especially, we take a very punitive and moralistic attitude toward such inclinations. However, he—like the therapist, and like others in our Western society—is a product of our culture. We are brought up in a society in which pedophilia is strongly discouraged and even condemned. The question, then, for the pedophile is why he has not come to be similarly inhibited. Often there are family-life situations that have been conducive to the development of pedophilia. (In Chapter Two I have discussed these in detail.) One must explore the particular factors that were operative in the patient's own atypical development—atypical, at least, for our society. If he himself was molested as a child, then he has to come to appreciate that this probably played a role in his own pedophilic tendencies. With regard to his feelings about himself, he has to be helped to take the attitude that he, like the child he molested, is "more to be pitied than scorned." He has had a certain amount of bad luck with regard to the early childhood experiences that were conducive to the development of his pedophilia. He has also had back luck with regard to the place and time he has born with regard to social attitudes toward pedophilia. However, these are not reasons to condemn himself. They are not reasons to indulge the pedophilia either. Rather, although unlikely with regard to the time and place that the genetic dice fell for him and the unlucky early life experiences he had, he still must learn to control himself if he is to protect himself from the Draconian punishments meted out to those in our society who act out their pedophilic impulses. The therapist does well to explore these areas in great detail, appreciating that every patient has his/her own pattern of contributory factors.

As mentioned elsewhere (Gardner, 1992c), low self-esteem is complex and many factors contribute to it. The therapist does well to explore for these contributing factors in great detail. Everything the patient is thinking, feeling, and doing that may contribute to feelings of low self-worth must be identified and attempts made to reduce these etiological factors. Such inquiry should not simply involve areas related to the sexual molestation, but all other areas of life as well. To the degree that one is successful in raising the patient's self-esteem, to that degree one is likely to reduce the pedophilic tendencies. However, it is important to appreciate that individuals whose pedophilia is deep-seated and has been the primary sexual pattern over many years are not likely to be changed significantly by the psychotherapeutic process. They can, however, suppress the acting-out of their pedophilic drives.

Dealing with Guilt (Or Lack of It)

Some pedophiles are psychopathic and have little if any guilt over their molestation of children. Others, however, feel very guilty about what they have done and the guilt in such individuals may be formidable. Of course, one does well to consider there to be a continuum, from those who are excessively guilty to those that have no guilt at all. The therapist should explore the guilt issue with the patient and ascertain at what point on this continuum the patient's guilt (or lack of it) lies.

For fathers who have little or no guilt, the therapeutic goal is to increase it. Such fathers may rationalize that pedophilia is an ancient tradition, a worldwide practice, and that there is nothing at all to be guilty about. Such fathers have to be helped to appreciate that although what they say on this point is true, this does not justify its practice in *our* society, even though our society overreacts to it. It is because our society overreacts to it that children suffer. If our society did not overreact to it, it is far less likely that children would suffer—especially if the sexual encounter has not been coercive, sadistic, or brutal (sometimes the case and sometimes not). Even if the molestation has been tender and kind, the father has to be helped to appreciate that such activities may have the effect of "locking" the child into sexualized relationships with people who are significantly older. And this can be a significant disadvantage in the dating phase of life as well as in the ability to form meaningful and stable marriages. Furthermore, if the father rationalizes the behavior with the argument "She wanted it" or "She didn't object, so she must have liked it," he has to be helped to appreciate that this is not a justifiable excuse for pedophilic behavior. Children are immature and helpless. We do not give them everything they want. We know that it is important to say no to them for their own good. Indulging a child's every whim interferes significantly with the child's ultimate adjustment in the world. Denying the child, at times, is necessary for survival in the world into which the child has been born. And denying sexual involvement with a child who invites it is a form of denial in this category.

If the father is extremely psychopathic, then the treatment may not be effective. Psychopaths are notoriously poor candidates for psychotherapeutic treatment. They have little if any guilt, no internal conflict, little if any guilt-evoking empathy for their victims, little insight into the fact they have problems, hence little if any motivation for treatment. If they are in treatment, it is usually because of some external reason; there is something to be gained for them that has nothing to do with changing themselves. For pedophiles with psychopathic tendencies, the most common reason for requesting treatment is that it has been ordered by a court and the failure to involve oneself may result in serious consequences, even imprisonment. Accordingly, therapists do well, at the outset, to "smoke out" such specious reasons for requesting therapy.

Over the years, I have occasionally had psychopathic people come to me for treatment. Invariably there was some external motivation, unrelated to the genuine desire to change themselves, e.g., "My girlfriend says she doesn't want to go with me anymore, and will certainly never marry me, because I lie so much," "The judge ordered me to go into treatment," and "My wife said she'll divorce me unless I go into therapy." Not surprisingly, all of them have attempted (with varying degrees of success) to exploit me with regard to the payment of my fees. Accordingly, in the last few years I have taken a special approach with regard to the payment for appointments by people who I suspect from the outset are psychopathic. Before describing the procedure it is important for the reader to appreciate that I make all my appointments myself, from the first to the nth. My secretary makes none of my appointments. All new callers receive a 10- to 15-minute free interview, during which time I get an idea about the primary problems. If, during the course of this conversation, I conclude that there is strong reason to believe that the patient is a psychopath, I will make the following statement:

> My experience with people with your kind of problem is that it is best that they pay for their therapy – in cash – at the beginning of each session. My standard fee is X dollars (my standard rate at that time) per 45-minute session. A consultation for an adult is generally an hour and a half, or 2X dollars. [I say absolutely nothing else and wait for the caller's response.]

Invariably, the caller will say something along these lines: "Well, let me think about it Doctor" or "I really don't have that kind of money." Sometimes the person will try to bargain with me and suggest we discuss the fee arrangement at the time of the consultation. Obviously, this I refuse to do. Needless to say, I have not once had the experience of such people agreeing to this program.

In contrast, fathers who have too much guilt, who are overreacting to the molestation, must be helped to appreciate that the practice is ancient and ubiquitous. They have to be helped to appreciate how strongly our society overreacts, and come to recognize that they are taking on society's attitude. Of course, it is very difficult to reduce such guilt in a world where there is such overreaction. However, this should not stop the therapist from making every attempt to put the "crime" in proper perspective. My experience has been, however, that there are many more pedophiles that have too little guilt than there are those who have too much.

Dealing with Isolation

The father may be in that category of pedophile who removes himself from society and uses his family as his own personal "harem." He may be an individual who basically fears involvement in the world and cannot relate meaningfully to others. His whole life is his family, and he uses his family members for just about all interpersonal gratifications, sexual and nonsexual. Such a pattern may be extremely difficult to modify by treatment. Going out of the home makes the father feel like "a fish out of water." Some of these individuals actually have their employment in their homes, especially in such situations as farms or home-based businesses. These individuals are less likely to be helped than those who have some experiences outside the home, especially in the workplace. Obviously, in the course of treatment, one must help these homebound individuals gain gratification in the extradomestic realm and have living experiences that such involvements can be enriching and maturing. This will lessen the need for their dependence on their family members as their sole source of human gratification. Sometimes group therapy can be useful in that it provides opportunities for intimate involvements—in a nonsexual way—with other individuals. It is here that the heterogeneous group is likely to be most valuable.

The father may have an impaired tolerance for the unpredictability and stresses of the extradomestic world, but he has to be helped to cope with its vicissitudes if he is to be successful in bringing about adaptation to and comfort with that world. For most patients therapy involves teaching coping mechanisms, i.e., teaching people how to deal better with the inevitable frustrations, disappointments, and rejections of life. Pedophiles in this category need more instruction within the therapeutic sessions regarding how to deal with the inevitable problems of life with which we are all confronted. However, this is only the "lecture" part of the course. Actual experiences in the outside "laboratory" of the world are required if these changes are to be brought about.

Dealing with the Exaggerated Need to Control and/or Dominate

The need to dominate and subjugate weaker individuals (especially women and children) is an ancient tradition. In fact, it has been the norm throughout the history of the world (with rare exception) and is very much the norm at this time, recent enlightenment and improvements notwithstanding. I suspect, as well, that there is genetic programming for men to be the more dominant and for women to be the more submissive. The more dominant men were more capable of surviving, especially in past years when the hunter-warrior role was the primary one assumed by men. But even later, when humanity moved into agricultural forms of survival, domination was still of survival value for men, especially when protecting themselves from enemies.

In contrast, women who were passive and submissive were more likely to be chosen as mates. Because docility was of selective survival value, it is probable that women are, even today, more genetically programmed to be passive. I am not placing any value judgments on this state of affairs; I am only stating what I consider to be the reality of the world. The therapist does well to give serious consideration to what I have said, and to recognize that he (she) should have limited goals with regard to changing significantly the dominating propensities of pedophiles in this category. However, this does not mean that therapists should not try to bring about some reduction of the pedophile's need to dominate. Such patients have to be helped to put themselves in the position of those whom they are subjugating. They have to be helped to develop sympathy and empathy for their victims. They have to be helped to gain esteem in other areas, areas that do not involve domination. They have to be helped to delegate authority to others.

Often there has been parental modeling for domineering behavior and this, of course, will lessen the likelihood of therapeutic success. Such men have to be helped to gain insight into certain psychodynamic factors that may have been operative in bringing about the domination, factors that are idiosyncratic and separate from factors that relate to modeling with the pedophile's father and other family males. Social and cultural influences have to be clarified as well, e.g., the domination factor commonly seen in violent movies, war stories, and similar kinds of macho fare. The idiosyncratic factors, i.e., those that are particularly relevant to the individual patient's development of pedophilia, have generally been added to the family and environmental factors. Insight has to be gained into all of these, and they have to be changed in therapy to the degree possible.

When investigating into the idiosyncratic factors, one should focus on low self-esteem, for which the domination may be a form of compensation. Thorough exploration into all areas in which thoughts, feelings, and behavior contribute to feelings of low self-worth should be explored. Anything that can be done to enhance self-worth should diminish the need to dominate. We see again here how low self-esteem is a central element in many forms of psychogenic psychopathology and how its alleviation can be viewed as a "universal antidote" for such difficulties (Gardner, 1992c).

Group therapy may also be useful. Here again, a heterogeneous group, especially one in which most of the people do not have domination problems, can be useful. Sometimes some of these father do not appreciate that domination of women is not "the way of the world" and that there are others who do not deal with women and children in this way. The domination problem may be part of generalized sadomasochism that has been a deep-seated family problem generations in the making. Under such circumstances, it is not likely to be helped to any significant degree by the psychotherapeutic process.

Dealing with the Excessively
Moralistic Pedophile

It may initially appear that the term *excessively moralistic pedophile* is an oxymoron, a contradiction in terms. It would appear that pedophiles do not have *enough* morality, otherwise they would not perpetrate their heinous acts. However, there are some pedophiles who are excessively moralistic, and their moralism is a reaction formation to underlying strong sexual cravings over which they feel excessively guilty. The blanket denunciation of sexuality in all its forms serves as a cover-up and is a method of suppressing and repressing strong sexual urges that they cannot allow to emerge into conscious awareness. However, suppressive and repressive forces may weaken, and there may thereby be a breakthrough of sexual impulses into conscious awareness. And the next step, of course, is the actual physical gratification of such impulses. A clergyman, for example, who chooses a stringent religious life as a way of avoiding sexuality may find that the urges become so overpowering that they can no longer be repressed or suppressed. For that individual, the child may be viewed as the safest, most passive, and least likely-to-be-rejecting subject for a sexual encounter. As a clergyman, he is likely to be held in high esteem and less likely to be refused. Some of the "televangelist" preachers would be in this category. Their need to warn the world about the evils and sins of sex is merely an attempt to convince themselves. People who have to proselytize, especially if they must do so to audiences of millions, are usually trying to convince themselves under the guise of convincing others. They are vicariously identifying with the subjects of their ministrations. It is as if each time they preach to others they are preaching to their projected selves. Their campaign, which attempts to obliterate sexual behavior in their constituents, serves to protect themselves from the temptations that would be engendered by the observation of sexual manifestations. If they were to be successful in obliterating sexuality from the entire world, they would presumably be protected from the temptations that they fear.

Such individuals have to be helped to become more comfortable with their sexual urges and to feel less guilty about them. We see here a good example of how the therapist's values play an important role in the psychotherapeutic process. As mentioned elsewhere (Gardner, 1992b), successful psychotherapy inevitably involves the transmission of the therapist's values to the patient. It is hoped that such transmission will be in the patient's best interests. I recognize that for some people in this category, the therapy might involve a career change. But this is not a unique situation. There are many people in therapy who decide on a career change and recognize that it is part of healthy growth and development. They come to appreciate that the career choice they made prior to treatment was injudicious and that neurotic factors contributed to it. As they become healthier, they decide to leave that career and direct their skills and talents into healthier paths.

Dealing with Impulsivity

Impulsivity may also have a high genetic loading. I believe it is reasonable to say that men are generally more impulsive than women. Up to this century (and in many places during this century) impulsivity was of survival value for men. The impulsive man was more likely to survive as hunter and warrior than the more cautious person. The warrior who thinks, as he holds his spear, "If I kill that man, his wife and children may starve" may be exhibiting a high level of civilized sensitivity. However, during the time that he is pausing for these noble considerations, he may get a spear thrust into his chest. The "shoot first and ask questions later" motto is a valuable principle to subscribe to on the battlefield—the obvious cruelty and sadism of the dictum notwithstanding. In contrast, impulsivity was just the opposite of what most men wanted in women. Sedentary behavior, especially comfort with forethought and planning, is an important quality to have if one is to be a successful child-rearer.

In addition to these genetic factors, there are certainly environmental influences that encourage impulsive behavior in men. Violence as part of the macho image is a good example. The macho man does not deliberate very long before taking action. He is "quick on the draw" and asks questions later. For the pedophile, there may be a longstanding pattern of impulsivity with regard to sexual gratification. Their urges are likely to be strong, and they demand quick release. Here again, biological loading is probably operative (we are much more like animals than we would like to believe). The impulsivity may be so great that pedophiles do not give proper consideration to the consequences of their behavior. Accordingly, one must help pedophiles "count to ten" and follow the principle: "Stop, look, think, and listen." They need significant experience with the implementation of these important principles, in both the sexual and nonsexual realms. Therapy in a heterogeneous group may be useful here in that it may provide the impulsive pedophile with the opportunity to have intimate contact with others whose healthy suppression of their impulses has been a lifelong pattern. (I am not referring here to extremely inhibited individuals, but to those who exhibit a *healthy* degree of suppression of their drives.)

Dealing with Homosexuality

Some pedophiles are basically homosexual, i.e., they are males who confine themselves primarily, if not exclusively, to male children as their sexual partners. They have little if any interest in having sex with female children. It is of interest to me that homosexual rights groups have distanced themselves significantly from this subgroup of homosexuals. I have yet to see a homosexual pedophile appear in the public media promulgating for gay rights. Homosexual groups know quite well that exposure of the pedophilic subgroup to the public eye will hurt their cause terribly. Homosexuals who are oriented toward peer sexual relationships have enough trouble getting public acceptance. They recognize the excessively punitive social attitudes toward pedophilia and appreciate that involvement with this subgroup will hurt their cause immeasurably.

Most therapists agree that homosexuals—especially those

who are and have always been homosexual—are not likely to be treated successfully with psychotherapy. Like all things in this world, there is a continuum. There are those whose homosexuality is only a transient and isolated part of their lives, and there are those for whom homosexuality is the only sexual orientation they have ever had. Of course, there are people who are all points in between the ends of this continuum. The closer the individual is to the exclusively homosexual end of the continuum, the poorer a candidate for treatment that person is. And this is especially the case if the individual is an adult at the time of the therapy. Furthermore, there is good reason to believe that there is a biological loading for many (if not most) homosexuals and this, too, gives them a poorer prognosis with regard to changing their sexual orientation via the psychotherapeutic process.

It is important for therapists to appreciate that homosexuals run the gamut from those who are interested in young children, to those who are interested primarily in adolescents, to those who are interested primarily in peers of their own age, and, to a lesser degree, to those who are interested in older people. Heterosexuals, as well, run the same gamut of interests, the range going from primary attraction to children to primary attraction to older people. The likelihood of psychotherapy changing homosexuals to heterosexuals is as great as the likelihood of changing heterosexuals to homosexuals. Therapists who do not believe this are likely to cause both themselves and their patients significant frustration. Accordingly, therapists do well to have very modest goals with regard to changing the homosexual pedophile's sexual orientation. And this is especially the case if the patient's pedophilia was "locked in" in childhood by having been the subject of sexual molestation himself over a long period during the formative years. Such programming makes the therapeutic prognosis for change even poorer.

Because of the relative degree of immutability of homosexual pedophilia, one's approach should be directed toward providing the child with safety and structuring the situation in such a way that there is no opportunity for acting out on the pedophilic impulses.

Dealing with Substance Abuse

As mentioned in Chapter Two, pedophilic acts commonly take place when the perpetrator is under the influence of alcohol or an addicting drug. Under such circumstances, the individual's judgment is impaired, control of impulses decrease, and the appreciation of the consequences of the behavior is reduced. I have mixed feelings about many of the treatment resources commonly utilized for the treatment of substance abuse at this time. For example, Alcoholics Anonymous (AA) is probably the favorite referral source. I cannot deny that it has certain benefits, especially with regard to helping individuals gain the support of others who have similar problems. At such meetings alcoholics feel less self-loathing and can be helped to gain some conscious control over their addiction.

One drawback of AA, in my opinion, is its reliance on higher powers to bring about change. There is a magical quality about this approach that does not appeal to me. Although the AA approach is to encourage conscious control, there is still much talk about the alcoholic's fate being in "higher hands." Accordingly, there is something contradictory about these messages, which, I am certain, lessens the likelihood that some alcoholics will exert as much conscious control as warranted. Of course, one could argue that alcoholics "need all the help they can get," both on earth and from heaven. Furthermore, there is too much emphasis on the here and now ("live from day to day"), with a corresponding deemphasis on the future. We certainly should, to some extent, live day to day. Life is short, in fact, much too short. I suspect that many people who get the most out of life are those who are exquisitely sensitive to this painful reality. However, we also must think about the future to a reasonable degree if we are to protect ourselves from future discomforts, pains, and even calamities. Another drawback of the AA approach is that it keeps brain circuits spinning with thoughts and feelings related to alcoholism and does not give proper attention to other areas of functioning, areas that should also have their circuits spinning in the brain.

Accordingly, when I do refer people to AA, I advise them of these drawbacks of the program, and I try to help them as well in my individual therapeutic sessions. It is important for therapists to appreciate that alcoholics are "notorious liars." They lie to themselves, and they lie to others. Lying is a central element in their problem and this, of course, makes it difficult to treat them therapeutically. They are also notorious rationalizers, and it is difficult to help them gain insight into their rationalizations. Many alcoholics do need a kind of rehabilitation program in which it is impossible for them to get alcohol while they are "drying out." The recidivism rate of such programs is quite high, but the programs certainly do have a place in the treatment of alcoholics. Office therapy should focus on the sources of tension and anxiety that are being relieved by the alcohol as well as other psychodynamic factors that are operative in the pathogenesis and perpetuation of the alcoholism.

It is important to appreciate that alcoholism has become part of the individual's lifestyle, similar to sadomasochism, domination/submission, and other personality patterns that may be generations in the making. The individual may not be comfortable with nonalcoholics, thus the attraction of AA. When not talking about alcohol, the person may have little to discuss. These factors have to be taken into consideration in the treatment of alcoholics, and one must do everything possible to expand their horizons and encourage involvements in a wide variety of other areas. This is one situation in which a heterogeneous group has benefits over the homogeneous group (which is what AA basically is).

With regard to drug abuse, there is much overlap with alcoholism. It too has become the lifestyle. Drug abusers, although they probably lie less than alcoholics, are still not completely free of this particular propensity. The leaders of such groups are generally abusers themselves, with a spotty history with regard to their own "cure." They are often proselytizers and have few if any skills outside the "skill" of being a drug-abuse counselor. They therefore do not serve as good models for their "patients." There are some drug-abuse programs that discourage the patients from having contact with people who are not ex-drug abusers themselves. I consider this to be extremely poor advice. It keeps the drug-abuse circuits spinning in the brain and doesn't give non-drug-abuse brain circuits enough opportunity to develop to a proper degree. These drawbacks notwithstanding, I still recommend such programs, but apprise patients in advance of what I consider to be their drawbacks. In my own work with the patient, I try to focus on the particular factors that were operative in bringing about and promulgating the drug abuse.

In short, to the degree that one can help the father reduce drug and/or alcohol abuse, to that degree will the therapist lessen the likelihood that the child will be sexually abused, especially if the abuse took place when the father was under the influence of the substance.

Counseling with the Mother and Father Together

Even if a divorce is going to take place because of the sex abuse, the parents should still be seen together in counseling. Therapists who hold that divorcing people should *not* be seen together are compromising significantly their psychotherapeutic efforts. The counseling can help the divorce be less traumatic. Furthermore, both are still the parents of the child and both need to cooperate and communicate in the child's best interests. Although therapy is certainly a primitive art, and although it leaves much to be desired with what it can accomplish, there is no question that joint sessions are a very effective way of improving people's cooperation and communication. The argument that the couple will only use the therapeutic session as a forum for arguing is not a reason to avoid such counseling. The arguments are the therapist's points of departure for psychotherapeutic interchanges. When there is danger of litigation, this should be strongly discouraged; the parents should be warned about the pitfalls of such a course of action, both for themselves and their children. Litigation predictably causes psychopathology for all involved parties and works against any psychotherapeutic process, whether it be for sex abuse or other problems. Elsewhere (Gardner, 1986), I have discussed these issues in greater detail.

If the parents are not separating, there is a high likelihood that there have been difficulties in their sexual relationship and that such difficulties may have been playing a role in bringing about the sexual abuse of the child. I have already discussed the kinds of sexual problems in each of the parents that can contribute to the sexual abuse of the child. The treatment of sexual problems between parents, even when there has been no sexual abuse of their children, is optimally accomplished when there is some involvement in treatment on the part of both sexual partners, even though one partner may not be the primary individual in treatment. People tend to deny, to varying degrees, their sexual problems. This is especially the case in a society (such as ours) that puts a high premium on sexual performance. The person who can be most objective about another individual's sexual functioning is the sexual partner. I am not claiming that these individuals can be completely objective, only that they have more intimate information than others. Accordingly, both partners should be seen in the counseling because of the information that each can provide about the other. In some situations, referral to a therapist particularly experienced and skilled in the treatment of sexual problems may be warranted. To the degree that the therapist can accomplish the goal of a good sex life between the parents, to that degree will he (she) lessen the likelihood of a repetition of the molestation.

In addition to focusing on the sexual problems, the therapist does well to focus on nonsexual sources of difficulties in the relationship. There may be power imbalances, especially of the domination/subjugation type. The parents may have a sadomasochistic relationship. Of course, there are many other marital problems that may be present. These create general dissension and unhappiness in the home and are likely to contribute to the need of the father to gain physical and emotional gratifications from the child. Last, it is important to repeat that the treatment of the wide variety of other symptoms described thus far, symptoms in the child, the mother, and the father, are more likely to be alleviated if the therapist keeps in mind that joint interviews and even full-family counseling may be useful. By full-family counseling, I not only mean the child and both parents but also other children in the family, as warranted.

Progesterone Acetate

Some therapists (to the best of my knowledge they are in the minority) recommend *progesterone acetate* injections to decrease the production of testosterone and, therefore, the sexual urges of sexual offenders who repeatedly molest children. If the offender himself wishes such treatment, I would give it consideration. However, I myself would not pressure a patient into taking such injections. My main reason for this position is that progesterone is a very powerful substance and is very likely to have other effects on the human body, some that are known and some that have yet to be learned. All of us, when we take any kind of medication, no matter how many years it has been in use, are still voluntarily serving as guinea pigs for the next generation. It is for these reasons that I am very much against courts mandating such treatment, if they could. It is probably unconstitutional for a court to require such treatment, but this has not stopped some judges from ordering such therapy. It may come as a surprise to some readers that judges do many things that are unconstitutional, and this is especially seen in the realm of child sex abuse. People are handcuffed and dragged off to jail, merely on the allegation that a three-year-old girl made in the office of a "validator." And people have remained in jail for years on the basis of hearsay information provided through grapevines. The punishments meted out to sexual molesters are certainly "cruel and unusual" and clearly not consistent with the protections provided all U.S. citizens by the Eighth Amendment of the U.S. Constitution.

CLINICAL EXAMPLES

The Girl and the Bus Driver

Jane, a four-and-a-half-year-old girl, was brought for consultation because of a severe obsession with sexuality of three months' duration. The parents described normal development, sexual and otherwise. They stated that three months prior to the consultation she began to become obsessed with sex. Specifically, she would try to put her hands inside her mother's bra to feel her breasts. She would try to pick up her mother's dress in order to put her hands in her mother's crotch area. She would frequently try to zip open her father's pants in order to see his genitals and grab his penis. These were not transient and half-hearted attempts; rather, the parents literally had to physically restrain her and "fight her off" in order to protect themselves from these "sexual attacks." With her parents' friends and relatives, as well, she would attempt the same sexual encounters.

The mother belonged to a local YMCA and frequently brought the child along with her to engage in a wide variety of gymnastic and other activities. Whereas previously she had absolutely no problem with her in the locker rooms or the showers, during the three months prior to my initial consultation the situation changed drastically. She would look at other women lasciviously and, with them as well, attempt to grab and fondle their breast and genital areas. But even when restrained, Jane made the women feel uncomfortable—so salacious were her glances and staring. This behavior reached the point where the mother could no longer take her into the locker room. At social gatherings as well, the patient was a constant source of embarrassment in that no person was exempt from being prey to her sexual overtures. There were no special verbalizations other than "I want to feel your boobies," "I want to put my hand in your 'gina'," and "I want to hold your peepee (penis)."

Naturally, when I first saw the patient I made an inquiry into the possibility that she was being sexually abused. The parents had also thought about this possibility, but claimed that they could not think of any situation in which the child might have been sexually abused. In my own inquiry, as well, I could not learn of any person who might have been a sex-abuse perpetrator, or any situation that was even suspicious of sex abuse. In fact, the parents were somewhat overprotective and had not yet put Jane in situations where she might be away from them for significant periods. She had not yet gone to day camp, nor had she had sleepover dates with friends or relatives. In fact, there wasn't a night in the child's life when she had not slept at home with both parents. From my detailed inquiry regarding undressing habits in the home, I found nothing to suggest that she was being unduly exposed to nudity or other potentially sexually provocative situations. The parents' sex life was private; they kept the door locked at night, and there had never been an occasion when Jane had any opportunity to observe parental sexual activity. She was an only child, and so there was no opportunity for sexual exposure or involvement with siblings. The parents carefully monitored her television and were certain that she had not been exposed to any R-rated movies. They did not possess sexually explicit videotapes or other sexual materials that the child might have observed or been involved with. In the initial inquiry I learned that the patient had started nursery school two months prior to the onset of her symptoms and that things there were going well. However, Jane's teacher had noticed the progressive increase in sexual comments and, not surprisingly, the teacher was also an object of Jane's sexual overtures. However, these were not so frequent and insistent that Jane created a classroom problem.

My conclusion at the end of my initial consultation was that there were two possibilities: (1) the patient was (and possibly was continuing to be) sexually molested, yet we still had to find out by whom and under what circumstances this was taking place, and (2) there was no sexual molestation, but Jane was a very early developer and sex hormones were flowing in her blood stream in much higher concentration and at a much earlier time than the vast majority of children in our society. I recommended that I see her on a weekly basis, as part of an extended evaluation, in the hope that information would be forthcoming that would give us a clue regarding what was going on.

During the first three sessions I learned absolutely nothing new that could be of assistance in my understanding of the causes of this child's hypersexualization. Jane made a number of attempts to grab my genitals and unzip my pants. Naturally, she was strictly told that this was not permitted, and Jane respected my request that she make no further attempts of this kind. The mother came into the fourth session quite upset and told me that she was quite sure that she had finally learned the cause of Jane's sexual obsessions. She related that during the preceding week Jane had once again tried to put her hand under her mother's dress. When her mother refused to allow her to do this, Jane angrily blurted out, "Nelly lets me do that to her." Immediately, everything fell into place. Nelly was the nursery school bus driver. From her gait, demeanor, and vocal intonations, the mother suspected that she might be gay. More importantly, the mother was starting to have a problem with Nelly in that she was frequently bringing Jane home late, even though the child was one of the first on the route to be dropped off. Nelly explained the lateness by claiming that she and Jane had a very good relationship and that the child asked that she be allowed to accompany Nelly throughout the course of her whole route and then leave Jane off last. On further inquiry with the child, the mother learned that it was Nelly who originated the idea of the circuitous route, a route that would enable her to bring Jane home as the last child. She also learned from Jane that prior to dropping her off, Nelly would park in an abandoned parking lot and would sexually molest the child.

The mother brought this to the attention of school authorities. Nelly reluctantly admitted that she had indeed molested Jane, and she was discharged. The mother asked my opinion regarding reporting Nelly to the police (these events took place in the late 1970s, before the reporting of such molestation was mandatory). I discouraged the mother from doing so with the argument that the child would be subjected to a series of police investigations and might possibly be involved in a criminal trial. Although such reporting might be of some benefit to society, there was no question that Jane herself would be psychologically damaged. Furthermore, I told the mother that it would make it much more difficult for me to treat Jane because such exposures would interfere with the natural desensitization process, would be likely to enhance guilt, and would have other untoward psychological effects. The mother heeded my advice, and Nelly was not reported.

From what we could learn, the child was being molested at a frequency of two to three times a week over a period of about two to three months. From what we could ascertain, the primary sexual encounters were masturbatory. Most often Jane would masturbate Nelly, but, on occasion, Nelly would fondle Jane, but not to the point of orgasm. These encounters, as best I could determine, were the causes of Jane's high level of sexual excitation. Fortunately for Jane, there was a significant diminution in her sexual preoccupations once Nelly was removed from the scene. These diminished to almost the zero level over a three-week period. During this time—as is my usual practice—I let the patient decide how much or how little she wanted to talk about her encounters with Nelly. Interestingly, she had very little to say about them. I did not believe that she had been significantly traumatized by these encounters. Although there had been a certain amount of sexual frustration that was not gratified, and although there was significant negative feedback from those toward whom she made sexual overtures, so many other things in her life were going well that these negative effects did not prove consequential.

Accordingly, I spent very little time discussing sexual matters directly. The child was told that what *Nelly* was doing was "bad" and "wrong," but that *she herself* had not done anything bad or wrong. Attempts were made to get Jane to understand that Nelly had some kind of a "problem," but I do not really believe that the child fully understood exactly what we were talking about with regard to the word *problem*. I also got across the message that when Jane is older, and that if she and a loving boyfriend and/or husband wanted to do such things with one another, and they were both approximately the same age, then there was nothing bad or wrong about that. What is bad or wrong is for an adult to do such things to a child.

Because there were no further problems, and because the patient did not verbalize anything to suggest residual difficulties, I discontinued the treatment four sessions after the mother had told me she had learned that Nelly was sexually molesting Jane. I believe that continuing the treatment beyond that point might have had the untoward effect of engendering in Jane the notion that a terrible thing had happened to her and this could contribute to feelings that she had been somehow victimized. Although she had to some extent been a victim, it was a short-lived victimization, and I did not want to have her grow up feeling that she had been "a victim!" Furthermore, Jane had no deep sense that she had been traumatized, there was little need for a desensitization process, and what little residual preoccupations she had were dissipated naturally. And I certainly was not going to make trouble for her by encouraging repetitious recall of her experiences with Nelly in order to help her "work through" this problem. Despite the fact that this is a common procedure, even in the 1970s I had serious reservations about this approach and considered it to be harmful to patients. This a view I still hold.

The Boy and the Pediatrician

Bill was brought to me at the age of four years eleven months, with a four-month history of preoccupation with sexual matters. On a number of occasions he took out his penis and said to his mother, "Suck on it." His mother also found him putting his penis into the mouth of his sister's dolls. Bill was obsessed with the desire to pull down the panties of little girlfriends and would cry bitterly when restrained from doing so. On such occasions the mother observed him to have an erection, while crying bitterly, "I want it, I want it, I want it." The mother was certain that he was experiencing significant sexual frustration, which he somehow believed would be relieved by having the opportunity to pull down little girls' panties. When they were driving in the car together he would frequently say, "Let's go over and visit Mary," "Let's go over and see Gloria," and "Let's go over and see Joan." (These girls were Bill's classmates in nursery school or children of his mother's friends.)

During the three months prior to my initial interview, Bill began to play a particular "game" with his mother and grandparents. The child would insist that the adults who were in the home at the time (usually the mother, and sometimes one or both grandparents) all go into the bathroom with him, lock the door, stand in the bathtub, and close the shower curtains around them. They would all stand there together listening for the "bad man." Bill would periodically ask someone to peek out the door to see if the bad man was still there. It would generally take 30 to 45 minutes, during which time there was intermittent peeking, before the child was reassured that the bad man was not there. Then they would hesitantly step out of the tub and tiptoe out of the bathroom.

The mother and grandparents were certain that the child had been sexually abused and reported this to the local child protection services. In the course of my inquiry, when the mother was asked about any unusual experiences, she reported that about one month prior to the onset of symptoms the child had a very upsetting experience. Specifically, Bill was supposed to be a shepherd in his nursery school's Christmas play. (Bill's nursery school was affiliated with the church the parents attended.) Bill's parents and grandparents came to the event, and everyone was eagerly awaiting Bill's appearance. However, when Bill was to walk on the stage he saw a certain clergyman and he suddenly became panic-stricken. Bill ran off the stage and jumped into his mother's arms. There was no consoling him. He was screaming so loudly, "I want to go home, I want to go home," that the parents had no choice but to take him out of the auditorium. The parents suspected that the clergyman might have been the abuser, but they were not sure. They reported this event to the child protection services and the man was investigated. His denials were believed by some and doubted by others. The prosecutor did not consider there to be enough evidence to press charges against the minister. Accordingly, I began treatment with the belief that the child had been sexually molested, but did not know who had molested him. My hope was that in the course of the therapy I might learn something more specific that would lead us to learn who the molester might be.

I proceeded with the treatment under the assumption that

the child was sexually abused. Because I believed—with a high degree of certainty—that Bill had been sexually abused, I was comfortable proceeding with the treatment without knowing exactly who the molester was. Had I significant doubt about whether molestation had occurred, I would not have embarked on the treatment program. And this is an important point. As described in Chapter Ten, the so-called "treatment" of children who were not molested can cause significant psychological harm. Basically, I viewed Bill's treatment as much more an extended evaluation, during which I was trying to elicit information that might be helpful to me in understanding the circumstances of his molestation. Bill was seen once a week, during which time he preferred making up stories and creating fantasies around miniature dolls and animals. None of the human figures were naked, nor was there any particular use of materials that were explicitly sexual. A theme emerged of "someone jumping on top of someone." Comments such as these were usually associated with doll play, in which a figure or animal was assaulting another figure. I speculated that the child might be reenacting his sexual molestation, but I certainly could not be sure. In response, I provided messages in which an assaulted party would call for help from adult authorities and other more powerful figures. I also introduced the theme of running away. The coping mechanisms I introduced were not specific to sexual molestation, but related to any situation in which Bill was being overwhelmed by a dangerous and/or coercive force or greater power.

I also advised the mother about dealing with Bill's sexual cravings. She was receptive to my suggestion that she encourage him to masturbate. Accordingly, when he would have erections and cry bitterly to be allowed to pull down the panties of little girls, she would encourage him to go into the bedroom, play with himself, and do what he wanted with his penis. Both she and I recommended this approach and, to the best of our knowledge, he utilized it.

Videotapes were made of each session and, interestingly, Bill would ask to see them between sessions, sometimes two and three times. The mother found him transfixed when he watched the videotaped sessions, and he would often quote my statements. For reasons still unknown to me, the mother discontinued treatment with me after about three months and switched to another therapist. When I asked her whether she would like to discuss her reasons for the transfer, she was evasive and so I did not press the point.

About three months after the transfer, the mother called me quite excitedly. She told me that she had learned who the molester was. It turned out to have been a doctor, a pediatrician. She told me that everything came out when Bill was scheduled for a follow-up appointment with the doctor. As soon as she told Bill that she was taking him to the pediatrician, Bill went into a state of panic and began screaming that he didn't want to go back. Of course, she asked him why, and it took her about an hour to learn that he did not want to return because the pediatrician had put his penis in Bill's mouth and had made him promise that he would never tell anyone. He had threatened the child that he would put needles in his eyes if he ever told anyone about the sexual encounter. Bill told his mother that "sticky stuff" was in his mouth afterward, and that he spit it out. Bill also told his mother that the pediatrician held his head while forcing him to perform fellatio.

The mother realized, in retrospect, that the molestation took place on the day that she had brought the child for an examination, during the week prior to the onset of symptoms. About a week before the appointment, the doctor himself called her and told her that he would not be able to keep the original appointment, but he could see the child on the following Saturday. He told her that he would come to the office on that day just to see patients whom he couldn't see during the week. When she arrived at the office that Saturday, she thought it quite strange that there were no assistants there. However, she did not make any comments about that. Furthermore, the doctor did another unusual thing, namely, he walked off with the child alone, rather than having the mother accompany him (the usual procedure). While leading the child away he said, "Bill's old enough now to come with me alone." She noted also that the child was in with the doctor longer than usual, and that when Bill came out he was somewhat tense and quiet.

The mother pressed charges against the pediatrician; however, the child was very uncooperative in the course of his interviews with the prosecutor and other investigators. He became panic-stricken, hysterical, and completely uncooperative. Accordingly, the charges were dropped because of "lack of evidence."

The Boy and the Virgins

Tom, a fifteen-year-old boy, was brought to me by his mother and father (each then divorced and remarried) because his three-year-old stepsister had told her mother that Tom had touched her "wee-wee hole." I had known the family over a period of approximately 10 years and had treated Tom from ages eight to nine because of behavior problems in school. At that time, his parents were having significant marital difficulties and there was talk of divorce. They subsequently did divorce, and each remarried. The three-and-a-half-year-old half sister was the product of the mother's second marriage. Tom was living with his mother, stepfather, and half sister. The father's new wife had four children, two daughters and two sons. The oldest, a boy, was already out of the house, and the father's new household consisted of the two girls and her brother, all teenagers.

On inquiry, I learned that Tom was very inhibited sexually. He told me that he planned to be a virgin when he got married and that he considered premarital sex "a sin." He described sexual urges, but considered masturbation to be "sick and wrong." He believed that people who engaged in this practice were "perverts." Although ashamed and guilty, he did describe two or three occasions when, while babysitting for his half sister, he spent significant time looking at her genitals and touching them. He agreed that there was a certain amount of sexual excitation associated with these activities, but he describes them as much more satisfying his curiosity than satisfying sexual cravings. He denied any other sexual activities, nor did his half sister describe such.

In my interviews with the half sister, I found no evidences for significant psychological trauma. In fact, she had reported the sexual encounters in a giggling and laughing way, without any suggestion that she had been traumatized or was reacting negatively to them. Accordingly, I decided not to treat the half sister. This is in the line with the old maxim, "If it's not broken, don't fix it." There are many children who have had experiences similar or identical to this child who are given intensive "treatment," based on the assumption that such an encounter must indeed be psychologically detrimental.

I believed that it was Tom who needed the treatment, treatment for his sexual inhibition problem. My hope was that he would loosen up, become more comfortable with his sexual impulses, and not have to gratify them in this inappropriate and, in our society, very dangerous way. In my sessions with him I discussed the subject of sex, how normal it is, how the urges need release, and that at his age the best releases were via involvements with girls his own age with whom he might have some kinds of mutually enjoyable sexual experiences. We also discussed masturbation as a healthy outlet, pin-up magazines, porno films, and other sexually explicit materials. I believe I was successful in reducing Tom's guilt about sex and encouraged, as well, his dating—which he did. We discussed masturbation and, with my encouragement, he began to do so using his own fantasies as well as pin-up magazine centerfolds as stimuli. We discussed in detail his involvements with girlfriends, and I was able to help him overcome his inhibitions and shyness in the dating situation. My goal here was twofold. First, I believed that his sexual inhibition problems warranted treatment in their own right, even if he had never involved himself in sexual encounters with his half sister. In addition, my hope was that reduction of his inhibitions in age-appropriate sexual activities would lessen the likelihood that he would look to his half sister as a source of sexual gratification.

I did not believe, however, that Tom's sexual involvement with his half sister was purely a sexual act, and that other factors might have been operative. On exploration of these other factors,

I learned that there was an anger element. Tom was angry at his mother and stepfather, especially his stepfather, who was an extremely domineering and coercive individual. At some level, he knew that the child would divulge the molestation and this would "drive my stepfather bonkers" (which it did). Accordingly, attempts were made in family interviews to reduce these sources of tension and to improve Tom's relationship with his stepfather.

The patient made videotapes of all of his sessions and routinely watched them between sessions. They provided a reiteration of my therapeutic messages and, I believe, quickened the pace of Tom's treatment. I often say that people who make videotapes of their sessions are getting two sessions for the price of one. However, this only applies if one confines oneself simply to the time element, i.e., replaying the session at no cost to the patient. Actually, much more is gained, e.g., intensification of the relationship with the therapist, entrenchment of the therapeutic messages, and the opportunity to show others (when appropriate) segments of the session as a point of departure for spinoff discussions with significant others.

In Tom's case, however, there was yet another benefit to the videotapes—a benefit that I could not have anticipated. Specifically, the molestation had ripple effects in his father's new family, which, as mentioned, consisted of Tom's new stepmother and her four children (and her three teenaged children who were still living with their mother). The stepmother, from the outset, was extremely reluctant for Tom to visit, mainly because she was jealous of the time the father spent with Tom. Her own ex-husband had abandoned her and their four children, and she was hoping to reestablish a nuclear family with Tom's father—with no interferences by Tom and any other people from her new husband's former life. Tom's father, then, was in a loyalty conflict. He felt like a rope in a tug of war between Tom and his wife.

When Tom's stepmother learned of the molestation she, too, "went bonkers." Her reaction was to ban Tom from the house completely. She called him a "sex pervert" and claimed that there was a high risk that he would rape her two teenaged girls. (She insisted her daughters were virgins, and she had every intention they remain in the state of chastity until the time of their marriage. Tom had good reason to believe that these girls, ages 15 and 17, had already been "deflowered," but this is irrelevant to my already complex story.) Reassurances by Tom, Tom's father, and me that it would be unlikely that he would "gang rape" these two helpless virgins – in a setting where their older brother, mother, and father were present – proved futile. The stepmother managed to sweep the girls up in her hysteria, which reached the point that the mere mentioning of Tom's name generated in the girls severe anxiety reactions and hysterical outbursts. Interestingly, none of these three women (neither the stepmother nor her two daughters) had had much experience with Tom, so formidable were the previous exclusionary maneuvers utilized by the stepmother. The hysteria reached the point where the stepmother would not even allow the girls to have joint sessions in which Tom, Tom's father, the two girls, and she herself were present. Even in my presence, she feared Tom would "rape" her daughters.

At the point where I felt all my therapeutic efforts were proving futile, Tom, with no suggestion on my part, offered to let the stepmother and girls select any of the videotapes of his sessions and view them. Tom believed that if they were to have the opportunity to do this, they would see that he was not the dangerous pervert they believed him to be. Interestingly, this served its purpose. The girls watched some of the tapes and came to appreciate that Tom wasn't the sex maniac they had been led to believe he was. In fact, they came to see that he was "a nice guy" and thus prevailed upon the mother to let him in the house. Although reluctant, the mother eased up on Tom and allowed him more visits to the home, even though such involvement compromised her fantasy of a new "nuclear family." I am not claiming that the whole problem of Tom's relationship with his stepmother was thereby solved; I am only claiming that the videotapes played a significant role in reducing it.

This case demonstrates well the importance of the therapist working with other individuals who are significantly involved with one's patients. I am not stating that we should automatically conduct family therapy for every patient whom we see. We should, however, try to bring in those individuals who are involved significantly with our patients, especially those individuals whose actions have a direct effect on what goes on with our patients. I am not claiming either that all of these people become officially designated as our patients. I am only claiming that we involve them in the treatment process and not concern ourselves with the exact label applied to them. In Tom's case, I was involved with two families: the mother's new family and the father's new family. Yet, these families were not seen separately. There were three or four meetings in which all four parental figures (Tom's two parents and two stepparents) were in the same room together. As mentioned elsewhere (Gardner, 1991b, 1991c), such a therapeutic program can be an extremely valuable one when parents are divorced and remarried, and I cannot recommend this approach highly enough. Tom was involved with a complex network of individuals, all of whom were interacting with one another in ways relevant to Tom's difficulties. To view Tom's molestation as simply that of a teenage boy touching the genitals of his three-and-a-half-year-old half sister is to take a very narrow, limited, and oversimplified view of the situation. Child protection services focus almost exclusively on the sexual act and reflexively make efforts to remove either the child or the "alleged perpetrator" from the home. Competent evaluators appreciate that the sexual act is one manifestation of a host of factors that may be operative in bringing it about. Competent therapists do everything possible to work with the network in order to bring about an alleviation of the wide variety of problems that have contributed to the abuse. This is true "protection" of the child. This is the only reasonable way to make the child "safe" from future molestations.

One last point. This family's therapy demonstrates, once again, that the treatment of children who are sexually abused should not necessarily involve direct work with the abused child. In many cases the therapist does well to do nothing. To do something with the child may do that child more harm than good. Those who reflexively "treat" are going to harm many children who would have been much better off without such "treatment." In some cases the focus should be only on the molester. In other cases, other people have to be brought in if the therapy is to be effective. And this was certainly the case in Tom's situation.

The Girl in the Wedding

I first saw Gloria when she was four-and-a-half years old. She was brought to me for consultation because two months previously she had been sexually molested by her 14-year-old cousin. He lived in Ohio and was visiting Gloria's family in New York City. Gloria had a two-year-old sister, and the cousin, Bob, babysat for the two girls on two weekend nights in the course of his one-week visit. After he left, Gloria reported to her mother that "Bob tried to put his pee-pee in my pee-pee." On further inquiry, the mother learned that on each of those two nights Bob had rubbed Gloria's vulva, kissed it, and asked her if she would let him put his penis in her vagina. The child claimed that she became frightened and refused. Bob did not then press her for further sexual activities. The mother also learned that Bob had threatened, "I'll kill you if you tell anyone." Although Gloria was initially upset by this threat, she did not believe that her cousin would kill her, and when she told her mother about these events, she was not particularly frightened. She did, however, wait until Bob had left the home before divulging these experiences.

The parents reported the molestation to Bob's parents in Ohio, who reported the matter to the local police authorities after the mother said to them, "If you don't call the local police there, I'm going to." During the subsequent two months Gloria was preoccupied with Bob's following her around the house, and reassurances that he was back in Ohio were only of limited value. She would also ask her mother to repeatedly say to a fantasized Bob, "Go away and don't come back here." The mother played out these little fantasized scenarios, and they appeared to be reassuring to the patient. Of course, we see here the kinds of coping mechanisms that abused children will often create for themselves. These are the kinds of coping mechanisms for which we should have the greatest respect, because they are indicators to us as to whether we should barge in with what we consider to be better modes of adaptation.

I subsequently saw Gloria in treatment for a period of about six weeks, with sessions once a week. Over this period I provided reinforcement of Gloria's own coping mechanisms and reassurances that her parents would never again be leaving Bob alone with her. Furthermore, I reiterated that her parents had no intentions of inviting Bob to their home in the immediate future and that she lived in New York City and Bob lived in Ohio, which was "far, far, away." Her desensitization play and preoccupation with coping mechanisms gradually diminished to a zero level over a six-week period and so I discontinued treatment. I advised the mother to call me if she noted any recurrence of these preoccupations. Furthermore, it was clear that Gloria was a healthy stable child, living in a healthy stable home, and she exhibited no other evidences for psychopathology. Accordingly, I found no other reason to keep Gloria in treatment. (Interestingly, the child protection services in Ohio never followed up on Bob's molestation of Gloria, nor did Gloria's family have any further information regarding whether Bob was in treatment.)

Two-and-a-half years later, when Gloria was about seven, her mother brought her back for a consultation. The main complaint at that time was lying and antisocial behavior in school. The mother informed me that there had been no reappearance of symptoms related to Gloria's sexual abuse. Early in this second round of treatment, the mother informed me that a relative in Ohio was getting married and that she, her husband, and Gloria were invited to the wedding. Bob was also going to be at the wedding, and the question was raised regarding whether Gloria should attend. The mother wanted to go to the wedding, as did Gloria, but the father was reluctant. This was discussed in a family meeting, and I myself expressed my opinion that it would be useful for Gloria to go and that all of us need extended family members. I tried to get across the point that, from everything I knew about him, Bob was not a low-life animal and that he was a human being who could be part of Gloria's family network support system, the sexual problem notwithstanding. Furthermore, we were not speaking here about Bob's babysitting again; rather, we were only talking about Bob and Gloria being together at a wedding in the presence of a couple of hundred people.

The following is a segment from a videotape made two days after Gloria attended the wedding in Ohio:

> *Therapist:* Okay, what else is happening with you?
> *Patient:* (no response)
> *Mother* (whispers to patient): What did we do Saturday?
> *Patient:* What Saturday?
> *Mother:* Where did we go?
> *Patient:* Oh, we went to a wedding.
> *Gardner:* You went to a wedding. Okay, let's hear. Where was that wedding? I heard about that wedding.
> *Patient:* Cleveland.
> *Gardner:* In Cleveland. Okay. Let's talk about that wedding.
> *Mother* (interrupting): Who was there?
> *Patient:* Uncle John.
> *Gardner:* John, your Uncle John. Okay.
> *Patient:* I wasn't so nasty to Bob.
> *Gardner:* So you weren't nasty?
> *Patient:* Yeah.
> *Gardner:* Hhmm. Were you scared there?
> *Patient* (nodding negatively): Uh-uh.
> *Gardner:* You didn't think anything would happen to you there?
> *Patient* (nodding positively): Uh-huh.
> *Gardner:* And what did he . . . . Did he come over and say hello to you and things like that?
> *Patient:* Yes.
> *Gardner:* Uh-huh. And were you scared then?
> *Patient:* No.
> *Gardner:* Uh-huh. Did he try to bother you in any way?
> *Patient:* No.
> *Gardner:* Uh-huh. Did you have a good time there?
> *Patient* (nodding positively): Hh-hmm.
> *Gardner:* Was there any trouble there of any kind?
> *Patient:* Nope!

We can see here that the patient did not suffer any untoward effects from being with Bob. This was what I had predicted. She would be provided with the living experience that she would be protected. This is far more valuable than mere verbal reassurances. The child's having actual experiences lend verification to such reassurances.

Gardner: But your dad wasn't there? Is that right? As I recall, he didn't want to go? Do you know *why* he didn't want to go? What was your understanding?

Patient: I don't know why he didn't want to go.

Gardner: Well, I recall our talking about that here last time, about his not wanting to go. Do you remember why?

Patient (nodding negatively): Uh-uh.

Gardner: Let's ask your mom.

Mother: He didn't want to go because he's still a little bit angry.

Patient: Why?

Mother: He's still upset about the past.

Patient: What past?

Gardner: What is your mother talking about when she says the past?

Patient: I don't know.

Gardner: She's talking about Bob, right? What about Bob. What's the past?

Patient: I don't know.

Gardner: You don't know or you'd rather not talk about it.

Patient: I'd rather not talk about it.

Gardner: Okay, because it's important. If you don't know it makes me think that maybe you don't remember, and it's very important here to be honest. Do you know that?

Patient: Hh-hmm.

Gardner: Honesty is the number one thing here—lying is just the opposite of what we do here. In this room it's 100 percent honest. So that if you don't want to talk about something you say, "I'd rather not discuss it." But you don't say, "I don't know," because that's a little bit of a lie, you know. It's not a *big* lie. It doesn't hurt anybody, but it's really not true. Right? Am I correct?

Patient: Correct.

Gardner: Okay, so we don't tell anything here that isn't 100 percent perfectly truthful. *Truth* is the key word here. All right?

Patient: Hh-hmm.

Gardner: Truth is the key word here. All right?

My elaboration here on the importance of telling the truth relates to the chief complaints that brought the patient back to treatment, namely, lying and other forms of antisocial behavior. I was not simply addressing myself to the relatively narrow issue of the patient telling me the truth in treatment, especially with regard to whether or not she knew the answer to my question, but expanded this principle to lying in general. In this way, I was able to get across the principle of the importance of telling the truth, without producing the embarrassment and shame that might result from talking about lying in specific areas, especially those lies that brought her back into treatment. I then turned to the mother and continued.

> *Gardner* (now talks to the mother): You see my dilemma—maybe it's a strong word—but my conflict here is this. Traumas of this kind, like many other kinds of trauma, cause a dilemma for the therapist. On the one hand, you don't want to muckrake, you don't want to keep the thing exposed when it's going to die, and be buried, and be laid to rest and lost in the past memories of the human brain. On the other hand, you don't want to leave simmering abscesses and pus pockets there that may be infecting a person's brain and life. And the question is whether going to this wedding where Bob was, for the first time since the event, was traumatic for her. I don't know if there had been some kind of strong reaction. If she had strong reactions that would rekindle all this, I want to know about it. If she handled it well, and didn't have any strong reactions, then it tells me that things probably have been laid to rest.

Here I explained to the mother the dilemma therapists should have regarding inquiries into child sex abuse, especially when the child is asymptomatic. As mentioned, the therapist should not muckrake; however, the therapist should provide therapy when there has been failure to resolve issues relevant to the trauma. I was not simply instructing a mother here regarding my therapeutic approach but was, without mentioning it, giving her advice on how to handle Gloria with regard to her experiences with Bob and her subsequent reactions to him.

> *Mother:* She was very positive in her reactions to him at the reception. She went over and hugged him and stayed in the same

room as him. As a matter of fact, I think at one point she was sitting in the same chair together, right?

Patient: (nods affirmatively)

Mother: Yeah. She felt very comfortable, I felt. There were two other little girls that she was running around with. This was a reception in a home and so there were five different rooms that people were in and she set herself up for some difficulties once or twice, and I was surprised, because she let herself be the object of the person being teased.

Patient: Who?

Mother: Anyway, it was a little strange, but as far as her relationship with Bob, she did very well and I was . . .

Gardner: Okay, so you didn't see any strong reactions?

Mother: No.

Gardner: Okay, I think that was good, that you (speaking to Gloria) didn't get too upset about that. Okay.

Mother: She did put herself in a position that I thought was very strange. She had been gone about five minutes and I walked into the room. She was on the floor being sort of held down by my niece—who was the bride—and they were trying to get her to open her mouth so they could pop in a piece of candy and I don't know what precipitated that, but it was very strange. Also, when I walked into the room, there was also a stranger that I thought she was behaving rather forward to and with. And she said it was because he was a friend of the bride that she felt comfortable in teasing him and really physically coming down on him very hard. I thought she was being very aggressive with him and I thought it was inappropriate. But we discussed it and she simply said . . . I told her that's not the way to treat people and that's not the way to behave with strangers ever. And she said, "Well, he's a friend of the bride."

The mother is making reference here to some of the antisocial behavior that brought Gloria back into treatment. On the one hand, one could argue that this was normal rambunctiousness at a wedding where children are likely to get "wound up." However, Gloria was much more readily wound up than most children and would probably be one of the first to involve herself in horseplay. In this regard, she was much more like a typical seven-year-old boy than a seven-year-old girl. In fact, I considered Gloria to have some of the genetic programming that boys traditionally have, i.e., programming for rough-and-tumble play. I believe that this is a derivative of the selective survival of the warrior-hunter-protective types of men. In contrast, there was selective survival of the more sedentary, empathic types of women, women who better served child-rearing purposes. (I am not placing any values on these evolutionary developments; I am only stating the facts as I see them.)

> *Gardner:* When your mother says physically aggressive, what was she talking about. What is she talking about now? Tell me exactly what that was.
> *Patient:* Stranger.
> *Gardner:* What's that?
> *Patient:* Strangers.
> *Gardner:* Strangers. And what were you doing. Now physically aggressive. Do you know what *physically aggressive* means?
> *Patient:* What?
> *Gardner:* You don't know. What you should have said to your mother is: "You know, I don't understand what physically aggressive means." Do you understand that? Because she thought that you knew what that meant. Since your mother was there, why don't we have her tell us exactly what the physical aggression was. *Physical* means with your body, right? And *aggression* means— aggression means you can hurt someone. That's what aggression means. It means to fight or insult someone. Do you know what *insult* means? Or knock against them. Or be mean. Aggression can cover a lot of things. So that's what she means by physical aggression. It means that with your body you do something that bothers another person. You punch against them or you push against them.

One of the patient's problems in treatment was that she would frequently "space out" and not register what was being said to her. Such tuning out made it very difficult to engage her therapeutically, and I would often have to interrupt the conversation and define words, even the simplest words. Sometimes, even these repetitions did not register.

> *Mother:* Or step on their toes. I think that's what you told me you started out by doing—by stepping on his toes?

Patient (nodding affirmatively): Hh-hmm.

Gardner: That would be an example.

Mother: And he was sitting in the chair.

Gardner (looking at patient): Hh-hmm. I see. So she told you to cool it, huh, on that stuff?

Patient: Hh-huh.

Gardner: Why were you doing that? Who was she singling out for this?

Mother: This was a young gentleman, maybe 19 or 20.

Gardner: Hh-hmm.

Mother: He was very friendly. He was one of the gang that was around. This was a young wedding.

Patient: His name was Sam.

Mother: His name was Sam. Okay.

Patient (spelling): S-A-M.

Mother: Okay. And he probably was very playful.

Gardner: Oh, so it was probably part of the horsing around that was going on at the wedding.

Mother: Yeah, but I just was a little disturbed that she really became overly comfortable with it and, as I said, she really came down on him rather hard because she felt it was safe territory.

Gardner: Hh-hmm.

Mother: And I don't want her to develop that.

Gardner: Okay. On the one hand, you don't want to be too uptight. You don't want to squelch too much of the childhood rambunctiousness and horseplay, which is healthy and lets out hostility in a socially acceptable way and is fun. You know, there is a teasing quality in it and it's a form of interaction. And you don't want to squelch that completely. On the other hand, you don't want to allow full abandon, you know. There's some point in between and I don't know you well enough to know where you're at on that continuum—whether you're too uptight.

Mother: No, I'm not too reserved. I'm not . . .

Gardner: You allow for that?

Mother: Yes.

Gardner: You think she was just going a little overboard?

Mother: Yeah, I do. My concern is that if anyone is going to be an exhibitionist, or if anyone is going to take things too far, I know it's going to be Gloria and I have to teach her where the limits are. And that's my major concern.

Gardner: Hh-hmm. Yeah. Okay, so I am just asking that, but it sounds like you've been taking a good middle-of-the-road position on this. If I'm wrong here, time will tell. Now, I would like to go back to your husband's not attending.

At that point, I believed that I had enough information to conclude that the mother was dealing appropriately with Gloria's rambunctiousness. Accordingly, I decided to discontinue further discussion on that point and go back to the failure of the father to attend the wedding. I believed that that was an important issue to focus on because of its implications for Gloria's attitudes toward Bob and her subsequent relationship with him. As mentioned, I believe all of us need reasonable degrees of love and affection and that we should not preclude any kind of a relationship whatsoever with an individual who may have sexually molested us. Certainly, everything should be done to protect a child from further molestation; but everything should also be done to preserve and encourage good relationships with nearest of kin.

> *Mother:* Hh-hmm.
> *Gardner:* What's your opinion of that?
> *Mother:* I think he is being rigidly unforgiving and just a little too, um, just plain rigid.
> *Gardner:* And you told him that?
> *Mother:* No, because for a long time in our lives . . . there is just so much major tension and it has been on my mind and I was hoping that basically, religiously, that he would be able to get some messages about forgiving and letting the past go and start dealing with where time is. So I was letting this past six months go by because we are in the middle of getting into the Ten Commandments and I thought, "Boy, that's a perfect time."
> *Gardner:* Oh, so you said nothing at this point.
> *Mother:* No.

When the mother spoke about waiting until they came to that part of the Ten Commandments that relates to forgiving, before she would talk to her husband about his dealing with Bob, I recognized immediately that she was procrastinating. I knew that I would focus on this point soon. However, I wished to lay some foundation for that area of exploration by first pointing out the importance of maintenance of the family network and the father's support of Gloria's continuing involvement with Bob, the sexual molestation notwithstanding.

> *Gardner:* You see, there are a couple of thoughts I have on it. One is that in a mild way it works against the therapeutic process for her in dealing with this trauma because Bob is your brother's son.
>
> *Mother:* Hh-hmm.
>
> *Gardner:* He's a relative. Like all relatives in this world, he has things you like and things you don't like. You feel you want to continue with your family network, their problems notwithstanding, to the degree that you want. And you want Gloria to have some involvement with her family. Clearly, the older she gets, the more she will be able to protect herself from any kind of overtures on Bob's part and his power over her will lessen. This is what I consider to be the best and healthiest route for her to take with regard to this: And that is that it doesn't mean that because he has this deficiency that you wash your hands of him for the rest of your life, that you scorn him forever, and that you treat him as a noxious, loathsome worm that you won't be in the same room with—because it robs her of some freedom, too. And it robs her of a more natural way of dealing with this problem. So I feel that, for Gloria's sake, your husband should have been there. Bob's not going to do anything at a wedding in front of the parents.
>
> *Mother:* Right!
>
> *Gardner:* That crazy he is not! Do you think your husband would have gone had this not happened?
>
> *Mother:* I don't know. My husband, if he's tired he won't do anything for anyone. He simply pulls in for himself and he would not drive that far, that kind of a distance.
>
> *Gardner:* Oh, so he wouldn't have gone anyway?
>
> *Mother:* Well, it's possible.
>
> *Gardner:* I see, but would you say that when he was weighing the considerations, this was a heavy consideration—tipping the balance in the negative?
>
> *Mother* (nodding affirmatively): Hh-hmm.
>
> *Gardner:* You see, I think that what parents *do*—I'm very big on modeling—it's one of my favorite words in this field—that what parents *do*—more than what they *say*—is what determines how a child is going to react. A good example here is a parent who smokes a cigarette. That parent is in no position to tell a teenager not to smoke.

Mother: Right.

Gardner: They can have all the charts of all the diseases and everything else. So your husband is saying, "This boy is noxious. I don't want to be in the same room with him and I will have nothing to do with him." Your husband believes that this may be a lifelong pattern of his. That's not good for Gloria in terms of continuing with hate, never forgiving, and so from a psychological point of view it's not good and, you know, it doesn't fit in with the precepts of your religious beliefs either. So it's another reason.

Mother: I completely agree.

Gardner: I feel that your statement, "I'll wait until we reach that part in our religious studies," I think was an unnecessary procrastination.

Mother: Hh-hmm.

Gardner: Do you know what I mean? If there was some more urgent precept that was broken, "Thou shall not kill" or "Thou shall not covet thy neighbor's wife," you wouldn't have waited until you reached that part. Do you know what I mean?

Mother (laughing): Right, right. (Both therapist and mother laugh together.) But I thought that having a year of talking about being forgiving and just what is set up in the commandments that—when we're his godparents—that's to me where the major issue is. We do have a responsibility for him and I feel in particular because of that we do have a responsibility. And that's where we are. And I was not willing to sit there and argue with my husband with him saying "Absolutely no" and I'm saying, "I think you're wrong." It doesn't go anywhere. And so that's why I thought . . . it's not that important.

Gardner: Okay. I see some passivity here and some justification for yourself for not confronting him.

Mother: Hh-hmm.

Gardner: You don't have to argue. It takes two to argue. You can say, "This is my position. Let's discuss it a little bit." You don't have to have the whole day spent on harangues and big arguments; but you should let your position be known. Your saying "it's not important" is to justify your passivity.

Mother: Hh-hmm.

Gardner: Whether it's from a religious point of view or whether it's from a psychological point of view, just standing there and saying nothing, because it's a minor thing, is not going to help the situation. Minor things can often lead to major things. But my job is to select those things, even though minor, that I consider to be psychological problems.

Mother: Right.

Gardner: If somebody were to steal a penny off my desk, it would be my job to bring it to his or her attention.

Mother: Hh-hmm.

Gardner: Even if the person said, "Oh, it's only a penny. What are you worried about a penny?" it's an issue. It's a theft. So, it's a mild thing, it's a minor thing, but it's an issue. You're using religious tenets and your view that he's religious as rationalizations for nonaction. And what I'm also concerned about is this rigidity. Is this a pattern? Is this one example of a pattern of rigidity, and if it is, is this one example of your submission to rigidity without speaking up?

I asked here a very important question, namely, whether the rigidity she describes in her husband is an ongoing pattern or whether this is simply an isolated instance. It is crucial that the therapist ask questions along these lines, because focus on an isolated behavioral manifestation is rarely of any value therapeutically. All people get rigid at times, especially under stressful circumstances. There is little to work with therapeutically with such occasional, predictable, forms of inappropriate or atypical behavior. One is much more interested in *patterns*. These are the areas to focus on in treatment. And I also want to know whether the mother's passivity, as well, is a pattern, or whether the incident being described here is an isolated one.

Mother: I would say absolutely yes.

Gardner: Yes.

Mother: Absolutely.

Gardner: Okay. Let's hear a couple of more examples. His rigidity, your passivity.

Once the mother states that his rigidity/her passivity problem is a pattern, I do not accept her statement immediately. I want to have further *specific examples* of the pattern in order to be sure that it is indeed the pattern she considers it to be. As mentioned so many times throughout the course of this book, without specific examples the therapist is ill equipped to come to conclusions regarding a particular issue. Abstractions and generalizations are of little communicative value; specific examples are the richest sources of information regarding whether or not something is indeed happening.

> *Mother:* I think he said to you that he's not a person who can deal with a quick answer or a quick judgment on something most of the time. If you say to him . . .
> *Gardner* (talking to patient): Are you getting bored with this?
> *Patient:* (nods affirmatively)

We see here one of the drawbacks of my working together with both a child patient and a parent. When too much time is spent in a discussion with the parent, the child may very well "tune out." All therapeutic approaches have their drawbacks, and having the mother serve as "assistant therapist" is no exception to this principle. However, this drawback notwithstanding, I believe its advantages far outweigh its disadvantages.

> *Gardner:* Okay, listen. We're going to try to make this a short discussion and we'll get to our games and talk, but this is very important. We're really talking about things that pertain to you. I know it's a little boring for you, but we'll try to make it short.
> *Mother:* I will say, "Guess where we're gonna spend the summer? I just picked up a contact in New Mexico or we're going to live in Italy for the summer." His first answer is absolutely rejection. A flat outright no. He's not interested.

The mother's career sometimes enabled her to have the opportunity for extended work in various parts of the United States and occasionally abroad. Such assignments readily lent themselves to combinations of work and recreation. The father's business also allowed him the flexibility to join her on many of these assignments.

> *Gardner:* Okay, and what will happen then?
> *Mother:* And then when he has a few weeks to do his own research and to get information on the subject, then he usually

totally gives the opposite answer and now New Mexico or Italy is in his bloodstream and . . .

Gardner: Okay, what do you do in this period when he's mulling over?

Mother: I try to help supply information so that he can see what's going on and get more information.

Gardner: So you do it in a way that he likes to believe it's his own decision?

Mother: It is his own decision to come.

Gardner: But you're working on him from the sidelines.

Mother: I made my decision to go.

Gardner: Yeah, but you're kind of feeding him info that will help him agree to go with you.

Mother: Yeah, I'll bring him brochures.

Gardner: Okay, so you have time to do it that way. I have no problem with that. But here you had a wedding, a one-time event with very short notice.

Mother: Very short notice, right.

Gardner: That's right, and I see your pull back. I'm just earmarking that for future reference.

Mother: Right.

Gardner: You brought up an issue, and if it's a *pattern*, I'm interested in it because we're dealing here with certain behavior patterns of Gloria's and I have to try to figure out what's going on in the family that might be affecting this pattern.

Mother: Right. Okay. That is definitely the way we work. His answers are usually a negative. His response usually on a quick decision is almost 90 percent of the time a negative response.

Gardner: And I am particularly concerned when such interactions affect Gloria directly. Can you think of any incident where it affects her directly when this happens?

Mother: Golly. You mean in front of her that she's aware of?

Gardner: Yeah.

Mother: Not that I can think of.

Gardner: Okay. I believe this may likely be playing a role in the problem of fabrication and the antisocial behavior.

Mother: Okay.

Gardner: How it does I don't know. But often these things do have some effect.

Mother: Well, I am constantly trying to avoid having confrontations with him.

Gardner: Okay.

Mother: And I am constantly making her aware of that—that you must not disturb Daddy, that we can't do this until we make amends, like clean up the mess or don't want him to get more hassled than he usually is.

Gardner: Okay, in the course of that tiptoeing around, do you in any way give messages that communicate "Don't say things, cover up, and even lie"?

Mother: No, I simply say, "We don't want to get Daddy angry, you know, because he's going to be angry that this wasn't cleaned up."

Gardner (directed at patient): I'll ask you a question, because I know you have been a little bored here while your mother and I have been talking. Do you know what your mother was just saying? Were you listening or not? What were we just talking about?

Patient (whispers): About my daddy.

Gardner: What were we saying about your daddy?

Patient: That we don't disturb him.

Gardner: You don't disturb him. Okay, does that happen a lot, that your mother says, "Let not get him upset"?

Patient: Yes.

Gardner: Does it happen every day?

Patient: No.

Gardner: How often would you say it happens?

Patient: Hh-hmm, maybe like three days.

Gardner: Okay, let's hear from your mom. How often do you say it happens?

Mother: Often. About 50 percent of the time.

The discussion then progressed further into the mother's passivity in her relationships with her husband, and the pent-up anger that she felt over such passivity. In addition, we focused on the effects of this pattern on Gloria, especially the factor of the mother's serving as a model for such passivity. We then focused on the pent-up resentment that was thereby being engendered in Gloria, resentment that might be discharged through antisocial behavior. I will not elaborate further on this aspect of the therapy because it takes us somewhat afield from the primary purpose of this chapter, which is to focus on the treatment of child sex abuse. This segment was presented because it provides a good exampie of the kind of treatment one should provide such children. In this case, Gloria's treatment demonstrated my point that delving into the sex-abuse problem was not warranted because it appeared that she had worked through her initial reactions during her therapy two-and-a-half years previously. Here I was encouraging rapprochement with her cousin Bob (the sex abuser) and attempted to deal with environmental factors (here the father's reluctance for rapprochement) that might be interfering with that process.

TWELVE
BELATED REALIZATION OF
CHILD SEX ABUSE BY AN ADULT

INTRODUCTION

In recent years we have witnessed a new phenomenon, namely, an adult (usually a woman) claiming that she recently realized — after many years of absolutely no recollection — that she was sexually abused as a child (usually by her father). First, I wish to emphasize that I believe that some of these accusations are indeed true. As mentioned on so many occasions throughout the course of this book, child sex abuse is a widespread and ancient phenomenon. Children who are sexually abused grow up and become adults. Children who are sexually abused may very well repress their memories of such abuse for many years. There is no question, however, that some adults are making false accusations and that it is extremely important that we develop guidelines for differentiating between true and false accusations in this category. It is my purpose in this chapter to focus on the false accusations, especially with regard to the manifestations that suggest strongly that they are false.

Commonly, the revelation occurs in the office of a therapist who has a reputation for being particularly skilled in bringing such long-repressed memories into conscious awareness. The moment of revelation is considered to be a turning point in the woman's life, and now all unanswered questions about her psychological health are answered. Everything now has "fallen into place." All the years of emotional turmoil, psychiatric treatment (including hospitalizations), wrecked marriages, and other forms of psychological dysfunction are now understood. It was the sex abuse that occurred during childhood that was the cause of all these years of grief. Now that the cause is known, the "healing" process can now *really* begin. (All previous therapies were a waste of time and money.) The treatment may take many years and may involve a significant degree of hardship for the nearest of kin, but it will be worth it. The woman continually extols the brilliance of her new therapist—who saw what others failed to see—and toward whom this woman will have a lifelong debt.

Commonly, the next step is to remove oneself totally from the alleged perpetrator, who is generally a man in declining years. His initial reaction is often one of astonishment and immediate denial, often supported by his wife. The sessions may extend over days, weeks, months, and sometimes even years. Nothing the father can say will convince his daughter that no sex abuse ever took place. Commonly, the father—who previously may have had a reasonably good relationship with his daughter—now finds himself totally rejected and isolated. His wife, who supports her husband, is also rejected, as well as anyone else who may support the father's position. The distraught parents feel impotent as every relative whose assistance they wish to enlist is cut off as well and the daughter maintains contact only with those friends and relatives who will support her accusation.

The next step often involves the daughter's appearance on television programs, interviews for newspapers and magazines, and personal presentations to any group willing to listen. One of the purposes here is to help other women (and there are millions out there) "discover" their own childhood molestations in order that they too might now, for the first time, deal properly and effectively with the effects of their childhood exploitations. Whereas most women who are sexually molested traditionally feel some shame over their experiences, both for themselves and their families, these women are just the opposite. If they had the opportunity to appear on "Prime Time" syndicated television, they would seize it. Clubs of such "victims" and "incest survivors" are formed and pressures placed on legislators to provide public funding for the treatment of such women, which, it is predicted, will require many years in order for them to "heal." In some cases, we are told, the trauma has been so formidable that these women may require treatment for the rest of their lives.

As mentioned throughout this book, there is no question that child sex abuse is widespread. Obviously, there is also no question that the vast majority of sexually abused children become adults. However, there is no question that most of the women who satisfy the false-accusation criteria described in this chapter have never been sexually abused. As I will elaborate upon below, these cases satisfy many more of the indicators of the false rather than the true sex-abuse accusation. In fact, I have already mentioned two of the indicators of the false accusation, namely, the strong need to bring the abuse to the attention of the public and the belief that all of one's psychological problems are derivatives of the abuse.

THE ACCUSERS

Why Do They Do This?

Release of Anger   Generally, these are very angry women. When the problems generating anger are not resolved, anger builds up and presses for release. Society always provides targets that facilitate such release, and these change with the times. Various rules and regulations are set up that strictly define which areas of release are acceptable and which are not. Some of the more common vehicles for release in our society are competition, gossip, worthy and noble causes, sports (both as a spectator and as a participant), family squabbles, and violent themes in books, television, and cinema. Family members are safe targets for such anger because they are often captive and are less likely to retaliate as strongly as strangers. In short, they cannot readily escape (especially if they are children and spouses), and they can be relied upon to be less punitive in their retaliatory maneuvers. The socially sanctioned targets change with the times and place.

In recent years, many women have found that men can serve as useful targets for their hostility. There is no question that women have been terribly subjugated since the beginning of civilization and that the process is still going on in just about every part of the world. There is no question that the women's liberation movement is, overall, a constructive force in human progress. However, every movement has its fanatics and zealots, and the women's movement is no exception. Most women have some justification for feeling angry at men in general. However, those who believe that the best way to deal with this is to destroy every man in sight are certainly not making constructive use of their anger. Actually, such women do the women's movement much more harm than good, give it a bad name, and work against its progress. Such utilization of men as scapegoats is a form of bigotry. If scapegoatism is to work, it is important that the scapegoat be close by. And this is an important element in prejudice. One can be intellectually prejudiced against people who live thousands of miles away, but they are not available as targets for the release of anger. Accordingly, one must find a scapegoat close by, even in the next house or neighborhood. Husbands and fathers satisfy this proviso quite well.

Sexual Factors Most of this book has been devoted to a discussion of the release of such anger via the sex-abuse accusation against a separated husband. Here I focus on an adult woman's venting this rage on her own father, who, for many women, was once the most important person in their lives and, at the time of the accusation, may still occupy the number one (or possibly the number two) level in the hierarchy of men who have influenced them. If one looks over the last 15 to 20 years with regard to what has been going on in the field of sex-abuse accusations, it might have been predicted that false sex-abuse accusations toward husbands would spread to fathers.

Contrary to popular opinion, children are capable of having strong sexual urges. Although there is generally an intensification of such urges around the time of puberty, they are present before that and have the capacity to be intensified—even to adult levels. Children's sexual urges are generalized, and children have to learn which individuals are "proper" to involve themselves with in the particular environment in which they are raised. In our society, where the incest taboo is quite strong, little girls have to learn that their fathers are "off limits" when it comes to the expression and gratification of their sexual feelings. The suppression and repression of such feelings may produce some clinical and behavioral squelching, but they may press for release nonetheless. One way of dealing with them is via the mechanism of projection. In this way the individual is saying, "It is not I who harbor strong sexual desires toward my father; it is he who has strong sexual desires toward me." The next step is to have the fantasy that these desires were realized in reality. To call all this an "Oedipus complex" or "Electra complex" adds no new information. Freud considered these particular desires to be the central element in the development of most psychoneurotic problems. I am in disagreement with him on this point, but I do agree that these intrafamilial sexual urges do play an important role in our lives. Of importance here is that such urges may contribute to a child's professing that a parent sexually abused him (her) and later in life, as an adult, claiming that he (she) was sexually abused as a child.

Paranoia

The Ubiquity of Paranoia   Paranoia is much more common than is generally appreciated. Most know that a paranoid is a person who harbors delusions of persecution, that is, the individual believes that he (she) is being persecuted by another individual, and there is absolutely no evidence that such is the case. Most believe that such people are to be found mainly in mental institutions, locked up in closed wards. This belief is in itself a delusion. The reality is that for every paranoid who is in a mental hospital, there are probably hundreds "on the outside," and many of these people are not even recognized as being mentally ill. Crichton-Miller, the English psychiatrist, once said (Kolb and Brodie, 1982):

> For every fully developed case of paranoia in our mental hospitals, there must be hundreds if not thousands, who suffer from minor degrees of suspicion and mistrust; whose lives are blighted by this barrier to human harmony; and who poison the springs of social life for the community. (p. 446)

Sometimes the paranoia may fuel worthy causes, and the individual achieves a certain amount of stability and even social respectability (especially from those who have joined the cause). The anger is vented toward those who are considered to be contributing to the perpetuation of various social abominations, and sometimes even constructive things come out of these movements. I am not claiming that *all* people who devote themselves assiduously to worthy causes are paranoid. I am only claiming that some of the people who are involved in such movements – those who are the most fanatic and consumed – may very well be paranoid. The rage that fuels the paranoia is being channeled into a socially constructive venture and good may come of it. There are others, however, whose paranoia blurs their reality, and they distort significantly the object of their indignation. They may see the situation as worse than it is, and attribute malevolent motives to those they are trying to reform or otherwise change. They misconceive events and oversimplify. Because of their blurred perceptions, their own colleagues may find them progressively less useful to the movement.

The Content of Paranoid Delusions   The content of paranoid delusions is not created de novo in the brain of the patient. Rather, the material is derived from ambient social phenomena that may serve well as a focus for the paranoid's preoccupation. There are not too many people in our society whose paranoia involves evil spirits, but this was certainly the concern of people in societies where evil spirits were considered to play an important role in the lives of the individuals. In 1692, in Salem, some of the people who believed that they (or others) were possessed by witches were, I am certain, paranoid. (I am not claiming that *all* who believed this were paranoid, only some.) In the World War II era, Nazi spies were frequently incorporated into the delusion of paranoids. Although there certainly were Nazi spies in the United States, it is not likely that a network of them devoted themselves to spying on paranoid patients, especially those in mental hospitals. In contrast, in Germany, Jews were commonly incorporated into the delusions of paranoids, Adolph Hitler being the most famous example. In my residency days, in the 1950s, many paranoids considered themselves to be persecuted by Russian spies. Without doubt, the McCarthy hearings contributed to the development of delusions involving impending persecution by Communists. In reality, there actually were Russian spies in the U.S., and they were given particular attention in the public media. However, there was no good reason to believe that these spies were as numerous as paranoids believed them to be and that networks of them were devoting themselves 24 hours a day to spy upon these particular patients. Not surprisingly, since the end of the cold war, fewer paranoids are being persecuted by Russian spies. But other potential persecutors are not hard to find. Being followed by the police and FBI are common preoccupations of paranoid people. Wiretapping is another concern for paranoids, again as a spinoff from a practice that certainly occurs in our society.

I could go on and on and give many examples throughout the history of the human race to demonstrate this point. What is pertinent here is that sex abuse has become the most recent concern for paranoids, and there is no question that *some* of the women who are accusing their fathers of having sexually abused them as children are paranoid individuals who have selected from the society the in-vogue scapegoat to serve as the target for the paranoid rage.

The Projection Element in Paranoia   Paranoia serves functions other than the release of pent-up anger. Central to the paranoid mechanism is projection. Specifically, paranoid individuals project out onto others thoughts and feelings that they themselves have, but they wish to disown. Because of guilt and other ego-debasing mechanisms, they do not wish to accept that they themselves have particular urges. Accordingly, by projecting them onto others, they can consider themselves free of these undesirable thoughts and feelings. Murderous rage is a good example. Most people would not be willing to accept the fact that they harbor within themselves the kind of murderous rage that causes some people to kill others. By projecting such anger out onto others, the paranoid can say: "It is not *I* who wish to kill him; it is *he* who wishes to kill me." And this mechanism can relate to sexual feelings as well. The sexually inhibited person may say: "It is not *I* who have sexual feelings toward him; it is *he* who has sexual feelings toward me." And this is one of the elements that may be operative in the false sex-abuse accusation.

The Oversimplification Element in Paranoia   Another element operative in paranoia is oversimplification. Most problems are complex and the solutions to most of the problems in the world are not easy ones. A multiplicity of factors is operative in any phenomenon, and problems are not dealt with by simple solutions. The paranoid solution generally involves an oversimplification of the problem and offers a quick and easy solution. And this is one of the elements in paranoid prejudice. Such people are essentially saying, "If we only get rid of those people, all our problems will be solved." Although history has repeatedly shown that this is not the case, the delusion still persists. A woman who has suffered with a wide variety of psychological difficulties throughout the course of her life is likely to embrace a simple solution that promises to cure all of her problems. If she can come to believe that her father's sexual activities with her in early childhood were the cause of all her difficulties, then she has a simple answer and, presumably, a simple solution, or at least the route to a simple solution. It is for this reason that such women are likely to say, "Now everything is understandable. Now I understand why I have all these years of grief. Thank God I met Ms. So-and-so, my brilliant counselor, who has shown me the path to the cure."

Resistance to Alteration by Logic and/or Confrontation with Reality
Another characteristic of paranoia is that the belief is not altered by confrontations with reality, no matter how compelling. Paranoia, after all, is a form of delusion. And a delusion, by definition, has no basis in reality and is a product of internal psychological processes rather than external realities. There are strong psychological forces within the individual that compel the person to maintain the belief, no matter how much at variance it may be with reality. Accordingly, those who try to alter the belief of paranoids by logic, argument, and confrontations with reality suffer nothing but frustration and a sense of futility. Accordingly, when the father, mother, and other family members try to convince the accusing woman that her beliefs are false and that some of the elements in her scenario are absurd and even impossible, their arguments fall on deaf ears. Or, if she does feel the need to respond, she provides some kind of an explanatory justification that may be as implausible as the original scenario. However, paranoids are notorious for their avoidance of such confrontations and provide a never-ending stream of justifications for not involving themselves in such conversations. When they *are* willing to discuss their accusations, they are often ingenious in providing rationalizations to justify their distortions. This principle is well demonstrated by an anecdote from my residency days. It is the story about a man who comes to a psychiatrist. The following interchange takes place:

> *Psychiatrist:* How can I help you?
> *Patient:* Doctor, I'm dead.
> *Psychiatrist:* Let me ask you this. Can a dead man bleed?
> *Patient:* Of course not. A dead man can't bleed.
> *Psychiatrist* (takes a pin, pricks the man's finger tip, and expresses a drop of blood): What do you think about this (while pointing to the drop of blood on the man's fingertip)?

Patient (after a long pause): Well, what do you know. This is the first time in the history of the world that a dead man has bled!

Paranoid women who accuse their fathers of sexually abusing them provide similar rationalizations to support the maintenance of their delusion. When their mothers try to convince them that the accusation has no basis in reality, they will claim that the mother is only trying to protect the father in order to preserve her marriage. It is a no-win situation when one tries to change a paranoid's mind regarding the validity of a delusion.

Low Self-Esteem in Paranoia   Paranoids basically suffer with deep-seated feelings of insecurity. This is one of the factors contributing to the need for projection. People with stronger egos are willing to tolerate socially unacceptable impulses within themselves and have enough compensatory assets to counterbalance personality weaknesses and socially unacceptable thoughts and feelings that they may harbor. Paranoids do not have the ego-strength to do this. Not only does this problem contribute to the mechanism of projection—wherein they project out onto others their own inadequacies (or presumed inadequacies)—but this weakness contributes to other problems as well. One such problem is their inability to admit that they were wrong. Admitting that one makes mistakes also requires a certain degree of ego-strength. And this is one of the reasons they are so resistant to logic, arguments, and confrontations that might demonstrate that their thinking is awry. For a paranoid, such an admission is tantamount to admitting that one is "crazy," and this, of course, is very difficult for anyone to do.

The feelings of low self-worth may also be compensated for by the individual developing the feeling that she is more astute than others regarding the ability to appreciate the significance of information. In general, paranoids consider themselves quite skillful in detecting innuendo, slights, and trifling disparagements that pass others by. They pride themselves on their ability to detect the hostility in everyday inadvertencies. For women who promulgate false sex-abuse accusations against their fathers, they may, in retrospect, pride themselves on their new-found sensitivity to the most subtle manifestations of sexual abuse, manifestations that others were too blind and/or stupid to detect. In the extreme, this compensatory mechanism for ego-enhancement may result in grandiosity and an all-pervasive feeling of superiority over others. This feeling of superiority, then, serves to strengthen the individual against those around them, who inevitably react with hostility to the paranoid's accusations. A vicious cycle then ensues in which those who disagree and argue with the paranoid unwittingly contribute to the strengthening of the paranoia and its derivative symptoms.

The Spread of Paranoia Paranoia tends to spread and expand. Whereas the delusions may start with a single individual, they frequently spread to others. I have already mentioned the phenomenon in which all family members and friends are divided into two categories: those who agree that the sex abuse has taken place and those who do not. When a sex-abuse accusation is the central mechanism in an adult woman's paranoia, she may consider all individuals who support the father's position to be capable of aiding and abetting his abuse—even at present. Although, as an adult, she considers herself strong enough to resist any present advances, her children would certainly not be able to protect themselves. Accordingly, grandchildren, who previously may have had a loving and warm relationship with their grandfather, are now removed entirely from the opportunity to have any contact with him—even by mail and telephone. Gifts are returned with the excuse that these are likely to be "bribes," the purpose of which is to entice the grandchildren into sexual encounters. And his wife, as one who has openly supported her husband's denials, is considered to be similarly untrustworthy. Because she "looked the other way" or was "too stupid to see what was going on" when the accuser was molested as a child, the woman now suspects that her mother would be similarly incapable of preventing her husband from perpetrating similar abuses on her own children. Aunts and uncles as well, who have not come forth to align themselves with the accusing woman, are similarly distrusted and viewed as potential facilitators of her father's sexual abuse of her children. As a result, many of these women go into hiding, move to distant states, and cut off entirely any and all communication with the accused father as well as his extended family and friends.

Paranoia and the Legal System People who are angry to the degree described here often want to wreak vengeance on those whom they believe have abused them. Our legal system provides a ready and willing vehicle for gratifying this morbid desire. There are generally two tracks along which such women can operate. On the civil track, they can ask for damages and payment for their "therapy." Because the trauma has been "enormous," the amount of money that can provide compensation is generally an amount equal to the total value of the assets of the father. And because the therapy must be intense and prolonged (no one can predict *how* long—it may be *life*long), then payment for such treatment is also justified. In some cases the blackmail element here is easily seen. I have seen letters written by such women in which their fathers were told that if they did not come forth with the indicated amount of payment, the daughter would consider herself to have no choice but to press criminal charges, with the threat of years of incarceration.

And this brings us to the second track, the criminal track. Here, too, such women will find willing accomplices in the legal apparatus. There is a sea of prosecutors and district attorneys who are quite happy to enhance their images in the public eye by bringing "justice" to these kinds of "perverts." And the public media, as well, are happy to provide these individuals with the notoriety (and future promotions and salary increments) that they crave. In most states the punishment for sexual abuse of a child is Draconian, far above and beyond the punishments meted out for most other crimes (including murder). Life sentences for fondling little girls are commonplace, and there are hundreds (and possibly thousands) of individuals who have been convicted of such a crime—some of whom may very well be guilty but many of whom, I am convinced, are not. In either case, their punishments are far beyond what was visualized by the Founding Fathers when they framed the U.S. Constitution, which was designed to protect an accused individual from "cruel and unusual punishment."

Conclusion   It would be an error for the reader to conclude that I believe that *all* adult women who promulgate false sex-abuse accusations against their fathers are paranoid. Rather, I believe that *some* (and possibly many) of them are, but it is too early to know approximately what percentage of these accusers fall into this category. Some are preparanoid and may be moving along the paranoid track, with the false sex-abuse accusation enhancing movement along that path. I suspect that with more knowledge and experience, we will see other types of psychopathology in these women. I am certain, however, that all of them will have demonstrated significant degrees of psychopathology in the earlier parts of their lives, long antedating the outbreak of the psychopathology associated with the sex-abuse accusation.

The Search for a "Therapist"

Some of the women I describe here have developed their delusional systems in the course of "treatment." There are others, however, who have not had the opportunity for such "therapy," but who have read or heard about the phenomenon of adult women learning in treatment about their childhood sex abuse and thereby found the "key" to all of their psychological problems. They, too, decide that they also would like to find out whether they can find this kind of simple solution to their own problems. This factor, plus the presence of a wide variety of other predisposing forms of psychopathology, result in their searching for a therapist who will help them delve into their past and possibly uncover similar evidences of sex abuse. Not just any therapist will do, however. One wants someone who specializes in this particular area, one who is well known for her expertise in uncovering this material, which may be very deeply buried in the innermost recesses of the unconscious mind. (I refer to the therapist as "her" because there are far more female than male therapists who satisfy this proviso.) These days it is not hard to find a therapist who is a "specialist" in this area, so ubiquitous is the sex-abuse hysteria. Especially attractive is the therapist who has the reputation of finding sex abuse in the vast majority, if not all, of the patients who come her way. Predictably, the therapist will be found; the sex abuse will be uncovered; the prophecy will have been fulfilled; the row of dominoes will begin to tumble—with tragic results for the woman, her father, her children, her friends, and her family network.

THE "THERAPISTS"

Who Are These People?

Anyone who believes that people who refer to themselves as therapists are psychologically healthy is also suffering with a delusion, just a little less pathological than the delusions that I have been focusing on thus far. And anyone who believes that people who are therapists are adequately trained and that most of them know what they are doing is also entertaining a belief that is easily contradicted by reality. In most (if not all) states, any individual can go into business with the title of "therapist." One cannot legally say that one is a psychiatrist (a subspecialty of medicine) or that one is a psychologist, or that one is a psychiatric social worker. Generally, people who practice therapy in the context of these disciplines require a certain amount of prescribed training and state certification. There are other disciplines, as well, that *may* require specific training and certification, e.g., family counselors, psychiatric nurse practitioners, and pastoral counselors. In addition, there is a sea of therapists out there who are "in practice," are self-styled and self-trained, and have not progressed along any of the aforementioned more formal paths. I am certain that most of these people are incompetent and many are dangerous. But there are thousands who *have* trained within the aforementioned disciplines who have, in my opinion, little or no competence. Even within these formal disciplines, there are many schools of thought and a wide variety of therapeutic approaches with only limited scientific validity. Accordingly, it is predictable that a certain segment of these individuals will also be dangerous, although not as high a percentage as those who have no formal training and monitoring of their activities.

In addition, with so many "therapists" per square inch, it is not surprising that there is significant competition for patients. It is indeed a buyer's market. One way for therapists to make a buck — in this competitive arena — is to pander to individuals who are involved in the latest fad of psychiatric disorder. At this point, sexual abuse is probably number one. There are probably more sexually abused patients seeking treatment today than ever before in the history of psychiatry. Accordingly, sex-abuse "experts" are sprouting up in every field, coming out from under every stone, and suddenly appearing from behind every tree. Considering the competition in the market place, one can easily find "treatment" no matter how little money one has. Some of these therapists are so fanatic that they will treat patients for nothing, so noble do they consider to be their cause. If someone has money to give away, there will always be someone who will be pleased to take it. For such people there will always be the exploiters and the psychopathic types, those who have no belief at all that their patients were indeed sexually abused, but who are quite happy to take money from any gullible individual who is willing to give it to them.

There are other "therapists," however, who really believe that most of the patients who come their way have indeed been sexually abused. Interestingly (but not surprisingly), most of these therapists are women. (I will elaborate soon as to why this is the case.) Accordingly, for simplicity of presentation, I will refer to the therapist as a female, although there are certainly some men who have jumped on the bandwagon as well (especially men in the aforementioned psychopathic category). Some of these women have actually been sexually abused themselves when younger. Not having come to terms with their own sexual abuse, and not having worked out whatever residual psychological problems may have resulted for them, they harbor ongoing animosity toward men. It is not simply their fathers (or their uncles, grandfathers, or whoever else it was who abused them), but *all* men must pay for the sins of these individuals. If they had their way, they would wreak vengeance on all *man*kind (not *woman*kind). What better way to wreak vengeance on men than to become a therapist and use one's patients to act out one's morbid hostility. One can become even more effective in the implementation of this grand plan if one sees sex abuse in just about every patient who comes one's way. In this way, all men can pay for their depravity. The possibility that an accused man may be innocent does not cross their minds.

These are the people who are ever waving the banner "children never lie" and are deeply committed to the dictum that if a child claims he (she) was sexually abused, it must have happened. The extension of this is "adult women who profess sexual abuse in childhood also never lie." The principle is: "If you have a fantasy that it happened, it must have happened. Otherwise, where else would the fantasy come from?" In the opinion of these individuals, a fantasy must relate to some external reality. A fantasy cannot be the result of external suggestion or internal psychological processes. As long as they follow this principle, they can gratify the pathological motives that operate in their having selected the profession of sex-abuse therapist.

Some of these therapists are overtly paranoid. They may even have been graduates of a prestigious and well-recognized kind of therapeutic program (e.g., psychiatry, psychology, and social work). Some have been trained by paranoids, thereby transmitting the pathology down yet another generation. Such paranoid therapists are particularly attractive to adult women who claim their fathers sexually abused them. These therapists may not have been sexually abused themselves, or they may have. In either case, they are paranoids and they will predictably bring preparanoid patients into the paranoid realm and, when already paranoid, make them worse. What develops is what we refer to in psychiatry as a *folie-à-deux* relationship. This is a disorder in which one party, a more assertive and aggressive individual, inculcates his (her) psychopathology into a weaker and more passive individual. Attempts by family members to convince the accusing woman that her therapist is making her sicker, not better, prove futile. The bonding between these two women becomes unbreakable. Even the slightest criticism will not be tolerated.

What Do These People Do?

Ignorance and/or Failure to Accept Well-Established Concepts of Memory In order to understand exactly how these therapists work, it is important for the reader to have some background on the phenomenon of memory. Obviously, it is beyond my purposes here to discuss the phenomenon of memory in detail. Rather, I will focus on certain aspects of memory that are particularly relevant to the adult woman who accuses her father of sex abuse. Further, I will focus on the ways in which these therapists ignore and/or distort well-established principles of human memory.

Encoding, Storage, and Retrieval One can break down memory into three large categories: encoding, storage and retrieval. Encoding (registration) refers to the process by which an external stimulus is transmitted into the brain, where it is stored. Storage (retention) refers to the processes by which the material is retained in the brain. Retrieval (recall or decoding) refers to the process by which the stored memory is brought into conscious awareness. The analogy to a camera's making a photograph is applicable here. When a camera takes a picture, it reproduces on the film (the storage place) a fairly accurate reproduction of what has been transmitted through the lens. This is not what happens with human beings. Whereas the camera is indiscriminate and sees "everything," the human is selectively attentive to that which the individual wants to see and selectively inattentive to those things that the brain does not wish to register. A wide variety of psychological mechanisms are operative in determining what will pass through the human eye in a meaningful way. Most important are our wishes and mechanisms of guilt, shame, and denial. These modify significantly what will be encoded and then stored in the brain.

Now to carry the analogy further. The retrieval process can be compared to removal of the photograph from the camera, album, or file. Generally, the photograph is the same (with the exception of situations in which it might be marred or destroyed, and the likelihood of this increases over time). The view that human memories remain fixed in the brain, especially over time, is not consistent with the best research on the subject. Rather, the already distorted renditions of reality that have been stored are reworked and restructured in the storage compartments of the brain (primarily the hippocampus). And this is an extremely important point. The memory does not sit there like a rock in a box, unchanged over the years. Rather, it becomes reworked, reconstructed, and integrated with other memories, each of which is distorted and changed over time. An important element determining what happens to this memory is what we *want* to happen to it. If the memory involves material that makes us uncomfortable, ashamed, or guilty, it is very likely that it will be altered in a direction that will remove these unpleasant thoughts and feelings. Memories are reconstructed; they are not reproduced. Furthermore, there is a certain amount of reorganization that takes place in order to give the memory a consistency and logical sequence that it may not otherwise possess. An example of this phenomenon is what we do with dreams. Dreams enter conscious awareness in what to us appears to be a disorganized format. Most often when we relate a dream, we automatically give it a continuity that it does not intrinsically possess.

And the retrieval process, separate from the storage process, also involves selective attention and reworking. Here too we ignore what makes us unhappy and uncomfortable and rework the memory into a format that pleases us. And this final "memory" may have little if anything to do with the original reality of which it is a derivative. And it is this final product that we call the memory. And even this may be altered over time as our views about the original event warrant further modification. Dawes (1991) puts it well: "It is the story that creates the memory, rather than vice versa."

With regard to childhood memories, the distortions may be introduced by parents and other family members. It is extremely important to appreciate this universal principle. When an individual talks about an early childhood experience, it is often useful (if possible) to get the parents' input regarding the validity of the child's rendition of the event. I am not claiming that the parents' version is going to be the "right" one (for the reasons already mentioned); I am only claiming that it is more likely to be a more accurate reflection of reality. A common phenomenon is a person's remembering an event that either never occurred, or had occurred at a time when the person was really too young to remember it but still believes that it took place. What the person is remembering is the parents' version of the event, told at the time or possibly later. The French psychologist Piaget provided an excellent example of this phenomenon from his own life. For many years he told about an early memory in which he recalled his nurse foiling an attempt to kidnap him from his carriage when he was two years old. Years later this nurse, then retired, sent a letter to his parents informing them that there was no such kidnapping attempt and that she had concocted the story in order to impress the parents with her efficiency and vigilance. Piaget had heard the story so often from his parents that he actually came to believe that he was witness to the event (Toufexis, 1991).

Therapists of the kind I describe here take many liberties with the aforementioned well-founded principles. They believe that if an individual has a memory of a childhood sexual experience, it must be true. They do not believe that our mind can play tricks on us and that we can actually have visual images of things that never happened. They do not believe in the restructuring of memories over the passage of time. They believe that memories are like rocks in a box or permanent photographs. Obviously, such ignoring of well-established scientific principles serves to maintain the *folie-à-deux* relationships they have with their patients.

Flashbacks Another area of memory with which the therapists described here take liberties relates to the phenomenon of the "flashback." A flashback is basically an eruption into conscious awareness of a buried memory that has generally been traumatic.

Usually, the flashback is brought into conscious awareness by some external stimulus that evokes it. Often, the stimulus has some similarity to the original traumatic event. An example would be the war veteran who has been traumatized in battle. Years later, exposure to situations that might be peripherally similar to the original battlefield conditions may evoke visual imagery (and associated thoughts and feelings) of actual battlefield scenes.

An important element in the flashback phenomenon is that there is generally no prolonged period in which the traumatized individual is completely free of flashbacks. Rather, as time goes on, their frequency diminishes, sometimes even to the point where they will be rare. Obviously, the greater the trauma, the longer will be the period of flashbacks and the less the likelihood that they will disappear completely. Individuals who suffer from flashbacks do not generally have the experience of many years of freedom from them and then their sudden reappearance 15, 20, or 30 years later. There are just too many environmental stimuli that can potentially evoke the flashback to allow for such a prolonged symptom-free period.

Therapists of the kind I am describing here do not subscribe to this well-established principle. Rather, they believe that a girl who was sexually abused at three can be completely free of flashbacks for many decades and then, at age 43, for example, can suddenly experience flashbacks about her experiences. Sexual intercourse with her husband (even after years of marriage) may have served as the evoking stimulus. Although the woman may have had sexual relations with her husband hundreds of times, and although she may have had multiple sexual experiences with other lovers (past and present), this particular sexual encounter — one that occurred in the course of treatment — now becomes the evoking stimulus for the flashback. Or, if she is not in treatment, it may have occurred after she read an article about it or learned about a friend who had this experience. (We see here once again the power of human suggestibility and gullibility.) In either case, the flashback is considered to be "proof" of the abuse, and the therapist is likely to point to the phenomenon's inclusion in the *DSM-III-R* as one of the manifestations of the post-traumatic stress disorder (PTSD), the diagnosis most often applied to people who have been raped and/or sexually traumatized in other ways.

Body Memory A related phenomenon, subscribed to by the kinds of therapists I am talking about here, is sometimes referred to as "body memories." This is a relatively new term, appearing only within the last few years, and it is said to be a kind of flashback in which physical contact (usually of a sexual kind) evokes a flood of memories involving a similar kind of body experience. The individual then experiences particular physical symptoms, which are presumably identical to those that were experienced at the time of the abuse. Whereas flashbacks are generally psychological, body memories are considered to be the physical analogy of the flashback. They are considered to provide even more compelling confirmation that the abuse took place. The body memory theory has been especially invoked in situations in which the abuse occurred before the age of one or two, the age below which human beings are not considered capable of recall. The *mind* may not remember the event, but the *body* is able to. Accordingly, when an individual claims that she was sexually abused at the age of four months, it is not her brain that is bringing about the recall, but the body's memory of the event, especially those parts of the body that were directly engaged in the sexual acts. The theory here is that these organs have some kind of a memory that acts independently of the brain.

Certain circumstances may have the effect of "reminding" these latent memory cells about certain past events (especially sexual traumas that the particular organ was subjected to), and they are thereby brought into action and produce the physical sensations that the individual experienced at the time of the original trauma. This concept is a true testament to the ability of the human being to rationalize the preposterous. If this theory is true, then we have been wrong all these years when we have believed that memory resides only in the brain. According to these people, there are *also* memory cells in those organs involved in sexual activities, e.g., the vagina, the penis, and the anus. Of course, no one has yet demonstrated these pockets of neurological memory cells in these organs, but this does not dissuade the believers from their conviction for their existence. Actually, I should be less mocking of these people and should appreciate that they may be on to something that can be a boon to medicine and should be a source of hope for people with Alzheimer's disease, brain tumors, and other degenerative diseases of the brain. These pockets of memory cells could be transplanted from the genital organs or anus to the brain, thereby restoring the individual to normal memory. Or, people might be able to be trained to use these cells as satellite brain replacements. Such brain cells in the genitals could conceivably contribute to a reduction in unwanted pregnancies (please excuse the pun) and sexually transmitted diseases (including AIDS). Furthermore, an individual might even be trained to think with his (her) anus!

Accretion   Another principle of memory that is important to appreciate here is that of accretion. Normally, we forget a vast majority of all things that happen to us. If we were to continually keep in memory—especially conscious awareness—all the things that occur, we would be driven insane. There must be a process of repression and suppression. There must be a process of relegation to the unconscious of the vast majority of memories. All of us may exhibit the phenomenon of progressive elaboration of a memory after initial recall. More specifically, a long-forgotten event may be brought into memory by some external evoking stimulus (such as a friend or relative reminding us of the experience). Initially, we may recall only a small fragment of the event. However, with further discussion and "mental searching," we may be able to retrieve from our memory bank progressively more material about the event. This is normal.

"Therapists" will frequently use a fragmentary memory of a presumably long-past sexual encounter as the point of departure for the accretion process. They will continually encourage their patients to think deeper and harder in order to extract from the storage compartments of their mind ever more detail about the alleged sexual encounter with the father. When the patient complies with these requests, the elicited "memories" are considered to be verifications of the fact that there was indeed sexual trauma. What is not considered is an alternative explanation, namely, that the progression of provided fantasies have nothing to do with the aforementioned accretion process but are related to the suggestions of friends, relatives, the therapist, the public media, the ambient sex hysteria, and the wish of the patient to provide such material. Ostensibly, the process for both true and false accusations is the same. However, two very different things are going on here. In the case of the true accusation, the process of accretion is normal and expected. In the case of the false accusation, the process of accretion results from human fantasy and suggestibility. These therapists will provide support for their position by pointing to the fact that there are indeed sexually abused women who do indeed exhibit the accretion phenomenon and will—quite honestly and accurately—provide increasing details of actual sexual experiences. Their critics argue that one can obtain the same results by the process of suggestibility. This is one of the knottiest problems confronting those who are trying to differentiate between true and false sex-abuse accusations. In such cases, one must look to other sources of information, information unrelated to the accretion phenomenon, in order to decide whether the accusation is true or false.

Commitment to the Concept of a Memory-Free Hiatus   A typical scenario provided by adult women who claim that they were sexually abused as children is one in which they learn, sometime in adult life, that they were sexually abused in childhood, often in infancy. As mentioned, they usually claim total amnesia for the events until the moment of recent revelation. There are certain aspects of this hiatus that can provide examiners with important information regarding whether the accusation is true or false. First, anyone who claims to recall events that occurred before the age of one is probably providing a false accusation. Most people cannot recall any events in their lives prior to the age of four or so. There are some who appear to be recalling accurately events that took place when they were three. Most knowledgeable experts in this area agree that memories dating back to the age of two are more likely to be repetitions of parental renditions that, over the years, have become believed by the child. These memories would be in the category of those described already by Piaget regarding his memory of his nursemaid protecting him from a kidnapper when he was two years old. Those who claim memory back to the age of one, in the opinion of most experts, must be fantasizing. The general consensus is that the child's brain cannot cognitively recall and organize events well enough to provide coherent memories of events during the first year of life. The therapists that I am describing here have no suspicions about memories of events that took place in the second and third year of life and are even deeply committed to memories that took place in the first year of life. (They are helped along here by their commitment to the aforementioned concept of "body memories.") This receptivity lessens their credibility when claiming that the sex-abuse accusations have credibility.

In addition, these therapists have a deep commitment to the concept of the memory-free hiatus, during which time there was absolutely no recall of the sexual events. In some situations, the hiatus of repression may have credibility; in others it is highly improbable (if not impossible) and lends weight to the conclusion that the accusation is false. For example, if a woman claims that she was sexually abused throughout her childhood and adolescence, left the home at 18 because of a desire to remove herself from the indignities to which she was being subjected, then remembered nothing of her sexual experience until age 36 when the memories were uncovered in therapy, it is highly unlikely that she was sexually abused. If one is to believe this scenario, one has to believe that from age 18 to 36 she was completely amnesiac for events that occurred from ages 2 to 18. Anyone who believes this is as suggestible as the patients being described here. More possible (I am not saying probable) is the situation in which a woman may have been abused from ages four to seven, then repressed the memories of the trauma, and then recalled it in her mid-thirties, with or without "therapy." Repression at age six or seven of events that occurred over a two-to-three-year period is more credible than repressing memory of events that took place from ages 2 to 18. Less important than the time span over which the abuse occurred is the age at which the abuse stopped. It is understandable that one may forget events that took place when one was about five (all of us do). It is less credible to completely obliterate from memory experiences that took place throughout the teen years, especially if they were viewed as traumatic. Examiners do well, then, when trying to assess whether such an accusation is true or false, to define as clearly as possible the time frame of the original alleged abuse, the time frame of the hiatal period of alleged amnesia, and the age at which the individual came to the realization that she had been sexually abused.

This leads us to a central problem faced by those asked to ascertain whether an adult's previously repressed accusation of sex abuse is true or false. The principle that I follow is best introduced by two vignettes that demonstrate the extremes on a continuum. At the one end, for example, is a woman of 25 who was sexually abused between ages three and five and repressed the memories for 20 years, first recalling them at the age of 25. Furthermore, if such recollection did not take place in the hands of an overzealous therapist of the kind described above, it may very well be true. At the other end of the continuum is the 25-year-old woman who claims that she was sexually abused between ages 3 and 21, repressed entirely memories of the abuse for four years, and then realized she had been abused while in treatment with an overzealous therapist. Under these circumstances, the accusation is likely to be false. The guidelines, then, are these: the longer the period of abuse, especially abuses that extend into the teen period (and even later), the less the likelihood of its being repressed. In addition, the shorter the period of repression, especially repressions in which the time frame is completely within the confines of adult life, the greater the likelihood the accusation is false. In the hands of an overzealous therapist, these criteria for the false accusation are more likely to be satisfied.

Another factor relevant to this hiatal period is the absence of symptoms (as opposed to memory). If indeed the individual was traumatized during the time frame of the abuse, it is likely that there will not only be memories of the trauma (especially if the trauma was discontinued in the teen period), but residual symptoms that can be directly related to the trauma and not inferred by some great leap of illogical logic. The greater the freedom from symptoms during this hiatal period, the greater the likelihood the accusation is false. Overzealous therapists often justify the symptom-free hiatus with the argument that even *DSM-III-R* provides for a delayed-onset type of PTSD. It is certainly true that *DSM-III-R* describes a delayed-onset type of PTSD. However, what they fail to appreciate is that *delayed onset* is not necessarily synonymous with *symptom free*. What is being referred to in *DSM-III-R* is a situation in which, following the trauma, the individual did indeed have symptoms, but they were not great enough and frequent enough to warrant the PTSD diagnosis. Then, possibly because of other stresses, the individual does warrant the diagnosis. Viet Nam veterans with the delayed-onset type of PTSD have not left the combat zone clean-free of symptoms. Rather, they do suffer with symptoms prior to the period when the PTSD diagnosis becomes warranted.

Hypnotherapy   Not surprisingly, many of the therapists I am talking about here have a deep commitment to hypnotherapy. They view hypnotherapy to be an extremely valuable tool for uncovering repressed material. Whether hypnotherapy is truly capable of doing this is a point of controversy. What is less controversial is the fact that there is a strong relationship between hypnotizability and suggestibility. In order for one to be hypnotized, one must be suggestible. Basically, when one goes into what is referred to as a hypnotic trance, one is putting oneself in a dependent position in relationship to another person and demonstrating a willingness to comply with the requests and suggestions made by the hypnotherapist. I am not simply referring here to such mechanical acts as lying down, shutting one's eyes, and raising and lowering one's arms in compliance with the suggestions made by the therapist. These are obviously the most objective and easily observable manifestations of the patient's receptivity to comply with the therapist's suggestions. More subtle, and more difficult to objectify, is the patient's willingness to provide the specific kind of information that the therapist is requesting. Considering what I know of human suggestibility, I believe that there are many situations in which the patient and therapist together enter into a fantasy world in which the patient provides just the kind of fantasies that the therapist is asking for. These may have absolutely no basis in reality, but are provided because the therapist is asking for them and the patient, for a wide variety of reasons, wishes to comply with this request.

Probably one of the more dramatic examples of this phenomenon was seen many years ago, when significant attention was given to a book about a woman named Ruth Simmons who, in the skilled hands of a hypnotherapist, was not only able to regress to the earliest weeks of her life, but regressed back to a previous existence (as Bridey Murphy) in Ireland many years before her birth. She had never been to Ireland, but her recounting of a wide variety of experiences that allegedly occurred to her earlier self were convincing with regard to the detail they provided about life in Ireland during the early eighteenth century. Controversy raged regarding whether these fantasies reflected bona fide experiences in a previous life or resulted from genuine early childhood experiences that served as nuclei for the fantasies provided the hypnotherapist. The book not only served to enhance general belief in the power of hypnotherapy to uncover unconscious memories, but gave support to the theory of reincarnation. Accordingly, we are not dealing here merely with the suggestibility of the patient and the therapist, but the suggestibility of the people who believed these preposterous revelations that were allegedly uncovered by hypnotherapy.

I do believe that hypnotherapy *can* play a role in the treatment of *some* patients for *certain* specific conditions. I do not believe, however, that it is any more effective in bringing into conscious awareness unconscious material than simply relaxing in an environment without competing stimuli and trying consciously to recall earlier events. More important, however, is my belief that more suggestible people are more likely to be "hypnotized," that is, they enter into that altered state of attention that we refer to when we use that word. The fact that more suggestible people are more likely to be hypnotized increases the likelihood that these same people are more likely to "remember" childhood sex abuse than those who are not so easily hypnotized. Accordingly, those who seek hypnotherapy and those who are good candidates for hypnotherapy are also the same people who are more likely to provide fantasies about sex abuses that never took place.

Belief in the Child's Capacity to Make Extremely Subtle Differentiations   Most good and devoted fathers undress their children, bathe them, and help them when they go to the bathroom. Such activities inevitably involve a certain amount of contact with the child's genitals. When the contact involves the hand of the parent to the genitals of the child, it is extremely difficult—if not impossible—for the child to differentiate between contact that is associated with sexual arousal on the adult's part and contact that is not. And this is especially the case if the adult is a female. But even if the adult is a male, there may not be an apparent erection. But even if the adult's penis was erect, it is not likely that the three-year-old child is going to appreciate the link between that phenomenon and sexual arousal. Therapists who promulgate false sex-abuse accusations ignore children's inability to appreciate such differentiations and accept as valid the patient's statement that the activity was engaged in with sexual intent on the part of the parent.

Belief in Preposterous and Extremely Unlikely Events   One of the hallmarks of the false accusation is the inclusion of preposterous and even impossible events. One accusing woman stated that she was so embarrassed by the fact that her father had put his finger in her vagina when she was three years old that she did not permit her mother to bathe her thereafter. Her mother—now the wife of the father she was accusing of having molested her—denied that this was the case and claimed that she had continued to bathe this child up to the age of eight or nine, after which time she could trust her to bathe herself. The mother claimed, as well, that she certainly would have been concerned about her three-year-old child refusing to be bathed. Further-more, the mother pointed out the obvious fact that three-year-old children are not famous for their ability to bathe themselves and no one ever complained about this child's hygiene. Not surprisingly, the accusing woman's therapist accepted her patient's rendition as completely valid. Also not considered here was the fact that the insertion of a finger into the vagina of a three-year-old is likely to produce pain and bleeding, so tender are the hymenal and surrounding tissues at that age. Under these circumstances it is hard to imagine the child's not bringing this to the attention of the mother, either voluntarily or involuntarily.

Another woman claimed that following her "rape" at the age of two-and-a-half, there was extensive bleeding that lasted two or three weeks. She described herself as literally sopping up large amounts of blood and hiding the blood-stained rags and towels in various parts of the home because her father had threatened her with dire consequences if she ever divulged the sexual activities to the mother. I will not address myself to the question of whether such extensive loss of blood would have produced fainting, dizziness, and at least some symptoms of anemia. More important here is the incredibility of the story because if it is true, one has to believe that the mother never once found any of these rags and towels that were saturated with blood. Two-and-a-half-year-old children are not famous for their ability to hide blood-saturated materials in various parts of their home. Yet, both the mother and the daughter agreed on this point: the blood saturated rags were never found by the mother. Of course, once again, the therapist believed that the patient's rendition had to be valid because the divulgence was made in the course of a hypnotic trance. Also ignored is the fact that the insertion of an adult male penis into the vagina of a two-and-a-half-year-old would not only result in pain and bleeding, but lacerations that would require immediate medical attention involving suturing of lacerations, which, because of the age of the child, would usually have to be done under general anesthesia.

In one case in which I was involved, the mother claimed that she was sexually molested by her uncle when she was between ages two and five. She had gone into therapy suspecting sex abuse, but it was only in treatment that her "brilliant" therapist helped her uncover these memories of this now deeply repressed trauma. And hypnotherapy (thank God for it) was of invaluable assistance in the uncovering process. She did not disclose recognition of this abuse until about two years into therapy, at which time she engaged the services of a lawyer and started to move down the legal track. The uncle consulted an attorney and informed him that during the time frame when his niece was allegedly abused, he was serving in the U.S. Navy in the South Pacific (from 1942 to 1945). During this time frame he had not once set foot in the United States. When the accusing woman learned, through her attorney, that this was the case, she and the therapist quickly came up with the explanation that they had gotten the ages wrong and that it was really ages five to seven. The delusion had to be changed to justify its perpetuation, but this alteration appeared to be a "minor adjustment" and the case rolled on.

Examiners do well, then, to remember that the greater the number of improbable, preposterous, and even impossible elements included in the scenario, the greater the likelihood that the accusation is false.

Failure to Interview the Accused Father Typically, these therapists show little if any interest in speaking directly with the accused father. I personally have not yet come across one case (in the category of sex-abuse accusations being discussed in this chapter) in which the father has been invited to meet with the therapist, and in all those cases that have come my way, the therapist has refused to meet with the father, even when he has beseeched her to do so. The usual reason for refusing to see the father—a reason provided both by the therapist and the accusing daughter—is, "There was no point in wasting my valuable time on him because he would only deny it anyway." Such rejection only produces a deepening of the father's sense of helplessness, frustration, and a feeling of impotent rage. It must be remembered that these therapists are generally angry women, many of whom are on a lifelong vendetta against men. Anything they can do to hurt men provides them with a sense of morbid gratification. A truly neutral therapist, a therapist who had a balanced view regarding whether or not the abuse took place, would welcome input from the father in order to get information that might help make the differentiation. The failure to see the father is a strong statement of the therapist's bias and is one of the hallmarks of the false sex-abuse accusation.

The Destruction of the Father-Daughter Psychological Bond
The failure to interview is only the first step in a process that leads to the attenuation and ultimately the destruction of the father-daughter psychological bond. Most competent therapists appreciate that even if the sex abuse did indeed take place, this in itself is not necessarily a reason to eliminate the father-daughter bond. And this is especially the case if there has been a reasonably good relationship between the father and the daughter. This is even more the case if there are grandchildren who themselves have had a good relationship with the alleged abuser. Rather, such therapists believe that the best way for these women to "work through" their reactions to the abuse is to remove themselves entirely from their fathers. In the course of the "treatment," they are taught to hate their fathers and to view him as a despicable individual who deserves only scorn, rejection, and punishment. Any positive thing he may have done, either at the time of the alleged abuse or subsequently, is not considered to have any redeeming value. So heinous has been the crime he has committed that nothing good he may have done in the whole life of the accusing woman can in any way counterbalance the traumatic effects of the abuse. The therapy, then, fans the flames of hatred that come to consume the patient. And the hatred then extends to all those who may support the father's position. This misguided and sadistic approach to the father is also one of the hallmarks of the false sex-abuse accusation.

Commonly, these therapists conduct group therapy. In some cases, all members of the group are individuals who have been sexually abused as children and they meet in order to provide "support" for one another and to help each other deal with the residual traumatic effects of their abuse. In other cases, there are individuals who have come to treatment for a variety of problems and never considered the possibility that they are the result of childhood sex abuse. One of the purposes of introducing them into the group is to help them uncover what they have probably repressed and, predictably, with enough group support and encouragement, they inevitably uncover this repressed unconscious material. This, of course, is another statement of the gullibility of the human being, a gullibility which is necessary for the success of these "operators."

The Assumption that a Sexual Encounter Between an Adult and a Child Is Automatically Psychologically Detrimental As mentioned earlier in this book, sexual activities between adults and children are a universal phenomenon, have been practiced all over the world, and exist even to this day to a significant degree in every culture. Although less common in countries which are part of the Judaeo-Christian ethic, the practice is still highly prevalent in these countries as well. One can view adult-child sexuality to be related to the subjugation of women which is also an ancient tradition. Women and children, being weaker than men, have been easily exploited by the more powerful. However, and this is an extremely important point, such encounters are *not* necessarily traumatic. The determinant as to whether the experience will be traumatic is the social attitude toward these encounters. As Hamlet said: "There is nothing either good or bad, but thinking makes it so." In Chapter One I have given examples of societies in which such experiences were not traumatic and, even in our society, not all adult-child sexual encounters are psychological damaging. Studies of our culture—which do not start with the bias that they must be psychologically damaging—provide clear demonstration of this. In short, there are many women who have had sexual encounters with their fathers who do not consider them to have affected their lives detrimentally. There are others, however, who have been seriously damaged by these encounters. Again, I am not recommending the practice; I am only describing the reality of the world. Of relevance here is the belief by many of these therapists that a sexual encounter between an adult and a child—no matter how short, no matter how tender, loving, and non-painful—automatically and predictably *must* be psychologically traumatic to the child. This belief, of course, justifies the ongoing therapy ("No one knows how long it will take. It will certainly take many years."). Obviously, if the therapist did not take this position, then she would not be able to enjoy the financial rewards attendant to this conviction. A derivative of this is the encouragement of lawsuits, the purpose of which is to extract as much money as possible from the father, money which will presumably allow vengeance gratification, but which will also pay for the treatment.

THE "ENABLERS"

Alcoholics Anonymous uses the term "enablers" to refer to those individuals with whom alcoholics involve themselves—individuals who contribute to the promulgation of the drinking problem. They are also referred to as "codependants." These are people who have a vested interest in the maintenance of the problem because it feeds into their own psychopathology in some morbid way. Women who promulgate false accusations of sex abuse against their fathers typically surround themselves with enablers. I have already mentioned the process by which those who support the father are rejected and are removed entirely from the life of the mother and her children. This is part of the process by which these women acquire their enablers and weed out those who will not provide support. Often the accusing woman is married to a man who passively goes along with his wife's accusation. My experience with these men is that they suffer with one or more of the following defects: passivity, limited intelligence, fear of asserting themselves against their wives, defective independent thinking, and shared paranoia. In some cases they have involved themselves in a folie-à-deux relationship with their wives. They know, however, that if they were to actively claim that the sex-abuse accusation sounds "hokey," they may very well find themselves divorced. They have been observer to the quick rejection of all those who even suggest that the father might be innocent, and they fear that they too will quickly be thrown on the garbage heap if they express any doubt about the validity of the accusation.

The accusation may result in a civil war within the family. All brothers and sisters are required to join one side or the other. Those who are neutral and want to "stay out of it" may similarly find themselves rejected. Only those who come out directly in support of the accusation have any chance of having a relationship with the accuser. A therapist of the father, who might want to enlist the aid of one of the siblings, is not likely to be successful. Any sibling on the side of the father is rejected, scorned, or treated as if he (she) did not even exist. Accordingly, that person's assistance cannot be elicited by the therapist to help resolve the family problems. If the person is on the side of the accusing daughter, it is extremely unlikely that he (she) is going to accept an invitation to come to the father's therapist's office for purposes of bringing about rapprochement. And, not surprisingly, invitations by the father for his daughter to come to *another* therapist with him—even for the purpose of a consultation—are routinely rejected. There is only *one* therapist such women trust and that is the one with whom they have the folie-à-deux relationship.

Throughout the United States there is a network of groups that provide support for battered and abused women. Many of these have "underground" divisions which provide protection for women whose husbands would indeed pursue, beat, and even kill them if they were to be found. There is no doubt that such groups may play an important role for *some* women who are physically abused by their husbands. This is especially so because legal and other community services designed to protect such women generally operate at an extremely low level of efficiency. However, my experience has been that the people who administer such groups are somewhat indiscriminate with regard to the women whom they take under their wings. My experience also has been that *some* (I am not saying all) of the women who are active in these groups are so filled with rage that they lose their objectivity with regard to dealing with the husbands of the women they are sheltering, as well as men in general. Many are fanatic and some are paranoid. Operating with such a head of rage, they are likely to lose objectivity with regard to discriminating between women who genuinely need their services and those who are using them for other purposes. Women who promulgate false sex-abuse accusations may very well enter the system in order to go into hiding and gain assistance for relocation in a secret place. For many such accusing women there is no distance great enough to provide them with safety. Moving 3000 miles away may not be considered inconvenient if it can provide them with a feeling of some safety.

It is important to appreciate that some (I did not say all) of the women who organize and administer such protective group networks and "underground railroads" for women, abused children, and other groups seeking safety from persecutors may be operating with the utilization of the reaction formation mechanism. Their obsession with protecting children may be a thin disguise for their basic desire to harm them. In one case I was involved with the worker in such a "shelter" stated: "When these kids come in most of them deny they were sexually abused. But, after a few days here, after speaking to other kids who were abused, they become more comfortable talking about it, and after a week or so everybody discloses their abuse." The idea that these children are exhibiting the "keeping-up-with-the-Joneses" phenomenon is not even considered. Denial of this possibility provides them with an excellent opportunity to vent rage on all the men against whom sex-abuse accusations are made, accusations derived from this setting. Under the guise of helping and protecting children, they are really setting up a situation that results in their destroying them. It is not surprising, then, when some of these people are then subsequently brought up on charges of abusing children themselves. In such cases, the reaction formation mechanisms break down and the basic sadistic impulses reveal themselves.

Of course, the aforementioned therapists and the therapeutic groups that they provide must also be listed among the enablers. This is especially the case if the groups consist entirely of people who are trying to provide "support" for one another because they have all been sexually abused as children. Friends in the neighborhood and supporting relatives should also be added to the list. Adult women who were genuinely abused in childhood do not generally need to surround themselves with such a coterie of supporting individuals. The need for such a group belies the underlying weakness of the allegation, which is basically like a house of cards and could be "blown out of the window" by reasonable and healthy individuals. In many cases, it is so patently absurd that only a retarded or psychotic person would believe it. Yet, so great is the gullibility and suggestibility of many human beings that even the most preposterous scenarios may gain credibility. Because the accusation is basically weak, the woman needs to surround herself with supporting individuals who will help maintain the delusion. The presence of the coterie of enablers is one of the hallmarks of the false sex-abuse accusation and is generally not seen in women who have been genuinely abused.

THE MONEY/POWER FACTOR

Sex abuse is big business. There is lots of money to be made by a whole parade of individuals who involve themselves in these cases. Adult women who accuse their fathers of child sex abuse may very well turn to a lawyer for assistance. Considering the fact that in the United States there is approximately one practicing lawyer for every 340 people (1991 figures), it is reasonable to say that there is a sea of hungry lawyers out there who are happy to take money from any client, no matter how absurd the complaint. I am not claiming that *all* lawyers are this greedy and indiscriminate with regard to whom they take on as a client; I am only claiming that there are enough such types around to make it quite easy for women in this category to obtain legal assistance. Then, there are the subgroup of lawyers who are paranoid. Paranoids gravitate toward the law because, in part, it provides them with compensation for feelings of inadequacy via the utilization of a powerful structure which insures that "justice will be done" and that "wrongs" will be made "right." Not surprisingly, those paranoid women who find paranoid therapists are also likely to gravitate toward paranoid lawyers. We then have a folie-à-trois which will predictably cause the accused father formidable grief. Paranoia and litigation go hand in hand. Waving the flag that justice must be done, the three together seek to gain redress in a court of law and thereby obtain "proof" that the abuse did indeed take place. Because the allegation is basically like a house of cards resting on sand, the need for this external and formidable proof becomes more compelling.

The lawyer, of course, has been enlisted not only to prove in a court of law that the father is guilty but to gain punitive damages and money for the woman's therapy. And the lawyer, obviously, must also be paid for his services. This is only "just" because it was the father who caused all this trouble in the first place by his indulging himself in animal behavior with an innocent child who was too tender in years to protect herself. As mentioned, in many of these cases the blackmail element is apparent especially when the mother threatens the father that if he does not pay X amount of megabucks, she will press criminal charges and not just keep the case in the civil courts. When there is money to be made, exploiters will be quick to jump on the bandwagon. I was involved recently in a case in which an ex-daughter-in-law approached her former father-in-law—a man of affluence—and told him that if he did not provide her with $500,000 (tax free), she would accuse him of sexually abusing his grandchildren (with whom he had a deep relationship). Thus rebuffed, she reported him to the local child protection services who, predictably, descended upon this man like gangbusters. Naturally, the "validators" were armed with their anatomical dolls and, predictably, they concluded that all five of his grandchildren were victims of sex abuse. Although he did not submit to this blackmail, it cost him thousands of dollars in legal fees to exonerate himself.

In recent years, legislators have been besieged by requests for increasingly more money to be allocated to clinics serving people who have been sexually abused. Most of this money has gone for the evaluation and treatment of children but, considering the increasing number of adult women who are belatedly alleging sex abuse, these clinics are now facing a new "challenge," namely, dealing with yet another segment of the population requiring their services. It is not very "political" for a legislator to refuse to vote for money for such a worthy cause. Furthermore, these clinics are easily demonstrating an ever-growing population of abused individuals who are in *desperate* need of their services. When money is allocated *only* for the treatment of abused people, it is obvious that those who are falsely alleging abuse (those who are lying or delusional) are not likely to be designated as such because if the clinic does so, it will have less justification for demanding funds.

In the last few years, we have seen yet another development—a development that could almost have been predicted. I am referring here to modifications of statutes of limitations. Traditionally, those who commit criminal acts have enjoyed a certain period beyond which an accuser could no longer gain redress in a court of law. For example, seven years is a common limitation for initiating accusations of homicide. And lesser crimes generally involve shorter statutes of limitations. Obviously, a woman claiming sex abuse 35 years after the alleged crime could not press charges unless there had been some modification of the statutes of limitations. In many states, recently, such statutes have been changed so that the statute's time frame is not calculated from the actual date of the crime's commission, but from the time the woman first realized she had been abused. Accordingly, if a woman was allegedly abused at age three and at the age of 40 (37 years later), while in hypnotherapy uncovers unconscious material that leads her to the conclusion that she was abused at age three, she could press charges up to the age of 47 (under a seven-year statute of limitations calculated from the day she appreciated she was sexually abused). If the accused had murdered his daughter, there would only be a seven-year statute of limitations. However, because he is accused of committing the abominable crime of sex abuse, the statute of limitations (for him) has been extended to 44 years. We see here yet another example of how Constitutional safeguards are being ignored in the service of prosecuting individuals who are being accused of sex abuse.

Our founding fathers crafted our Constitution ever mindful of the abominations that those in power have perpetrated upon the

weaker and helpless. Constitutional safeguards, more than anything else, were designed to protect individuals from these de-
pravities. Statutes of limitation are an excellent example. Statutes
of limitation serve two primary purposes: (1) they protect defendants against irrational and excessive punishments that are likely
to be meted out in times of hysteria, and (2) they increase the
likelihood that defendants will be able to avail themselves of credible witnesses. In most states, there is a three-year statute of
limitation on most misdemeanors and a five-year statute of limitations on felonies. Adult women who claim they were sexually
abused as children are clamoring for changes in these laws,
changes that would calculate the beginning of the period of the
accused's vulnerability from the time she first realized she had
been sexually abused. Some of these women have been sexually
abused, and some of them have not. In either case, this change in
the statutes would deprive such defendants of a fundamental
constitutional right, considered to be one of the cornerstones of the
U.S. Constitution. The modification of these laws would deprive
sex-abuse defendants of these safeguards in an atmosphere that is
exactly of the kind the founding fathers were trying to protect
defendants from, namely, an atmosphere of hysteria in which
defendants would be deprived of credible witnesses. Not surprisingly, most lawyers are in favor of these modifications because
they would provide more opportunities for lawsuits, lawsuits that
the present statutes of limitation would prohibit. Because many (if
not most) legislators are lawyers who combine private practice
with their legislative obligations, it is likely that these modifications will be instituted in most, if not all, states. At this point (July
1992), the best information I have is that 21 states have now passed
such legislation and many others are in the process of giving
serious consideration to these changes. In short, the trend is
"sweeping the nation" at a very rapid rate, and the likelihood of
the trend reversing itself in the near future is extremely small.

I have a real question as to whether those states that have
introduced these modifications are passing laws that are unconstitutional. Even murderers are protected by statutes of limitations, generally five to seven years. There is no question that

murderers today are given shorter prison sentences than sex abusers and are more likely to get out on parole earlier. This is just one example of the hysteria of our times, hysteria that is prevailing over reason and justice. I can appreciate the desire of those who have been genuinely abused to take action against those who have victimized them. However, until we have developed exquisitely sensitive criteria for differentiating between true and false sex-abuse accusations in this category (the guidelines presented here are an initial offering), changes in the statutes of limitations would be dangerous. They would open the floodgates for the hysterical false accusers, with tragic consequences for the victims of their false accusations.

Mention has been made of the immunity from lawsuits enjoyed by those who promulgate false allegations of sex abuse. Such immunity also serves the ends of the money/power structure. Individuals who falsely accuse cannot be countersued for perjury or libel unless malice can be proven. Because malice is an internal psychological state which cannot be objectively measured, it is almost impossible to prove malice in such cases. Although it may be obvious that the motives were indeed malicious, it is very difficult to prove this in a court of law. Because false accusers cannot be brought up on charges of perjury and libel, that route of redress is not available to the accused. Such statutes, although passed with the ostensible motive of protecting individuals from being sexually exploited, has the effect of keeping in business the power/money structure that thrives on sex-abuse allegations, whether they be true or false.

CONCLUDING COMMENTS

At the time I write this (July 1992) I have the feeling that belated sex-abuse accusations by adult women is only in the earliest stages of its growth. The combination of human suggestibility, gullibility, and avarice will predictably fuel this expansion of the phenomenon. I suspect that there will be many more such accusations in the immediate future. Recently (1992) the False Memory Syndrome Foundation (an organization recently set up by falsely accused parents), conducted a survey among their members. The following "therapy techniques" were described to have been utilized in bringing about the disclosures:

Satanism expert brought in	Yoga
Prayer therapy	Fasting
Primal scream therapy	Massage therapy
Sodium amytal	Astrology
Psychodrama	Channeling
Meditation	Crystals
Trance writing	Reflexology
Regression therapy	Massage therapy
Neuro-linguistic programming	

These sources of the disclosure are testament to the conclusion that fanaticism is running rampant here.

The crucial question is: What can be done about this? I believe that books such as mine may play a role (admittedly small) in bringing to the attention of all concerned parties what is going on. Perhaps with more appreciation by the public of how its monies are being spent, there will be a tightening up of legislative funding of those clinics that are contributing to the promulgation of this scandal. I believe that the immunity from being countersued that sex-abuse accusers enjoy has done much more harm than good. I believe that such laws should be rescinded. If this is accomplished, then it will be much easier to institute lawsuits against false accusers and this may have the effect of discouraging frivolous accusations. To the best of my knowledge, there have not been enough lawsuits against "therapists." Fortunately, those who operate along traditional professional tracks (such as psychiatry, psychology, and social work) are protected from malpractice suits under the principle that a professional is only expected to practice at the level of competence standard for peers in that same community. The therapists I have described here are not alone. In fact, there are thousands of "therapists" who will be willing to come to court and claim validity to the "therapeutic" modalities I have described here. I am certain that these therapists can provide a much longer parade of supporters than people like myself. My hope is that books such as this will contribute to a change in this situation.

A compelling argument against the notion that ongoing traumatic childhood experiences can be totally repressed over many years can be provided by the experiences of the Holocaust survivors. I am convinced that if one were to obtain a list of people who were released from Nazi concentration camps in 1945, and one were to trace these people for interviewing in 1992, it would be a rare person who would have totally forgotton the experience. I cannot imagine such a person saying, "concentration camp? What concentration camp? I have absolutely no memory of the experience" or "I had obliterated entirely any memories of having been in concentration camp." The whole experience was totally repressed. However, in the skillful hands of my therapist I gradually recovered memories of the cattle cars, firing squads, rape of women, gas chambers, and the crematoria." Possibly, there might be a very small percentage who did indeed repress some of their experiences, but there certainly would not be a flood of people claiming now dramatic "recall" of their childhood traumas.

Furthermore, I am certain that *these* survivors would not be found to have developed a multiple personalilty disorder, nor would they *suddenly* exhibit the signs and symptoms of a post-traumatic stress disorder 30 to 40 years after their release. And this would be true of other people who were subjected to other forms of prolonged childhood trauma, such as chronic physical illness, physical abuse, wars, earthquakes, and ongoing emotional abuse.

In short, if we are to believe these "victims" and their "therapists," we have to consider childhood sexual traumas to be such a special kind of experience that a whole series of well accepted psychological principles are inapplicable, and an entirely new set of psychological theories has to be invented to explain its alleged derivative symptoms. A new set of psychological principles has to be accepted, principles totally at variance with everything we know about childhood trauma, our capacity for repressing it, and its residual manifestations in adult life. This, then, brings me once again to a dictum I have repeatedly stated throughout the course of this book: "The most likely things are most likely." The evaluator who keeps this obvious wisdom in mind will be in the best position to ascertain whether a sex-abuse accusation is true or false.

CONCLUDING COMMENTS

> I have discovered the missing link
> between the higher apes and
> civilized man: it is we!
>
> Konrad Lorenz

INTRODUCTORY COMMENTS

This book ends on a note of anger, frustration, and pessimism. I am not ashamed of these feelings, nor do I consider them to be neurotic. I consider them to be a manifestation of my concern for the innocent victims of the sea of incompetents who are causing enormous grief because of their ignorance and/or stupidity. There is a difference between ignorance and stupidity. Ignorant people *do* have the basic intellectual capacity to know better, but they do not know how little they know. Sometimes the teachers who taught them were similarly ignorant. In contrast, stupid people do not have the brain substance to know better, and no amount of teaching is going to raise their level of competence. The incompetents I am referring to here are the parade of individuals who have been involved at many levels in promulgating false accusations of sex abuse. They are the "validators," "therapists," "child advocates," psychologists, psychiatrists, social workers, lawyers, district attorneys, detectives, judges, juries, and an assortment of other individuals who self-righteously scream "sex abuser" at anyone who is unfortunate enough to cross their path and get swept up in their delusion. The reader will note that advanced degrees in the most prestigious professions do not make people necessarily immune to being incompetent.

As a teenager I realized that there is an enormous gap between what the world is and what it potentially could be. I recognized also that this has probably always been the case and that it may be that things are better in this regard now than they ever have been. Some confirmation of this is suggested by the fact that at this time in history more people are literate and more people have been "educated" than ever before in the history of the world. I place quotes around the word *educated* because it is quite clear that what is passing for an education is much more often just a charade in which a gullible public is led to believe that taxpayers' money is actually being spent on learning experiences. Often, what is really happening is that poorly educated people are passing down their ignorance to the next generation, basically a situation in which the "blind are leading the blind." Rather than transmitting knowledge, they are transmitting ignorance. The students are not learning to open their eyes, observe the world around them, and make judicious decisions about what is happening. Rather, they are learning to gobble up indiscriminately what they are being "taught" and then periodically vomit forth this information on examinations, which, with grade inflation, lead the students to believe that they have been educated and are even "smart."

Most people today view people of the past as having been "ignorant," especially because they typically were swept up in superstition and the belief in the impossible. I do not believe that things have changed. The percentage of people who are swept up in believing the impossible, or only infinitesimally possible, is probably no different today from what it was in the past. What is different is the *nature* of the impossible things that are believed. In ancient Rome augury was widely practiced. Augurs claimed that they could foretell the future by the study of what would appear to others to be unimportant and trivial events, such as the behavior of animals and the movement of celestial bodies. Omens were omnipresent for those with the sensitivity to be alerted to them. The examination of the entrails of sacrificed beasts was considered by them to be an important source of information about future events. Their prognostications were not only taken seriously by the population at large, but even by emperors and generals. Cato the Censor, a Roman skeptic, said, "I am amazed that one augur can pass another without grinning." The belief in astrology and such superstitions as a black cat crossing one's path bringing bad luck are present-day residua of augury.

In the Middle Ages, most people believed in demons who did the work of the devil, and many forms of undesirable human behavior were attributed to these spirits. In our "modern times," most people do not hold to these "primitive" explanations for human behavior. However, those who really believe that we have advanced significantly in this realm are misguided. In the late 20th century we are witnessing what is only a slight modification of these earlier explanations for human behavior. Specifically, there are hundreds of thousands (and probably millions) who believe that satanic influences are playing a role in driving sex-abuse perpetrators to subject their victims to their abominations. This theory not only explains bona fide sex abuse but is expanded to include fantasized sex abuse as well, so that sex abuse is considered to have taken place in situations in which there is absolutely no evidence (other than that which can easily be extracted from a three-year-old child). Those too sophisticated to impute their woes to Satan consider childhood sex abuse to be the cause of all their grief. They share this delusion with their therapists and a wide variety of other "experts" from a multiplicity of disciplines. Mass hysteria prevails with millions running scared. The specter of sex abuse has descended upon the land, like the plague in Europe during the 14th century, and no one may be safe. Shakespeare's Puck said it well in *A Midsummer Night's Dream:* "Lord, what fools these mortals be!" (*III, ii,* 115).

One of my favorite metaphors for life is that it is a circus and that human beings are the performing clowns. The sex-abuse scene is indeed a circus, involving many people who act just like clowns. The aforementioned parade of "professionals," e.g., the "validators," "child advocates," lawyers, psychiatrists, social workers, are indeed clowns. But the metaphor breaks down somewhat because clowns know they are clowning. Many of these people actually believe in what they are doing. For others it is just a business. The clowns in the sex-abuse circus—both the "true believers" and those for whom it is just a business that enables them to exploit the gullible—are all serious. They do not realize that they are acting like clowns, and this is one of the reasons why they are so dangerous.

I have been providing testimony in courtrooms for approximately 32 years. I have spent thousands of hours sitting on the witness stand, watching carefully what is going on in front of me. I have good reason to believe that I am different from most witnesses in that position in that I do not just passively go along with the sport (which is what the courtroom scene basically is in that it is a competitive game with spectators), but I think seriously about the spectacle, and I assess it from the vantage point of a psychiatrist and psychoanalyst who is ever thinking about *the reasons why* people do what they do. It is from this vantage point that the circus metaphor is most applicable. In fact, it is a three-ring circus. In one ring is the accuser, the prosecutor, the detectives, the district attorney, the "child advocates," the "validators," and the attorneys who are there to zealously support their clients' position, whether or not they have any conviction for it. (Often the lawyers know the accusing woman is "crazy," but they are happy to take her money as long as it lasts; they have basically been taught in law school that this is "ethical.") In another ring is the defendant and his lawyers (who may or may not have any conviction for his position). However noble and honorable the defense attorneys may be, they are still involving themselves in the adversary system, which, in its present form, warrants the circus metaphor. In the third ring is the judge. He (she) too is swept up in the adversarial system and generally believes that it is the best method for finding out whether the abused did indeed once put his hand on the vulva of this three-year-old child when he took her to the toilet. His belief that the courtroom setting is the best way to find out whether this happened also makes him a clown. One could argue that I, too, am a clown and that I am sitting there in the fourth ring. From 1988 to 1991 I quit going to the "circus" of the courtroom, in *part* because of my revulsion of the scene. One of the important reasons for my returning is that there were many people who were falsely accused of sex abuse who were pleading for my services, and to deprive them of my testimony increased the likelihood that they would be jailed. Accordingly, I am back in the circus and suffer the indignities attendant to that decision—with the recognition that it is the price I must personally pay if I am to be of help to some of the unfortunate victims of false sex-abuse accusations.

SEX-ABUSE HYSTERIA

About a year-and-a-half ago, I described in detail the sex-abuse hysteria that we are witnessing (Gardner, 1991a). It is difficult to say whether things have improved since the publication of that book. On the positive side, I believe that there are now more people who are aware of the fact that many sex-abuse accusations are false. However, this positive side is probably more than outweighed by the increasing number of people who believe that "children never lie" and if a child professes sex abuse (even after being programmed by a "validator"), the allegation must be true. Whether or not things are better or worse, there is still no question that things are very, very bad. There are still hundreds (and probably thousands) of innocent people who are in jail who, I am convinced, are innocent. One need only look at the newspapers; it is not difficult to find evidences for the hysteria. One component of hysteria is overreaction. Whether or not the particular instance of sex abuse actually occurred, we see formidable overreaction—one manifestation of which is the Draconian punishments meted out to sex abusers.

I could give many examples of the hysteria from the daily

newspapers. One such example: The February 4, 1992, (Ryckman, 1992) edition of *The Plain Dealer* (Cleveland, Ohio) describes the plight of a woman named Denise Perrigo, who noted that, when breastfeeding her 2-1/2-year-old child, she was experiencing sexual arousal. She called a community volunteer center "hotline" to obtain the telephone number of her local La Leche League, a breastfeeding advocacy and support group. The volunteer, after hearing her question, referred her to the local "Rape Crisis Center," which she naively called. (In retrospect, this is probably the biggest mistake she ever made in her 29 years on earth.) The Rape Crisis Center called the "child abuse hotline." Soon thereafter, Ms. Perrigo was arrested and her daughter taken away by the Department of Social Services (DSS), which decided that breastfeeding a child at the age of 2-1/2 is de facto sex abuse. The fact that the international average length of nursing is 4.2 years meant absolutely nothing to DSS or to the judges involved in Ms. Perrigo's case. The child was placed in a foster home; even the maternal grandparents were not considered to be fit guardians because they did not consider their daughter to have sexually abused their grandchild. The judge who finally concluded that no sex abuse had taken place still viewed Ms. Perrigo as neglectful because she had subjected her daughter to DSS interviews by making the telephone call in the first place. We see here the kind of no-win situation in which falsely accused people often find themselves with the legal and social apparatus designed to "help" them.

In another example of the hysteria, a group that refers to itself as the Roper Organization sent out a book entitled *Unusual Personal Experiences* to 100,000 mental health professionals in May 1992. The pamphlet is devoted to visitations to earth by space aliens. In the introduction, John E. Mack, M.D., a professor of psychiatry at the Harvard Medical School, urges readers to believe patients who recall being abused by space aliens (Mack, 1992). The Roper Organization survey indicates that two percent of Americans now remember being abused by space aliens. There are two possibilities here: One is that these people are relating actual experiences and that we should heed Dr. Mack's advice.

The other is that they have not been so visited and that their beliefs are manifestations of psychiatric disturbance, including hysteria and paranoia. I personally believe that the latter explanation is far more likely than the former.

I do believe that there are probably thousands and even millions of places in the universe that could accommodate the kind of life we enjoy here on earth. I also believe that light travels at the speed of 186,000 miles per second, i.e., in one second light can travel a distance approximately equal to 7-1/2 times the circumference of the earth. I believe also that the nearest star (sun) that could *possibly* (I did not say *probably*) have a planet that could accommodate life is four light years away. I believe also that "aliens" could not survive as aliens if they could be brought to travel at the speed of light, especially because matter cannot exist in the form of matter when it travels at that speed. Accordingly, the only kind of visitation by aliens that could be possible would involve life-sustaining colonies, traveling at much lower speeds, that would have to prepare to exist over hundreds of generations as a space colony before landing on some distant place such as Earth. Of course, this presupposes a life form similar to ours.

Even if my reasoning is faulty here, especially because my brain cannot think logically about alternative life forms, of this I am certain: No demonstrable evidence of such landings has ever been found. Certainly, no aliens have ever been captured, nor residua of their "space ships," which have been confirmed to be extraterrestial in origin. Of course, many *claims* have been made about such evidence and there are thousands who will swear by everything that is holy to them that they have met space aliens, but there is a big difference between those who claim that they have met them and those who have actually introduced them to the rest of us. Somehow, all those who have met space aliens share in common one thing: the alien has never stayed around long enough to have a press conference, have its photograph taken, appear on the talk shows, etc. In short, we see here how people who enjoy the most prestigious positions in famous universities are not immune from being swept up by hysteria.

We are living in dangerous times, similar to Nazi Germany

under Hitler and Communist Russia under most of its dictators. The similarities are greater than the differences. People are not being roasted in ovens and relegated to slave labor in gulags. They are, however, being jailed with Draconian punishments that are unconstitutional and made pariahs of their families and communities.

The hysteria appears to be worsening. I believe it is reasonable to say that at this time there are millions of people in the United States who are either directly accusing or supporting false sex-abuse accusations and/or are reacting in an extremely exaggerated fashion to situations in which bona fide sex abuse has occurred. People are running scared. Nursery schools are videotaping throughout the course of the day, especially when the child is taken to the bathroom. Divorced fathers are afraid to bathe their children. No sane teacher would counsel a child alone in a room, behind a closed door. Grandfathers are scared to hug their grandchildren and uncles are scared to hug their nieces and nephews, lest they be accused of "bad touching." Scout masters travel in clusters, rather than alone. People are constantly surrounding themselves with "witnesses" in order to protect themselves from false sex-abuse accusations.

THE MULTIPLE PERSONALITY DISORDER

When I was in medical school and residency training, I was taught that the multiple personality disorder (MPD) was extremely rare. I saw no such patients in medical school and saw only one patient with MPD throughout the five years of my internship and residency training. In recent years, many psychiatrists hold that the disorder is much more common than previously realized and that an important etiological factor is childhood trauma that is dealt with by *dissociation*. Grinspoon (1992a) provides an excellent definition of dissociation:

> Dissociation can be described as a process or experience in which the unity of consciousness is disrupted, normal integrated awareness is disturbed, and mental functions are separated into

complexes that operate autonomously. Connections, continuity, and consistency are lost; the sense of identity changes, groups of memories, feelings, and perceptions are relegated to separate compartments or buried in oblivion from which they may suddenly emerge. (p. 1)

People who have devoted themselves to the study of individuals with MPD claim that it is frequently associated with childhood physical and/or sexual abuse and that the dissociative process serves to protect the individual from conscious awareness of the painful thoughts and feeling associated with the abuse. Not surprisingly, people who feel the need to support a false sex-abuse accusation have jumped on the MPD bandwagon. Now we are taught that it is much more common than we have previously realized and that MPD is the plight of many sexually abused individuals. Of course, the individual may not realize that he (she) is suffering with MPD, but this is not surprising because the disorder involves the process of "dissociation," which, by definition, means that the individual is not consciously aware of what is going on within himself. (However, the therapist is.)

And this brings us to one of the central problems in psychoanalytic theory and treatment. The theory is based on the assumption that there are mental processes that are beyond the realm of conscious awareness, i.e., in the unconscious compartment of the mind. I personally believe that there are unconscious processes, dreams being an excellent example. One of the problems with psychoanalytic theory is that of demonstrating and/or proving that specific thoughts and feelings are indeed stored in a particular individual's unconscious mind. Often what is considered to be present in the *patient's unconscious mind* is present only in the *psychoanalyst's conscious mind*. If the patient denies any awareness of such material, the analyst can say, "Of course you don't know about it. It's in your *unconscious*." This presents a no-win situation for the patient as well as anyone who might be dubious about the validity of the analyst's statement. As a psychoanalyst myself, and as someone who has served for many years on the faculty of a psychoanalytic institute, I am familiar with this problem. It is *one* of the reasons why I no longer serve on a psychoanalytic faculty. Imputing unconscious memories of childhood sex abuse is one recent offshoot of psychoanalytic theory.

Until recently, the controversy within psychiatry regarding the prevalence of MPD was a relatively minor one and was confined to whether it was a *very rare* or just a *rare* disorder. No one paid very much attention. Now it has become center stage, not, I believe, because it has gotten more common, but because the childhood trauma factor has enabled overzealous and even fanatic examiners to seize upon this medical-psychiatric disorder to give "scientific credibility" to their allegations. This is similar to the way the post-traumatic stress disorder has been utilized for this purpose. Because there is no "sex abuse syndrome," over-zealous examiners have to find other *DSM-III-R* entities to justify and provide credibility for their allegations. Abused children who deny they were abused are considered to have been abused but are "dissociating" the thoughts and feelings associated with their trauma. These children are considered to be individuals who will ultimately become diagnosed as MPD. Interestingly, many of these people say "dissassociating" rather than *dissociating*. Their misspelling of the term is yet another example of their ignorance of the sources from which they are borrowing material. (So widespread is their misuse of the word that I would not be surprised if theirs becomes standard spelling within the next few years.) Adults who are not consciously aware of the fact that their psychiatric problems are derived from childhood sexual abuse can be considered to be suffering with MPD and, in the hands of an allegedly skilled therapist, will be able to tease out conscious awareness of their abuse. Coons (1986) describes in detail this delicate process.

Aldridge-Morris (1989) is critical of the widespread application of the MPD diagnosis, especially as a way of justifying sex abuse. Aldridge-Morris states, "One should only diagnosis multiple personality when there is corroborative evidence that complex and integrated alter egos, with amnesic barriers, existed prior to therapy and emerge without hypnotic intervention by clinicians." I am in full agreement with Aldridge-Morris. He recognizes that there are some individuals who indeed suffer with MPD and that this disorder might very well have resulted from early childhood traumas, including sexual. However, he also holds that it is being overdiagnosed and that one way of differentiating between those who genuinely warrant the diagnosis and those who do not is to use the criterion regarding whether the disorder existed prior to "therapy," especially therapeutic techniques such as hypnotherapy. The reader who is interested in a sober statement on the dissociative disorders does well to refer to Grinspoon's articles (1992a, 1992b).

PROBABILITY THEORY

Many years ago, while in medical school, we were often reminded that "the most likely things are most likely." This warning was considered important because of the traditional tendency of medical students to diagnose those diseases that they had read about the night before. For some, this tendency related to the fact that the diagnosis was the first to come to mind when puzzled about a patient's disease. For others it was an attempt to try to impress upon their instructors their diagnostic acumen, an acumen that enabled them to see esoteric diseases when others (especially senior people) did not. Under such circumstances, a student would proudly state that his (her) patient had a particularly rare tropical disease, and the professor might comment, "It looks like the old garden variety of viral gastroenteritis to me." The admonition that the *most likely things are most likely* may seem absurd to the point of being inane; however, I consider it to be a great wisdom. It is unfortunate that the vast majority of people in this world do not heed it. It is indeed sad that many (if not most) people in this world do not appreciate this obvious truth. One of the central problems with which we are dealing in the false-sex-abuse allegation realm is basically this one. Those who believe many false accusations seem to operate on just the opposite principle, namely, "The most *un*likely things are most likely." One could argue that less educated and/or less intelligent people might be forgiven their failure to appreciate this principle. Unfortunately, the ignorance goes way beyond people in those two categories, even to the highest levels of professional expertise.

I have often had the desire to have the opportunity to give a simple lecture on basic probability theory to judges and juries. Unfortunately, I have not had such an opportunity (and I doubt if I ever will). I would start off with the traditional coin-flipping examples. I would try to demonstrate how the chances of flipping a *heads* with one flip is *one* out of *two*, or 1/2. I would then go on to talk about the chances of flipping two heads in a row, which would be 1/2 *times* 1/2 or 1/4. Specifically, of four sets of two flips each (a total of eight flips), only two flips (i.e., one set) are likely to result in two heads. In addition, there is likely to be one set of two tails, one set of a head and a tail, and one set of a tail and a head. I would then go on to explain how the chances of flipping three heads in a row would be 1/2 x 1/2 x 1/2 or 1/8, i.e., the chances are that only one of eight sets of three flips each (a total of 24 flips) would result in three heads being flipped. I would then demonstrate the basic mathematical principle that the probability of a series of events occurring is obtained by *multiplying* the probability of each event.

I would then go on to demonstrate this principle when applied to less common events, events that might have a probability of occurring once out of 10 times. The probability of two such events occurring together would be 1/100 (1/10 x 1/10), and three such events, 1/1,000 (1/10 x 1/10 x 1/10). I would carry this further to demonstrate that the probability of 10 such events occurring would be 1/10,000,000,000 (1 over 10^{10}) or one in 10 billion sets. I would try to apply this to the sex-abuse situation by giving a probability of 10 percent to each of the events. I would then go on and try to apply the same principle to events with a much lower likelihood, like 5 percent and 2 percent. My hope would be that the listeners would ultimately appreciate how remote is the possibility of *all* of these events having taken place under the same circumstances. Unfortunately, I suspect that my efforts would prove futile. I believe that the vast majority of individuals would not understand what I was trying to get across, and I would lose the attention of many judges and juries before I got very far along. I do not believe that this relates to the complexity of these concepts. Nor do I believe that their failure to follow what I am saying relates to impaired intelligence. Rather, I believe it relates to the low level of education that most people receive, especially with regard to being required to figure things out by themselves. Moreover, I believe that their logical processes would be compromised and dulled by the prevailing hysteria of our times.

PREVALENCE

The issue of prevalence comes up frequently when dealing with child sex abuse. Newspaper reporters will often ask me, "How widespread is child sex abuse?" Obviously, this is an impossible question to answer, not only because people are not going to divulge the abuse but also because there are many borderline situations in which the determination as to whether the act warrants the name *abuse* is very much "within the eye of the beholder." We cannot go from door to door surveying people with the question, "Excuse me sir (ma'am), can you tell me if you've ever sexually abused a child?" Nor can we use courtroom convictions because, I am certain, there are many abusers who have not been found guilty and many innocents who have been. Furthermore, when a teenage babysitter bathes a child and rubs the crotch area with sexual intent, how is one going to know that this has happened? Accordingly, we do not know whether there has been more child abuse occurring in recent years than there was in the past. At this point, I suspect that the frequency is no greater. There is no question, however, that media coverage of abuse has expanded enormously in recent years. Another question asked is: "How widespread are false accusations of child sex abuse?" Again, this is an impossible question to answer, and anyone who provides specific figures on this subject is "pulling them out of the sky." Even if one is to confine oneself to specific categories of false accusations, e.g., those that occur in the context of child custody disputes, it is impossible to know how prevalent such false accusations are, again for the same reasons just given.

The high prevalence of paranoia is not given the attention it deserves. The general consensus is that paranoid people are locked up in back wards of mental hospitals and have delusions that they are being persecuted by spies and foreign agents. I am convinced that for every paranoid in that category there are at least a hundred who are walking the streets and who look like "normal" individuals. I am convinced that many of the people involved in false sex-abuse accusations are paranoid. As described in detail in Chapter Twelve, they exhibit the most important characteristics of paranoid delusional thinking: projection, oversimplification, resistance to alteration by logic and confrontation with reality, and the protection of a fragile ego. Evaluators do well, therefore, to give serious consideration to the paranoid factor that may be fueling a false sex-abuse accusation.

Psychologists are likely to consider using the *Minnesota Multiphasic Personality Inventory-2* (MMPI-2) (Hathaway and McKinley, 1989) for detecting paranoia that might not be clinically apparent, or as a way of confirming paranoia in order to support the argument that the accusation is false. Those who are knowledgeable about the MMPI-2 recognize that it is not foolproof in this regard; however, it certainly may provide support that paranoia is present. I have recently had a few cases in which I was convinced that the sex-abuse allegation was false. The falsely accusing mother exhibited elevations both on the Paranoia and the Psychopathic Deviate Scales of the MMPI-2. Interestingly, in these cases, the falsely accused fathers *also* exhibited elevations on these very same scales. I considered the findings in the mothers to be consistent with the clinical picture, but not with the fathers. The mothers were delusional with regard to their belief in the sex-abuse accusation, and there was absolutely no good supporting evidence for the accusation. In addition, they were psychopathic with regard to the absence of guilt they exhibited over the effects on the father of the accusation. In contrast, I found absolutely nothing in these fathers to support clinically the MMPI-2 findings. What they shared in common was the fact that they had been dragged through two to three years of courtroom litigation and were subjected thereby to formidable psychological trauma. Their MMPI-2 paranoia scale elevations were the result of answering questions in which they described themselves as being persecuted and feeling that people were plotting against them. These individuals were not paranoid; they *were indeed* being persecuted. There *were* others who were actually plotting against them, people like their wives, "validators," lawyers, detectives, prosecutors, etc. And their elevations on the Psychopathic Deviate scale were, I believe, derived from their having reached the point of being willing to consider utilizing illegal and antisocial methods to protect themselves from further indignities and punishments. These are initial findings. I suspect that future studies will corroborate these findings.

Another phenomenon that I have come to appreciate as more prevalent than I had previously recognized relates to females who use males as "sperm donors" and then dispense with their services entirely. I believe that this is a widespread phenomenon that has not been given the attention it deserves. I believe that the craving to have children is genetically stronger in women than in men and that the frustration the "barren" woman feels is much greater than that which the fatherless male feels. I am not claiming that men have no paternal instincts; I am only claiming that the *maternal* instinct is stronger than the *paternal*. I believe it is important to differentiate between sexual drive and parental instinct. I do not know whether the sexual drive in the average man is greater than that in the average woman. I do believe that the average man is genetically programmed to be more promiscuous than the average woman and that the woman's sexual arousal is more related to relationship factors than simple sexual drive.

Women certainly want men as providers, but this can be separated from their services as protectors. Women no longer need husbands as on-site protectors, in contrast to the need in earlier times, when the world was so predatory that on-site guards were extremely important to have and were often necessary for survival. In the 20th century, as was true in the past, most women still need men as providers. Also, in the 20th century, money is the primary vehicle by which such providing is accomplished. Accordingly, what many (if not most) women want after conception is *money*. And this can certainly be provided from a distance, without their having to suffer the inconveniences and discomforts of the provider's presence. Many (if not most) women prefer the company of females over males. Basically, most women want relationships (primarily with other women and their own children, men occupying the third level slot) and incidentally want sex. Men want primarily to "get laid" and incidentally have the gratifications attendant to a relationship—but not as strong as women's for any of the three types: male, female, or with children. Men who have been falsely accused of sex abuse by their wives will often describe a longstanding history of exclusionary maneuvers, maneuvers that may date back to the birth of the child. I have seen a couple of cases in which such women did not even want the husband in the delivery room. Recently (Gardner, 1992a) I described these in detail in association with the development of the parental alienation syndrome. But such maneuvers may take many years to bring about the ultimate exclusion of the male. A sex-abuse accusation can achieve this result within hours. Literally, within hours of the accusation the man can be put in jail. Sometimes, the jail sentence will be lifelong. It is better than murdering him, because murder may result in the woman herself suffering unpleasant consequences. A sex-abuse accusation accomplishes the same thing without any risk to herself. There is no blood to wipe up, guns to hide, or alibis to provide. It is all clean, neat, and in the open. In fact, the woman may be viewed as having contributed to the cleansing of society for having put one more "pervert" behind bars. I cannot emphasize this point strongly enough, and I suggest that evaluators give consideration to this factor when evaluating a sex-abuse accusation.

FINAL COMMENTS

As the reader can appreciate, writing this book has been a prodigious task. It pulls together approximately 10 years of work in which I have been trying to find criteria for differentiating between true and false sex-abuse accusations. It brings in, however, over 20 years of *previous* experience in child psychiatry, experience and knowledge that have served as a foundation for this more recent endeavor. One problem (of the many) I had while writing this book was the continual flow of information that I considered pertinent to include. Every week more information came to my attention that warranted inclusion. Accordingly, I was continually going back and plugging in more material in various chapters. As the reader probably appreciates, I am not the kind of a person who gets paralyzed in the course of writing a book and obsesses about whether it is yet ready to go to the printer. I can usually satisfy myself that the book is not "perfect" (whatever that means) and that, to the best of my knowledge, everything therein is basically what I believe and is as accurate as I can possibly determine. At this point, this book satisfies these criteria. However, I am convinced that once it is at the printer, and once it has reached the point of no return, I will have more information that I would want to put in. This is predictable because of the rapid expansion of this field and the fact that there are others (not as many as I would like) who are also addressing themselves to this very difficult differentiation and whose research is under way at this point.

It is my belief that the criteria that I have proposed in this book should prove useful to evaluators who are willing to undertake the intensive kinds of evaluations necessary to utilize them. I believe that *if properly utilized,* they will enable the examiner to make this important differentiation in the vast majority of cases being evaluated. As mentioned so frequently throughout the book, such evaluations are optimally done in circumstances in which the same examiner has the opportunity to interview the accuser, the accused, and the alleged child victim (individually and jointly, as warranted). I am *not* suggesting that the child be automatically placed in the same room with the alleged perpetrator, but that the examiner should have the opportunity for such a joint interview if he (she) considers it safe and warranted. An automatic restriction from such an interview will compromise significantly and unnecessarily many evaluations. I emphasize the fact that the individual will have to "undertake the intensive kinds of evaluations necessary" for implementing these criteria because they obviously cannot be utilized in a short period. Like most things in life, quick investigations and quick solutions are likely to be insufficient and lead to incorrect conclusions. Examiners must insist upon being given the opportunity for lengthy evaluations (in the majority of cases) if they are to provide meaningful conclusions. Not to do so is to promulgate the enormous problems that result from an inadequate evaluation—problems that may cause formidable grief to all parties involved in the evaluation, whether the accusation be true or false.

ADDENDUM I

PROVISIONS FOR ACCEPTING AN INVITATION TO SERVE AS AN IMPARTIAL EXAMINER IN SEX ABUSE LITIGATION

Whenever possible, I make every reasonable attempt to serve as a court-appointed impartial examiner, rather than as an advocate, in sex abuse litigation. I recognize that this is more easily accomplished in civil, as opposed to criminal, litigation. Furthermore, I make no promise beforehand to support the position of the inviting party.

Sex abuse evaluations are of greatest use to the court when the examiner has the opportunity to interview the accuser, the accused, and the alleged child victim—individually and in combination, as warranted. This does not mean that the examiner will automatically place the alleged child victim and the accused in the room together, but should be given the opportunity to do so if he (she) considers such interviews warranted. The greater the number of compromises made with regard to this ideal, the less valuable will be the evaluator's services to the court.

Before accepting an invitation for involvement, I ask that the following steps be taken:

1) The inviting parties will ask the adversary parties to join with them in requesting that the presiding judge appoint me impartial examiner. In such cases the court order should indicate that I will be given the opportunity to interview the accuser, the accused, and the alleged child victim(s).

2) If step #1 is not successfully accomplished, then the inviting parties will ask the court to order the unreceptive side to participate in the evaluation. Such order should require the evaluation of the accuser, the accused, and the alleged child victim(s). Although recognized in such circumstances as the advocate of the inviting parties, I will still conduct the evaluation as if I were serving as an impartial examiner and therefore make no promise beforehand that I will support the position of the inviting parties, even though deemed by the court to be their advocate.

3) If step #2 is not successfully accomplished, my evaluation will be seriously compromised because I will not be given the opportunity to evaluate all involved parties. Under such circumstances, I will be willing to review materials and conduct whatever interviews I can in order to make a decision about whether or not I can support the inviting parties' position. If I can do so with conviction, I will be willing to testify in court on behalf of that side, with the full recognition that answers to some of my questions will have to be considered hypothetical.

My fee for conducting a sex abuse evaluation is $250 per full hour of my time. Time spent in interviewing, as well as time expended in report preparation, dictation, telephone conversations, court preparation, and any other time involved in association with the evaluation will be billed at the $250 per hour rate. My fee for court appearances in the Greater New York City area is $350 per hour while in court, and $150 per hour travel time to and from my office. During the data-collection phase of the evaluation, payment shall be made at the time services are rendered. Payment for court appearances shall be made in advance—in accordance with estimates provided prior to the rendering of these services. My fee schedule for providing legal services beyond the Greater New York City area is available on request.

I also request at the outset an advance security deposit of $2500. This will not serve as an advance retainer, in that the aforementioned fees will not be drawn against it—unless there has been a failure to pay my fees. Of course, when my services are no longer warranted, this deposit (with proper adjustments) will be returned to the payer(s). My fee schedule for conducting evaluations and/or providing court testimony beyond the New York City area is available on request.

Please know that if you do wish to enlist my services, I will do my utmost to provide a thorough and fair evaluation.

Richard A. Gardner, M.D.
Clinical Professor of
  Child Psychiatry
Columbia University,
College of Physicians
  and Surgeons

RAG/dll

ADDENDUM II

Dear

This is in response to your request for my involvement in your sex abuse litigation. Enclosed please find materials that should prove of interest and value to you before making a final decision regarding my involvement.

      1) The document, "Provisions for Accepting an Invitation to Serve as an Impartial Examiner in Sex-Abuse Litigation." Outlined therein are the provisions that must be satisfied before I will agree to participate.

      2) A summary of my curriculum vitae (taken from the jackets of recent books). My qualifications for conducting such evaluations is outlined therein. A full curriculum vitae is available on request.

      3) Copies of brochures from recent conferences in which I have provided presentations on sex abuse and related subjects to legal and mental health professionals. Also enclosed are descriptive materials of my books on child sex abuse.

Upon receipt of the materials described in the provisions document, I will be pleased to proceed with the evaluation as rapidly as is feasible. Please know that if you do wish to enlist my services, I will do my utmost to provide you with a thorough and fair evaluation.

                         Sincerely,

                         Richard A. Gardner, M.D.
                         Clinical Professor of
                           Child Psychiatry
                         Columbia University
                         College of Physicians
                           and Surgeons

RAG/dll
encls.

REFERENCES

Abel, G. G., Barlow, D. H., Blanchard, E. B., and Mavissakalian, M. (1975), Measurement of a sexual arousal in male homosexuals: the effects of instruction and stimulus modality. *Archives of Sexual Behavior*, 4:623-629.

───────────── , Becker, J. V., Cunningham-Rathner, J., Mittelman, M. S., and Rouleau, J. L. (1988), Multiple paraphilic diagnoses among sex offenders. *Bulletin of the American Academy of Psychiatry and the Law*, 16(2):153-168.

Abeles, N. (1986), Minutes of the annual meeting of the council of representatives. *American Psychologist*, 41:633-663.

Aldridge-Morris, R. (1989), *Multiple Personality: An Exercise in Deception*. Hove, East Sussex, United Kingdom: Lawrence Erlbaum Associates.

Alter-Reid, K. Gibbs, M. S., Lachenmeyer, J. R., Sigal, J., and Massoth, N. A. (1986), Sexual abuse of children: a review of the empirical findings. *Clinical Psychology Review*, 6:249-266.

American Academy of Child and Adolescent Psychiatry (1988), Guidelines for the clinical evaluation of child and adolescent sexual abuse: position statement of the American academy of child and adolescent psychiatry. *Journal of the American Academy of Child and Adolescent Psychiatry*, 27(5):655-657.

American Academy of Pediatrics, Committee on Child Abuse and Neglect (1991), Guidelines for the evaluation of sexual abuse of children. *Pediatrics*, 87(2):254-260.

The American Psychiatric Association (1952), *Diagnostic and Statistical*

Manual of Mental Disorders. Washington, D.C.: American Psychiatric Association.

_____ (1968), *Diagnostic and Statistical Manual of Mental Disorders, Second Edition (DSM-II).* Washington, D.C.: American Psychiatric Association.

_____ (1980), *Diagnostic and Statistical Manual of Mental Disorders, Third Edition (DSM-III).* Washington, D.C.: American Psychiatric Association.

_____ (1987), *Diagnostic and Statistical Manual of Mental Disorders, Third Edition, Revised (DSM-III-R).* Washington, D.C.: American Psychiatric Association.

American Psychological Association (February 8, 1990), *Statement on the Use of Anatomically Detailed Dolls in Forensic Evaluations.* Washington, D.C.: American Psychological Association.

August, R. L. and Forman, B. D. (1989), A comparison of sexually abused and nonsexually abused children's behavioral responses to anatomically correct dolls. *Child Psychiatry and Human Development,* 20(1):39-46.

Ayalon, O. (1984), Sexual exploitation of children: an overview of its scope, impact, and legal ramifications. *FBI Law Enforcement Bulletin,* 2:15-20.

Becker, J. V., Kaplan, M. S., Cunningham-Rathner, J., and Kavoussi, R. (1986), Characteristics of adolescent incest perpetrators: preliminary findings. *Journal of Family Violence,* 1:85-87.

Behrman, R. E. and Vaughan, V. C. (1983), *Textbook of Pediatrics.* Philadelphia: W. B. Saunders Co.

Bell, A. P. and Weinberg, M. S. (1978), *Homosexualities: A Study of Diversity among Men and Women.* New York: Simon & Schuster.

_____ , _____ , and Hammersmith, S. K. (1981), *Sexual Preference: Its Development in Men and Women.* Bloomington, Indiana: Indiana University Press.

Bellak, L. and Bellak, S. S. (1949), *Children's Apperception Test.* Larchmont, New York: C.P.S. Co.

_____ (1963), *The Supplement to the Children's Apperception Test-Supplement (CAT-S).* Larchmont, New York: C.P.S. Co.

Benedek, E. P. and Schetky, D. H. (1987), Problems in validating allegations of sexual abuse, Part 2, Clinical Evaluation. *Journal of The American Academy of Child and Adolescent Psychiatry,* 26(6):916-921.

Bess, B. and Janssen, Y. (1982), Incest: a pilot study. *Hillside Journal of Clinical Psychiatry,* 4:39-52.

Bieber, I., Dain, H., Dince, P., Drellich, M., Grand, H., Gundlach, R., Dremer, M., Rifkin, A., Wilbur, C., and Bieber, T. (1962), *Homosexuality: A Psychoanalytic Study of Male Homosexuals.* New York: Basic Books, Inc.

Birkin, A. (1979), *J. M. Barrie and the Lost Boys: The Love Story That Gave Birth to "Peter Pan."* New York: Clarkson N. Potter.

Blush, G. J. and Ross, K. L. (1987), Sexual allegations in divorce: the SAID syndrome. *Conciliation Courts Review,* 25(1):1-11.

Boat, B. W. and Everson, M. D. (1988), Interviewing young children with anatomical dolls. *Child Welfare,* 67(4):337-351.

Brainerd, C. and Ornstein, P. A. (1991), Children's memory for witnessed events: the developmental backdrop. In *The Suggestibility of Children's Recollections,* ed. J. Doris, pp. 10-20. Washington, D.C.: American Psychological Association.

British Psychological Society (1986), Report from the working group on the use of the polygraph in criminal investigation and personnel screening. *Bulletin of the British Psychological Society,* 39:81-93.

Bullough, V. (1983), Lewis Carroll. *Medical Aspects of Human Sexuality,* 17:134-140.

Ceci, S. J. (1991), Some overarching issues in the children's suggestibility debate. In *The Suggestibility of Children's Recollections,* ed. J. Doris, pp. 1-9. Washington, D.C.: American Psychological Association.

Chasnoff, I. J., Burns, W. J., Schnoll, S. H., Burns, K., Chisum, G., and Kyle-Sproe, L. (1986), Maternal-neonatal incest. *American Journal of Orthopsychiatry,* 56:577-580.

Clancy, P. E. and Firpo, P. A. (1991), *A System Out of Balance* (videotape). Walnut Creek, California: Clancy, Firpo, and Weisinger (law firm).

Clarke-Stewart, A., Thomson, W. C., and Lepore, S. (1989), Manipulating children's interpretations through interrogation. In *Can children provide accurate eyewitness reports?* G. S. Goodman (Chair), Symposium conducted at the biennial meeting of the Society for Research in Child Development, Kansas City, Missouri.

Cohen, M. L., Seghorn, T., and Calnas, W. (1969), Sociometric study of the sex offenders. *Journal of Abnormal Psychology,* 74:249-255.

Cohen, M. N. (1978), *Lewis Carroll, Photographer of Children: Four Nude Studies.* New York: Clarkson N. Potter and Crown Publishers.

Coleman, L. (1989), Medical examination for sexual abuse: have we been misled? *Issues in Child Abuse Accusations,* 1(3):1-9.

Condy, S. R., Templer, D. I., Brown, R., and Veaco, L. (1987), Parameters of sexual contact of boys with women. *Archives of Sexual Behavior,* 16(5):379-394.

Coons, P. M. (1986), Child abuse and multiple personality disorder: review of the literature and suggestions for treatment. *Child Abuse & Neglect,* 10:455-462.

Crewdson, J. (1988), *By Silence Betrayed.* Boston: Little, Brown and Co.

Davies, G. (1991), Concluding comments. In *The Suggestibility of Children's Recollections,* ed. J. Doris, pp. 177-187. Washington, D.C.: American Psychological Association.

_____ , Stevenson-Robb, Y., and Flin, R. (1988), Tales out of school: children's memory for an unexpected event. In *Practical Aspects of Memory: Current Research and Issues,* ed. M. M. Gruneberg, P. E. Morris, and R. N. Sykes, pp. 122-127. Chichester, England: Wiley.

_____ , Tarrant, A., and Flin, R. (1989), Close encounters of a witness kind: children's memory for a simulated health inspection. *British Journal of Psychology,* 80:415-429.

Dawes, R. M. (1991), Biases of retrospection. *Issues in Child Abuse Accusations,* 1(3):25-28.

Dawkins, R. (1976), *The Selfish Gene.* London: Oxford University Press.

DeJong, A. R., Weiss, J. C., and Brent, R. L. (1982), Condyloma acuminata in children. *American Journal of Diseases of Children,* 136:704-706.

Demause, L. (1991), The universality of incest. *The Journal of Psychohistory,* 19(2):123-164.

Dent, H. R. (1991), Experimental studies of interviewing child witnesses. In *The Suggestibility of Children's Recollections,* ed. J. Doris, pp. 138-146. Washington, D.C.: American Psychological Association.

Denton, L. (1987), Child abuse reporting laws: are they a barrier to helping troubled families? *The American Psychological Association Monitor,* 18(6):188.

DiLeo, J. H. (1973), *Children's Drawings as Diagnostic Aids.* New York: Brunner/Mazel Publishers.

D'Udine, B. (1990), The modification of sexual behavior through imprinting: a rodent model. In *Pedophilia: Biosocial Dimensions,* ed. J. R. Feierman, pp. 221-241. New York: Springer-Verlag.

Dunn, L. M., and Dunn, L. M. (1981), *The Peabody Picture Vocabulary Test-Revised.* Circle and Pines, Minnesota: Amercian Guidance Service.

Eibl-Eibesfeldt, I. (1990), Dominance, submission, and love: sexual pathologies from the perspective of ethology. In *Pedophilia: Biosocial Dimensions,* ed. J. R. Feierman, pp. 150-175. New York: Springer-Verlag.

Emans, S. J., Woods, E. R., Flagg, N. T., and Freeman, A. (1987), Genital findings in sexually abused, symptomatic and asymptomatic, girls. *Pediatrics,* 79(5):778-785.

Encyclopaedia Britannica, Micropedia (1982), Children's Crusade, II:840-841.

Faller, K. C. (1987), Women who sexually abuse children. *Violence and Victims,* 2(4):263-276.

_____ (1989), Characteristics of a clinical sample of sexually abused children: how boy and girl victims differ. *Child Abuse and Neglect,* 13:281-291.

False Memory Syndrome Foundation (1992), *FMS Foundation Newsletter*, May 1, 1992, p. 2.

Finkel, M. A. (1989), Anogenital trauma in sexually abused children. *Pediatrics*, 84(2):317-322.

Finkelhor, D. (1979), *Sexually Victimized Children*. New York: Macmillan.

—————— (1984), *Child Sex Abuse, New Theory and Research*. New York: The Free Press.

—————— (1986), *A Sourcebook on Child Sexual Abuse*. Beverly Hills, California: Sage Publications, Inc.

—————— , Williams, L. M., and Burns, N. (1989), *Nursery Crimes: Sexual Abuse in Day Care*. Newbury Park, California: Sage Publications, Inc.

Flin, R. (1991), A grand memory for forgetting. In *The Suggestibility of Children's Recollections*, ed. J. Doris, pp. 21-23. Washington, D.C.: American Psychological Association.

Freud, S. (1905), Three contributions to the theory of sex: II—infantile sexuality. In *The Basic Writings of Sigmund Freud*, ed. A. A. Brill, pp. 592-593. New York: Random House, Inc. (The Modern Library), 1938.

—————— (1909), A phobia in a five-year-old boy. In *Collected Papers*, vol. 3, pp. 149-209. New York: Basic Books, Inc. (1959)

—————— (1930), *Civilization and Its Discontents*. London: The Hogarth Press, Ltd., 1950.

Freund, K. (1963), A laboratory method of diagnosing predominance of homo-or-hetero erotic interest in the mail. *Behavior Research and Therapy*, 1:85-93.

—————— , McKnight, C. K., Langevin, R., and Cibiri, S. (1972), The female child as a surrogate object. *Archives of Sexual Behavior*, 2(2): 119-133.

Friedman, R. C. (1988), *Male Homosexuality: A Contemporary Analytic Perspective*. New Haven, Connecticut: Yale University Press.

Frisbie, L. (1969), *Another Look At Sex Offenders in California*. California Department of Mental Hygiene, Research Monograph No. 12, Sacramento, California.

Fromuth, M. E. and Burkhart, B. R. (1987), Childhood sexual victimization among college men: definitional and methodological issues. *Violence and Victims*, 2:241-253.

Frost, M. A. (1986), "Weird science" and child sex abuse cases. *The Champion*, January/February 1986, pp. 17-18.

Fuller, A. K. (1989), Child molestation and pedophilia: an overview for the physician. *Journal of the American Medical Association*, 261(4):602-606.

Gabriel, R. M. (1985), Anatomically correct dolls in the diagnosis of sexual abuse of children. *Journal of the Melanie Klein Society*, 3(2):40-51.

Gardner, R. A. (1968), The mutual storytelling technique: use in alleviating childhood oedipal problems. *Contemporary Psychoanalysis,* 4:161-177.

_____ (1969), Guilt, Job, and JB. *Medical Opinion and Review,* 5(2):146ff.

_____ (1970), The use of guilt as a defense against anxiety. *The Psychoanalytic Review,* 57:124-136.

_____ (1971), *Therapeutic Communication with Children: The Mutual Storytelling Technique.* New York: Jason Aronson, Inc.

_____ (1973), *The Talking, Feeling, and Doing Game.* Cresskill, New Jersey: Creative Therapeutics.

_____ (1975), *Psychotherpeutic Approaches to the Resistant Child.* Northvale, New Jersey: Jason Aronson, Inc.

_____ (1976), *Psychotherapy with Children of Divorce.* Northvale, New Jersey: Jason Aronson, Inc.

_____ (1979), *The Parents Books About Divorce* (paperback edition). New York: Bantam Books, Inc.

_____ (1982), *Family Evaluation in Child Custody Litigation.* Cresskill, New Jersey: Creative Therapeutics.

_____ (1985), Recent trends in divorce and custody litigation. *The Academy Forum,* 29(2):3-7. New York: The American Academy of Psychoanalysis.

_____ (1986), *Child Custody Litigation: A Guide for Parents and Mental Health Professionals.* Cresskill, New Jersey: Creative Therapeutics.

_____ (1987), *The Parental Alienation Syndrome and the Differentiation Between Fabricated and Genuine Child Sex Abuse.* Cresskill, New Jersey: Creative Therapeutics.

_____ (1988a), *The Storytelling Card Game.* Cresskill, New Jersey: Creative Therapeutics.

_____ (1988b), *Psychotherapy with Adolescents.* Cresskill, New Jersey: Creative Therapeutics.

_____ (1989), *Family Evaluation in Child Custody Mediation, Arbitration, and Litigation.* Cresskill, New Jersey: Creative Therapeutics.

_____ (1991a), *Sex Abuse Hysteria: Salem Witch Trials Revisited.* Cresskill, New Jersey: Creative Therapeutics.

_____ (1991b), *The Parents Book About Divorce, Second Edition* (hardcover). Cresskill, New Jersey: Creative Therapeutics.

_____ (1991c), *The Parents Book About Divorce, Second Edition* (paperback). New York: Bantam Books, Inc.

_____ (1992a), *The Parental Alienation Syndrome: A Guide for Mental Health and Legal Professionals.* Cresskill, New Jersey: Creative Therapeutics.

_____ (1992b), *The Psychotherapeutic Techniques of Richard A. Gardner, Revised Edition*. Cresskill, New Jersey: Creative Therapeutics.

_____ (1992c), *Self-Esteem: Psychodynamics and Psychotherapy*. Cresskill, New Jersey: Creative Therapeutics.

Garland, R. J. and Dougher, M. J. (1990), The abused/abuser hypothesis of child sexual abuse: a critical review of theory and research. In *Pedophilia: Biosocial Dimensions*, ed. J. R. Feierman, pp. 488-509. New York: Springer-Verlag.

Gebhard, P. H. and Gagnon, J. H. (1964), Male sex offenses against very young children. *American Journal of Psychiatry*, 121:576-579.

Gibbon, E. (1983), *The History of the Decline and Fall of the Roman Empire*. New York: Modern Library.

Glaser, D. and Collins, C. (1989), The response of young, non-sexually abused children to anatomically correct dolls. *Journal of Child Psychology and Psychiatry*, 30(4):547-560.

Goff, C. W., Burke, K. R. , Rickenback, C., and Buebendorf, D. P. (1989), Vaginal opening measurement. *American Journal of Diseases of Children*, 143:166-168.

Goleman, D. (1988), Lies can point to mental disorders or signal normal growth. *The New York Times*, Science Times, p. C1, May 17, 1988.

Goodman, G. S. (1991), On stress and accuracy in research on children's testimony. In *The Suggestibility of Children's Recollections*, ed. J. Doris, pp. 77-82. Washington, D.C.: American Psychological Association.

_____ and Clarke-Stewart, A. (1991), Suggestibility in children's testimony: implications for sexual abuse investigations. In *The Suggestibility of Children's Recollections*, ed. J. Doris, pp. 92-105. Washington, D.C.: American Psychological Association.

Goodwin, J. (1987), Developmental impacts of incest. In *Basic Handbook of Child Psychiatry*, ed. J. D. Call, R. L. Cohen, S. I. Harrison, I. N. Berlin, and L. A. Stone, vol. V, pp. 103-111. New York: Basic Books, Inc.

_____ and DiVasto, P. (1989), Female homosexuality: a sequel to mother-daughter incest. In *Sexual Abuse: Incest Victims and Their Families, Second Edition*, ed. J. M. Goodwin, pp. 140-146. Chicago: Year Book Medical Publishers, Inc.

Green, A. H. and Schetky, D. H. (1988), True and false allegations of child sexual abuse. In *Child Sexual Abuse*, ed. D. H. Schetky and A. H. Green, pp. 104-124. New York: Brunner/Mazel Publishers.

Green, R. (1985), Gender identity in childhood and later sexual orientation: follow-up of 78 males. *American Journal of Psychiatry*, 142(3):339-441.

_____ (1987), *The "Sissy Boy Syndrome" and the Development of Homosexuality*. New Haven, Connecticut: Yale University Press.

Grinspoon, L. (1992a), Dissociation and dissociative disorders: Part I. *The Harvard Mental Health Letter,* 8(9):1-4. Conclus.

——————— (1992b), Dissociation and dissociative disorders: Part II. *The Harvard Mental Health Letter,* 8(10):1-4.

Groth, A. N. (1979a), Sexual trauma in the life histories of rapists and child molesters. *Victimology,* 4:10-16.

——————— (1979b), *Men Who Rape.* New York: Plenum Publishing Co.

——————— (1984), *Anatomical Drawings: For Use in the Investigation and Intervention of Child Sex Abuse.* Newton Centre, Massachusetts: Forensic Mental Health Associates.

——————— , Hobson, W. F., and Gary, T. S. (1982), The child molester: clinical observations. In *Social Work and Child Sex Abuse,* ed. J. Conte, pp. 129-144. New York: Haworth Press, Inc.

Hathaway, S. R. and McKinley, J. C. (1989), *Minnesota Multiphasic Personality Inventory-2.* Minneapolis, Minnesota: University of Minnesota Press. 4-40.

Hauggaard, J. J. and Reppucci, N. D. (1988), *The Sexual Abuse of Children.* San Francisco: Jossey-Bass.

Henson, D. E. and Rubin, H. B. (1971), Voluntary control of eroticism. *Journal of Applied Behavior Analysis,* 4:37-44.

Herdt, G. H. (1981), *Guardians of the Flutes: Idioms of Masculinity.* New York: McGraw-Hill.

——————— (1984) (Ed.), *Ritualized Homosexuality in Melanesia.* Berkeley, California: University of California Press.

Herman-Giddens, M. E. and Frothingham, T. E. (1987), Prepubertal female genitals: examination for evidence of abuse. *Pediatrics,* 80:203-208.

Hibbard, R. A., Roghmann, K., and Hoekelman, R. A. (1987), Genitalia in children's drawings: an association with sexual abuse. *Pediatrics,* 79:129-137.

Hicks, R. D. (1991), *In Pursuit of Satan: The Police and the Occult.* Buffalo, New York: Prometheus Books.

Hobbs, C. J. and Wynne, J. M. (1986), Buggery in childhood: a common syndrome of child abuse. *Lancet,* 2(8510):792-796.

——————— (1987), Child sexual abuse: an increasing rate of diagnosis. *Lancet,* 2(8563):837-841.

Horowitz, D. A. (1987), Physical examination of sexually abused children and adolescents. *Pediatrics in Review,* 9(1):25-29.

Hoyt, E. P. (1974), *Horatio's Boys: The Life and Works of Horatio Alger, Jr.* Radnor, Pennyslvania: Chilton Books.

Jampole, L. and Weber, M. K. (1987), An assessment of the behavior of sexually abused and nonsexually abused children with anatomically correct dolls. *Child Abuse and Neglect,* 11:187-192.

Johnson, R. L. and Shrier, D. (1987), Past sexual victimization by females of male patients in an adolescent medicine clinic population. *American Journal of Psychiatry*, 144:650-138.

Johnston, F. A. and Johnston, S. A. (1986), Differences between human figure drawings of child molesters and control groups. *Journal of Clinical Psychology*, 42:638-647.

Kahr, B. (1991), The sexual molestation of children: historical perspectives. *The Journal of Psychohistory*, 19(2):191-214.

Kanner, L. (1935), *Child Psychiatry, Third Edition*. Springfield, Illinois: Charles C Thomas Publisher.

Kaplan, J. M. (1986), Pseudoabuse—the misdiagnosis of child abuse. *Journal of Forensic Science*, 31:1420-1428.

Kaufman, T. B. (1987), Where the legal process and the therapeutic process intersect. *New Jersey Psychologist*, 37(2):12-14.

King, M. A. and Yuille, J. C. (1987), Suggestibility and the child witness. In *Children's Eyewitness Memory*, ed. S. J. Ceci, M. P. Toglia, and D. F. Ross, pp. 24-35. New York: Springer-Verlag.

Kinsey, A. C., Pomeroy, W. B., Martin, C. E., and Gebhard, P. (1948), *Sexual Behavior in the Human Male*. Philadelphia: W. B. Saunders Co.

_____ (1953), *Sexual Behavior in the Human Female*. Philadelphia: W. B. Saunders Co.

Kiser, L. J., Ackerman, B. J., Brown, E., Edwards, N. B., McColgan, E., Pugh, R., and Pruitt, D. B. (1988), Post-traumatic stress disorder in young children: a reaction to purported sexual abuse. *Journal of the American Academy of Child and Adolescent Psychiatry*, 27(5):645-654.

Kohut, H. (1977), *The Restoration of the Self*. New York: International Universities Press.

Kolb, L. C. and Brodie, H. K. H. (1982), *Modern Clinical Psychiatry*. Philadelphia: W. B. Saunders Co.

Konker, C. (1992), Rethinking child sexual abuse: an anthropological perspective. *American Journal of Orthopsychiatry*, Vol. 62(1):147-153.

Koppitz, E. M. (1968), *Psychological Evaluation of Children's Human Figure Drawings*. New York: Grune & Stratton.

Kritzberg, N. I. (1966), A new verbal projective test for the expansion of the projective aspects of the clinical interview. *Acta Paedopsychiatrica*, 33(2):48-62.

Krivacska, J. J. (1989), *Designing Child Sex Abuse Prevention Programs*. Springfield, Illinois: Charles C Thomas, Publisher.

Krug, R. S. (1989), Adult male report of childhood sexual abuse by mothers: case descriptions, motivations, and long-term consequences. *Child Abuse and Neglect*, 13:111-120.

Lanning, K. V. (1989), Satanic, occult, ritualistic crime: a law enforcement perspective. *The Police Club*, October 1989, pp. 62-83.

_____ (1992), *Investigator's Guide to Allegations of "Ritual" Child Abuse*. Quantico, Virginia: U.S. Dept. of Justice. National Center for the Analysis of Violent Crime.

Larson, N., Maison, S., and Gilgun, J. (1987), Female sex offenders: understanding and treatment. Paper presented at the Sixth World Congress for Sexology, Heidelberg, Federal Republic of Germany.

Laws, D. R. and Rubin, H. B. (1969), Instructional control of an autonomic sexual response. *Journal of Applied Behavioral Analysis*, 2:93-99.

Leahy, M. M. (1991), Child sexual abuse: origins, dynamics and treatment. *Journal of the American Academy of Psychoanalysis*, 19(3):385-395.

Lechmann, C. (1987), Erzwungene Liebe. *Psychologie heute*, 10:63-67.

Legrand, R., Wakefield, H., and Underwager, R. (1989), Alleged behavioral indicators of sexual abuse. *Issues in Child Abuse Accusations*, 1(2):1-5.

Levy, D. M. (1939), Release therapy. *The American Journal of Orthopsychiatry*, 9(4):713-736.

_____ (1940), Psychotherapy and childhood. *The American Journal of Orthopsychiatry*, 10(4):905-910.

Lew, M. (1990), *Victims No Longer: Men Recovering from Incest and Other Child Sexual Abuse*. New York: Harper & Row.

Lindberg, M. (1991), An interactive approach to assessing the suggestibility and testimony of eyewitnesses. In *The Suggestibility of Children's Recollections*, ed. J. Doris, pp. 47-55. Washington, D.C.: American Psychological Association.

Loftus, E. F. (1975), Leading questions and the eyewitness report. *Cognitive Psychology*, 7:560-572.

_____ and Davies, G. M. (1984), Distortions in the memory of children. *Journal of Social Issues*, 40:51-67.

_____ , Donder, D., Hoffman, H. G., and Schooler, J. W. (1989), Creating new memories that are quickly accessed and confidently held. *Memory and Cognition*, 17:607-616.

_____ , Miller, D. G., and Burns, H. J. (1978), Semantic integration of verbal information into a visual memory. *Journal of Experimental Psychology: Human Learning and Memory*, 4:19-31.

_____ and Palmer, J. C. (1974), Reconstruction of automobile destruction: an example of the interaction between language and memory. *Journal of Verbal Learning and Verbal Behavior*, 13:585-589.

_____ , Schooler, J., and Wagenaar, W. (1985), The fate of memory: comment on McCloskey and Zaragoza. *Journal of Experimental Psychology: General*, 114:375-380.

Longo, R. E. (1982), Sexual learning and experience among adolescent sexual offenders. *International Journal of Offender Therapy and Comparative Criminology*, 26:235-241.

Lourie, I. S. and Blick, L. C. (1987), Child sex abuse. In *Basic Handbook of Child Psychiatry*, ed. J. D. Noshpitz, vol. V, pp. 280-286. New York: Basic Books, Inc.

Lukianowicz, N. (1972), Incest. I: Paternal incest. II: Other types of incest. *British Journal of Psychiatry*, 120:301-313.

Luria, A. R. (1968), *The Mind of a Mnemonist.* New York: Basic Books, Inc.

Lykken, D. T. (1985), The probity of the polygraph. In *The Psychology of Evidence and Trial Procedure*, ed. S. M. Kassin and L. S. Wrightsman. Beverly Hills, California: Sage Publishing Co.

Lyons, A. S. and Petrucelli, R. J. (1978), *Medicine: An Illustrated History.* New York: Harry N. Abrams, Inc.

Mack, J. E. (1992), Mental health professionals and the Roper poll. *Unusual Personal Experiences: An Analysis of the Data from Three National Surveys Conducted by the Roper Organization*, pp. 7-8. Las Vegas: Bigelow Holding Corp.

Mappan, M. (1980), *Witches and Historians.* Malabar, Florida: Robert E. Krieger Publishing Co.

Margolin, L. (1991), Child sexual abuse by nonrelated caregivers. *Child Abuse & Neglect*, 15:213-221.

Mathews, R., Matthews, J. K., and Speltz, K. (1989), *Female Sexual Offenders: An Exploratory Study.* Orwell, Vermont: The Safer Society Press.

Matthews, J. K., Mathews, R., and Speltz, K. (1991), Female sexual offenders: a typology. In *Family Sexual Abuse: Frontline Research and Evaluation*, ed. M. Q. Patton, pp. 147-161. Newbury Park, California: Sage Publications, Inc.

Matzner, F. J. (1991), Does satanism exist? *Journal of the American Academy of Child and Adolescent Psychiatry*, 30(5):848.

May, W. F. (1991), The molested. *Hastings Center Report*, 21(3):9-20.

McCann, J. (1988), *Health Science Response to Child Maltreatment Conference.* San Diego, California, January 21, 1988.

——————— (1990), Use of the colposcope in childhood sexual abuse examinations. *Medical Clinics of North America*, 37(4):863-880.

——————— , Voris, J., and Simon, M. (1988), Labial adhesions and posterior fourchette injuries in childhood sexual abuse. *American Journal of Diseases of Children*, 142:659-662.

——————— , ——————— , ——————— , and Wells, R. (1989), Perianal findings in prepubertal children selected for nonabuse: a descriptive study. *Child Abuse & Neglect*, 13(2):179-193.

——————— , Wells, R., Simon, M., and Voris, J. (1990), Genital findings in prepubertal girls selected for nonabuse: a descriptive study. *Pediatrics*, 86(3):428-438.

McCarty, L. M. (1986), Mother-child incest: characteristics of the offender. *Child Welfare*, 65(5):447-458.

McGough, L. S. (1991a), Sexual abuse and suggestibility. In *The Suggestibility of Children's Recollections*, ed. J. Doris, pp. 115-117. Washington, D.C.: American Psychological Association.

_____ (1991b), Assessing the credibility of witnesses' statements. In *The Suggestibility of Children's Recollections*, ed. J. Doris, pp. 165-167. Washington, D.C.: American Psychological Association.

McIver, W. F. (1986), The case for a therapeutic interview in situations of alleged sexual molestation. *The Champion*, 10(1):11-13.

_____ , Wakefield, H., and Underwager, R. (1989), Behavior of abused and nonabused children in interviews with anatomically correct dolls. *Issues in Child Abuse Accusations*, 1(1):39-48.

Medicus, G. and Hopf, S. (1990), The phylogeny of male/female differences in sexual behavior. In *Pedophilia: Biosocial Dimensions*, ed. J. R. Feierman, pp. 122-149. New York: Springer-Verlag.

Medlyn, B. (1989), The plethysmograph: evaluating the sexual deviant. *Arizona Attorney*, December 1989, pp. 27-28.

Menninger, K. A. (1957), *The Human Mind, Third Edition*. New York: Alfred Knopf.

Minneapolis Family Renewal Center, Sexual Abuse Project (1979). Fairview Southdale Hospital, Minneapolis, Minnesota.

Money, J. (1990), Pedophilia: a specific instance of new phylism theory as applied to paraphilic lovemaps. In *Pedophilia: Biosocial Dimensions*, ed. J. R. Feierman, pp. 445-463. New York: Springer-Verlag.

_____ and Russo, A. J. (1979), Homosexual outcome of discordant gender activity role in childhood: longitudinal follow-up. *Journal of Pediatric Psychology*, 4:29-49.

Muram, D. (1989a), Child sexual abuse – genital tract findings in prepubertal girls, I. The unaided medical examination. *American Journal of Obstetrics and Gynecology*, 160(2):328-333.

(1989b), Child sexual abuse: relationship between sexual acts and genital findings. *Child Abuse & Neglect*, 13:211-216.

_____ and Elias, S. (1989), Child sexual abuse – genital tract findings in prepubertal girls, II. Comparison of colposcopic and unaided examinations. *American Journal of Obstetrics and Gynecology*, 160(2):333-335.

Murray, H. (1936), *The Thematic Apperception Test*. New York: The Psychological Corp.

Myles-Worsley, M., Cromer, C., and Dodd, D. (1986), Children's preschool script reconstruction: reliance on general knowledge as memory fades. *Developmental Psychology*, 22:2-30.

Naitove, C. E. (1982), Arts therapy with sexually abused chidren. In *Handbook of Clinical Intervention in Child Sexual Abuse*, ed. S. S. Sgroi, pp. 269-308. Lexington, Massachusetts: Lexington Books (D. C. Heath and Co.).

O'Connor, A. A. (1987), Female sex offenders. *British Journal of Psychiatry*, 150:615-620.

Overholser, J. C. and Beck, S. (1986), Multimethod assessment of rapists, child molesters, and three control groups on behavioral and psychological measures. *Journal of Consulting and Clinical Psychology*, 54:682-687.

Panton, J. H. (1979), MMPI profile configurations associated with incestuous and non-incestuous child molesting. *Psychological Reports*, 45:335-338.

Paul, D. M. (1977), What really did happen to Baby Jane? The medical aspects of the investigation of alleged sexual abuse of children. *Medical Science Law*, 26:85-102.

Peters, D. (1991), The influence of stress and arousal on the child witness. In *The Suggestibility of Children's Recollections*, ed. J. Doris, pp. 60-76. Washington, D.C.: American Psychological Association.

Peters, J. J. (1976), Children who are victims of sexual assault and the psychology of offenders. *American Journal of Psychotherapy*, 30:398-421.

Phongpaichit, P. (1982), *From Peasant Girls to Bangkok Masseuses*. Geneva: International Labor Organization.

Quinsey, V. L. and Bergerson, S. G. (1976), Instructional control of penile circumference. *Behavioral Therapy*, 6:202-212.

Raskin, D. C. and Esplin, P. W. (1991), Assessment of children's statements of sexual abuse. In *The Suggestibility of Children's Recollections*, ed. J. Doris, pp. 153-164. Washington, D.C.: American Psychological Association.

_____ and Steller, M. (1989), Assessing credibility of allegations of child sexual abuse: polygraph examinations and statement analysis. In *Criminal Behavior and the Justice System*, ed. H. Wegener, F. Loesel, and J. Haisch, pp. 290-302. New York: Springer-Verlag.

_____ and Yuille, J. C. (1989), Problems in evaluating interviews of children in sexual abuse cases. In *Perspectives on Children's Testimony*, ed. S. J. Ceci, D. C. Ross, and M. P. Toglia, pp. 184-207. New York: Springer-Verlag.

Ravitch, D. and Finn, C. E. (1987), *What Do Our 17-Year-Olds Know?* New York: Random House, Inc.

Realmuto, G. M., Jensen, J. B., and Wescoe, S. (1990), Specificity and sensitivity of sexually anatomically correct dolls in substantiating abuse: a pilot study. *Journal of the American Academy of Child and Adolescent Psychiatry*, 29(5):743-746.

Reeves, T. (1981), Loving boys. In *The Age Taboo*, ed. D. Tsang. Boston: Alyson Publications.

Renshaw, D. C. (1987), Evaluating suspected cases of child sexual abuse. *Psychiatric Annals*, 17(4):262-270.

Richardson, J. T., Best, J., and Bromley, D. G. (1991), *The Satanism Scare.* Hawthorne, New York: Aldine De Gruyter.

Risin, L. I. and Koss, M. P. (1987), The sexual abuse of boys: prevalence and descriptive characteristics of childhood victimizations. *Journal of Interpersonal Violence,* 2(3):309-323.

Robson, B. (1991), The scars of Scott county. *Minneapolis/St. Paul,* March 1991, pg. 48ff.

Rorschach, H. (1921), *The Rorschach Test.* New York: The Psychological Corp.

Ross, K. L. and Blush, G. J. (1990), Sex abuse validity discriminators in the divorced or divorcing family. *Issues in Child Abuse Accusations,* 2(1):1-6.

Roumajon, Y. (1960), 3. Kongress der Deutschen Gesellschaft für Psychotherapie und Tiefenpsychologie in Paris (oral report).

Rowan, E. L., Rowan, J. B., and Langelier, P. (1990), Women who molest children. *The Bulletin of the American Academy of Psychiatry and the Law,* 18(1):79-83.

Russell, D. (1986), *The Secret Trauma: Incest in the Lives of Girls and Women.* New York: Basic Books, Inc.

Ryckman, L. L. (1992), Phone call costs mother one year with daughter. *The Plain Dealer* (Cleveland, Ohio), February 4, 1992, pp. 1Aff.

Safire, W. (1989), The polygraph virus. *The New York Times,* January 2, 1989, p. A25.

Saywitz, K. J. (1987), Children's testimony: age-related patterns of memory errors. In *Children's Eyewitness Memory,* ed. S. J. Ceci, M. P. Toglia, and D. F. Ross, pp. 36-52. New York: Springer-Verlag.

Schetky, D. H. (1988), The clinical evaluation of child sexual abuse. In *Child Sexual Abuse,* ed. D. H. Schetky and A. H. Green, pp. 57-81. New York: Brunner/Mazel Publishers.

Segal, Z. V. and Marshall, W. L. (1985), Heterosexual social skills in a population of rapists and child molesters. *Journal of Consulting and Clinical Psychology,* 53:55-63.

Selkin, J. (1991), *The Child Sex Abuse Case in the Courtroom, Second Edition.* Denver, Colorado: Private publication by James Selkin, Ph.D.

Sgroi, S. M., Porter, F. S., and Blick, L. C. (1982), Validation of child sexual abuse. In *Handbook of Clinical Intervention in Child Sexual Abuse,* ed. S. M. Sgroi, pp. 39-79. Lexington, Massachusetts: Lexington Books (D.C. Heath and Co.).

Shanor, K. (1978), *The Shanor Study: The Sexual Sensitivity of the American Male.* New York: Dial Press.

Shore, W. B. and Winklestein, J. A. (1971), Nonvenereal transmission of gonococcal infections to children. *The Journal of Pediatrics,* 79:662-663.

Sigston, A. and White, D. G. (1975), Conformity in children as a function of age level. *British Journal of Social and Clinical Psychology,* 3:388-419.

Silcner, N. A. and Hanson, S. R. (1989), Guidelines for videotape interviews in child sexual abuse cases. *American Journal of Forensic Psychology*, 7(1):61-74.

Silva, D. C. (1990), Pedophilia: an autiography. In *Pedophilia: Biosocial Dimensions*, ed. J. R. Feierman, pp. 464-487. New York: Springer-Verlag.

Simon, W. T. and Schouten, P. G. W. (1990), *Plethysmography in the Assessment and Treatment of Sexual Deviants: An Overview* (unpublished manuscript).

Sivan, A. B., Schor, D. P., Koeppl, G. K., and Noble, L. D. (1988), Interaction of normal children with anatomical dolls. *Child Abuse and Neglect*, 12:295-304.

Spelman, C. (1985), *Talking About Child Sexual Abuse*. Chicago, Illinois: The National Committee for Prevention of Child Abuse.

Steller, M. (1991), Rehabilitation of the child witness. In *The Suggestibility of Children's Recollections*, ed. J. Doris, pp. 106-109. Washington, D.C.: American Psychological Association.

Stewart, F. H., Stewart, G. K., Guest, F., and Hatcher, R. A. (1987), *Understanding Your Body: Every Woman's Guide to a Lifetime of Health*. New York: Bantam Books.

Stoller, R. J. (1975), *Perversion: The Erotic Form of Hatred*. New York: Pantheon.

——————— (1979), *Sexual Excitement: Dynamics of Erotic Life*. New York: Pantheon.

——————— (1985), *Observing the Exotic Imagination*. New Haven, Connecticut: Yale University Press.

Stone, E. M. (1988), *American Psychiatric Glossary*. Washington, D. C.: American Psychiatric Press, Inc.

Strassmann, B. I. (1981), Sexual selection, parental care, and concealed ovulation in humans. *Ethology and Sociobiology*, 2:31-40.

Summit, R. C. (1983), The child sexual abuse accommodation syndrome. *Child Abuse & Neglect*, 7:177-193.

——————— (1991), *State of Florida vs. Bob Fijnje*. Deposition of Roland C. Summit, January 8, 1991. pp. 50-51.

Thompson, W. C., Clarke-Stewart, A., Meyer, J., Pathak, M. K., and Lepore, S. (1991), *Children's susceptibility to suggestive interrogation*. Paper presented at the annual meeting of the American Psychological Association, San Francisco, California.

Toglia, M. P. (1991), Memory impairment—it is more common than you think. In *The Suggestibility of Children's Recollections*, ed. J. Doris, pp. 40-46. Washington, D.C.: American Psychological Association.

Tollison, C. D. and Adams, H. E. (1979), *Sexual Disorders: Treatment, Theory, and Research*. New York: Gardner Press.

Toufexis, A. (1991), When can memories be trusted? *Time*, October 28, 1991, pp. 86-87.

Travin, S., Cullin, K., and Protter, B. (1990), Female sex offenders: severe victims and victimizers. *Journal of Forensic Sciences*, 35(1):140-150.

Tripp, C. A. (1987), *The Homosexual Matrix*. New York: New American Library.

Underwager, R. C. and Wakefield, H. (1990), *The Real World of Child Interrogations*. Springfield, Illinois: Charles C Thomas Publisher.

_____ (1991), Cur allii, prae aliis? (Why some, and not others?) *Issues in Child Abuse Accusations*, 3(3):178-193.

Undeutsch, U. (1989), The development of statement reality analysis. In *Credibility Assessment*, ed. J. C. Yuille, pp. 101-120. Dordrecht, The Netherlands: Kluwer.

Upham, C. W. (1867), *Salem Witchcraft*. Boston: Boston Publishing Co.

Victor, J. S. (1991), The satanic cult scare and allegations of ritual child abuse. *Issues in Child Abuse Accusations*, 3(3):135-143.

Wakefield, H. and Underwager, R. (1988), *Accusations of Child Sex Abuse*. Springfield, Illinois: Charles C Thomas Publisher.

_____ (1990), Personality characteristics of falsely accusing parents in custody disputes. Presented at the Sixth Annual Symposium in Forensic Psychology, Las Vegas, Nevada, March 13, 1990 (unpublished manuscript).

_____ (1991), Female child sexual abusers: a critical review of the literature. Paper presented at the Seventh Annual Symposium on Forensic Psychology, Newport Beach, California, May 7, 1991.

_____ , Rogers, M., and Underwager, R. (1990), Female sexual abusers: a theory of loss. *Issues in Child Abuse Accusations*, 2(4):181-195.

Warren-Leubecker, A. (1991), The influence of stress and arousal on the child witness. In *The Suggestibility of Children's Recollections*, ed. J. Doris, pp. 83-85. Washington, D.C.: American Psychological Association.

Wechsler, D. (1974), *Wechsler Intelligence Scale for Children—Revised*. New York: The Psychological Corp.

Weinberg, K. S. (1962), *Incest Behavior*. New York: Citadel Press.

Weiner, I. (1962), Father-daughter incest. *Psychiatric Quarterly*, 36:601-632.

Wells, G. L., and Loftus, E. F. (1991), Is this child fabricating? Reactions to a new assessment technique. In *The Suggestibility of Children's Recollections*, ed. J. Doris, pp. 168-171. Washington, D.C.: American Psychological Association.

White, S. T., Ingram, D. L., and Lyna, P. R. (1989), Vaginal diameter in the evaluation of sexual abuse. *Child Abuse & Neglect*, 13(2):217-224.

White, S., Strom, G. A., and Santilli, G. (1985), A protocol for interviewing preschoolers with the sexually anatomically correct dolls (unpublished manuscript). Case Western Reserve University School of Medicine, Cleveland, Ohio.

_____ and Halpin, B. M. (1986), Interviewing young sexual abuse victims with anatomically correct dolls. *Child Abuse & Neglect,* 10:519-529.

Winnicott, D. W. (1968), The value of the therapeutic consultation. In *Foundations of Child Psychiatry,* ed. E. Miller, pp. 593-608. London: Pergamon Press.

Wyatt, G. (1985), The sexual abuse of Afro-American and white women in childhood. *Child Abuse & Neglect,* 10:231-240.

Yates, A., Beutler, L., and Crago, M. (1985), Drawings by child victims of abuse. *Child Abuse and Neglect,* 9:183-189.

_____ and Musty, T. (1988), Preschool children's erroneous allegations of sexual molestation. *American Journal of Psychiatry,* 145(8):989-992.

_____ and Terr, L. (1988a), Anatomically correct dolls: should they be used as the basis for expert testimony? *Journal of the American Academy of Child and Adolescent Psychiatry.*

_____ (1988b), Anatomically correct dolls: should they be used as the basis for expert testimony? *Journal of the American Academy of Child and Adolescent Psychiatry,* 27(3):387-388.

Yuille, J. C. (1988), The systematic assessment of children's testimony. *Canadian Psychology,* 19(3):47-261.

_____ , and Farr, V. (1987), Statement validity analysis: a systematic approach to the assessment of children's allegations of child sexual abuse. *British Columbia Psychologist,* Fall, 1987, 19-27.

_____ , Hunter, R., and Harvey, W. (1990), A coordinated approach to interviewing in child sexual abuse investigations. *Canada's Mental Health,* 38(2/3):14-18.

Zaragoza, M. S. (1991), Preschool children's susceptibility to memory impairment. In *The Suggestibility of Children's Recollections,* ed. J. Doris, pp. 27-39. Washington, D.C.: American Psychological Association.

Zuger, B. (1970), Gender role determination. *Psychosomatic Medicine,* 32:449-67.

_____ (1976), Monozygotic twins discordant for homosexuality: report of a pair and significance of the phenomenon. *Comprehensive Psychiatry,* 17:661-69.

_____ (1984), Early effeminate behavior in boys: outcome and significance for homosexuality. *Journal of Nervous and Mental Disorders,* 172(2):90-97.

AUTHOR INDEX

Mack, J.E., 686
Maison, S., 82
Mappan, M., 117–118, 120, 132, 136, 138
Margolin, L., 76
Marshall, W.L., 59
Martin, C.E., 36, 61
Massoth, N.A., 51
Matthews, J.K., 76, 77, 78, 79, 80, 81, 82, 84
Matthews, R., 76, 77, 78, 79, 80, 81, 82, 84
Matzner, F.J., 473
Mavissakalian, M., 260
May, W.F., 171
McCann, J., 234, 237, 238, 242, 243, 245, 246, 247, 248–249, 250, 252, 255, 257
McCarty, L.M., 77, 79–80, 81, 82
McColgan, E., 95
McGough, L.S., 109–110, 111
McIver, W.F., 271, 351
McKinley, J.C., 211, 694
McKnight, C.K., 260
McIver, W.F., 302
Medicus, G, 56, 70
Medlyn, B., 259
Menninger, K.A., xxix,
Meyer, J., 351
Miller, D.G., 103
Mittelman, M.S., 49–50, 60, 64
Money, J., 39, 52, 53, 70
Muram, D., 235, 238, 253–254
Murray, H., 271, 346, 438
Musty, T., 180, 221
Myles-Worsley, M., 101

Naitove, C.E., 433
Noble, L.D., 350

O'Connor, A.A., 77
Ornstein, P.A., 101
Overholser, J.C., 55, 58

Palmer, J.C., 103
Panton, J.H., 59
Pathak, M.K., 351
Paul, D.M., 254–255
Peters, D., 105
Peters, J.J., 52, 56, 58
Petrucelli, R.J., xxix,
Phongpaichit, P., 68
Pomeroy, W.B., 36, 61
Porter, F.S., 58
Protter, B., 82, 83, 84
Pruitt, D.B., 95
Pugh, R., 95

Quinsey, V.L., 260

Raskin, D.C., 111–112, 151, 175
Ravitch, D., 315
Realmuto, G.M., 351
Reeves, T., 68
Renshaw, D.C., 94, 493
Reppucci, N.D., 55, 59, 65
Richardson, J.T., 477
Rickenback, C., 245
Rifkin, A., 39
Risin, L.I., 76, 85
Robson, B., 515–516
Rogers, M., 79
Roghmann, K., 434–435
Rohrschach, H., 211, 346
Ross, K.L., 161, 222, 227
Rouleau, J.L., 49–50, 60, 64
Roumajon, Y., 57
Rowan, E.L., 74, 76, 77, 81, 82, 83
Rowan, J.B., 74, 76, 77, 81, 82, 83
Rubin, H.B., 260
Russell, D., 75, 82
Russo, A.J., 39
Ryckman, L.L., 686

Safire, W., 261
Santilli, G., 342, 344, 350, 360
Saywitz, K.J., 113–114
Schetky, D.H., 221, 433, 496

SUBJECT INDEX

Child protection services, 377,
        518-519
Children
    age of
        and credibility of information,
            391-393
        having advanced sexual
            knowledge for, 151-153
        programming and , 194
        and sex-abuse hysteria, 461
    antisocial, 177-178
    attitude toward their genitals,
        156-157
    as being similar to females and
        male pedophilia, 70
    and borrowed scenarios, 163-165
    and capacity to make subtle dif-
        ferentiations, 666
    chronicity of sexual abuse,
        175-176
    and confrontations with accused,
        377-380
    and criteria for discriminating
        between true and false accu-
        sations, 133-180
    and dealing with cognitive dis-
        tortions, 501-507
    and dealing with emotional
        problems, 507-511
    depressed, 165-166
    differentiating between truth and
        lie, 270-274, 403-406
    fantasies of
        distortion of normal, 466-468
        oedipal, 125
    exposure to sex-abuse educa-
        tional materials, 188-189
    fears, tension, and anxiety in,
        136-137, 179-180
    hatred of father, 509-510
    interviewing of, 391-440
    involved in nursery school sex-
        abuse hysteria, 460-480

and litany, 161-163
and masturbation, xxx-xxxi, 15,
    122-123, 154, 290-292,
    544-545, 580-581
memory and suggestibility of,
    99-114
and naming body parts,
    275-276
obsessed with grabbing genitals,
    155
olfactory gratification and sexual
    activity in, 16, 123
and orgasms, 15, 154, 290-291,
    400, 543
and parental alienation
    syndrome, 126-131
parents blaming alleged perpe-
    trator for psychopathology
    of, 453-454
and pathological feeling about
    sex, 507-509
pathologizing normal behavior
    of, 452-453
preposterousness of allegations,
    469-472
protecting from further abuse,
    537-539
and pseudomaturity, 176-177
psychodynamic factors operative
    in false accusations of,
    114-133
psychotherapeutic approaches to
    symptoms of abused,
    543-576
school attendance and perfor-
    mance in, 178-179
severe psychopathology in, 180
sexual excitation in, 121-126,
    153-156
symptoms of sexually abused,
    477-478, 532-535
threats and bribes concerning,
    159

Expert See *Evaluator; Impartial
    Examiner; Mental health
    evaluator; Therapist; Vali-
    dators*
Extended family
    mother's exclusion of accused
        parent's, 215
False accusation
    and incorporation of satanic rit-
        uals in abuse, 472–477
Falsely accused. *See Accused; Fa-
    ther*
Falsely accusing parent, 183–230,
    see also Accuser; Mother
    common psychodynamic factors
        operative in, 218–228
        borderline personality disor-
            der, 227
        family pattern reproduction,
            223–224
        hysteria, 221–223
        intellectual impairment,
            227–228
        projection and paranoia,
            219–221
        rage and vengeance, 218–219
        sperm-donor concept of
            males, 224–227, 695–696
    dealing with, 511–513
    and "hired gun" mental health
        professionals, 198–199
    and history of wreaking ven-
        geance on accused, 199–200
    indicators of
        from early life, 185–188
        from events preceding evalua-
            tion, 188–204
        obtained during course of
            evaluation, 204–218
    lack of punitive treatment for,
        519–520
    probability theory regarding,
        691–693

False Memory Syndrome Founda-
    tion, 678
Family
    breaking up of, 560, 561
    extended, mother's exclusion of
        accused parent's, 215
    joint interviews with, 514–515
    pattern, reproduction of,
        206–207, 223–224, 387–388,
        582–584
    surrogate, 560
Family dysfunction, 70–71
    and development of pedophilia,
        51, 79–80
Family therapy, 536–537
    crucial role of, 498–499
Fantasies, 351, *see also Lies*
    distortion of normal childhood,
        466–468
    oedipal, 125
    projection of onto dolls,
        435–436
    and reality, 100
    role-reversal, 471–472
    sexual, 6
Father, *see also Accused; Parents;
    Pedophilia*
    child's hatred of, 509–510
    dealing with the falsely accused,
        513–514
    failure to notify of sex-abuse
        accusation, 196–198
    and rationalizing pedophilia,
        594–595
    surrogate, 539
    treatment of the, 586–608
        and denial of abuse, 586–588
Father-child relationship
    destruction of psychological
        bond, 669–670
    improving, 590–592
    psychotherapeutic approaches to
        problems with, 571–573

Fears
  of children, 179–180
  psychotherapeutic approaches
    to, 560–562
Feces
  and sexual arousal, 30–31
Female genital findings, 244–249
  normal, 244–249
  in sexually abused, 250–255
Female impersonator, 27–28
Female pedophilia. *See Pedophilia*
Feminists
  as validators, 333
Fetishism, 21–22, 29–30
  definition of, 21
  transvestic, 27–28
Fifth Amendment, 375, 445
First-memory question, 416–418
Flashbacks, 657–659
Follow-up studies, 515–517
Freud
  polymorphous perversity, 14–15,
    121, 144, 155
  psychoanalysis, 353
Frog-leg position, supine, 234–235,
    241–244, 245–248
Frotteurism
  definition of, 22
  gender differences in, 22–23
Games, therapeutic, 346–347,
    355–356, 363–364, 425–430,
    437–438, 506
Gender
  differences
    in mating patterns, 2–7
    in sexual arousal/behavior,
      40–41, 225
    of false accusing parents,
      183–184
    and the paraphilias of DSM-III-
      R, 18–32
    and pedophilia, 69
    and relationships, 695–696

  of therapists, 653–654
Gender identity disorder of child-
    hood, 38
Gene survival and transmission,
    Dawkins's theory of, 7–13
Genetics
  and environment, 14
  and gender differences in mating
    patterns, 2–3
  and homosexuality, 34–35
  and paraphilias, 32–33
  and pedophilia, 67
Genitals
  children obsessed with grabbing,
    155
  children's attitude toward their,
    156–157
  medical findings regarding
    four categories of, 253
    normal, 244–250
    in sexually abused children,
      250–255
Genital warts, 256–257
Gestures, leading, 361–368
Gonococcal infection, 256–257
Gonorrhea, 255–257
Group therapy, 539, 583, 597–598,
    602
  for dealing with isolation,
    597–598
  for excessive domination and
    control problems, 599
  for fathers, 588, 589–590
  homogeneous vs. heterogeneous,
    577–578, 589, 670
  for mothers, 577–578
Guilt, 222, 393, 510
  and age, 576
  of child concerning participation
    in sexual acts, 139–142,
    548–549
  as a component of self-denigra-
    tion of depression, 459–550

Self-assertion, 568–569
    male pedophilia and impaired, 58
Self-created story, 431–432
Self-esteem, 422, 478–479
    enhancing fathers', 592–594
    in paranoia, 648–649
    problems, psychotherapeutic approaches to, 552–554
Self-loathing, 422, 539, 550
Self-protection
    child learning methods of, 554
Septate hymenal configuration, 236
Sex-abuse accommodation syndrome, 531–532
Sex-abuse evaluators. *See Evaluator; Impartial Examiner; Mental health evaluator; Therapist; Validators*
Sex-abuse hysteria, 685–688, *see also Hysteria*
    nursery school/day-care center, 443–490
Sex Abuse in Divorce Syndrome (SAID), 161, 222
Sex-Abuse Legitimacy Scale (SAL Scale), xxxiv-xxxvi
Sex-abuse prevention programs, 156
Sex-abuse scenario
    changes and inconsistencies in, 468–469
    nightmares and, 467–468
    truth as code-term for, 505–506
Sex abuse syndrome, 294
Sexual abuse, *see also Child sexual abuse*
    accusation, 93–181
        child's memory and suggestibility concerning, 99–114
        criteria for differentiating between true and
        false, xxxiv-xxxv, 95–99, 133–180

psychodynamic factors operative in false, 114–133
tracing the evolution of, 385–387
behavioral manifestations of, 94
belated realization of by adults, 639–680
childhood history of and development of pedophilia, 53–54, 82–83
children who have experienced
    clinical examples of treatment for, 608–637
    not needing treatment, 535–536
    psychotherapeutic approaches to symptoms of, 543–576
    symptoms of, 532–535
chronicity of, 175–176
credibility of the description of, 144–151
degree of hesitancy to reveal, 134–136
and denial, 195–196, 462
direct coercive techniques concerning disclosure of, 304–305
disclosure as proof of, 303–304
educational material, exposing child to, 188–189
evaluations, prevention of the traumatic effects of, 517–521
failure to notify father of accusation, 196–198
high risk for, xxxviii-xxxix
important types of questions to ask regarding, 398–401
indicators, 286–287
    considered not to be related to abuse, 292–294
    and validators pathologizing normal behavior, 287–292